ENHANCED
WebAssign

The perfect homework management tool to support McKeague's traditional books for the modern student

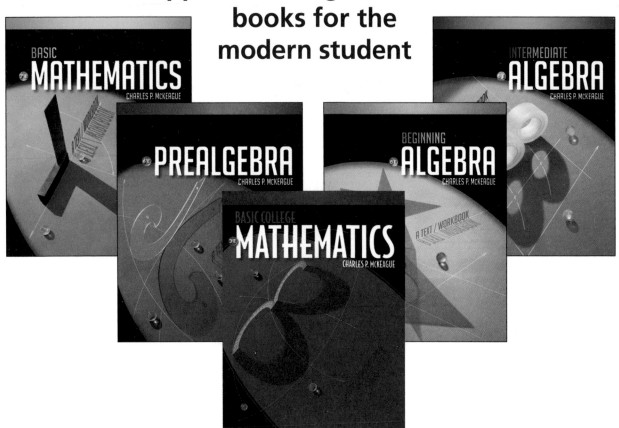

Pat McKeague's passion for teaching mathematics is reflected in his texts, which provide students with plenty of guided practice, review, and reinforcement to build skills. At the same time, McKeague meets today's students on their own terms, with contemporary applications they can relate to, and that help them "get" and connect concepts.

But there's one improvement that's a welcome addition to even the most well-crafted text: interactive, visual learning support that so many students need.

That's why this text is integrated with **Enhanced WebAssign.** This easy-to-use homework management system provides automatic grading that saves you time. It also provides interactive, visual tutorial assistance along with examples and practice exercises—thousands of them—that reinforce the book's pedagogical approach.

Intrigued?
Look inside to learn more about how Enhanced WebAssign can work for you and your students.

Enhanced WebAssign at a glance . . .

Content Features

- *Randomized, algorithmic problems based on over 1,400 text exercises* for unlimited practice

- *Algorithmic solutions,* allowing students to see how problems are solved step-by-step (instead of simply seeing the answer)

- *Interactive examples* from the text

- *Step-by-step tutorials* for specific examples and/or problems

- *Videos* that provide additional instruction on text examples and/or problems

- *Careful feedback* to help guide students to understanding

- *Relevant eBook* pages from the text

- *Live online* tutoring via whiteboarding, email, and instant messaging

Program and Technical Features

- Simple, friendly user interface
- Course creation in two easy steps; assignment creation in five minutes
- Instructor gradebook with weighted categories and scores
- Automatic grading of online homework assignments
- Intuitive *Question Editor* that allows questions to be edited or added without learning a programming language
- Proper display of mathematical expressions
- Timed, secure, password- and IP-restricted exercises
- Student forums, bulletin boards, messaging, and built-in calendar and communication tools
- Compatible with all recent operating systems (Windows, Apple Macintosh, Linux, Sun Solaris)
- Works with most web browsers (e.g., Mozilla Firefox, Internet Explorer, Safari)
- No proprietary plug-ins required

Enhanced WebAssign content is available with these developmental mathematics textbooks from Brooks/Cole:

Aufmann/Lockwood:
New! *Basic College Mathematics: An Applied Approach,* 9th Edition
New! *Essential Mathematics with Applications,* 8th Edition
New! *Introductory Algebra,* 8th Edition
New! *Intermediate Algebra: An Applied Approach,* 8th Edition
New! *Prealgebra and Introductory Algebra: An Applied Approach,* 2nd Edition
New! *Algebra: Introductory and Intermediate,* 5th Edition
New! *PREALG,* 1st Edition

Aufmann/Barker/Lockwood:
Prealgebra, 5th Edition
Beginning Algebra with Applications, Media Enhanced Edition, 7th Edition
Intermediate Algebra with Applications, Media Enhanced Edition, 7th Edition
Algebra: Beginning and Intermediate, Media Enhanced Edition, 2nd Edition

Gustafson/Karr/Massey:
New! *Beginning Algebra,* 9th Edition
New! *Intermediate Algebra,* 9th Edition
New! *Beginning and Intermediate Algebra: An Integrated Approach,* 6th Edition

Kaufmann/Schwitters:
Beginning Algebra (paperbound)
Intermediate Algebra (paperbound)
New! *Elementary Algebra,* 9th Edition
New! *Intermediate Algebra,* 9th Edition
New! *Algebra for College Students,* 9th Edition
Elementary and Intermediate Algebra, 5th Edition

Larson:
Elementary Algebra, 5th Edition
Intermediate Algebra, 5th Edition
Elementary and Intermediate Algebra, 5th Edition

McKeague:
New! *Basic College Mathematics,* 3rd Edition
Basic Mathematics, 7th Edition
Prealgebra, 6th Edition
Beginning Algebra: A Text and Workbook, 8th Edition
Intermediate Algebra: A Text and Workbook, 8th Edition
Elementary Algebra, 8th Edition
Intermediate Algebra, 8th Edition
Elementary and Intermediate Algebra, 3rd Edition

Tussy/Gustafson/Koenig:
New! *Basic Mathematics for College Students,* 4th Edition
New! *Prealgebra,* 4th Edition
Developmental Mathematics for College Students, 2nd Edition
New! *Introductory Algebra,* 4th Edition
New! *Intermediate Algebra,* 4th Edition (paperbound)
Elementary Algebra, 4th Edition
Intermediate Algebra, 4th Edition (hardbound)
Elementary and Intermediate Algebra, 4th Edition

Van Dyke/Rogers/Adams:
Fundamentals of Mathematics, 9th Edition

Sign up today!
www.webassign.net/cengage

Basic College Mathematics

A TEXT/WORKBOOK

THIRD EDITION

Charles P. McKeague
CUESTA COLLEGE

BROOKS/COLE
CENGAGE Learning

Australia • Brazil • Japan • Korea • Mexico • Singapore • Spain • United Kingdom • United States

BROOKS/COLE
CENGAGE Learning·

Basic College Mathematics: A Text/Workbook,
Third Edition
Charles P. McKeague

Acquisitions Editor: Marc Bove

Assistant Editor: Stefanie Beeck

Editorial Assistant: Kyle O'Loughlin

Media Editor: Heleny Wong

Marketing Manager: Gordon Lee

Marketing Assistant: Angela Kim

Marketing Communications Manager:
Katy Malatesta

Content Project Manager: Jennifer Risden

Creative Director: Rob Hugel

Art Director: Vernon Boes

Print Buyer: Karen Hunt

Rights Acquisitions Account Manager, Text:
Bob Kauser

Rights Acquisitions Account Manager, Image:
Don Schlotman

Production Service: XYZ Textbooks

Text Designer: Diane Beasley

Photo Researcher: Kathleen Olson

Illustrator: Kristina Chung/XYZ Textbooks

Cover Designer: Irene Morris

Cover Image: Pete McArthur

Compositor: Devin Christ/XYZ Textbooks

For product information and technology assistance, contact us at
Cengage Learning Customer & Sales Support, 1-800-354-9706

For permission to use material from this text or product,
submit all requests online at **www.cengage.com/permissions**
Further permissions questions can be emailed to
permissionrequest@cengage.com

Library of Congress Control Number: 2010922074

ISBN-13: 978-0-8400-5310-7

ISBN-10: 0-8400-5310-X

Brooks/Cole
20 Davis Drive
Belmont, CA 94002-3098
USA

Cengage Learning is a leading provider of customized learning solutions with office locations around the globe, including Singapore, the United Kingdom, Australia, Mexico, Brazil, and Japan. Locate your local office at:
www.cengage.com/global

Cengage Learning products are represented in Canada by Nelson Education, Ltd.

To learn more about Brooks/Cole, visit **www.cengage.com/brookscole**
Purchase any of our products at your local college store or at our preferred online store **www.CengageBrain.com**

Printed in the United States of America
1 2 3 4 5 6 7 14 13 12 11 10

Brief Contents

Contents

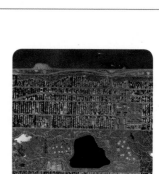

Preface to the Instructor

I have a passion for teaching mathematics. That passion carries through to my textbooks. My goal is a textbook that is user-friendly for both students and instructors. For students, this book forms a bridge to beginning algebra with clear, concise writing, continuous review, and interesting applications. For the instructor, I build features into the text that reinforce the habits and study skills we know will bring success to our students.

The third edition of *Basic College Mathematics* builds upon these strengths.

Applying the Concepts   Students are always curious about how the mathematics they are learning can be applied, so we have included applied problems in most of the problem sets in the book and have labeled them to show students the array of uses of mathematics. These applied problems are written in an inviting way, many times accompanied by new interesting illustrations to help students overcome some of the apprehension associated with application problems.

Getting Ready for the Next Section   Many students think of mathematics as a collection of discrete, unrelated topics. Their instructors know that this is not the case. The new Getting Ready for the Next Section problems reinforce the cumulative, connected nature of this course by showing how the concepts and techniques flow one from another throughout the course. These problems review all of the material that students will need in order to be successful, forming a bridge to the next section, gently preparing students to move forward.

Maintaining Your Skills   One of the major themes of our book is continuous review. We strive to continuously hone techniques learned earlier by keeping the important concepts in the forefront of the course. The Maintaining Your Skills problems review material from the previous chapter, or they review problems that form the foundation of the course—the problems that you expect students to be able to solve when they get to the next course.

The Basic Mathematics Course as a Bridge to Further Success

Basic mathematics is a bridge course. The course and its syllabus bring the student to the level of ability required of college students, while getting them ready to make a successful start in introductory algebra.

Our Proven Commitment to Student Success

After two successful editions, we have developed several interlocking, proven features that will improve students' chances of success in the course. We place practical, easily understood study skills in the first five chapters scattered throughout the sections. Here are some of the other, important success features of the book.

Chapter Pretest   These are meant as a diagnostic test taken before starting the work in the chapter. Much of the material here is learned in the chapter so proficiency on the pretests is not necessary.

Getting Ready for Chapter X   This is a set of problems from previous chapters that students need in order to be successful in the current chapter. These are review problems intended to reinforce the idea that all topics in the course are built on previous topics.

Getting Ready for Class   Just before each problem set is a list of four questions under the heading Getting Ready for Class. These problems require written responses from students and are to be done before students come to class. The answers can be found by reading the preceding section. These questions reinforce the importance of reading the section before coming to class.

Blueprint for Problem Solving   Found in the main text, this feature is a detailed outline of steps required to successfully attempt application problems. Intended as a guide to problem solving in general, the blueprint takes the student through the solution process to various kinds of applications.

A Glimpse of Algebra   These sections, found in most chapters, show how some of the material in the chapter looks when it is extended to algebra.

Chapter Openings   Each chapter opens with an introduction in which a real-world application is used to stimulate interest in the chapter. We expand on these opening applications later in the chapter.

End-of-Chapter Summary, Review, and Assessment

We have learned that students are more comfortable with a chapter that sums up what they have learned thoroughly and accessibly, and reinforces concepts and techniques well. To help students grasp concepts and get more practice, each chapter ends with the following features that together give a comprehensive re-examination of the chapter.

Chapter Summary   The chapter summary recaps all main points from the chapter in a visually appealing grid. In the margin, next to each topic, is an example that illustrates the type of problem associated with the topic being reviewed. Our way of summarizing shows students that concepts in mathematics do relate—and that mastering one concept is a bridge to the next. When students prepare for a test, they can use the chapter summary as a guide to the main concepts of the chapter.

Chapter Review   Following the chapter summary in each chapter is the chapter review. It contains an extensive set of problems that review all the main topics in the chapter. This feature can be used flexibly, as assigned review, as a recommended self-test for students as they prepare for examinations, or as an in-class quiz or test.

Cumulative Review   Starting in Chapter 2, following the chapter review in each chapter is a set of problems that reviews material from all preceding chapters. This keeps students current with past topics and helps them retain the information they study.

Chapter Test   A set of problems representative of all the main points of the chapter. These don't contain as many problems as the chapter review, and should be completed in 50 minutes.

Chapter Projects Each chapter closes with a pair of projects. One is a group project, suitable for students to work on in class. Group projects list details about number of participants, equipment, and time, so that instructors can determine how well the project fits into their classroom. The second project is a research project for students to do outside of class and tends to be open ended.

Supplements for the Instructor

Please contact your sales representative.

Annotated Instructor's Edition ISBN-10: 0840053118 | ISBN-13: 9780840053114
This special instructor's version of the text contains answers next to all exercises and instructor notes at the appropriate location.

Complete Solutions Manual ISBN-10: 0840061595 | ISBN-13: 9780840061591
This manual contains complete solutions for all problems in the text.

Enhanced WebAssign

Instant feedback and ease of use are just two reasons why WebAssign is the most widely used homework system in higher education. WebAssign's homework delivery system allows you to assign, collect, grade, and record homework assignments via the web. And now, this proven system has been enhanced to include links to textbook sections, video examples, and problem-specific tutorials. For further utility, students will also have the option to purchase an online multimedia eBook of the text. Enhanced WebAssign is more than a homework system—it is a complete learning system for math students.

PowerLecture with ExamView® Algorithmic Equations
ISBN-10: 0840061609 | ISBN-13: 9780840061607
This CD-ROM provides the instructor with dynamic media tools for teaching. Create, deliver, and customize tests (both print and online) in minutes with *ExamView® Computerized Testing Featuring Algorithmic Equations*. Easily build solution sets for homework or exams using *Solution Builder's* online solutions manual. Microsoft® PowerPoint® lecture slides and figures from the book are also included on this CD-ROM.

Text-Specific Videos ISBN-10: 0840053134 | ISBN-13: 9780840053138
This set of text-specific videos features segments taught by the author, worked-out solutions to many examples in the book. Available to instructors only.

Supplements for the Student

Enhanced WebAssign

Get instant feedback on your homework assignments with Enhanced WebAssign (assigned by your instructor). This online homework system is easy to use and includes helpful links to textbook sections, video examples, and problem-specific tutorials. For further ease of use, purchase an online multimedia eBook via WebAssign.

Student Solutions Manual ISBN-10: 0840053126 | ISBN-13: 9780840053121
This manual contains complete annotated solutions to all odd problems in the problem sets and all chapter review and chapter test exercises.

Acknowledgments

I would like to thank my editor at Cengage Learning, Marc Bove, for his help and encouragement with this project. Devin Christ, the head of production at our office, was a tremendous help in organizing and planning the details of putting this book together. Mary Gentilucci, Staci Truelson and Tammy Fisher-Vasta assisted with error checking and proofreading. Special thanks to my other friends at Cengage Learning and Jennifer Risden, project manager, who did a great job of coordinating everyone and everything in order to publish this book.

Pat McKeague
February 2010

Preface to the Student

I often find my students asking themselves the question "Why can't I understand this stuff the first time?" The answer is "You're not expected to." Learning a topic in mathematics isn't always accomplished the first time around. There are many instances when you will find yourself reading over new material a number of times before you can begin to work problems. That's just the way things are in mathematics. If you don't understand a topic the first time you see it, that doesn't mean there is something wrong with you. Understanding mathematics takes time. The process of understanding requires reading the book, studying the examples, working problems, and getting your questions answered.

How to Be Successful in Mathematics

1. If you are in a lecture class, be sure to attend all class sessions on time. You cannot know exactly what goes on in class unless you are there. Missing class and then expecting to find out what went on from someone else is not the same as being there yourself.

2. Read the book. It is best to read the section that will be covered in class beforehand. Reading in advance, even if you do not understand everything you read, is still better than going to class with no idea of what will be discussed.

3. Work problems every day and check your answers. The key to success in mathematics is working problems. The more problems you work, the better you will become at working them. The answers to the odd-numbered problems are given in the back of the book. When you have finished an assignment, be sure to compare your answers with those in the book. If you have made a mistake, find out what it is, and correct it.

4. Do it on your own. Don't be misled into thinking someone else's work is your own. Having someone else show you how to work a problem is not the same as working the same problem yourself. It is okay to get help when you are stuck. As a matter of fact, it is a good idea. Just be sure you do the work yourself.

5. Review every day. After you have finished the problems your instructor has assigned, take another 15 minutes and review a section you have already completed. The more you review, the longer you will retain the material you have learned.

6. Don't expect to understand every new topic the first time you see it. Sometimes you will understand everything you are doing, and sometimes you won't. That's just the way things are in mathematics. Expecting to understand each new topic the first time you see it can lead to disappointment and frustration. The process of understanding takes time. It requires that you read the book, work problems, and get your questions answered.

7. Spend as much time as it takes for you to master the material. No set formula exists for the exact amount of time you need to spend on mathematics to master it. You will find out as you go along what is or isn't enough time for you. If you end up spending 2 or more hours on each section in order to master the material there, then that's how much time it takes; trying to get by with less will not work.

8. Relax. It's probably not as difficult as you think.

Whole Numbers

Introduction

The Hoover Dam, as shown in an image from Google Earth, sits on the border of Nevada and Arizona and was the largest producer of hydroelectric power in the United States when it was completed in 1935. Hydroelectric power is the most widely used form of renewable energy today, accounting for about 19% of the world's electricity. Hydroelectricity is a very clean source of power as it does not produce carbon dioxide or any waste products.

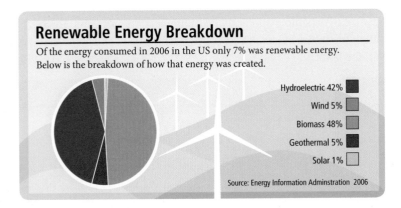

Renewable Energy Breakdown

Of the energy consumed in 2006 in the US only 7% was renewable energy. Below is the breakdown of how that energy was created.

Hydroelectric 42%
Wind 5%
Biomass 48%
Geothermal 5%
Solar 1%

Source: Energy Information Adminstration 2006

As the chart indicates, the demand for energy is soaring, and developing new sources of energy production is more important than ever. In this chapter we will begin reading and understanding this type of chart.

1

The pretest below contains problems that are representative of the problems you will find in the chapter. Those of you studying on your own, or working in a self-paced course, can use the pretest to determine which parts of the chapter will require the most work on your part.

1. Write 7,062 in expanded form. $7000 + 60 + 2$

2. Write 3,409,021 in words.   Three million, four hundred nine thousand, twenty-one

3. Write eighteen thousand, five hundred seven with digits instead of words.   18,507 .

4. Add.

$$\begin{array}{r} 341 \\ +256 \\ \hline 597 \end{array}$$

5. Add.

$$\begin{array}{r} 1,029 \\ +4,381 \\ \hline 5,410 \end{array}$$

6. Subtract.

$$\begin{array}{r} 512 \\ -301 \\ \hline 211 \end{array}$$

7. Subtract.

$$\begin{array}{r} 1,700 \\ -1,436 \\ \hline 264 \end{array}$$

8. Multiply.

$$\begin{array}{r} 27 \\ \times\ 8 \\ \hline 216 \end{array}$$

9. Multiply.

$$\begin{array}{r} 536 \\ \times\ 40 \\ \hline 21,440 \end{array}$$

10. Divide.

$$18\overline{)576} \quad 32$$

11. Divide.

$$23\overline{)4,018} \quad 174\text{ R }16$$

Round.

12. 513 to the nearest ten   510

13. 6,798 to the nearest hundred   6,800

Simplify.

14. $7 + 3 \cdot 2^3$ 31

15. $4 + 5[2 + 6(9 - 7)]$ 74

16. Write the expression using symbols, then simplify.

6 times the difference of 12 and 8. $6(12 - 8) = 24$

Getting Ready for Chapter 1

To get started in this book, we assume that you can do simple addition and multiplication problems. To check to see that you are ready for the chapter, fill in each of the tables below. If you have difficulty, you can find further practice in Appendix A and Appendix B at the back of the book.

TABLE 1

Addition Facts

+	0	1	2	3	4	5	6	7	8	9
0	0	1	2	3	4	5	6	7	8	9
1	1	2	3	4	5	6	7	8	9	10
2	2	3	4	5	6	7	8	9	10	11
3	3	4	5	6	7	8	9	10	11	12
4	4	5	6	7	8	9	10	11	12	13
5	5	6	7	8	9	10	11	12	13	14
6	6	7	8	9	10	11	12	13	14	15
7	7	8	9	10	11	12	13	14	15	16
8	8	9	10	11	12	13	14	15	16	17
9	9	10	11	12	13	14	15	16	17	18

TABLE 2

Multiplication Facts

×	0	1	2	3	4	5	6	7	8	9
0	0	0	0	0	0	0	0	0	0	0
1	0	1	2	3	4	5	6	7	8	9
2	0	2	4	6	8	10	12	14	16	18
3	0	3	6	9	12	15	18	21	24	27
4	0	4	8	12	16	20	24	28	32	36
5	0	5	10	15	20	25	30	35	40	45
6	0	6	12	18	24	30	36	42	48	54
7	0	7	14	21	28	35	42	49	56	63
8	0	8	16	24	32	40	48	56	64	72
9	0	9	18	27	36	45	54	63	72	81

Place Value and Names for Numbers

Introduction . . .

The two diagrams below are known as Pascal's triangle, after the French mathematician and philosopher Blaise Pascal (1623–1662). Both diagrams contain the same information. The one on the left contains numbers in our number system; the one on the right uses numbers from Japan in 1781.

PASCAL'S TRIANGLE IN JAPAN
From Mural Chūzen's *Sampō Dōshi-mon* (1781)

A Place Value

Our number system is based on the number 10 and is therefore called a "base 10" number system. We write all numbers in our number system using the *digits* 0, 1, 2, 3, 4, 5, 6, 7, 8, and 9. The positions of the digits in a number determine the values of the digits. For example, the 5 in the number 251 has a different value from the 5 in the number 542.

The *place values* in our number system are as follows: The first digit on the right is in the *ones column*. The next digit to the left of the ones column is in the *tens column*. The next digit to the left is in the *hundreds column*. For a number like 542, the digit 5 is in the hundreds column, the 4 is in the tens column, and the 2 is in the ones column.

If we keep moving to the left, the columns increase in value. The table shows the name and value of each of the first seven columns in our number system:

Millions Column	Hundred Thousands Column	Ten Thousands Column	Thousands Column	Hundreds Column	Tens Column	Ones Column
1,000,000	100,000	10,000	1,000	100	10	1

EXAMPLE 1 Give the place value of each digit in the number 305,964.

SOLUTION Starting with the digit at the right, we have:

4 in the ones column, 6 in the tens column, 9 in the hundreds column, 5 in the thousands column, 0 in the ten thousands column, and 3 in the hundred thousands column.

Instructor Note
The notes you will find in color throughout this annotated edition of the book are for you. They are simply things that I would point out to you if I were showing you through the book. I hope you enjoy the book and that you find these notes useful.
  Charles P. McKeague

Note Next to each Example in the text is a Practice Problem with the same number. After you read through an Example, try the Practice Problem next to it. The answers to the Practice Problems are at the bottom of the page. Be sure to check your answers as you work these problems. The worked-out solutions to all Practice Problems with more than one step are given in the back of the book. So if you find a Practice Problem that you cannot work correctly, you can look up the correct solution to that problem in the back of the book.

PRACTICE PROBLEMS

1. Give the place value of each digit in the number 46,095.

Answer
1. 5 ones, 9 tens, 0 hundreds, 6 thousands, 4 ten thousands

NASA

Large Numbers

The photograph shown here was taken by the Hubble telescope in April 2002. The object in the photograph is called the *Cone Nebula.* In astronomy, distances to objects like the Cone Nebula are given in light-years, the distance light travels in a year. If we assume light travels 186,000 miles in one second, then a light-year is 5,865,696,000,000 miles; that is

5 trillion, 865 billion, 696 million miles

To find the place value of digits in large numbers, we can use Table 1. Note how the Ones, Thousands, Millions, Billions, and Trillions categories are each broken into Ones, Tens, and Hundreds. Note also that we have written the digits for our light-year in the last row of the table.

TABLE 1

Trillions			Billions			Millions			Thousands			Ones		
Hundreds	Tens	Ones	Hundreds	Tens	Ones	Hundreds	Tens	Ones	Hundreds	Tens	Ones	Hundreds	Tens	Ones
		5	8	6	5	6	9	6	0	0	0	0	0	0

EXAMPLE 2
Give the place value of each digit in the number 73,890,672,540.

SOLUTION The following diagram shows the place value of each digit.

Ten Billions	Billions	Hundred Millions	Ten Millions	Millions	Hundred Thousands	Ten Thousands	Thousands	Hundreds	Tens	Ones
7	3,	8	9	0,	6	7	2,	5	4	0

B   Expanded Form

We can use the idea of place value to write numbers in *expanded form.* For example, the number 542 can be written in expanded form as

$$542 = 500 + 40 + 2$$

because the 5 is in the hundreds column, the 4 is in the tens column, and the 2 is in the ones column.

Here are more examples of numbers written in expanded form.

EXAMPLE 3
Write 5,478 in expanded form.

SOLUTION $5,478 = 5,000 + 400 + 70 + 8$

We can use money to make the results from Example 3 more intuitive. Suppose you have $5,478 in cash as follows:

---

2. Give the place value of each digit in the number 21,705,328,456.

3. Write 3,972 in expanded form.

Answers
2. 6 ones, 5 tens, 4 hundreds, 8 thousands, 2 ten thousands, 3 hundred thousands, 5 millions, 0 ten millions, 7 hundred millions, 1 billion, 2 ten billions
3. 3,000 + 900 + 70 + 2

$5,000 $400 $70 $8

Using this diagram as a guide, we can write

$$\$5,478 = \$5,000 + \$400 + \$70 + \$8$$

which shows us that our work writing numbers in expanded form is consistent with our intuitive understanding of the different denominations of money.

EXAMPLE 4   Write 354,798 in expanded form.

SOLUTION $354,798 = 300,000 + 50,000 + 4,000 + 700 + 90 + 8$

EXAMPLE 5   Write 56,094 in expanded form.

SOLUTION   Notice that there is a 0 in the hundreds column. This means we have 0 hundreds. In expanded form we have

$$56,094 = 50,000 + 6,000 + 90 + 4$$

↑
Note that we don't have to include the 0 hundreds

EXAMPLE 6   Write 5,070,603 in expanded form.

SOLUTION   The columns with 0 in them will not appear in the expanded form.

$$5,070,603 = 5,000,000 + 70,000 + 600 + 3$$

4. Write 271,346 in expanded form.

5. Write 71,306 in expanded form.

6. Write 4,003,560 in expanded form.

STUDY SKILLS

Some of the students enrolled in my mathematics classes develop difficulties early in the course. Their difficulties are not associated with their ability to learn mathematics; they all have the potential to pass the course. Research has identified three variables that affect academic achievement. These are (1) how much math you know before entering a course, (2) the quality of instruction (classroom atmosphere, teaching style, textbook content and format), and (3) your academic self concept, attitude, anxiety, and study habits. As a student, you have the most control over the last variable. Your academic self concept is a significant predictor of mathematics achievement. Students who get off to a poor start do so because they have not developed the study skills necessary to be successful in mathematics. Throughout this textbook you will find tips and things you can do to begin to develop effective study skills and improve your academic self concept.

Put Yourself on a Schedule

The general rule is that you spend two hours on homework for every hour you are in class. Make a schedule for yourself in which you set aside two hours each day to work on this course. Once you make the schedule, stick to it. Don't just complete your assignments and then stop. Use all the time you have set aside. If you complete the assignment and have time left over, read the next section in the book, and then work more problems. As the course progresses you may find that two hours a day is not enough time to master the material in this course. If it takes you longer than two hours a day to reach your goals for this course, then that's how much time it takes. Trying to get by with less will not work.

Answers
4. $200,000 + 70,000 + 1,000 + 300 + 40 + 6$
5. $70,000 + 1,000 + 300 + 6$
6. $4,000,000 + 3,000 + 500 + 60$

C Writing Numbers in Words

The idea of place value and expanded form can be used to help write the names for numbers. Naming numbers and writing them in words takes some practice. Let's begin by looking at the names of some two-digit numbers. Table 2 lists a few. Notice that the two-digit numbers that do not end in 0 have two parts. These parts are separated by a hyphen.

TABLE 2			
Number	In English	Number	In English
25	Twenty-five	30	Thirty
47	Forty-seven	62	Sixty-two
93	Ninety-three	77	Seventy-seven
88	Eighty-eight	50	Fifty

The following examples give the names for some larger numbers. In each case the names are written according to the place values given in Table 1.

EXAMPLE 7 Write each number in words.

a. 452   b. 397   c. 608

SOLUTION a. Four hundred fifty-two
  b. Three hundred ninety-seven
  c. Six hundred eight

EXAMPLE 8 Write each number in words.

a. 3,561   b. 53,662   c. 547,801

SOLUTION a. Three thousand, five hundred sixty-one

↑

Notice how the comma separates
the thousands from the hundreds

  b. Fifty-three thousand, six hundred sixty-two
  c. Five hundred forty-seven thousand, eight hundred one

EXAMPLE 9 Write each number in words.

a. 507,034,005
b. 739,600,075
c. 5,003,007,006

SOLUTION a. Five hundred seven million, thirty-four thousand, five

  b. Seven hundred thirty-nine million, six hundred thousand, seventy-five

  c. Five billion, three million, seven thousand, six

---

7. Write each number in words.
   a. 724
   b. 595
   c. 307

8. Write each number in words.
   a. 4,758
   b. 62,779
   c. 305,440

9. Write each number in words.
   a. 707,044,002
   b. 452,900,008
   c. 4,008,002,001

Answers
7. a. Seven hundred twenty-four
   b. Five hundred ninety-five
   c. Three hundred seven
8. a. Four thousand, seven hundred fifty-eight
   b. Sixty-two thousand, seven hundred seventy-nine
   c. Three hundred five thousand, four hundred forty
9. a. Seven hundred seven million, forty-four thousand, two
   b. Four hundred fifty-two million, nine hundred thousand, eight
   c. Four billion, eight million, two thousand, one

STUDY SKILLS
Find Your Mistakes and Correct Them

There is more to studying mathematics than just working problems. You must always check your answers with the answers in the back of the book. When you have made a mistake, find out what it is, and then correct it. Making mistakes is part of the process of learning mathematics. I have never had a successful student who didn't make mistakes—lots of them. Your mistakes are your guides to understanding; look forward to them.

Here is a practical reason for being able to write numbers in word form.

Michael Smith
1221 Main Street
Anytown, NY 11001

1001

DATE 7/8/08

PAY TO THE
ORDER OF Campus Book Store $ 423.00

Four hundred twenty-three and no cents   DOLLARS

Michael Smith

⑆010015 0111332200233⑈ 1142232⑈

D Writing Numbers from Words

The next examples show how we write a number given in words as a number written with digits.

EXAMPLE 10   Write five thousand, six hundred forty-two, using digits instead of words.

SOLUTION   *Five thousand, six hundred forty-two*

$$5, \qquad 6 \qquad 42$$

EXAMPLE 11   Write each number with digits instead of words.
  a. Three million, fifty-one thousand, seven hundred
  b. Two billion, five
  c. Seven million, seven hundred seven

SOLUTION   **a.** 3,051,700

  b. 2,000,000,005

  c. 7,000,707

---

10. Write six thousand, two hundred twenty-one using digits instead of words.

11. Write each number with digits instead of words.
   a. Eight million, four thousand, two hundred
   b. Twenty-five million, forty
   c. Nine million, four hundred thirty-one

Answers
10. 6,221
11. a. 8,004,200
   b. 25,000,040
   c. 9,000,431

Sets and the Number Line

In mathematics a collection of numbers is called a *set*. In this chapter we will be working with the set of *counting numbers* and the set of *whole numbers*, which are defined as follows:

Counting numbers = {1, 2, 3, . . .}
Whole numbers = {0, 1, 2, 3, . . .}

The dots mean "and so on," and the braces { } are used to group the numbers in the set together.

Another way to visualize the whole numbers is with a *number line*. To draw a number line, we simply draw a straight line and mark off equally spaced points along the line, as shown in Figure 1. We label the point at the left with 0 and the rest of the points, in order, with the numbers 1, 2, 3, 4, 5, and so on.

FIGURE 1

The arrow on the right indicates that the number line can continue in that direction forever. When we refer to numbers in this chapter, we will always be referring to the whole numbers.

> **Note** Counting numbers are also called natural numbers.

STUDY SKILLS
Gather Information on Available Resources
You need to anticipate that you will need extra help sometime during the course. There is a form to fill out in Appendix A to help you gather information on resources available to you. One resource is your instructor; you need to know your instructor's office hours and where the office is located. Another resource is the math lab or study center, if they are available at your school. It also helps to have the phone numbers of other students in the class, in case you miss class. You want to anticipate that you will need these resources, so now is the time to gather them together.

Getting Ready for Class

After reading through the preceding section, respond in your own words and in complete sentences.

1. Give the place value of the 9 in the number 305,964.
2. Write the number 742 in expanded form.
3. Place a comma and a hyphen in the appropriate place so that the number 2,345 is written correctly in words below:

    two thousand three hundred forty five

4. Is there a largest whole number?

Problem Set 1.1

A Give the place value of each digit in the following numbers. [Examples 1, 2]

▶ **1.** 78
8 ones, 7 tens

2. 93
3 ones, 9 tens

▶ **3.** 45
5 ones, 4 tens

4. 79
9 ones, 7 tens

5. 348
8 ones, 4 tens,
3 hundreds

6. 789
9 ones, 8 tens,
7 hundreds

7. 608
8 ones, 0 tens, 6
hundreds

▶ **8.** 450
0 ones, 5 tens, 4
hundreds

▶ **9.** 2,378
8 ones, 7 tens, 3
hundreds,
2 thousands

10. 6,481
1 one, 8 tens,
4 hundreds,
6 thousands

▶ **11.** 273,569
9 ones, 6 tens, 5
hundreds,
3 thousands,
7 ten thousands, 2
hundred thousands

▶ **12.** 768,253
3 ones, 5 tens, 2
hundreds,
8 thousands,
6 ten thousands,
7 hundred thousands

Give the place value of the 5 in each of the following numbers.

▶ **13.** 458,992
Ten thousands

14. 75,003,782
Millions

▶ **15.** 507,994,787
Hundred millions

16. 320,906,050
Tens

17. 267,894,335
Ones

18. 234,345,678,789
Millions

▶ **19.** 4,569,000
Hundred thousands

20. 50,000
Ten thousands

B Write each of the following numbers in expanded form. [Examples 3–6]

▶ **21.** 658
600 + 50 + 8

22. 479
400 + 70 + 9

23. 68
60 + 8

24. 71
70 + 1

▶ **25.** 4,587
4,000 + 500 + 80 + 7

26. 3,762
3,000 + 700 + 60 + 2

▶ **27.** 32,674
30,000 + 2,000 + 600 + 70 + 4

28. 54,883
50,000 + 4,000 + 800 + 80 + 3

29. 3,462,577
3,000,000 + 400,000 + 60,000 + 2,000 + 500 + 70 + 7

30. 5,673,524
5,000,000 + 600,000 + 70,000 + 3,000 + 500 + 20 + 4

▶ **31.** 407
400 + 7

32. 508
500 + 8

33. 30,068
30,000 + 60 + 8

▶ **34.** 50,905
50,000 + 900 + 5

35. 3,004,008
3,000,000 + 4,000 + 8

36. 20,088,060
20,000,000 + 80,000 + 8,000 + 60

C Write each of the following numbers in words. [Examples 7–9]

▶ **37.** 29
Twenty-nine

38. 75
Seventy-five

▶ **39.** 40
Forty

40. 90
Ninety

▶ **41.** 573
Five hundred seventy-three

42. 895
Eight hundred ninety-five

43. 707
Seven hundred seven

44. 405
Four hundred five

▶ **45.** 770
Seven hundred seventy

46. 450
Four hundred fifty

47. 23,540
Twenty-three thousand, five hundred forty

48. 56,708
Fifty-six thousand, seven hundred eight

49. 3,004
Three thousand, four

50. 5,008
Five thousand, eight

▶ **51.** 3,040
Three thousand, forty

52. 5,080
Five thousand, eighty

53. 104,065,780
One hundred four million, sixty-five thousand, seven hundred eighty

54. 637,008,500
Six hundred thirty-seven million, eight thousand, five hundred

▶ **55.** 5,003,040,008
Five billion, three million, forty thousand, eight

56. 7,050,800,001
Seven billion, fifty million, eight hundred thousand, one

57. 2,546,731
Two million, five hundred forty-six thousand, seven hundred thirty-one

58. 6,998,454
Six million, nine hundred ninety-eight thousand, four hundred fifty-four

D Write each of the following numbers with digits instead of words. [Examples 10, 11]

▶ **59.** Three hundred twenty-five
325

▶ **60.** Forty-eight
48

61. Five thousand, four hundred thirty-two
5,432

62. One hundred twenty-three thousand, sixty-one
123,061

▶ **63.** Eighty-six thousand, seven hundred sixty-two
86,762

64. One hundred million, two hundred thousand, three hundred
100,200,300

65. Two million, two hundred
2,000,200

66. Two million, two
2,000,002

▶ **67.** Two million, two thousand, two hundred
2,002,200

68. Two billion, two hundred thousand, two hundred two
2,000,200,202

■ Applying the Concepts

▶ **69.** The illustration shows the average income of workers 18 and older by education.

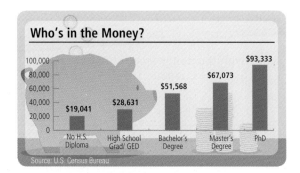

Who's in the Money?

100,000
80,000
60,000
40,000
20,000
0

$19,041 $28,631 $51,568 $67,073 $93,333

No H.S. Diploma   High School Grad/ GED   Bachelor's Degree   Master's Degree   PhD

Source: U.S. Census Bureau

Write the following numbers in words:
a. the average income of someone with only a high school education
   Twenty-eight thousand, six hundred thirty-one
b. the average income of someone with a Ph.D.
   Ninety-three thousand, three hundred thirty-three

▶ **70.** Write the following numbers in words from the information in the given illustration:

Such Great Heights

Petronas Tower 1 & 2
Kuala Lumpur, Malaysia
1,483 ft

Taipei 101
Taipei, Taiwan
1,670 ft

Sears Tower
Chicago, USA
1,450 ft

Source: www.tenmojo.com

a. the height in feet of the Taipei 101 building in Taipei, Taiwan
   One thousand, six hundred seventy
b. the height in feet of the Sears Tower in Chicago, Illinois
   One thousand, four hundred fifty

71. MP3s A new MP3 player has the ability to hold over 125,000 songs. Write the place value of the 1 in the number of songs.
Hundred thousands

72. Music Downloads The top three downloaded songs for one month on Amazon.com had a combined 450,320 downloads. Write the place value of the 3 in the number of downloads.
Hundreds

73. Baseball Salaries According to mlb.com, Major League Baseball's 2008 average player salary was $3,173,403, representing an increase of 7% from the previous season's average. Write 3,173,403 in words.

Average Player Salary

'07
'08 $3,173,40?
7% increase

Three million, one hundred seventy-three thousand, four hundred three

74. Astronomy The distance from the sun to the earth is 92,897,416 miles. Write this number in expanded form.
90,000,000 + 2,000,000 + 800,000 + 90,000 + 7,000 + 400 + 10 + 6

75. Web Searches The phrase "math help" was searched on Google approximately 21,480 times in one month in 2008. Write this number in words.

Twenty-one thousand, four hundred eighty

76. Web Searches The phrase "math help" was searched on Yahoo approximately 6,180 times in one month in 2008. Write this number in words.

Six thousand, one hundred eighty

Writing Checks In each of the checks below, fill in the appropriate space with the dollar amount in either digits or in words.

77.

```
Michael Smith                                      1002
1221 Main Street
Anytown, NY 11001                 DATE 7/8/08

PAY TO THE
  ORDER OF  Sunshine Apartment Complex    $ 750.00
  Seven hundred fifty dollars and no cents    DOLLARS
                              Michael Smith
  ⑈01001⑈   0111332200233⑈  1142232⑈
```

78.

```
Michael Smith                                      1003
1221 Main Street
Anytown, NY 11001                 DATE 7/8/08

PAY TO THE
  ORDER OF  Electric and Gas Company    $ 216.00
  Two hundred sixteen dollars and no cents    DOLLARS
                              Michael Smith
  ⑈01001⑈   0111332200233⑈  1142232⑈
```

Populations of Countries The table below gives estimates of the populations of some countries for mid-year 2008. The first column under *Population* gives the population in digits. The second column gives the population in words. Fill in the blanks.

Country	Population	
	Digits	**Words**
79. United States	304,000,000	Three hundred four million
80. People's Republic of China	1,330,000,000	One billion, three hundred thirty million
81. Japan	127,000,000	One hundred twenty-seven million
82. United Kingdom	61,000,000	Sixty-one million

(From U.S. Census Bureau, International Data Base)

Populations of Cities The table below gives estimates of the populations of some cities for mid-year 2008. The first column under *Population* gives the population in digits. The second column gives the population in words. Fill in the blanks.

City	Population	
	Digits	**Words**
83. Tokyo	36,000,000	Thirty-six million
84. Los Angeles	18,000,000	Eighteen million
85. Paris	10,900,000	Ten million, nine hundred thousand
86. London	7,500,000	Seven million, five hundred thousand

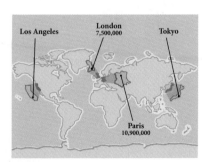

Addition with Whole Numbers, and Perimeter

1.2

Objectives

A Add whole numbers.

B Understand the notation and vocabulary of addition.

C Use the properties of addition.

D Find a solution to an equation by inspection.

E Find the perimeter of a figure.

Introduction . . .

The chart shows the number of babies born in 2006, grouped together according to the age of mothers.

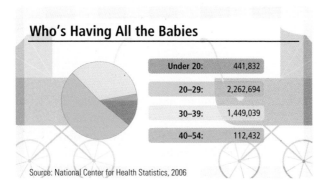

Who's Having All the Babies

Under 20:	441,832
20–29:	2,262,694
30–39:	1,449,039
40–54:	112,432

Source: National Center for Health Statistics, 2006

There is much more information available from the table than just the numbers shown. For instance, the chart tells us how many babies were born to mothers less than 30 years of age. But to find that number, we need to be able to do addition with whole numbers. Let's begin by visualizing addition on the number line.

Facts of Addition

Using lengths to visualize addition can be very helpful. In mathematics we generally do so by using the number line. For example, we add 3 and 5 on the number line like this: Start at 0 and move to 3, as shown in Figure 1. From 3, move 5 more units to the right. This brings us to 8. Therefore, $3 + 5 = 8$.

Instructor Note
Although there are no problems in the Problem Set that use the number line for addition, I always use the number line for several examples in class. Doing so prepares students for addition with negative numbers, where the number line is used extensively.

Start | 3 units → | 5 units → | End

0 1 2 3 4 5 6 7 8

FIGURE 1

If we do this kind of addition on the number line with all combinations of the numbers 0 through 9, we get the results summarized in Table 1 on the next page.

We call the information in Table 1 our basic addition facts. Your success with the examples and problems in this section depends on knowing the basic addition facts.

Note Table 1 is a summary of the addition facts that you *must* know in order to make a successful start in your study of basic mathematics. You *must* know how to add any pair of numbers that come from the list. You *must* be fast and accurate. You don't want to have to think about the answer to 7 + 9. You should know it's 16. Memorize these facts now. Don't put it off until later.

Appendix B at the back of the book has 100 problems on the basic addition facts for you to practice. You may want to go there now and work those problems.

TABLE 1										
					ADDITION TABLE					
+	**0**	**1**	**2**	**3**	**4**	**5**	**6**	**7**	**8**	**9**
0	0	1	2	3	4	5	6	7	8	9
1	1	2	3	4	5	6	7	8	9	10
2	2	3	4	5	6	7	8	9	10	11
3	3	4	5	6	7	8	9	10	11	12
4	4	5	6	7	8	9	10	11	12	13
5	5	6	7	8	9	10	11	12	13	14
6	6	7	8	9	10	11	12	13	14	15
7	7	8	9	10	11	12	13	14	15	16
8	8	9	10	11	12	13	14	15	16	17
9	9	10	11	12	13	14	15	16	17	18

We read Table 1 in the following manner: Suppose we want to use the table to find the answer to 3 + 5. We locate the 3 in the column on the left and the 5 in the row at the top. We read *across* from the 3 and *down* from the 5. The entry in the table that is across from 3 and below 5 is 8.

A Adding Whole Numbers

To add whole numbers, we add digits within the same place value. First we add the digits in the ones place, then the tens place, then the hundreds place, and so on.

EXAMPLE 1   Add: 43 + 52

SOLUTION   This type of addition is best done vertically. First we add the digits in the ones place.

$$\begin{array}{r} 43 \\ + \ 52 \\ \hline 5 \end{array}$$

Then we add the digits in the tens place.

$$\begin{array}{r} 43 \\ + \ 52 \\ \hline 95 \end{array}$$

EXAMPLE 2   Add: 165 + 801

SOLUTION   Writing the sum vertically, we have

$$\begin{array}{r} 165 \\ + \ 801 \\ \hline 966 \end{array}$$ ← Add ones place

Add tens place

Add hundreds place

PRACTICE PROBLEMS

1. Add: 63 + 25

Note To show *why* we add digits with the same place value, we can write each number showing the place value of the digits:

$$\begin{array}{r} 43 = 4 \text{ tens} + 3 \text{ ones} \\ + \ 52 = 5 \text{ tens} + 2 \text{ ones} \\ \hline 9 \text{ tens} + 5 \text{ ones} \end{array}$$

2. Add: 342 + 605

Answers
1. 88
2. 947

Addition with Carrying

In Examples 1 and 2, the sums of the digits with the same place value were always 9 or less. There are many times when the sum of the digits with the same place value will be a number larger than 9. In these cases we have to do what is called *carrying* in addition. The following examples illustrate this process.

EXAMPLE 3 Add: 197 + 213 + 324

SOLUTION We write the sum vertically and add digits with the same place value.

$$
\begin{array}{r}
\overset{1}{1}97 \\
213 \\
+\ 324 \\
\hline
4
\end{array}
$$

When we add the ones, we get 7 + 3 + 4 = 14
We write the 4 and carry the 1 to the tens column

$$
\begin{array}{r}
\overset{1\,1}{1}97 \\
213 \\
+\ 324 \\
\hline
34
\end{array}
$$

We add the tens, including the 1 that was carried over from the last step. We get 13, so we write the 3 and carry the 1 to the hundreds column

$$
\begin{array}{r}
\overset{1\,1}{1}97 \\
213 \\
+\ 324 \\
\hline
734
\end{array}
$$

We add the hundreds, including the 1 that was carried over from the last step

EXAMPLE 4 Add: 46,789 + 2,490 + 864

SOLUTION We write the sum vertically—with the digits with the same place value aligned—and then use the shorthand form of addition.

$$
\begin{array}{cccccc}
\overset{1}{4} & \overset{2}{6} & , & \overset{2}{7} & \overset{1}{8} & 9 \\
 & 2 & , & 4 & 9 & 0 \\
 & & & 8 & 6 & 4 \\
\hline
5 & 0 & , & 1 & 4 & 3
\end{array}
$$

← These are the numbers that have been carried

Write the 3; carry the 1	Ones
Write the 4; carry the 2	Tens
Write the 1; carry the 2	Hundreds
Write the 0; carry the 1	Thousands
No carrying necessary	Ten thousands

Adding numbers as we are doing here takes some practice. Most people don't make mistakes in carrying. Most mistakes in addition are made in adding the numbers in the columns. That is why it is so important that you are accurate with the basic addition facts given in this chapter.

B Vocabulary

The word we use to indicate addition is the word *sum*. If we say "the sum of 3 and 5 is 8," what we mean is 3 + 5 = 8. The word *sum* always indicates addition. We can state this fact in symbols by using the letters *a* and *b* to represent numbers.

3. Add.
  a. 375 + 121 + 473
  b. 495 + 699 + 978

 Note Notice that Practice Problem 3 has two parts. Part a is similar to the problem shown in Example 3. Part b is similar also, but a little more challenging in nature. We will do this from time to time throughout the text. If a practice problem contains more parts than the example to which it corresponds, then the additional parts cover the same concept, but are more challenging than Part a.

4. Add.
  a. 57,904 + 7,193 + 655
  b. 68,495 + 7,236 + 878 + 29 + 5

Answers
3. a. 969 **b.** 2,172
4. a. 65,752 **b.** 76,643

> **Definition**
> If a and b are any two numbers, then the **sum** of a and b is $a + b$. To find the sum of two numbers, we add them.

Table 2 gives some phrases and sentences in English and their mathematical equivalents written in symbols.

TABLE 2	
In English	**In Symbols**
The sum of 4 and 1	$4 + 1$
4 added to 1	$1 + 4$
8 more than m	$m + 8$
x increased by 5	$x + 5$
The sum of x and y	$x + y$
The sum of 2 and 4 is 6.	$2 + 4 = 6$

Note When mathematics is used to solve every-day problems, the problems are almost always stated in words. The translation of English to symbols is a very important part of mathematics.

C Properties of Addition

Once we become familiar with addition, we may notice some facts about addition that are true regardless of the numbers involved. The first of these facts involves the number 0 (zero).

Whenever we add 0 to a number, the result is the original number. For example,

$$7 + 0 = 7 \qquad \text{and} \qquad 0 + 3 = 3$$

Because this fact is true no matter what number we add to 0, we call it a property of 0.

> **Addition Property of 0**
> If we let a represent any number, then it is always true that
> $$a + 0 = a \qquad \text{and} \qquad 0 + a = a$$
> *In words:* Adding 0 to any number leaves that number unchanged.

A second property we notice by becoming familiar with addition is that the order of two numbers in a sum can be changed without changing the result.

$$3 + 5 = 8 \qquad \text{and} \qquad 5 + 3 = 8$$
$$4 + 9 = 13 \qquad \text{and} \qquad 9 + 4 = 13$$

This fact about addition is true for *all* numbers. The order in which you add two numbers doesn't affect the result. We call this fact the *commutative property of addition,* and we write it in symbols as follows.

Note When we use letters to represent numbers, as we do when we say "If a and b are any two numbers," then a and b are called variables, because the values they take on vary. We use the variables a and b in the definitions and properties on this page because we want you to know that the definitions and properties are true for all numbers that you will encounter in this book.

> **Commutative Property of Addition**
> If a and b are any two numbers, then it is always true that
> $$a + b = b + a$$
> *In words:* Changing the order of two numbers in a sum doesn't change the result.

STUDY SKILLS
Accept Definitions

It is important that you don't overcomplicate definitions. When I tell my students that my name is Mr. McKeague, they don't ask "why?" You should approach definitions in the same way. Just accept them as they are, and memorize them if you have to. If someone asks you what the commutative property is, you should be able to respond, "With addition, the commutative property says that if a and b are two numbers then $a + b = b + a$. In other words, you can change the order of two numbers you are adding without changing the result."

EXAMPLE 5   Use the commutative property of addition to rewrite each sum.

    a. $4 + 6$ **b.** $5 + 9$ **c.** $3 + 0$ **d.** $7 + n$

SOLUTION   The commutative property of addition indicates that we can change the order of the numbers in a sum without changing the result. Applying this property we have:

    a. $4 + 6 = 6 + 4$
    b. $5 + 9 = 9 + 5$
    c. $3 + 0 = 0 + 3$
    d. $7 + n = n + 7$

Notice that we did not actually add any of the numbers. The instructions were to use the commutative property, and the commutative property involves only the order of the numbers in a sum.

The last property of addition we will consider here has to do with sums of more than two numbers. Suppose we want to find the sum of 2, 3, and 4. We could add 2 and 3 first, and then add 4 to what we get:

$$(2 + 3) + 4 = 5 + 4 = 9$$

Or, we could add the 3 and 4 together first and then add the 2:

$$2 + (3 + 4) = 2 + 7 = 9$$

The result in both cases is the same. If we try this with any other numbers, the same thing happens. We call this fact about addition the *associative property of addition,* and we write it in symbols as follows.

Associative Property of Addition

If a, b, and c represent any three numbers, then

$$(a + b) + c = a + (b + c)$$

In words: Changing the grouping of three numbers in a sum doesn't change the result.

5. Use the commutative property of addition to rewrite each sum.
    a. $7 + 9$
    b. $6 + 3$
    c. $4 + 0$
    d. $5 + n$

Instructor Note
Some students will question the purpose of problems like the ones shown in Example 5: "Why isn't the answer for Example 5a just 10?" I point out that the purpose of this type of problem is to help them become familiar with a property or idea that may be new to them. These are not addition problems but are problems designed to illustrate something important that they will need later on in the course.

Note   This discussion is here to show why we write the next property the way we do. Sometimes it is helpful to look ahead to the property itself (in this case, the associative property of addition) to see what it is that is being justified.

Answer
5. a. $9 + 7$ **b.** $3 + 6$ **c.** $0 + 4$
    d. $n + 5$

6. Use the associative property of addition to rewrite each sum.
  a. $(3 + 2) + 9$
  b. $(4 + 10) + 1$
  c. $5 + (9 + 1)$
  d. $3 + (8 + n)$

EXAMPLE 6 Use the associative property of addition to rewrite each sum.

  a. $(5 + 6) + 7$ **b.** $(3 + 9) + 1$ **c.** $6 + (8 + 2)$ **d.** $4 + (9 + n)$

SOLUTION The associative property of addition indicates that we are free to regroup the numbers in a sum without changing the result.

  a. $(5 + 6) + 7 = 5 + (6 + 7)$
  b. $(3 + 9) + 1 = 3 + (9 + 1)$
  c. $6 + (8 + 2) = (6 + 8) + 2$
  d. $4 + (9 + n) = (4 + 9) + n$

The commutative and associative properties of addition tell us that when adding whole numbers, we can use any order and grouping. When adding several numbers, it is sometimes easier to look for pairs of numbers whose sums are 10, 20, and so on.

EXAMPLE 7 Add: $9 + 3 + 2 + 7 + 1$

SOLUTION We find pairs of numbers that we can add quickly:

$$9 + 3 + 2 + 7 + 1$$
$$= 10 + 10 + 2$$
$$= 22$$

7. Add.
  a. $6 + 2 + 4 + 8 + 3$
  b. $24 + 17 + 36 + 13$

D Solving Equations

We can use the addition table to help solve some simple equations. If n is used to represent a number, then the equation

$$n + 3 = 5$$

will be true if n is 2. The number 2 is therefore called a *solution* to the equation, because, when we replace n with 2, the equation becomes a true statement:

$$2 + 3 = 5$$

Equations like this are really just puzzles, or questions. When we say, "Solve the equation $n + 3 = 5$," we are asking the question, "What number do we add to 3 to get 5?"

When we solve equations by reading the equation to ourselves and then stating the solution, as we did with the equation above, we are solving the equation by *inspection*.

Note The letter n as we are using it here is a variable, because it represents a number. In this case it is the number that is a solution to an equation.

8. Use inspection to find the solution to each equation.
  a. $n + 9 = 17$
  b. $n + 2 = 10$
  c. $8 + n = 9$
  d. $16 = n + 10$

EXAMPLE 8 Find the solution to each equation by inspection.
  a. $n + 5 = 9$
  b. $n + 6 = 12$
  c. $4 + n = 5$
  d. $13 = n + 8$

SOLUTION We find the solution to each equation by using the addition facts given in Table 1.
  a. The solution to $n + 5 = 9$ is 4, because $4 + 5 = 9$.
  b. The solution to $n + 6 = 12$ is 6, because $6 + 6 = 12$.
  c. The solution to $4 + n = 5$ is 1, because $4 + 1 = 5$.
  d. The solution to $13 = n + 8$ is 5, because $13 = 5 + 8$.

Answers
6. a. $3 + (2 + 9)$ **b.** $4 + (10 + 1)$
  c. $(5 + 9) + 1$ **d.** $(3 + 8) + n$
7. a. 23 **b.** 90
8. a. 8 **b.** 8 **c.** 1 **d.** 6

E Perimeter

FACTS FROM GEOMETRY Perimeter

We end this section with an introduction to perimeter. Here we will find the perimeter of several different shapes called *polygons*. A *polygon* is a closed geometric figure, with at least three sides, in which each side is a straight line segment.

The most common polygons are squares, rectangles, and triangles. Examples of these are shown in Figure 2.

square   rectangle   triangle

FIGURE 2

In the square, s is the length of the side, and each side has the same length. In the rectangle, l stands for the length, and w stands for the width. The width is usually the lesser of the two. The b and h in the triangle are the base and height, respectively. The height is always perpendicular to the base. That is, the height and base form a 90°, or right, angle where they meet.

Note In the triangle, the small square where the broken line meets the base is the notation we use to show that the two line segments meet at right angles. That is, the height h and the base b are perpendicular to each other; the angle between them is 90°.

Definition

The **perimeter** of any polygon is the sum of the lengths of the sides, and it is denoted with the letter P.

EXAMPLE 9 Find the perimeter of each geometric figure.

a.

15 inches

b.

37 feet

24 feet

c.

36 yards   23 yards

24 yards   24 yards

12 yards

SOLUTION In each case we find the perimeter by adding the lengths of all the sides.

a. The figure is a square. Because the length of each side in the square is the same, the perimeter is

$$P = 15 + 15 + 15 + 15 = 60 \text{ inches}$$

b. In the rectangle, two of the sides are 24 feet long, and the other two are 37 feet long. The perimeter is the sum of the lengths of the sides.

$$P = 24 + 24 + 37 + 37 = 122 \text{ feet}$$

c. For this polygon, we add the lengths of the sides together. The result is the perimeter.

$$P = 36 + 23 + 24 + 12 + 24 = 119 \text{ yards}$$

9. Find the perimeter of each geometric figure.

a.

7 feet

b.

88 inches   33 inches

c.

44 yards   66 yards

77 yards

Answer
9. **a.** 28 feet **b.** 242 inches
   c. 187 yards

USING TECHNOLOGY

Calculators

From time to time we will include some notes like this one, which show how a calculator can be used to assist us with some of the calculations in the book. Most calculators on the market today fall into one of two categories: those with algebraic logic and those with function logic. Calculators with algebraic logic have a key with an equals sign on it. Calculators with function logic do not have an equals key. Instead they have a key labeled ENTER or EXE (for execute). Scientific calculators use algebraic logic, and graphing calculators, such as the TI-83, use function logic.

Here are the sequences of keystrokes to use to work the problem shown in Part c of Example 9.

Scientific Calculator: $36 \boxed{+} 23 \boxed{+} 24 \boxed{+} 12 \boxed{+} 24 \boxed{=}$

Graphing Calculator: $36 \boxed{+} 23 \boxed{+} 24 \boxed{+} 12 \boxed{+} 24 \boxed{\text{ENT}}$

Getting Ready for Class

After reading through the preceding section, respond in your own words and in complete sentences.

1. What number is the sum of 6 and 8?
2. Make up an addition problem using the number 456 that does not involve carrying.
3. Make up an addition problem using the number 456 that involves carrying from the ones column to the tens column only.
4. What is the perimeter of a geometric figure?

Problem Set 1.2

A Find each of the following sums. (Add.) [Examples 1–4]

1. 3 + 5 + 7
15

2. 2 + 8 + 6
16

3. 1 + 4 + 9
14

4. 2 + 8 + 3
13

5. 5 + 9 + 4 + 6
24

6. 8 + 1 + 6 + 2
17

7. 1 + 2 + 3 + 4 + 5
15

8. 5 + 6 + 7 + 8 + 9
35

9. 9 + 1 + 8 + 2
20

10. 7 + 3 + 6 + 4
20

A Add each of the following. (There is no carrying involved in these problems.) [Examples 1, 2]

11. 43
25
68

12. 56
23
79

13. 81
17
98

14. 37
22
59

15. 4,281
3,016
7,297

16. 2,749
1,250
3,999

17. 3,482
3,005
6,487

18. 2,496
7,503
9,999

19. 32
21
43
96

20. 521
340
135
996

21. 6,245
203
1,001
7,449

22. 27
4,510
342
4,879

A Add each of the following. (All problems involve carrying in at least one column.) [Examples 3, 4]

23. 49
16
65

24. 85
29
114

25. 74
28
102

26. 36
46
82

27. 682
193
875

28. 439
270
709

29. 638
191
829

30. 444
595
1,039

31. 4,963
5,428
10,391

32. 8,291
7,489
15,780

33. 6,205
9,999
16,204

34. 8,888
9,999
18,887

35. 56,789
98,765
155,554

36. 45,678
87,654
133,332

37. 52,468
58,642
111,110

38. 13,579
97,531
111,110

39. 4,296
8,720
4,375
17,391

40. 5,637
481
7,899
14,017

41. 4,994
449
9,449
14,892

42. 6,824
371
4,857
12,052

43. 12
34
56
78
180

44. 21
43
65
87
216

45. 999
444
555
222
2,220

46. 646
464
525
252
1,887

47. 9,245
672
8,341
27
18,285

48. 45
9,876
54
6,789
16,764

B Complete the following tables.

49.

First Number a	Second Number b	Their Sum a + b
61	38	99
63	36	99
65	34	99
67	32	99

50.

First Number a	Second Number b	Their Sum a + b
10	45	55
20	35	55
30	25	55
40	15	55

51.

First Number a	Second Number b	Their Sum a + b
9	16	25
36	64	100
81	144	225
144	256	400

52.

First Number a	Second Number b	Their Sum a + b
25	75	100
24	76	100
23	77	100
22	78	100

C Rewrite each of the following using the commutative property of addition. [Example 5]

▶ **53.** $5 + 9$
$9 + 5$

54. $2 + 1$
$1 + 2$

55. $3 + 8$
$8 + 3$

56. $9 + 2$
$2 + 9$

57. $6 + 4$
$4 + 6$

▶ **58.** $1 + 7$
$7 + 1$

C Rewrite each of the following using the associative property of addition. [Example 6]

59. $(1 + 2) + 3$
$1 + (2 + 3)$

▶ **60.** $(4 + 5) + 9$
$4 + (5 + 9)$

61. $(2 + 1) + 6$
$2 + (1 + 6)$

62. $(2 + 3) + 8$
$2 + (3 + 8)$

63. $1 + (9 + 1)$
$(1 + 9) + 1$

64. $2 + (8 + 2)$
$(2 + 8) + 2$

▶ **65.** $(4 + n) + 1$
$4 + (n + 1)$

66. $(n + 8) + 1$
$n + (8 + 1)$

D Find a solution for each equation. [Example 8]

▶ **67.** $n + 6 = 10$
$n = 4$

68. $n + 4 = 7$
$n = 3$

69. $n + 8 = 13$
$n = 5$

70. $n + 6 = 15$
$n = 9$

71. $4 + n = 12$
$n = 8$

72. $5 + n = 7$
$n = 2$

▶ **73.** $17 = n + 9$
$n = 8$

74. $13 = n + 5$
$n = 8$

B Write each of the following expressions in words. Use the word *sum* in each case. [Table 2]

▶ **75.** $4 + 9$
The sum of 4 and 9

76. $9 + 4$
The sum of 9 and 4

77. $8 + 1$
The sum of 8 and 1

78. $9 + 9$
The sum of 9 and 9

▶ **79.** $2 + 3 = 5$
The sum of 2 and 3 is 5.

80. $8 + 2 = 10$
The sum of 8 and 2 is 10.

B Write each of the following in symbols. [Table 2]

▶ **81. a.** The sum of 5 and 2 $5 + 2$
   b. 3 added to 8 $8 + 3$

82. a. The sum of a and 4 $a + 4$
   b. 6 more than x $x + 6$

83. a. m increased by 1 $m + 1$
   b. The sum of m and n $m + n$

84. a. The sum of 4 and 8 is 12. $4 + 8 = 12$
   b. The sum of a and b is 6. $a + b = 6$

E Find the perimeter of each figure. The first four figures are squares. [Example 9]

85.

3 in.

12 in.

▶ **86.**

9 in.

36 in.

87.

4 ft

16 ft

88.

2 ft

8 ft

89.

3 yd

10 yd

26 yd

▶ **90.**

1 yd

5 yd

12 yd

91.

5 in.   6 in.

7 in.

18 in.

▶ **92.**

4 in.   10 in.

12 in.

26 in.

E Applying the Concepts

▶ **93.** Classroom appliances use a lot of energy. You can save energy by unplugging or turning of unused appliances.

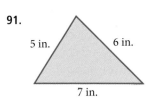

Energy Estimates
All units given as watts per hour.

Ceiling fan	125
Stereo	400
Television	130
VCR/DVD player	20
Printer	400
Photocopier	400
Coffee maker	1000

Source: dosomething.org 2008

Use the information in the given illustration to find the following:

a. the number of watts/hour saved by unplugging a DVD player and a television

150 watts/hour

b. the number of watts/hour saved by unplugging a ceiling fan and a coffee maker

1,125 watts/hour

94. The information in the illustration represents the number of picture messages sent for the first nine months of the year, in millions.

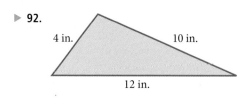

A Picture's Worth 1,000 Words

Jan 3 Feb 10 Mar 21 Apr 21 May 26 Jun 32 Jul 41 Aug Sep

Use the information to find the following:

a. the number of picture messages sent in all nine months

154 million picture messages

b. the number of picture messages sent in March and April

13 million picture messages

95. Checkbook Balance On Monday Bob had a balance of $241 in his checkbook. On Tuesday he made a deposit of $108, and on Thursday he wrote a check for $24. What was the balance in his checkbook on Wednesday?

$349

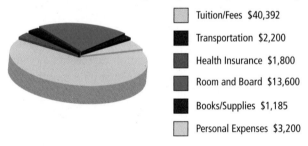

96. Number of Passengers A plane flying from Los Angeles to New York left Los Angeles with 67 passengers on board. The plane stopped in Bakersfield and picked up 28 passengers, and then it stopped again in Dallas where 57 more passengers came on board. How many passengers were on the plane when it landed in New York?

152 passengers

97. College Costs According to data from *The Chronicle of Higher Education*, the most expensive college in the country is George Washington University in Washington, D.C. According to the university's website, a student entering as a freshman during the 2008–09 academic year can expect to pay the expenses shown in the chart below:

2008-09 Costs for Attending George Washington University

Tuition/Fees $40,392
Transportation $2,200
Health Insurance $1,800
Room and Board $13,600
Books/Supplies $1,185
Personal Expenses $3,200

a. What are the total of the expenses for one year at George Washington University?
$62,377

b. How much of these total expenses are college related?
$55,177

c. What is the total amount for expenses that are not directly related to attending this college?
$7,200

98. Improving Your Quantitative Literacy Quantitative literacy is a subject discussed by many people involved in teaching mathematics. The person they are concerned with when they discuss it is you. We are going to work at improving your quantitative literacy, but before we do that we should answer the question, what is quantitative literacy? Lynn Arthur Steen, a noted mathematics educator, has stated that quantitative literacy is "the capacity to deal effectively with the quantitative aspects of life."

a. Give a definition for the word *quantitative*.

b. Give a definition for the word *literacy*.

c. Are there situations that occur in your life that you find distasteful or that you try to avoid because they involve numbers and mathematics? If so, list some of them here. (For example, some people find the process of buying a car particularly difficult because they feel that the numbers and details of the financing are beyond them.)

Introduction . . .

Many times when we talk about numbers, it is helpful to use numbers that have been *rounded off*, rather than exact numbers. For example, the city where I live has a population of 43,704. But when I tell people how large the city is, I usually say, "The population is about 44,000." The number 44,000 is the original number rounded to the nearest thousand. The number 43,704 is closer to 44,000 than it is to 43,000, so it is rounded to 44,000. We can visualize this situation on the number line.

Welcome to
San Luis Obispo
Founded 1772

Population 43,704

Further   Closer

43,000   43,704   44,000

A Rounding

The steps used in rounding numbers are given below.

> **Strategy**   **Rounding Whole Numbers**
> To summarize, we list the following steps:
>
> **Step 1:** Locate the digit just to the right of the place you are to round to.
>
> **Step 2:** If that digit is less than 5, replace it and all digits to its right with zeros.
>
> **Step 3:** If that digit is 5 or more, replace it and all digits to its right with zeros, and add 1 to the digit to its left.

> **Note**   After you have used the steps listed here to work a few problems, you will find that the procedure becomes almost automatic.

You can see from these rules that in order to round a number you must be told what column (or place value) to round to.

PRACTICE PROBLEMS

EXAMPLE 1   Round 5,382 to the nearest hundred.

SOLUTION   There is a 3 in the hundreds column. We look at the digit just to its right, which is 8. Because 8 is greater than 5, we add 1 to the 3, and we replace the 8 and 2 with zeros:

5,382   is   5,4**00**   to the nearest hundred

Greater than 5   Add 1 to   Put zeros
                        get 4   here

1. Round 5,742 to the nearest
   a. hundred
   b. thousand

EXAMPLE 2   Round 94 to the nearest ten.

SOLUTION   There is a 9 in the tens column. To its right is 4. Because 4 is less than 5, we simply replace it with 0:

94   is   9**0**   to the nearest ten

Less than 5   Replaced with zero

2. Round 87 to the nearest
   a. ten
   b. hundred

Answers
1. a. 5,700 **b.** 6,000
2. a. 90 **b.** 100

3. Round 980 to the nearest
   a. hundred
   b. thousand

4. Round 376,804,909 to the nearest
   a. million
   b. ten thousand

☐ House Payments **$10,200**

■ Taxes **$6,137**

■ Miscellaneous **$6,142**

☐ Entertainment **$2,142**

■ Car Expenses **$4,847**

☐ Savings **$2,149**

■ Food **$5,296**

5. Use the pie chart above to answer these questions.
   a. To the nearest ten dollars, what is the total amount spent on food and car expenses?
   b. To the nearest hundred dollars, how much is spent on savings and taxes?
   c. To the nearest thousand dollars, how much is spent on items other than food and entertainment?

EXAMPLE 3   Round 973 to the nearest hundred.

SOLUTION   We have a 9 in the hundreds column. To its right is 7, which is greater than 5. We add 1 to 9 to get 10, and then replace the 7 and 3 with zeros:

973   is   1,**000**   to the nearest hundred

Greater than 5 · Add 1 to get 10 · Put zeros here

EXAMPLE 4   Round 47,256,344 to the nearest million.

SOLUTION   We have 7 in the millions column. To its right is 2, which is less than 5. We simply replace all the digits to the right of 7 with zeros to get:

47,256,344   is   47,**000,000**   to the nearest million

Less than 5 · Leave as is · Replaced with zeros

Table 1 gives more examples of rounding.

TABLE 1			
		Rounded to the Nearest	
Original Number	Ten	Hundred	Thousand
6,914	6,910	6,900	7,000
8,485	8,490	8,500	8,000
5,555	5,560	5,600	6,000
1,234	1,230	1,200	1,000

Rule

If we are doing calculations and are asked to round our answer, we do all our arithmetic first and then round the result. That is, the last step is to round the answer; we don't round the numbers first and then do the arithmetic.

EXAMPLE 5   The pie chart in the margin shows how a family earning $36,913 a year spends their money.
   a. To the nearest hundred dollars, what is the total amount spent on food and entertainment?
   b. To the nearest thousand dollars, how much of their income is spent on items other than taxes and savings?

SOLUTION   In each case we add the numbers in question and then round the sum to the indicated place.
   a. We add the amounts spent on food and entertainment and then round that result to the nearest hundred dollars.

Food	$5,296
Entertainment	2,142
Total	$7,438 = $7,400 to the nearest hundred dollars

Answers
3. **a.** 1,000 **b.** 1,000
4. **a.** 377,000,000 **b.** 376,800,000

b. We add the numbers for all items except taxes and savings.

House payments	$10,200
Food	5,296
Car expenses	4,847
Entertainment	2,142
Miscellaneous	6,142
Total	$28,627 = $29,000 to the nearest thousand dollars

B Estimating

When we *estimate* the answer to a problem, we simplify the problem so that an approximate answer can be found quickly. There are a number of ways of doing this. One common method is to use rounded numbers to simplify the arithmetic necessary to arrive at an approximate answer, as our next example shows.

EXAMPLE 6 Estimate the answer to the following problem by rounding each number to the nearest thousand.

4,872
1,691
777
+ 6,124

SOLUTION We round each of the four numbers in the sum to the nearest thousand. Then we add the rounded numbers.

4,872	rounds to	5,000
1,691	rounds to	2,000
777	rounds to	1,000
+ 6,124	rounds to	+ 6,000
		14,000

We estimate the answer to this problem to be approximately 14,000. The actual answer, found by adding the original unrounded numbers, is 13,464.

Here is a practical application for which the ability to estimate can be a useful tool.

EXAMPLE 7 On the way home from classes you stop at the local grocery store to pick up a few things. You know that you have a $20.00 bill in your wallet. You pick up the following items: a loaf of wheat bread for $2.29, a gallon of milk for $3.96, a dozen eggs for $2.18, a pound of apples for $1.19, and a box of your favorite cereal for $4.59. Use estimation to determine if you will have enough to pay for your groceries when you get to the cashier.

SOLUTION We round the items in our grocery cart off to the nearest dollar:

wheat bread for $2.29	rounds to	$2.00
milk for $3.96	rounds to	$4.00
eggs for $2.18	rounds to	$2.00
apples for $1.19	rounds to	$1.00
+ cereal for $4.59	rounds to	+ $5.00
		$14.00

We estimate our total to be $14.00. Thus, $20.00 will be enough to pay for the groceries. (The actual cost of the groceries is $14.21.)

6. Estimate the answer by first rounding each number to the nearest thousand.

a. 5,287
2,561
888
+4,898

b. 702
3,944
1,001
+3,500

Note In Example 6 we are asked to *estimate* an answer, so it is okay to round the numbers in the problem before adding them. In Example 5 we are asked for a rounded answer, meaning that we are to find the exact answer to the problem and then round to the indicated place. In that case we must not round the numbers in the problem before adding.

Answer
5. a. $10,140 **b.** $8,300
c. $29,000
6. a. 14,000 **b.** 10,000

DESCRIPTIVE STATISTICS

Bar Charts

The table and chart below give two representations for the amount of caffeine in five different drinks, one numeric and the other visual.

TABLE 2	
Beverage (6-ounce cup)	**Caffeine** (in milligrams)
Brewed coffee	100
Instant coffee	70
Tea	50
Cocoa	5
Decaffeinated coffee	4

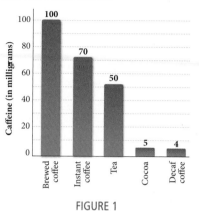

FIGURE 1

The diagram in Figure 1 is called a *bar chart*. The horizontal line below which the drinks are listed is called the *horizontal axis*, while the vertical line that is labeled from 0 to 100 is called the *vertical axis*.

Getting Ready for Class

After reading through the preceding section, respond in your own words and in complete sentences.

1. Describe the process you would use to round the number 5,382 to the nearest thousand.

2. Describe the process you would use to round the number 47,256,344 to the nearest ten thousand.

3. Find a number not containing the digit 7 that will round to 700 when rounded to the nearest hundred.

4. When I ask a class of students to round the number 7,499 to the nearest thousand, a few students will give the answer as 8,000. In what way are these students using the rule for rounding numbers incorrectly?

Problem Set 1.3

A Round each of the numbers to the nearest ten. [Examples 1–5]

▶ **1.** 42
40

2. 44
40

3. 46
50

4. 48
50

▶ **5.** 45
50

6. 73
70

7. 77
80

8. 75
80

▶ **9.** 458
460

10. 455
460

▶ **11.** 471
470

12. 680
680

▶ **13.** 56,782
56,780

14. 32,807
32,810

▶ **15.** 4,504
4,500

16. 3,897
3,900

Round each of the numbers to the nearest hundred. [Examples 1–5]

▶ **17.** 549
500

18. 954
1,000

19. 833
800

20. 604
600

▶ **21.** 899
900

22. 988
1,000

23. 1090
1,100

▶ **24.** 6,778
6,800

25. 5,044
5,000

▶ **26.** 56,990
57,000

27. 39,603
39,600

28. 31,999
32,000

Round each of the numbers to the nearest thousand. [Examples 1–5]

29. 4,670
5,000

▶ **30.** 9,054
9,000

31. 9,760
10,000

32. 4,444
4,000

▶ **33.** 978
1,000

34. 567
1,000

▶ **35.** 657,892
658,000

36. 688,909
689,000

▶ **37.** 509,905
510,000

38. 608,433
608,000

▶ **39.** 3,789,345
3,789,000

40. 5,744,500
5,745,000

▶ Selected exercises available online at www.webassign.net/brookscole

A Complete the following table by rounding the numbers on the left as indicated by the headings in the table. [Examples 1–5]

Original Number	Rounded to the Nearest		
	Ten	Hundred	Thousand
41. 7,821	7,820	7,800	8,000
42. 5,945	5,950	5,900	6,000
43. 5,999	6,000	6,000	6,000
44. 4,353	4,350	4,400	4,000
45. 10,985	10,990	11,000	11,000
46. 11,108	11,110	11,100	11,000
47. 99,999	100,000	100,000	100,000
48. 95,505	95,510	95,500	96,000

B **Estimating** Estimate the answer to each of the following problems by rounding each number to the indicated place value and then adding. [Example 6]

49. hundred
  750
  275
  + 120
  1,200

50. thousand
  1,891
  765
  + 3,223
  6,000

51. hundred
  472
  422
  536
  + 511
  1,900

52. hundred
  399
  601
  744
  + 298
  2,000

53. thousand
  25,399
  7,601
  18,744
  + 6,298
  58,000

54. thousand
  9,999
  8,888
  7,777
  + 6,666
  34,000

55. hundred
  9,999
  8,888
  7,777
  + 6,666
  33,400

56. ten thousand
  127,675
  72,560
  + 219,065
  420,000

57. ten thousand
  65,000
  31,000
  15,555
  + 72,000
  190,000

58. ten
  10,061
  10,044
  10,035
  + 10,025
  40,170

59. hundred
  20,150
  18,250
  12,350
  + 30,450
  81,400

60. hundred
  1,950
  2,849
  3,750
  + 4,649
  13,200

Applying the Concepts

61. Age of Mothers About 4 million babies were born in 2006. The chart shows the breakdown by mothers' age and number of babies. Use the chart to answer the following questions.

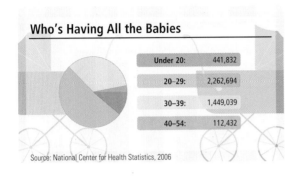

Who's Having All the Babies

Under 20:	441,832
20–29:	2,262,694
30–39:	1,449,039
40–54:	112,432

Source: National Center for Health Statistics, 2006

a. What is the exact number of babies born in 2006?
  4,265,997 babies

b. Using your answer from Part a, is the statement "About 4 million babies were born in 2006" correct?
  Yes

▶ c. To the nearest hundred thousand, how many babies were born to mothers aged 20 to 29 in 2006?
  2,300,000 babies

▶ d. To the nearest thousand, how many babies were born to mothers 40 years old or older?
  112,000 babies

62. Business Expenses The pie chart shows one year's worth of expenses for a small business. Use the chart to answer the following questions.

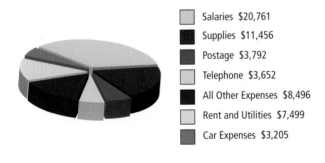

Salaries $20,761
Supplies $11,456
Postage $3,792
Telephone $3,652
All Other Expenses $8,496
Rent and Utilities $7,499
Car Expenses $3,205

a. To the nearest hundred dollars, how much was spent on postage and supplies?
  $15,200

b. Find the total amount spent, to the nearest hundred dollars, on rent and utilities and car expenses.
  $10,700

c. To the nearest thousand dollars, how much was spent on items other than salaries and rent and utilities?
  $31,000

d. To the nearest thousand dollars, how much was spent on items other than postage, supplies, and car expenses?
  $40,000

The bar chart below is similar to the one we studied in this section. It was given to me by a friend who owns and operates an alcohol dragster. The dragster contains a computer that gives information about each of his races. This particular race was run during the 1993 Winternationals. The bar chart gives the speed of a race car in a quarter-mile drag race every second during the race. The horizontal lines have been added to assist you with Problems 63–66.

Speed of a Race Car

▶ **63.** Is the speed of the race car after 3 seconds closer to 160 miles per hour or 190 miles per hour?

160 miles per hour

64. After 4 seconds, is the speed of the race car closer to 150 miles per hour or 190 miles per hour?

190 miles per hour

▶ **65.** Estimate the speed of the car after 1 second.

Answers will vary, but 70 miles per hour is a good estimate.

66. Estimate the speed of the car after 6 seconds.

Answers will vary, but 225 miles per hour is a good estimate.

67. Fast Food The following table lists the number of calories consumed by eating some popular fast foods. Use the axes in the figure below to construct a bar chart from the information in the table.

CALORIES IN FAST FOOD	
Food	Calories
McDonald's Hamburger	270
Burger King Hamburger	260
Jack in the Box Hamburger	280
McDonald's Big Mac	510
Burger King Whopper	630
Jack in the Box Colossus Burger	940

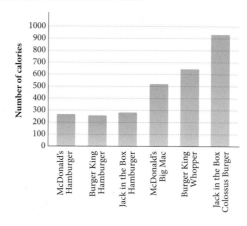

68. Exercise The following table lists the number of calories burned in 1 hour of exercise by a person who weighs 150 pounds. Use the axes in the figure below to construct a bar chart from the information in the table.

CALORIES BURNED BY A 150-POUND PERSON IN ONE HOUR	
Activity	Calories
Bicycling	374
Bowling	265
Handball	680
Jazzercise	340
Jogging	680
Skiing	544

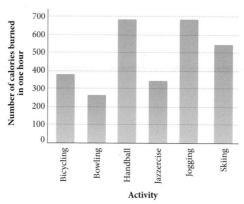

1.4

Introduction . . .

In business, subtraction is used to calculate profit. Profit is found by subtracting costs from revenue. The following double bar chart shows the costs and revenue of the Baby Steps Shoe Company during one 4-week period.

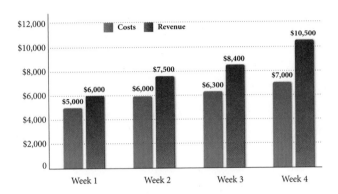

To find the profit for Week 1, we subtract the costs from the revenue, as follows:

Profit = $6,000 − $5,000
Profit = $1,000

Subtraction is the opposite operation of addition. If you understand addition and can work simple addition problems quickly and accurately, then subtraction shouldn't be difficult for you.

A Vocabulary

The word *difference* always indicates subtraction. We can state this in symbols by letting the letters a and b represent numbers.

Definition

The **difference** of two numbers a and b is $a − b$

Table 1 gives some word statements involving subtraction and their mathematical equivalents written in symbols.

TABLE 1	
In English	**In Symbols**
The difference of 9 and 1	$9 − 1$
The difference of 1 and 9	$1 − 9$
The difference of m and 4	$m − 4$
The difference of x and y	$x − y$
3 subtracted from 8	$8 − 3$
2 subtracted from t	$t − 2$
The difference of 7 and 4 is 3.	$7 − 4 = 3$
The difference of 9 and 3 is 6.	$9 − 3 = 6$

B The Meaning of Subtraction

When we want to subtract 3 from 8, we write

$$8 - 3, \qquad 8 \text{ subtract } 3, \qquad \text{or} \qquad 8 \text{ minus } 3$$

The number we are looking for here is the difference between 8 and 3, or the number we add to 3 to get 8. That is:

$$8 - 3 = ? \qquad \text{is the same as} \qquad ? + 3 = 8$$

In both cases we are looking for the number we add to 3 to get 8. The number we are looking for is 5. We have two ways to write the same statement.

Subtraction   Addition

$$8 - 3 = 5 \qquad \text{or} \qquad 5 + 3 = 8$$

For every subtraction problem, there is an equivalent addition problem. Table 2 lists some examples.

TABLE 2		
Subtraction		**Addition**
$7 - 3 = 4$	because	$4 + 3 = 7$
$9 - 7 = 2$	because	$2 + 7 = 9$
$10 - 4 = 6$	because	$6 + 4 = 10$
$15 - 8 = 7$	because	$7 + 8 = 15$

To subtract numbers with two or more digits, we align the numbers vertically and subtract in columns.

PRACTICE PROBLEMS

1. Subtract.
   a. $684 - 431$
   b. $7,406 - 3,405$

EXAMPLE 1   Subtract: $376 - 241$

SOLUTION   We write the problem vertically, aligning digits with the same place value. Then we subtract in columns.

$$\begin{array}{r} 376 \\ -\ 241 \\ \hline 135 \end{array}$$

←— Subtract the bottom number in each column from the number above it

2. a. Subtract 405 from 6,857.
   b. Subtract 234 from 345.

EXAMPLE 2   Subtract 503 from 7,835.

SOLUTION   In symbols this statement is equivalent to

$$7,835 - 503$$

To subtract we write 503 below 7,835 and then subtract in columns.

$$\begin{array}{ccccc} 7 & , & 8 & 3 & 5 \\ - & & 5 & 0 & 3 \\ \hline 7 & , & 3 & 3 & 2 \end{array}$$

$5 - 3 = 2$	Ones
$3 - 0 = 3$	Tens
$8 - 5 = 3$	Hundreds
$7 - 0 = 7$	Thousands

Answers
1. a. 253   b. 4,001
2. a. 6,452   b. 111

As you can see, subtraction problems like the ones in Examples 1 and 2 are fairly simple. We write the problem vertically, lining up the digits with the same place value, and subtract in columns. We always subtract the bottom number from the top number.

C Subtraction with Borrowing

Subtraction must involve *borrowing* when the bottom digit in any column is larger than the digit above it. In one sense, borrowing is the reverse of the carrying we did in addition.

EXAMPLE 3   Subtract: 92 − 45

SOLUTION   We write the problem vertically with the place values of the digits showing:

$$92 = 9 \text{ tens} + 2 \text{ ones}$$
$$\underline{-45 = 4 \text{ tens} + 5 \text{ ones}}$$

Look at the ones column. We cannot subtract immediately, because 5 is larger than 2. Instead, we borrow 1 ten from the 9 tens in the tens column. We can rewrite the number 92 as

$$9 \text{ tens} + 2 \text{ ones}$$
$$= 8 \text{ tens} + 1 \text{ ten} + 2 \text{ ones}$$
$$= 8 \text{ tens} + 12 \text{ ones}$$

Now we are in a position to subtract.

$$92 = 9 \text{ tens} + 2 \text{ ones} = 8 \text{ tens} + 12 \text{ ones}$$
$$\underline{-45 = 4 \text{ tens} + 5 \text{ ones} = 4 \text{ tens} + \ \ 5 \text{ ones}}$$
$$4 \text{ tens} + \ \ 7 \text{ ones}$$

The result is 4 tens + 7 ones, which can be written in standard form as 47.

Writing the problem out in this way is more trouble than is actually necessary. The shorthand form of the same problem looks like this:

```
  8   12 ←————————  This shows we have
  9    2            borrowed 1 ten to go
-  4    5           with the 2 ones
  ─────────
  4    7
  ↑    ↑
  │   12 − 5 = 7    Ones
  │
  8 − 4 = 4         Tens
```

This shortcut form shows all the necessary work involved in subtraction with borrowing. We will use it from now on.

Note The discussion here shows why borrowing is necessary and how we go about it. To understand borrowing you should pay close attention to this discussion.

Answer
3. a. 16 **b.** 129

The borrowing that changed 9 tens + 2 ones into 8 tens + 12 ones can be visualized with money.

$90 $2   = $80 $12

4. a. Find the difference of 656 and 283.

   b. Find the difference of 3,729 and 1,749.

EXAMPLE 4   Find the difference of 549 and 187.

SOLUTION   In symbols the difference of 549 and 187 is written

$$549 - 187$$

Writing the problem vertically so that the digits with the same place value are aligned, we have

$$\begin{array}{r} 549 \\ -\,187 \end{array}$$

The top number in the tens column is smaller than the number below it. This means that we will have to borrow from the next larger column.

$$\begin{array}{r} \overset{4}{\cancel{5}} \ \overset{14}{\cancel{4}} \ 9 \\ -\,1 \ \ 8 \ \ 7 \\ \hline 3 \ \ 6 \ \ 2 \end{array}$$

Borrow 1 hundred to go with the 4 tens

9 − 7 = 2   Ones

14 − 8 = 6   Tens

4 − 1 = 3   Hundreds

The actual work we did in borrowing looks like this:

5 hundreds + 4 tens + 9 ones

= 4 hundreds + 1 hundred + 4 tens + 9 ones

= 4 hundreds + 14 tens + 9 ones

Getting Ready for Class

After reading through the preceding section, respond in your own words and in complete sentences.

1. Which sentence below describes the problem shown in Example 1?
   a. The difference of 241 and 376 is 135.
   b. The difference of 376 and 241 is 135.

2. Write a subtraction problem using the number 234 that involves borrowing from the tens column to the ones column.

3. Write a subtraction problem using the number 234 in which the answer is 111.

4. Describe how you would subtract the number 56 from the number 93.

Answers
4. a. 373 **b.** 1,980

Problem Set 1.4

A Perform the indicated operation. [Examples 1, 2, 4]

▶ **1.** Subtract 24 from 56.
32

2. Subtract 71 from 89.
18

3. Subtract 23 from 45.
22

4. Subtract 97 from 98.
1

5. Find the difference of 29 and 19.
10

6. Find the difference of 37 and 27.
10

▶ **7.** Find the difference of 126 and 15.
111

▶ **8.** Find the difference of 348 and 32.
316

B Work each of the following subtraction problems. [Examples 1, 2]

▶ **9.**   975
  − 663
  ‾‾‾‾‾
   312

10.   480
  − 260
  ‾‾‾‾‾
   220

11.   904
  − 501
  ‾‾‾‾‾
   403

12.   657
  − 507
  ‾‾‾‾‾
   150

▶ **13.**   9,876
  − 8,765
  ‾‾‾‾‾‾
   1,111

14.   5,008
  − 3,002
  ‾‾‾‾‾‾
   2,006

▶ **15.**   7,976
  − 3,432
  ‾‾‾‾‾‾
   4,544

16.   6,980
  −   470
  ‾‾‾‾‾‾
   6,510

C Find the difference in each case. (These problems all involve borrowing.) [Example 3]

▶ **17.** $52 - 37$
15

18. $65 - 48$
17

19. $70 - 37$
33

20. $90 - 21$
69

▶ **21.** $74 - 69$
5

22. $31 - 28$
3

23. $51 - 18$
33

24. $64 - 58$
6

25. $329 - 234$
95

▶ **26.** $518 - 492$
26

27. $348 - 196$
152

▶ **28.** $759 - 661$
98

29.   932
  − 658
  ‾‾‾‾‾
   274

30.   895
  − 597
  ‾‾‾‾‾
   298

31.   647
  − 159
  ‾‾‾‾‾
   488

32.   842
  − 199
  ‾‾‾‾‾
   643

▶ **33.**   905
  − 367
  ‾‾‾‾‾
   538

34.   804
  − 238
  ‾‾‾‾‾
   566

▶ **35.**   600
  − 437
  ‾‾‾‾‾
   163

36.   800
  − 342
  ‾‾‾‾‾
   458

▶ **37.**   4,583
  − 2,973
  ‾‾‾‾‾‾
   1,610

38.   7,849
  − 2,957
  ‾‾‾‾‾‾
   4,892

39.   79,040
  − 32,957
  ‾‾‾‾‾‾‾
   46,083

40.   86,492
  − 78,506
  ‾‾‾‾‾‾‾
   7,986

▶ Selected exercises available online at www.webassign.net/brookscole

A Complete the following tables.

▶ **41.**

First Number a	Second Number b	The Difference of a and b a − b
25	15	10
24	16	8
23	17	6
22	18	4

42.

First Number a	Second Number b	The Difference of a and b a − b
90	79	11
80	69	11
70	59	11
60	49	11

43.

First Number a	Second Number b	The Difference of a and b a − b
400	256	144
400	144	256
225	144	81
225	81	144

44.

First Number a	Second Number b	The Difference of a and b a − b
100	36	64
100	64	36
25	16	9
25	9	16

A Write each of the following expressions in words. Use the word *difference* in each case.

▶ **45.** $10 - 2$
The difference of 10 and 2

46. $9 - 5$
The difference of 9 and 5

47. $a - 6$
The difference of a and 6

48. $7 - x$
The difference of 7 and x

▶ **49.** $8 - 2 = 6$
The difference of 8 and 2 is 6.

50. $m - 1 = 4$
The difference of m and 1 is 4.

▶ **51.** What number do you subtract from 8 to get 5?
3

52. What number do you subtract from 6 to get 0?
6

53. What number do you subtract from 15 to get 7?
8

54. What number do you subtract from 21 to get 14?
7

▶ **55.** What number do you subtract from 35 to get 12?
23

56. What number do you subtract from 41 to get 11?
30

A Write each of the following sentences as mathematical expressions.

▶ **57.** The difference of 8 and 3
$8 - 3$

58. The difference of x and 2
$x - 2$

59. 9 subtracted from y
$y - 9$

60. a subtracted from b
$b - a$

61. The difference of 3 and 2 is 1.
$3 - 2 = 1$

62. The difference of 10 and y is 5.
$10 - y = 5$

▶ **63.** The difference of 37 and 9x is 10.
$37 - 9x = 10$

64. The difference of 3x and 2y is 15.
$3x - 2y = 15$

▶ **65.** The difference of 2y and 15x is 24.
$2y - 15x = 24$

66. The difference of 25x and 9y is 16.
$25x - 9y = 16$

67. The difference of (x + 2) and (x + 1) is 1.
$(x + 2) - (x + 1) = 1$

68. The difference of (x − 2) and (x − 4) is 2.
$(x - 2) - (x - 4) = 2$

D Applying the Concepts

Not all of the following application problems involve only subtraction. Some involve addition as well. Be sure to read each problem carefully.

▶ **69. Checkbook Balance** Diane has $504 in her checking account. If she writes five checks for a total of $249, how much does she have left in her account?

$255

Instructor Note
The instructions to the word problems on this page point to a common feature of this book. Students will find that not all the word problems here involve subtraction. Also, there may be numbers given in the problem that are not a part of the solution to the problem.

▶ **70. Checkbook Balance** Larry has $763 in his checking account. If he writes a check for each of the three bills listed below, how much will he have left in his account?

Item	Amount
Rent	$418
Phone	$25
Car repair	$117

$203

▶ **71. Home Prices** In 1985, Mr. Hicks paid $137,500 for his home. He sold it in 2008 for $310,000. What is the difference between what he sold it for and what he bought it for?

$172,500

▶ **72. Oil Spills** In March 1977, an oil tanker hit a reef off Taiwan and spilled 3,134,500 gallons of oil. In March 1989, an oil tanker hit a reef off Alaska and spilled 10,080,000 gallons of oil. How much more oil was spilled in the 1989 disaster?

6,945,500 gallons

73. Wind Speeds On April 12, 1934, the wind speed on top of Mount Washington was recorded at 231 miles per hour. When Hurricane Katrina struck on August 28, 2005, the highest recorded wind speed was 140 miles per hour. How much faster was the wind on top of Mount Washington, than the winds from Hurricane Katrina?

91 miles per hour

74. Concert Attendance Eleven thousand, seven hundred fifty-two people attended a recent concert at the Pepsi Arena in Albany, New York. If the arena holds 17,500 people, how many empty seats were there at the concert?

5,748 seats

75. Computer Hard Drive You purchase a new computer with 320 gigabytes of hard drive capacity. (A gigabyte is roughly a billion bytes). After loading a variety of programs you discover that you have used 147 gigabytes of your hard drive's capacity. How much hard drive capacity do you still have available?

173 gigabytes

76. State Size Alaska is the largest state in the United States with an area of 663,267 square miles. Rhode Island is the smallest state with an area of 1,545 square miles. How many more square miles does Alaska have when compared to Rhode Island?

661,722 square miles

▶ **77. Wind Energy** The bar chart below shows the states producing the most wind energy in 2006.

Wind Energy

Texas	2,768 MW
California	2,361 MW
Iowa	936 MW
Minnesota	895 MW
Washington	818 MW

Source: American Wind Energy Association 2006

a. Use the information in the bar chart to fill in the missing entries in the table.

State	Energy (megawatts)
Texas	2,768
California	2,361
Iowa	936
Washington	818

b. How much more wind energy is produced in Texas than in California?

407 MW

78. Auto Insurance Costs The bar chart below shows the cities with the highest annual insurance rates in 2006.

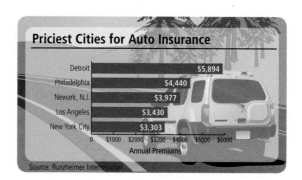

Priciest Cities for Auto Insurance

Detroit	$5,894
Philadelphia	$4,440
Newark, N.J.	$3,977
Los Angeles	$3,430
New York City	$3,303

0   $1000 $2000 $3000 $4000 $5000 $6000
Annual Premiums

Source: Runzheimer International

a. Use the information in the bar chart to fill in the missing entries in the table.

City	Cost (dollars)
Detroit	5,894
Philadelphia	4,440
Los Angeles	3,430
New York City	3,303

b. How much more does auto insurance cost in Detroit than in Los Angeles?

$2,464

Objectives

A Multiply whole numbers.

B Understand the notation and vocabulary of multiplication.

C Identify properties of multiplication.

D Find the area of squares and rectangles.

E Solve equations with multiplication.

Introduction . . .

A supermarket orders 35 cases of a certain soft drink. If each case contains 12 cans of the drink, how many cans were ordered?

To solve this problem and others like it, we must use multiplication. Multiplication is what we will cover in this section.

A Multiplying Whole Numbers

To begin, we can think of multiplication as shorthand for repeated addition. That is, multiplying 3 times 4 can be thought of this way:

$$3 \text{ times } 4 = 4 + 4 + 4 = 12$$

Multiplying 3 times 4 means to add three 4's. We can write 3 times 4 as 3×4, or $3 \cdot 4$.

EXAMPLE 1 Multiply: $3 \cdot 4{,}000$

SOLUTION Using the definition of multiplication as repeated addition, we have

$$3 \cdot 4{,}000 = 4{,}000 + 4{,}000 + 4{,}000$$
$$= 12{,}000$$

Here is one way to visualize this process.

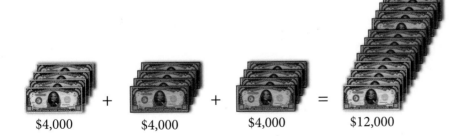

| $\$4{,}000$ | $\$4{,}000$ | $\$4{,}000$ | $\$12{,}000$ |

Notice that if we had multiplied 3 and 4 to get 12 and then attached three zeros on the right, the result would have been the same.

PRACTICE PROBLEMS

1. Multiply.
   a. $4 \cdot 70$
   b. $4 \cdot 700$
   c. $4 \cdot 7{,}000$

Answer
1. **a.** 280
   b. 2,800
   c. 28,000

Note The kind of notation we will use to indicate multiplication will depend on the situation. For example, when we are solving equations that involve letters, it is not a good idea to indicate multiplication with the symbol ×, since it could be confused with the letter *x*. The symbol we will use to indicate multiplication most often in this book is the multiplication dot.

Note We are assuming that you know the basic multiplication facts given in the table below. If you need some practice with these facts, go to Appendix 2 at the back of the book.

BASIC MULTIPLICATION FACTS

×	1	2	3	4	5	6	7	8	9
1	1	2	3	4	5	6	7	8	9
2	2	4	6	8	10	12	14	16	18
3	3	6	9	12	15	18	21	24	27
4	4	8	12	16	20	24	28	32	36
5	5	10	15	20	25	30	35	40	45
6	6	12	18	24	30	36	42	48	54
7	7	14	21	28	35	42	49	56	63
8	8	16	24	32	40	48	56	64	72
9	9	18	27	36	45	54	63	72	81

2. Identify the products and factors in the statement
$6 \cdot 7 = 42$

3. Identify the products and factors in the statement
$70 = 2 \cdot 5 \cdot 7$

B Notation

There are many ways to indicate multiplication. All the following statements are equivalent. They all indicate multiplication with the numbers 3 and 4.

$$3 \cdot 4, \quad 3 \times 4, \quad 3(4), \quad (3)4, \quad (3)(4), \qquad \begin{array}{r} 4 \\ \times 3 \\ \hline \end{array}$$

If one or both of the numbers we are multiplying are represented by letters, we may also use the following notation:

$5n$ means   5 times n
ab means a times b

Vocabulary

We use the word *product* to indicate multiplication. If we say "The product of 3 and 4 is 12," then we mean

$$3 \cdot 4 = 12$$

Both $3 \cdot 4$ and 12 are called the product of 3 and 4. The 3 and 4 are called *factors*.

TABLE 1	
In English	**In Symbols**
The product of 2 and 5	$2 \cdot 5$
The product of 5 and 2	$5 \cdot 2$
The product of 4 and n	$4n$
The product of x and y	xy
The product of 9 and 6 is 54	$9 \cdot 6 = 54$
The product of 2 and 8 is 16	$2 \cdot 8 = 16$

EXAMPLE 2   Identify the products and factors in the statement

$$9 \cdot 8 = 72$$

SOLUTION   The factors are 9 and 8, and the products are $9 \cdot 8$ and 72.

EXAMPLE 3   Identify the products and factors in the statement

$$30 = 2 \cdot 3 \cdot 5$$

SOLUTION   The factors are 2, 3, and 5. The products are $2 \cdot 3 \cdot 5$ and 30.

C Distributive Property

To develop an efficient method of multiplication, we need to use what is called the *distributive property*. To begin, consider the following two problems:

Problem 1   Problem 2
$3(4 + 5)$ $3(4) + 3(5)$
$= 3(9)$ $= 12 + 15$
$= 27$ $= 27$

The result in both cases is the same number, 27. This indicates that the original two expressions must have been equal also. That is,

$$3(4 + 5) = 3(4) + 3(5)$$

Answers
2. Factors: 6, 7; products: $6 \cdot 7$ and 42
3. Factors: 2, 5, 7; products: $2 \cdot 5 \cdot 7$ and 70

This is an example of the distributive property. We say that multiplication *distributes* over addition.

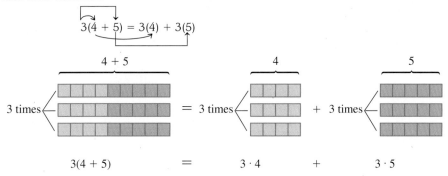

$$3(4 + 5) = 3(4) + 3(5)$$

$$3(4 + 5) \quad = \quad 3 \cdot 4 \quad + \quad 3 \cdot 5$$

We can write this property in symbols using the letters a, b, and c to represent any three whole numbers.

> **Distributive Property**
> If a, b, and c represent any three whole numbers, then
> $$a(b + c) = a(b) + a(c)$$

Suppose we want to find the product 7(65). By writing 65 as $60 + 5$ and applying the distributive property, we have:

$$
\begin{aligned}
7(65) &= 7(60 + 5) && 65 = 60 + 5 \\
&= 7(60) + 7(5) && \text{Distributive property} \\
&= 420 + 35 && \text{Multiplication} \\
&= 455 && \text{Addition}
\end{aligned}
$$

We can write the same problem vertically like this:

```
      60 + 5
  ×        7
          35   ←   7(5) = 35
  +      420   ←   7(60) = 420
         455
```

This saves some space in writing. But notice that we can cut down on the amount of writing even more if we write the problem this way:

STEP 2: 7(6) = 42; add the 3 we carried to 42 to get 45 →
$$
\begin{array}{r}
\overset{3}{6}5 \\
\times\ 7 \\
\hline
455
\end{array}
$$
STEP 1: 7(5) = 35; write the 5 in the ones column, and then carry the 3 to the tens column

This shortcut notation takes some practice.

EXAMPLE 4   Multiply: 9(43)

STEP 2: 9(4) = 36; add the 2 we carried to 36 to get 38 →
$$
\begin{array}{r}
\overset{2}{4}3 \\
\times\ 9 \\
\hline
387
\end{array}
$$
STEP 1: 9(3) = 27; write the 7 in the ones column, and then carry the 2 to the tens column

4. Multiply.
   a. 8(57)
   b. 8(570)

Answer
4. **a.** 456 **b.** 4,560

5. Multiply.
 a. 45(62)
 b. 45(620)

> **Note** This discussion is to show why we multiply the way we do. You should go over it in detail, so you will understand the reasons behind the process of multiplication. Besides being able to do multiplication, you should understand it.

6. Multiply.
 a. 356(641)
 b. 3,560(641)

EXAMPLE 5 Multiply: 52(37)

SOLUTION This is the same as 52(30 + 7) or by the distributive property

$$52(30) + 52(7)$$

We can find each of these products by using the shortcut method:

$$\begin{array}{r} 52 \\ \times\ 30 \\ \hline 1{,}560 \end{array} \qquad \begin{array}{r} \overset{1}{52} \\ \times\ 7 \\ \hline 364 \end{array}$$

The sum of these two numbers is $1{,}560 + 364 = 1{,}924$. Here is a summary of what we have so far:

$$\begin{aligned} 52(37) &= 52(30 + 7) & 37 = 30 + 7 \\ &= 52(30) + 52(7) & \text{Distributive property} \\ &= 1{,}560 + 364 & \text{Multiplication} \\ &= 1{,}924 & \text{Addition} \end{aligned}$$

The shortcut form for this problem is

$$\begin{array}{r} 52 \\ \times\ 37 \\ \hline 364 \\ +\ 1{,}560 \\ \hline 1{,}924 \end{array} \quad \begin{array}{l} \leftarrow\ 7(52) = 364 \\ \leftarrow\ 30(52) = 1{,}560 \end{array}$$

In this case we have not shown any of the numbers we carried, simply because it becomes very messy.

EXAMPLE 6 Multiply: 279(428)

SOLUTION
$$\begin{array}{r} 279 \\ \times\ 428 \\ \hline 2{,}232 \\ 5{,}580 \\ +\ 111{,}600 \\ \hline 119{,}412 \end{array} \quad \begin{array}{l} \leftarrow\ 8(279) = 2{,}232 \\ \leftarrow\ 20(279) = 5{,}580 \\ \leftarrow\ 400(279) = 111{,}600 \end{array}$$

USING TECHNOLOGY

Calculators

Here is how we would work the problem shown in Example 6 on a calculator:
Scientific Calculator: 279 [×] 428 [=]
Graphing Calculator: 279 [×] 428 [ENT]

Estimating

One way to estimate the answer to the problem shown in Example 6 is to round each number to the nearest hundred and then multiply the rounded numbers. Doing so would give us this:

$$300(400) = 120{,}000$$

Our estimate of the answer is 120,000, which is close to the actual answer, 119,412. Making estimates is important when we are using calculators; having an estimate of the answer will keep us from making major errors in multiplication.

Answers
5. a. 2,790 **b.** 27,900
6. a. 228,196 **b.** 2,281,960

EXAMPLE 7 A supermarket orders 35 cases of a certain soft drink. If each case contains 12 cans of the drink, how many cans were ordered?

SOLUTION We have 35 cases, and each case has 12 cans. The total number of cans is the product of 35 and 12, which is 35(12):

$$
\begin{array}{r}
12 \\
\times\ 35 \\
\hline
60 \quad\longleftarrow\quad 5(12) = 60 \\
+\ 360 \quad\longleftarrow\quad 30(12) = 360 \\
\hline
420
\end{array}
$$

There is a total of 420 cans of the soft drink.

7. If each tablet of vitamin C contains 550 milligrams of vitamin C, what is the total number of milligrams of vitamin C in a bottle that contains 365 tablets?

EXAMPLE 8 Shirley earns $12 an hour for the first 40 hours she works each week. If she has $109 deducted from her weekly check for taxes and retirement, how much money will she take home if she works 38 hours this week?

SOLUTION To find the amount of money she earned for the week, we multiply 12 and 38. From that total we subtract 109. The result is her take-home pay. Without showing all the work involved in the calculations, here is the solution:

$$38(\$12) = \$456 \qquad \text{Her total weekly earnings}$$
$$\$456 - \$109 = \$347 \qquad \text{Her take-home pay}$$

8. If Shirley works 36 hours the next week and has the same amount deducted from her check for taxes and retirement, how much will she take home?

EXAMPLE 9 In 1993, the government standardized the way in which nutrition information is presented on the labels of most packaged food products. Figure 1 shows one of these standardized food labels. It is from a package of Fritos Corn Chips that I ate the day I was writing this example. Approximately how many chips are in the bag, and what is the total number of calories consumed if all the chips in the bag are eaten?

SOLUTION Reading toward the top of the label, we see that there are about 32 chips in one serving, and 3 servings in the bag. Therefore, the total number of chips in the bag is

Nutrition Facts

Serving Size 1 oz. (28g/About 32 chips)
Servings Per Container: 3

Amount Per Serving

Calories 160	Calories from fat 90
	% Daily Value*
Total Fat 10 g	**16%**
Saturated Fat 1.5g	**8%**
Cholesterol 0mg	**0%**
Sodium 160mg	**7%**
Total Carbohydrate 15g	**5%**
Dietary Fiber 1g	**4%**
Sugars 0g	
Protein 2g	

Vitamin A 0%	•	Vitamin C 0%
Calcium 2%	•	Iron 0%

*Percent Daily Values are based on a 2,000 calorie diet

FIGURE 1

9. The amounts given in the middle of the nutrition label in Figure 1 are for one serving of chips. If all the chips in the bag are eaten, how much fat has been consumed? How much sodium?

Note The letter g that is shown after some of the numbers in the nutrition label in Figure 1 stands for grams, a unit used to measure weight. The unit mg stands for milligrams, another, smaller unit of weight. We will have more to say about these units later in the book.

$$3(32) = 96 \text{ chips}$$

This is an approximate number, because each serving is approximately 32 chips. Reading further we find that each serving contains 160 calories. Therefore, the total number of calories consumed by eating all the chips in the bag is

$$3(160) = 480 \text{ calories}$$

As we progress through the book, we will study more of the information in nutrition labels.

Answers
7. 200,750 milligrams
8. $323
9. 30 g of fat, 480 mg of sodium

10. If a 150-pound person bowls for 3 hours, will he or she burn all the calories consumed by eating two bags of the chips mentioned in Example 9?

EXAMPLE 10   The table below lists the number of calories burned in 1 hour of exercise by a person who weighs 150 pounds. Suppose a 150-pound person goes bowling for 2 hours after having eaten the bag of chips mentioned in Example 9. Will he or she burn all the calories consumed from the chips?

Activity	Calories Burned in 1 Hour by a 150-Pound Person
Bicycling	374
Bowling	265
Handball	680
Jazzercize	340
Jogging	680
Skiing	544

SOLUTION   Each hour of bowling burns 265 calories. If the person bowls for 2 hours, a total of

$$2(265) = 530 \text{ calories}$$

will have been burned. Because the bag of chips contained only 480 calories, all of them have been burned with 2 hours of bowling.

More Properties of Multiplication

Multiplication Property of 0
If a represents any number, then

$$a \cdot 0 = 0 \quad \text{and} \quad 0 \cdot a = 0$$

In words: Multiplication by 0 always results in 0.

Multiplication Property of 1
If a represents any number, then

$$a \cdot 1 = a \quad \text{and} \quad 1 \cdot a = a$$

In words: Multiplying any number by 1 leaves that number unchanged.

Commutative Property of Multiplication
If a and b are any two numbers, then

$$ab = ba$$

In words: The order of the numbers in a product doesn't affect the result.

Associative Property of Multiplication
If a, b, and c represent any three numbers, then

$$(ab)c = a(bc)$$

In words: We can change the grouping of the numbers in a product without changing the result.

Instructor Note
Again, we are emphasizing the properties of numbers in order to help with the transition to algebra.

Answer
10. No

To visualize the commutative property, we can think of an instructor with 12 students.

4 chairs across, 3 chairs back   =   3 chairs across, 4 chairs back

EXAMPLE 11 Use the commutative property of multiplication to rewrite each of the following products:

        a. $7 \cdot 9$ **b.** $4(6)$

SOLUTION Applying the commutative property to each expression, we have:

        a. $7 \cdot 9 = 9 \cdot 7$ **b.** $4(6) = 6(4)$

EXAMPLE 12 Use the associative property of multiplication to rewrite each of the following products:

        a. $(2 \cdot 7) \cdot 9$ **b.** $3 \cdot (8 \cdot 2)$

SOLUTION Applying the associative property of multiplication, we regroup as follows:

        a. $(2 \cdot 7) \cdot 9 = 2 \cdot (7 \cdot 9)$ **b.** $3 \cdot (8 \cdot 2) = (3 \cdot 8) \cdot 2$

D Formulas for Area

FACTS FROM GEOMETRY: Formulas for Area
A square and rectangle are shown in the following figures. Note that we have labeled the dimensions of each with variables. The formula for the area of each object is given in terms of its dimensions.

A Square   A Rectangle

Area $= s^2$ Area $= \ell w$

    The formula for area gives us a measure of the amount of surface the object has.

11. Use the commutative property of multiplication to rewrite each of the following products.
    a. $5 \cdot 8$
    b. $7(2)$

12. Use the associative property of multiplication to rewrite each of the following products.
    a. $(5 \cdot 7) \cdot 4$
    b. $4 \cdot (6 \cdot 4)$

Answers
11. a. $8 \cdot 5$ **b.** $2(7)$
12. a. $5 \cdot (7 \cdot 4)$ **b.** $(4 \cdot 6) \cdot 4$

13. Find the area of the figures in Example 13, with the following changes:
   a. $s = 4$ feet
   b. $l = 7$ inches
      $w = 5$ inches

EXAMPLE 13 Find the area of each figure.

a.

   5 ft

b.

   6 in.

   8 in.

SOLUTION We use the preceding formulas to find the area. In each case, the units for area are square units.

   a. Area $= s^2 = (5 \text{ feet})^2 = 25$ square feet
   b. Area $= lw = (8 \text{ inches})(6 \text{ inches}) = 48$ square inches

E Solving Equations

If n is used to represent a number, then the equation

$$4 \cdot n = 12$$

is read "4 times n is 12," or "The product of 4 and n is 12." This means that we are looking for the number we multiply by 4 to get 12. The number is 3. Because the equation becomes a true statement if n is 3, we say that 3 is the solution to the equation.

EXAMPLE 14 Find the solution to each of the following equations:

   a. $6 \cdot n = 24$ b. $4 \cdot n = 36$ c. $15 = 3 \cdot n$ d. $21 = 3 \cdot n$

SOLUTION
   a. The solution to $6 \cdot n = 24$ is 4, because $6 \cdot 4 = 24$.
   b. The solution to $4 \cdot n = 36$ is 9, because $4 \cdot 9 = 36$.
   c. The solution to $15 = 3 \cdot n$ is 5, because $15 = 3 \cdot 5$.
   d. The solution to $21 = 3 \cdot n$ is 7, because $21 = 3 \cdot 7$.

14. Use multiplication facts to find the solution to each of the following equations.
   a. $5 \cdot n = 35$
   b. $8 \cdot n = 72$
   c. $49 = 7 \cdot n$
   d. $27 = 9 \cdot n$

Getting Ready for Class

After reading through the preceding section, respond in your own words and in complete sentences.

1. Use the numbers 7, 8, and 9 to give an example of the distributive property.
2. When we write the distributive property in words, we say "multiplication distributes over addition." It is also true that multiplication distributes over subtraction. Use the letters a, b, and c to write the distributive property using multiplication and subtraction.
3. We can multiply 8 and 487 by writing 487 in expanded form as $400 + 80 + 7$ and then applying the distributive property. Apply the distributive property to the expression below and then simplify.

   $$8(400 + 80 + 7) =$$

4. Find the mistake in the following multiplication problem. Then work the problem correctly.

$$
\begin{array}{r}
43 \\
\times\ 68 \\
\hline
344 \\
+\ 258 \\
\hline
602
\end{array}
$$

Answers
13. a. 16 square feet
    b. 35 square inches
14. a. 7 b. 9 c. 7 d. 3

Problem Set 1.5

A Multiply each of the following. [Example 1]

▶ **1.** 3 · 100
300

2. 7 · 100
700

3. 3 · 200
600

4. 4 · 200
800

▶ **5.** 6 · 500
3,000

6. 8 · 400
3,200

7. 5 · 1,000
5,000

8. 8 · 1,000
8,000

▶ **9.** 3 · 7,000
21,000

10. 6 · 7,000
42,000

11. 9 · 9,000
81,000

12. 7 · 7,000
49,000

A Find each of the following products. (Multiply.) In each case use the shortcut method. [Examples 4–6]

▶ **13.**   25
      × 4
      100

14.   43
      × 9
      387

15.   38
      × 6
      228

16.   45
      × 7
      315

▶ **17.**   18
      × 2
      36

18.   29
      × 3
      87

19.   72
      × 20
      1,440

20.   68
      × 30
      2,040

▶ **21.**   19
      × 50
      950

22.   24
      × 40
      960

23.   69
      × 25
      1,725

24.   27
      × 36
      972

▶ **25.**   11
      × 11
      121

26.   12
      × 21
      252

27.   97
      × 16
      1,552

28.   24
      × 39
      936

▶ **29.**   168
      × 25
      4,200

30.   452
      × 34
      15,368

▶ **31.** 728
      × 91
      66,248

32. 680
      × 76
      51,680

33. 698
      × 400
      279,200

34. 879
      × 600
      527,400

▶ **35.** 111
      × 111
      12,321

36. 123
      × 321
      39,483

37. 532
      × 200
      106,400

38. 277
      × 900
      249,300

▶ **39.** 856
      × 232
      198,592

40. 455
      × 248
      112,840

41. 976
      × 628
      612,928

42. 432
      × 555
      239,760

43. 2,468
      × 135
      333,180

44. 2,725
      × 324
      882,900

▶ **45.** 24,563
      × 735
      18,053,805

46. 56,728
      × 852
      48,332,256

47. 44,777
      × 5,888
      263,646,976

48. 33,999
      × 2,555
      86,867,445

B Complete the following tables.

49.

First Number a	Second Number b	Their Product ab
11	11	121
11	22	242
22	22	484
22	44	968

▶ **50.**

First Number a	Second Number b	Their Product ab
25	15	375
25	30	750
50	15	750
50	30	1,500

51.

First Number a	Second Number b	Their Product ab
25	10	250
25	100	2,500
25	1,000	25,000
25	10,000	250,000

52.

First Number a	Second Number b	Their Product ab
11	111	1,221
11	222	2,442
22	111	2,442
22	222	4,884

▶ **53.**

First Number a	Second Number b	Their Product ab
12	20	240
36	20	720
12	40	480
36	40	1,440

54.

First Number a	Second Number b	Their Product ab
10	12	120
100	12	1,200
1,000	12	12,000
10,000	12	120,000

B Write each of the following expressions in words, using the word *product*.

▶ **55.** 6 · 7

The product of 6 and 7

56. 9(4)

The product of 9 and 4

57. 2 · *n*

The product of 2 and *n*

58. 5 · *x*

The product of 5 and *x*

▶ **59.** 9 · 7 = 63

The product of 9 and 7 is 63.

60. (5)(6) = 30

The product of 5 and 6 is 30.

B Write each of the following in symbols.

61. The product of 7 and *n*

7 · *n*

62. The product of 9 and *x*

9 · *x*

▶ **63.** The product of 6 and 7 is 42.

6 · 7 = 42

64. The product of 8 and 9 is 72.

8 · 9 = 72

▶ **65.** The product of 0 and 6 is 0.

0 · 6 = 0

66. The product of 1 and 6 is 6.

1 · 6 = 6

B Identify the products in each statement.

▶ **67.** 9 · 7 = 63

Products: 9 · 7 and 63

68. 2(6) = 12

Products: 2(6) and 12

69. 4(4) = 16

Products: 4(4) and 16

70. 5 · 5 = 25

Products: 5 · 5 and 25

B Identify the factors in each statement.

71. 2 · 3 · 4 = 24

Factors: 2, 3, and 4

72. 6 · 1 · 5 = 30

Factors: 6, 1, and 5

73. 12 = 2 · 2 · 3

Factors: 2, 2, and 3

74. 42 = 2 · 3 · 7

Factors: 2, 3, and 7

C Rewrite each of the following using the commutative property of multiplication. [Example 11]

75. 5(9)

9(5)

▶ **76.** 4(3)

3(4)

77. 6 · 7

7 · 6

78. 8 · 3

3 · 8

C Rewrite each of the following using the associative property of multiplication. [Example 12]

79. 2 · (7 · 6)

(2 · 7) · 6

▶ **80.** 4 · (8 · 5)

(4 · 8) · 5

81. 3 × (9 × 1)

(3 × 9) × 1

82. 5 × (8 × 2)

(5 × 8) × 2

C Use the distributive property to rewrite each expression, then simplify.

▶ **83.** 7(2 + 3)

7(2) + 7(3) = 35

84. 4(5 + 8)

4(5) + 4(8) = 52

85. 9(4 + 7)

9(4) + 9(7) = 99

86. 6(9 + 5)

6(9) + 6(5) = 84

▶ **87.** 3(x + 1)

3x + 3

88. 5(x + 8)

5x + 40

89. 2(x + 5)

2x + 10

90. 4(x + 3)

4x + 12

E Find a solution for each equation. [Example 14]

91. $4 \cdot n = 12$

n = 3

92. $3 \cdot n = 12$

n = 4

▶ **93.** $9 \cdot n = 81$

n = 9

94. $6 \cdot n = 36$

n = 6

95. $0 = n \cdot 5$

n = 0

96. $6 = 1 \cdot n$

n = 6

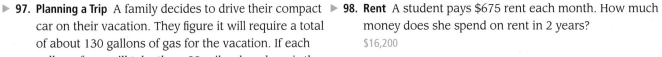

■ Applying the Concepts

Most, but not all, of the application problems that follow require multiplication. Read the problems carefully before trying to solve them.

▶ **97. Planning a Trip** A family decides to drive their compact car on their vacation. They figure it will require a total of about 130 gallons of gas for the vacation. If each gallon of gas will take them 22 miles, how long is the trip they are planning?

2,860 miles

▶ **98. Rent** A student pays $675 rent each month. How much money does she spend on rent in 2 years?

$16,200

99. Downloading Songs You receive a gift card for the Apple™ iTunes™ store for $25.00 and download 18 songs at $0.99 per song. How much is left on your gift card?

$7.18

100. Cost of Building a Home When you consider building a new home it is helpful to be able to estimate the cost of building that house. A simple way to do this is to multiply the number of square feet under the roof of the house by the average building cost per square foot. Suppose you contact a builder who estimates that, on average, he charges $142.00 per square foot. Determine the cost to build a 2,067 square foot house.

$293,514

101. World's Busiest Airport Atlanta, Georgia is home to the world's busiest airport, Hartsfield-Jackson Atlanta International Airport. According to the Federal Aviation Administration about 50 jets can land and take off every 15 minutes which is about 200 jets an hour. About how many jets land and take off in the month of July?

148,800 jets

102. Flowers It is probably no surprise that Valentine's Day is the busiest day of the year for florists. It is estimated that 214 million roses were produced for Valentine's Day in 2007 (Source: Society of American Florists). If a single rose costs a consumer $2.50, what was the total revenue for the roses produced?

$535,000,000

Exercise and Calories The table below is an extension of the table we used in Example 10 of this section. It gives the amount of energy expended during 1 hour of various activities for people of different weights. The accompanying figure is a nutrition label from a bag of Doritos tortilla chips. Use the information from the table and the nutrition label to answer Problems 103–108.

CALORIES BURNED THROUGH EXERCISE			
	Calories Per Hour		
Activity	120 Pounds	150 Pounds	180 Pounds
Bicycling	299	374	449
Bowling	212	265	318
Handball	544	680	816
Jazzercise	272	340	408
Jogging	544	680	816
Skiing	435	544	653

Nutrition Facts

Serving Size 1 oz. (28g/About 12 chips)
Servings Per Container About 2

Amount Per Serving

Calories 140   Calories from fat 60

	% Daily Value*
Total Fat 7g	11%
Saturated Fat 1g	6%
Cholesterol 0mg	0%
Sodium 170mg	7%
Total Carbohydrate 18g	6%
Dietary Fiber 1g	4%
Sugars less than 1g	
Protein 2g	

Vitamin A 0%   •   Vitamin C 0%
Calcium 4%   •   Iron 2%

*Percent Daily Values are based on a 2,000 calorie diet

▶ **103.** Suppose you weigh 180 pounds. How many calories would you burn if you play handball for 2 hours and then ride your bicycle for 1 hour?

2,081 calories

104. How many calories are burned by a 120-lb person who jogs for 1 hour and then goes bike riding for 2 hours?

1,142 calories

▶ **105.** How many calories would you consume if you ate the entire bag of chips?

280 calories

106. Approximately how many chips are in the bag?

About 24 chips

▶ **107.** If you weigh 180 pounds, will you burn off the calories consumed by eating 3 servings of tortilla chips if you ride your bike 1 hour?

Yes

108. If you weigh 120 pounds, will you burn off the calories consumed by eating 3 servings of tortilla chips if you ride your bike for 1 hour?

No

D Find the area of each figure. [Example 13]

▶ **109.**

1 in.

1 in.

1 in²

110.

15 mm

15 mm

225 mm²

▶ **111.**

0.75 in.

1.5 in.

1.125 in²

112.

1.5 cm

4.5 cm

6.75 cm²

● Estimating

Mentally estimate the answer to each of the following problems by rounding each number to the indicated place and then multiplying.

113. 750 hundred
$\times$ 12 ten
8,000

114. 591 hundred
$\times$ 323 hundred
180,000

115. 3,472 thousand
$\times$ 511 hundred
1,500,000

116. 399 hundred
$\times$ 298 hundred
120,000

117. 2,399 thousand
$\times$ 698 hundred
1,400,000

118. 9,999 thousand
$\times$ 666 hundred
7,000,000

● Extending the Concepts: Number Sequences

A *geometric sequence* is a sequence of numbers in which each number is obtained from the previous number by multiplying by the same number each time. For example, the sequence 3, 6, 12, 24, . . . is a geometric sequence, starting with 3, in which each number comes from multiplying the previous number by 2. Find the next number in each of the following geometric sequences. The definition given here for geometric sequences is used again in a number of *Extending the Concepts* problems.

119. 5, 10, 20, . . .
40

120. 10, 50, 250, . . .
1,250

121. 2, 6, 18, . . .
54

122. 12, 24, 48, . . .
96

Introduction . . .

Darlene is planning a party and would like to serve 8-ounce glasses of soda. The glasses will be filled from 32-ounce bottles of soda. In order to know how many bottles of soda to buy, she needs to find out how many of the 8-ounce glasses can be filled by one of the 32-ounce bottles. One way to solve this problem is with division: dividing 32 by 8. A diagram of the problem is shown in Figure 1.

32-ounce bottle   8-ounce glasses

FIGURE 1

As a division problem: As a multiplication problem:

$32 \div 8 = 4$ $4 \cdot 8 = 32$

A Notation

As was the case with multiplication, there are many ways to indicate division. All the following statements are equivalent. They all mean 10 divided by 5.

$$10 \div 5, \quad \frac{10}{5}, \quad 10/5, \quad 5\overline{)10}$$

The kind of notation we use to write division problems will depend on the situation. We will use the notation $5\overline{)10}$ mostly with the long-division problems found in this chapter. The notation $\frac{10}{5}$ will be used in the chapter on fractions and in later chapters. The horizontal line used with the notation $\frac{10}{5}$ is called the *fraction bar.*

Vocabulary

The word *quotient* is used to indicate division. If we say "The quotient of 10 and 5 is 2," then we mean

$$10 \div 5 = 2 \quad \text{or} \quad \frac{10}{5} = 2$$

The 10 is called the *dividend,* and the 5 is called the *divisor.* All the expressions, $10 \div 5$, $\frac{10}{5}$, and 2, are called the *quotient* of 10 and 5.

TABLE 1	
In English	**In Symbols**
The quotient of 15 and 3	$15 \div 3$, or $\dfrac{15}{3}$, or 15/3
The quotient of 3 and 15	$3 \div 15$, or $\dfrac{3}{15}$, or 3/15
The quotient of 8 and n	$8 \div n$, or $\dfrac{8}{n}$, or 8/n
x divided by 2	$x \div 2$, or $\dfrac{x}{2}$, or x/2
The quotient of 21 and 3 is 7.	$21 \div 3 = 7$, or $\dfrac{21}{3} = 7$

The Meaning of Division

One way to arrive at an answer to a division problem is by thinking in terms of multiplication. For example, if we want to find the quotient of 32 and 8, we may ask, "What do we multiply by 8 to get 32?"

$$32 \div 8 = ? \qquad \text{means} \qquad 8 \cdot ? = 32$$

Because we know from our work with multiplication that $8 \cdot 4 = 32$, it must be true that

$$32 \div 8 = 4$$

Table 2 lists some additional examples.

TABLE 2		
Division		**Multiplication**
$18 \div 6 = 3$	because	$6 \cdot 3 = 18$
$32 \div 8 = 4$	because	$8 \cdot 4 = 32$
$10 \div 2 = 5$	because	$2 \cdot 5 = 10$
$72 \div 9 = 8$	because	$9 \cdot 8 = 72$

B Division by One-Digit Numbers

Consider the following division problem:

$$465 \div 5$$

We can think of this problem as asking the question, "How many fives can we subtract from 465?" To answer the question we begin subtracting multiples of 5. One way to organize this process is shown below:

$$
\begin{array}{r}
90 \\
5{\overline{\smash{\big)}\,465}} \\
-450 \\
\hline
15
\end{array}
$$

⟵ We first guess that there are at least 90 fives in 465

⟵ $90(5) = 450$

⟵ 15 is left after we subtract 90 fives from 465

What we have done so far is subtract 90 fives from 465 and found that 15 is still left. Because there are 3 fives in 15, we continue the process.

```
    3   ←——— There are 3 fives in 15
   90
 5)465
 −450
   15
 − 15   ←——— 3 · 5 = 15
    0   ←——— The difference is 0
```

The total number of fives we have subtracted from 465 is

$$90 + 3 = 93$$

We now summarize the results of our work.

$465 ÷ 5 = 93$ which we check

with multiplication ⟶

```
   1
  93
 × 5
 465
```

The division problem just shown can be shortened by eliminating the subtraction signs, eliminating the zeros in each estimate, and eliminating some of the numbers that are repeated in the problem.

The shorthand form for this problem

```
    3
   90
 5)465
  450
   15
   15
    0
```

looks like this.

```
   93
 5)465
  45↓
   15
   15
    0
```

The arrow indicates that we bring down the 5 after we subtract.

The problem shown above on the right is the shortcut form of what is called *long division*. Here is an example showing this shortcut form of long division from start to finish.

EXAMPLE 1   Divide: $595 ÷ 7$

SOLUTION Because $7(8) = 56$, our first estimate of the number of sevens that can be subtracted from 595 is 80:

```
    8   ←——— The 8 is placed above the tens column
 7)595       so we know our first estimate is 80
  56↓   ←——— 8(7) = 56
   35   ←——— 59 − 56 = 3; then bring down the 5
```

Since $7(5) = 35$, we have

```
   85   ←——— There are 5 sevens in 35
 7)595
  56↓
   35
   35   ←——— 5(7) = 35
    0   ←——— 35 − 35 = 0
```

Our result is $595 ÷ 7 = 85$, which we can check with multiplication:

```
   3
  85
 × 7
 595
```

PRACTICE PROBLEMS

1. Divide.
 a. $296 ÷ 4$
 b. $2,960 ÷ 4$

Answer
1. **a.** 74 **b.** 740

2. Divide.
   a. 6,792 ÷ 24
   b. 67,920 ÷ 24

Division by Two-Digit Numbers

EXAMPLE 2   Divide: 9,380 ÷ 35

SOLUTION   In this case our divisor, 35, is a two-digit number. The process of division is the same. We still want to find the number of thirty-fives we can subtract from 9,380.

$$
\begin{array}{r}
2 \quad \longleftarrow \text{ The 2 is placed above the hundreds column} \\
35)\overline{9,380} \\
\underline{7\ 0}\downarrow \quad \longleftarrow 2(35) = 70 \\
2\ 38 \quad \longleftarrow 93 - 70 = 23; \text{ then bring down the 8}
\end{array}
$$

We can make a few preliminary calculations to help estimate how many thirty-fives are in 238:

$$5 \times 35 = 175 \qquad 6 \times 35 = 210 \qquad 7 \times 35 = 245$$

Because 210 is the closest to 238 without being larger than 238, we use 6 as our next estimate:

$$
\begin{array}{r}
26 \quad \longleftarrow \text{ 6 in the tens column means this estimate is 60} \\
35)\overline{9,380} \\
7\ 0 \\
\overline{2\ 38} \\
2\ 10\downarrow \quad \longleftarrow 6(35) = 210 \\
\overline{280} \quad \longleftarrow 238 - 210 = 28; \text{ bring down the 0}
\end{array}
$$

Because 35(8) = 280, we have

$$
\begin{array}{r}
268 \\
35)\overline{9,380} \\
\underline{7\ 0} \\
2\ 38 \\
\underline{2\ 10} \\
280 \\
\underline{280} \quad \longleftarrow 8(35) = 280 \\
0 \quad \longleftarrow 280 - 280 = 0
\end{array}
$$

We can check our result with multiplication:

$$
\begin{array}{r}
268 \\
\times\ \ 35 \\
\hline
1,340 \\
\underline{8,040} \\
9,380
\end{array}
$$

3. Divide.
   1,872 ÷ 9

EXAMPLE 3   Divide: 1,872 by 18.

SOLUTION   Here is the first step.

$$
\begin{array}{r}
1 \quad \longleftarrow \text{ 1 is placed above hundred column} \\
18)\overline{1,872} \\
\underline{1\ 8} \quad \longleftarrow \text{ Multiply 1(18) to get 18} \\
0 \quad \longleftarrow \text{ Subtract to get 0}
\end{array}
$$

Answer
2. a. 283 **b.** 2,830

The next step is to bring down the 7 and divide again.

$$
\begin{array}{r}
10 \\
18\overline{)1{,}872} \\
\underline{1\ 8}\downarrow \\
07 \\
\underline{\ \ 0} \\
7
\end{array}
$$

← 0 is placed above tens column. 0 is the largest number we can multiply by 18 and not go over 7

← Multiply 0(18) to get 0

← Subtract to get 7

Here is the complete problem.

$$
\begin{array}{r}
104 \\
18\overline{)1{,}872} \\
\underline{1\ 8}\downarrow\ | \\
07\ \ | \\
\underline{\ \ 0}\downarrow \\
72 \\
\underline{72} \\
0
\end{array}
$$

To show our answer is correct, we multiply.

$$18(104) = 1{,}872$$

Division with Remainders

Suppose Darlene was planning to use 6-ounce glasses instead of 8-ounce glasses for her party. To see how many glasses she could fill from the 32-ounce bottle, she would divide 32 by 6. If she did so, she would find that she could fill 5 glasses, but after doing so she would have 2 ounces of soda left in the bottle. A diagram of this problem is shown in Figure 2.

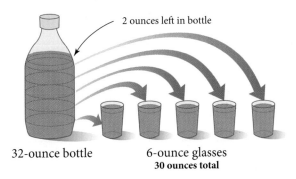

2 ounces left in bottle

32-ounce bottle

6-ounce glasses
30 ounces total

FIGURE 2

Writing the results in the diagram as a division problem looks like this:

$$
\begin{array}{r}
5 \\
6\overline{)32} \\
\underline{30} \\
2
\end{array}
$$

Divisor ⟶ | ← Quotient
← Dividend
← Remainder

4. Divide.
  a. $1{,}883 \div 27$
  b. $1{,}883 \div 18$

EXAMPLE 4   Divide: $1{,}690 \div 67$

SOLUTION Dividing as we have previously, we get

$$
\begin{array}{r}
25 \\
67\overline{)1{,}690} \\
1\ 34\downarrow \\
\hline
350 \\
335 \\
\hline
15 \leftarrow \text{15 is left over}
\end{array}
$$

We have 15 left, and because 15 is less than 67, no more sixty-sevens can be subtracted. In a situation like this we call 15 the *remainder* and write

These indicate that the remainder is 15

$$
\begin{array}{r}
25\ \text{R}\ 15 \\
67\overline{)1{,}690} \\
1\ 34\downarrow \\
\hline
350 \\
335 \\
\hline
15
\end{array}
\qquad \text{or} \qquad
\begin{array}{r}
25\frac{15}{67} \\
67\overline{)1{,}690} \\
1\ 34\downarrow \\
\hline
350 \\
335 \\
\hline
15
\end{array}
$$

Both forms of notation shown above indicate that 15 is the remainder. The notation R 15 is the notation we will use in this chapter. The notation $\frac{15}{67}$ will be useful in the chapter on fractions.

  To check a problem like this, we multiply the divisor and the quotient as usual, and then add the remainder to this result:

$$
\begin{array}{r}
67 \\
\times\ 25 \\
\hline
335 \\
1{,}340 \\
\hline
1{,}675 \leftarrow \text{Product of divisor and quotient}
\end{array}
$$

$$1{,}675 + 15 = 1{,}690$$

Remainder   Dividend

USING TECHNOLOGY

Calculators

Here is how we would work the problem shown in Example 4 on a calculator:

Scientific Calculator: 1690 ÷ 67 =

Graphing Calculator: 1690 ÷ 67 ENT

In both cases the calculator will display 25.223881 (give or take a few digits at the end), which gives the remainder in decimal form. We will discuss decimals later in the book.

Answer
4. a. 69 R 20, or $69\frac{20}{27}$
  b. 104 R 11, or $104\frac{11}{18}$

C Applications

EXAMPLE 5   A family has an annual income of $35,880. How much is their average monthly income?

SOLUTION   Because there are 12 months in a year and the yearly (annual) income is $35,880, we want to know what $35,880 divided into 12 equal parts is. Therefore we have

$$
\begin{array}{r}
2\,990 \\
12\overline{)35{,}880} \\
\underline{24} \\
11\,8 \\
\underline{10\,8} \\
1\,08 \\
\underline{1\,08} \\
00
\end{array}
$$

Because 35,880 ÷ 12 = 2,990, the monthly income for this family is $2,990.

Division by Zero

We cannot divide by 0. That is, we cannot use 0 as a divisor in any division problem. Here's why.

Suppose there was an answer to the problem

$$\frac{8}{0} = \,?$$

That would mean that

$$0 \cdot \,? = 8$$

But we already know that multiplication by 0 always produces 0. There is no number we can use for the ? to make a true statement out of

$$0 \cdot \,? = 8$$

Because this was equivalent to the original division problem

$$\frac{8}{0} = \,?$$

we have no number to associate with the expression $\frac{8}{0}$. It is undefined.

> **Rule**
> Division by 0 is undefined. Any expression with a divisor of 0 is undefined. We cannot divide by 0.

5. A family spends $1,872 on a 12-day vacation. How much did they spend each day on average?

Note   To estimate the answer to Example 5 quickly, we can replace 35,880 with 36,000 and mentally calculate
$$36{,}000 \div 12$$
which gives an estimate of 3,000. Our actual answer, 2,990, is close enough to our estimate to convince us that we have not made a major error in our calculation.

Getting Ready for Class

After reading through the preceding section, respond in your own words and in complete sentences.

1. Which sentence below describes the problem shown in Example 1?
   a. The quotient of 7 and 595 is 85.
   b. Seven divided by 595 is 85.
   c. The quotient of 595 and 7 is 85.

2. In Example 2, we divide 9,380 by 35 to obtain 268. Suppose we add 35 to 9,380, making it 9,415. What will our answer be if we divide 9,415 by 35?

3. Example 4 shows that $1,690 \div 67$ gives a quotient of 25 with a remainder of 15. If we were to divide 1,692 by 67, what would the remainder be?

4. Explain why division by 0 is undefined in mathematics.

Problem Set 1.6

A Write each of the following in symbols.

▶ **1.** The quotient of 6 and 3
6 ÷ 3

2. The quotient of 3 and 6
3 ÷ 6

3. The quotient of 45 and 9
45 ÷ 9

4. The quotient of 12 and 4
12 ÷ 4

5. The quotient of r and s
$r \div s$

6. The quotient of s and r
$s \div r$

▶ **7.** The quotient of 20 and 4 is 5.
20 ÷ 4 = 5

8. The quotient of 20 and 5 is 4.
20 ÷ 5 = 4

Write a multiplication statement that is equivalent to each of the following division statements.

▶ **9.** 6 ÷ 2 = 3
2 · 3 = 6

10. 6 ÷ 3 = 2
3 · 2 = 6

▶ **11.** $\dfrac{36}{9} = 4$
9 · 4 = 36

12. $\dfrac{36}{4} = 9$
4 · 9 = 36

13. $\dfrac{48}{6} = 8$
6 · 8 = 48

14. $\dfrac{35}{7} = 5$
7 · 5 = 35

▶ **15.** 28 ÷ 7 = 4
7 · 4 = 28

16. 81 ÷ 9 = 9
9 · 9 = 81

B Find each of the following quotients. (Divide.) [Examples 1–3]

▶ **17.** 25 ÷ 5
5

18. 72 ÷ 8
9

19. 40 ÷ 5
8

20. 12 ÷ 2
6

21. 9 ÷ 0
Undefined

▶ **22.** 7 ÷ 1
7

23. 360 ÷ 8
45

24. 285 ÷ 5
57

▶ **25.** $\dfrac{138}{6}$
23

26. $\dfrac{267}{3}$
89

▶ **27.** $5\overline{)7,650}$
1,530

28. $5\overline{)5,670}$
1,134

▶ **29.** $5\overline{)6,750}$
1,350

30. $5\overline{)6,570}$
1,314

31. $3\overline{)54,000}$
18,000

32. $3\overline{)50,400}$
16,800

▶ **33.** $3\overline{)50,040}$
16,680

34. $3\overline{)50,004}$
16,668

■ Estimating

Work Problems 35 through 38 mentally, without using a calculator.

▶ **35.** The quotient 845 ÷ 93 is closest to which of the following numbers?

    a. 10　　**b.** 100　　**c.** 1,000　　**d.** 10,000

    a

36. The quotient 762 ÷ 43 is closest to which of the following numbers?

    a. 2　　**b.** 20　　**c.** 200　　**d.** 2,000

    b

37. The quotient 15,208 ÷ 771 is closest to which of the following numbers?

    a. 2　　**b.** 20　　**c.** 200　　**d.** 2,000

    b

38. The quotient 24,471 ÷ 523 is closest to which of the following numbers?

    a. 5　　**b.** 50　　**c.** 500　　**d.** 5,000

    b

Mentally give a one-digit estimate for each of the following quotients. That is, for each quotient, mentally estimate the answer using one of the digits 1, 2, 3, 4, 5, 6, 7, 8, or 9.

39. 316 ÷ 289

    1

40. 662 ÷ 289

    2

41. 728 ÷ 355

    2

42. 728 ÷ 177

    4

43. 921 ÷ 243

    4

44. 921 ÷ 442

    2

45. 673 ÷ 109

    6

46. 673 ÷ 218

    3

B Divide. You shouldn't have any wrong answers because you can always check your results with multiplication. [Examples 1–3]

▶ **47.** 1,440 ÷ 32

    45

48. 1,206 ÷ 67

    18

49. $\dfrac{2,401}{49}$

    49

▶ **50.** $\dfrac{4,606}{49}$

    94

▶ **51.** $28\overline{)12,096}$

    432

52. $28\overline{)96,012}$

    3,429

53. $63\overline{)90,594}$

    1,438

54. $45\overline{)17,595}$

    391

▶ **55.** $87\overline{)61,335}$

    705

56. $79\overline{)48,032}$

    608

57. $45\overline{)135,900}$

    3,020

58. $56\overline{)227,920}$

    4,070

B Complete the following tables.

59.

First Number a	Second Number b	The Quotient of a and b $\frac{a}{b}$
100	25	4
100	26	3 R 22
100	27	3 R 19
100	28	3 R 16

60.

First Number a	Second Number b	The Quotient of a and b $\frac{a}{b}$
100	25	4
101	25	4 R 1
102	25	4 R 2
103	25	4 R 3

B The following division problems all have remainders. [Example 4]

▶ **61.** $6\overline{)370}$
61 R 4

62. $8\overline{)390}$
48 R 6

63. $3\overline{)271}$
90 R 1

64. $3\overline{)172}$
57 R 1

▶ **65.** $26\overline{)345}$
13 R 7

66. $26\overline{)543}$
20 R 23

67. $71\overline{)16,620}$
234 R 6

68. $71\overline{)33,240}$
468 R 12

69. $23\overline{)9,250}$
402 R 4

70. $23\overline{)20,800}$
904 R 8

▶ **71.** $169\overline{)5,950}$
35 R 35

▶ **72.** $391\overline{)34,450}$
88 R 42

C Applying the Concepts [Example 5]

The application problems that follow may involve more than merely division. Some may require addition, subtraction, or multiplication, whereas others may use a combination of two or more operations.

▶ **73. Monthly Income** A family has an annual income of $42,300. How much is their monthly income?
$3,525

▶ **74. Hourly Wages** If a man works an 8-hour shift and is paid $96, how much does he make for 1 hour?
$12

▶ **75. Price per Pound** If 6 pounds of a certain kind of fruit cost $4.74, how much does 1 pound cost?
79¢

76. Cost of a Dress A dress shop orders 45 dresses for a total of $2,205. If they paid the same amount for each dress, how much was each dress?
$49

77. Filling Glasses How many 32-ounce bottles of Coke will ▶
be needed to fill sixteen 6-ounce glasses?

3 bottles

78. Filling Glasses How many 8-ounce glasses can be filled
from three 32-ounce bottles of soda?

12 glasses

three 32-ounce bottles = _____ 8-ounce glasses

79. Filling Glasses How many 5-ounce glasses can be filled ▶
from a 32-ounce bottle of milk? How many ounces of
milk will be left in the bottle when all the glasses are
full?

6 glasses with 2 oz left over

80. Filling Glasses How many 3-ounce glasses can be filled
from a 28-ounce bottle of milk? How many ounces of
milk will be left in the bottle when all the glasses are
filled?

9 glasses with 1 oz left over

81. Boston Red Sox The annual payroll for the Boston
Red Sox for the 2007 season was about $156 million
dollars. If there are 40 players on the roster what is the
average salary per player for the Boston Red Sox?

$3,900,000

82. Miles per Gallon A traveling salesman kept track of his
mileage for 1 month. He found that he traveled 1,104
miles and used 48 gallons of gas. How many miles did
he travel on each gallon of gas?

23 miles

▶ **83. Milligrams of Calcium** Suppose one egg contains 25
milligrams of calcium, a piece of toast contains 40
milligrams of calcium, and a glass of milk contains
215 milligrams of calcium. How many milligrams of
calcium are contained in a breakfast that consists of
three eggs, two glasses of milk, and four pieces of
toast?

665 mg

84. Milligrams of Iron Suppose a glass of juice contains 3 milligrams of iron and a piece of toast contains 2 milligrams
of iron. If Diane drinks two glasses of juice and has three
pieces of toast for breakfast, how much iron is contained
in the meal?

12 mg

85. Fitness Walking The guidelines for fitness now indicate
that a person who walks 10,000 steps daily is physically fit. According to *The Walking Site* on the Internet,
it takes just over 2,000 steps to walk one mile. If that
is the case, how many miles do you need to walk in
order to take 10,000 steps?

5 miles

86. Fundraiser As part of a fundraiser for the Earth Day
activities on your campus, three volunteers work to stuff
3,210 envelopes with information about global warming.
How many envelopes did each volunteer stuff?

1,070 envelopes

2,000 steps = 1 mile

Exponents and Order of Operations

Exponents are a shorthand way of writing repeated multiplication. In the expression 2^3, 2 is called the *base* and 3 is called the *exponent*. The expression 2^3 is read "2 to the third power" or "2 cubed." The exponent 3 tells us to use the base 2 as a multiplication factor three times.

$$2^3 = 2 \cdot 2 \cdot 2 \quad \text{2 is used as a factor three times}$$

The expression 2^3 is equal to the number 8. We can summarize this discussion with the following definition.

> **Definition**
> An **exponent** is a whole number that indicates how many times the base is to be used as a factor. Exponents indicate repeated multiplication.

A Exponents

In the expression 5^2, 5 is the base and 2 is the exponent. The meaning of the expression is

$$5^2 = 5 \cdot 5 \quad \text{5 is used as a factor two times}$$
$$= 25$$

The expression 5^2 is read "5 to the second power" or "5 squared."

Here are some more examples.

EXAMPLE 1 3^2 The base is 3, and the exponent is 2. The expression is read "3 to the second power" or "3 squared."

EXAMPLE 2 3^3 The base is 3, and the exponent is 3. The expression is read "3 to the third power" or "3 cubed."

EXAMPLE 3 2^4 The base is 2, and the exponent is 4. The expression is read "2 to the fourth power."

As you can see from these examples, a base raised to the second power is also said to be *squared,* and a base raised to the third power is also said to be *cubed.* These are the only two exponents (^{2} and ^{3}) that have special names. All other exponents are referred to only as "fourth powers," "fifth powers," "sixth powers," and so on.

B Expressions with Exponents

The next examples show how we can simplify expressions involving exponents by using repeated multiplication.

EXAMPLE 4 $3^2 = 3 \cdot 3 = 9$

EXAMPLE 5 $4^2 = 4 \cdot 4 = 16$

PRACTICE PROBLEMS

For each expression, name the base and the exponent, and write the expression in words.

1. 5^2

2. 2^3

3. 1^4

Simplify each of the following by using repeated multiplication.
4. 5^2

5. 9^2

Answers
1–3. See solutions section.
4. 25 **5.** 81

6. 2^3

7. 1^4

8. 2^5

EXAMPLE 6 $\quad 3^3 = 3 \cdot 3 \cdot 3 = 9 \cdot 3 = 27$

EXAMPLE 7 $\quad 3^4 = 3 \cdot 3 \cdot 3 \cdot 3 = 9 \cdot 9 = 81$

EXAMPLE 8 $\quad 2^4 = 2 \cdot 2 \cdot 2 \cdot 2 = 4 \cdot 4 = 16$

USING TECHNOLOGY

Calculators

Here is how we use a calculator to evaluate exponents, as we did in Example 8:

Scientific Calculator: 2 $\boxed{x^y}$ 4 $\boxed{=}$

Graphing Calculator: 2 $\boxed{\wedge}$ 4 $\boxed{\text{ENT}}$ or 2 $\boxed{x^y}$ 4 $\boxed{\text{ENT}}$

(depending on the calculator)

Finally, we should consider what happens when the numbers 0 and 1 are used as exponents. First of all, any number raised to the first power is itself. That is, if we let the letter a represent any number, then

$$a^1 = a$$

To take care of the cases when 0 is used as an exponent, we must use the following definition:

Definition

Any number other than 0 raised to the 0 power is 1. That is, if a represents any nonzero number, then it is always true that

$$a^0 = 1$$

Simplify each of the following expressions.

9. 7^1

10. 4^1

11. 9^0

12. 1^0

EXAMPLE 9 $\quad 5^1 = 5$

EXAMPLE 10 $\quad 9^1 = 9$

EXAMPLE 11 $\quad 4^0 = 1$

EXAMPLE 12 $\quad 8^0 = 1$

C Order of Operations

The symbols we use to specify operations, $+$, $-$, $\cdot$, $\div$, along with the symbols we use for grouping, ( ) and [ ], serve the same purpose in mathematics as punctuation marks in English. They may be called the punctuation marks of mathematics.

Consider the following sentence:

Bob said John is tall.

It can have two different meanings, depending on how we punctuate it:

1. "Bob," said John, "is tall."

2. Bob said, "John is tall."

Answers
6. 8 **7.** 1 **8.** 32
9. 7 **10.** 4 **11.** 1 **12.** 1

Without the punctuation marks we don't know which meaning the sentence has.

Now, consider the following mathematical expression:

$$4 + 5 \cdot 2$$

What should we do? Should we add 4 and 5 first, or should we multiply 5 and 2 first? There seem to be two different answers. In mathematics we want to avoid situations in which two different results are possible. Therefore we follow the rule for order of operations.

Definition

Order of Operations When evaluating mathematical expressions, we will perform the operations in the following order:

1. If the expression contains grouping symbols, such as parentheses ( ), brackets [ ], or a fraction bar, then we perform the operations inside the grouping symbols, or above and below the fraction bar, first.

2. Then we evaluate, or simplify, any numbers with exponents.

3. Then we do all multiplications and divisions in order, starting at the left and moving right.

4. Finally, we do all additions and subtractions, from left to right.

According to our rule, the expression $4 + 5 \cdot 2$ would have to be evaluated by multiplying 5 and 2 first, and then adding 4. The correct answer—and the only answer—to this problem is 14.

$$
\begin{aligned}
4 + 5 \cdot 2 &= 4 + 10 \quad \text{Multiply first,} \\
&= 14 \quad \text{then add}
\end{aligned}
$$

Here are some more examples that illustrate how we apply the rule for order of operations to simplify (or evaluate) expressions.

EXAMPLE 13 Simplify: $4 \cdot 8 - 2 \cdot 6$

SOLUTION We multiply first and then subtract:

$$
\begin{aligned}
4 \cdot 8 - 2 \cdot 6 &= 32 - 12 \quad \text{Multiply first,} \\
&= 20 \quad \text{then subtract}
\end{aligned}
$$

EXAMPLE 14 Simplify: $5 + 2(7 - 1)$

SOLUTION According to the rule for the order of operations, we must do what is inside the parentheses first:

$$
\begin{aligned}
5 + 2(7 - 1) &= 5 + 2(6) \quad \text{Inside parentheses first,} \\
&= 5 + 12 \quad \text{then multiply,} \\
&= 17 \quad \text{then add}
\end{aligned}
$$

EXAMPLE 15 Simplify: $9 \cdot 2^3 + 36 \div 3^2 - 8$

SOLUTION

$$
\begin{aligned}
9 \cdot 2^3 + 36 \div 3^2 - 8 &= 9 \cdot 8 + 36 \div 9 - 8 \quad \text{Exponents first,} \\
&= 72 + 4 - 8 \quad \text{then multiply and divide, left to right.} \\
&= 76 - 8 \ \Big\} \quad \text{Add and subtract,} \\
&= 68 \ \Big\} \quad \text{left to right}
\end{aligned}
$$

Note To help you to remember the order of operations you can use the popular sentence **P**lease **E**xcuse **M**y **D**ear **A**unt **S**ally, or the acronym **PEMDAS**

Parentheses (or grouping)
Exponents
Multiplication and **D**ivision, from left to right
Addition and **S**ubtraction, from left to right

13. Simplify.
  a. $5 \cdot 7 - 3 \cdot 6$
  b. $5 \cdot 70 - 3 \cdot 60$

14. Simplify: $7 + 3(6 + 4)$

15. Simplify.
  a. $28 \div 7 - 3$
  b. $6 \cdot 3^2 + 64 \div 2^4 - 2$

Answers
13. a. 17 **b.** 170 **14.** 37
15. a. 1 **b.** 56

Calculators

Here is how we use a calculator to work the problem shown in Example 14:

SCIENTIFIC CALCULATOR: 5 $\boxed{+}$ 2 $\boxed{\times}$ $\boxed{(}$ $\boxed{(}$ 7 $\boxed{-}$ 1 $\boxed{)}$ $\boxed{=}$

GRAPHING CALCULATOR: 5 $\boxed{+}$ 2 $\boxed{(}$ $\boxed{(}$ 7 $\boxed{-}$ 1 $\boxed{)}$ $\boxed{\text{ENT}}$

Example 15 on a calculator looks like this:

SCIENTIFIC CALCULATOR: 9 $\boxed{\times}$ 2 $\boxed{x^y}$ 3 $\boxed{+}$ 36 $\boxed{\div}$ 3 $\boxed{x^y}$ 2 $\boxed{-}$ 8 $\boxed{=}$

GRAPHING CALCULATOR: 9 $\boxed{\times}$ 2 $\boxed{\wedge}$ 3 $\boxed{+}$ 36 $\boxed{\div}$ 3 $\boxed{\wedge}$ 2 $\boxed{-}$ 8 $\boxed{\text{ENT}}$

16. Simplify.
   a. $5 + 3[24 - 5(6 - 2)]$
   b. $50 + 30[240 - 50(6 - 2)]$

EXAMPLE 16   Simplify: $3 + 2[10 - 3(5 - 2)]$

SOLUTION   The brackets, [ ], are used in the same way as parentheses. In a case like this we move to the innermost grouping symbols first and begin simplifying:

$$
\begin{aligned}
3 + 2[10 - 3(5 - 2)] &= 3 + 2[10 - 3(3)] \\
&= 3 + 2[10 - 9] \\
&= 3 + 2[1] \\
&= 3 + 2 \\
&= 5
\end{aligned}
$$

Table 1 lists some English expressions and their corresponding mathematical expressions written in symbols.

TABLE 1	
In English	**Mathematical Equivalent**
5 times the sum of 3 and 8	$5(3 + 8)$
Twice the difference of 4 and 3	$2(4 - 3)$
6 added to 7 times the sum of 5 and 6	$6 + 7(5 + 6)$
The sum of 4 times 5 and 8 times 9	$4 \cdot 5 + 8 \cdot 9$
3 subtracted from the quotient of 10 and 2	$10 \div 2 - 3$

STUDY SKILLS
Read the Book Before Coming to Class

As we mentioned in the Preface, it is best to have read the section to be covered in class before getting to class. Even if you don't understand everything that you have read, you are still better off reading ahead than not. The Getting Ready for Class questions at the end of each section are intended to give you things to look for in the reading that will be important in understanding what is in the section.

Getting Ready for Class

After reading through the preceding section, respond in your own words and in complete sentences.

1. In the expression 5^3, which number is the base?
2. Give a written description of the process you would use to simplify the expression $3 + 4(5 + 6)$.
3. What is the first step in simplifying the expression $8 + 6 \div 3 - 1$?
4. How do you remember the correct Order of Operations?

Answers
16. a. 17 **b.** 1,250

Problem Set 1.7

A For each of the following expressions, name the base and the exponent. [Examples 1–3]

▶ **1.** 4^5
Base 4
Exponent 5

2. 5^4
Base 5
Exponent 4

3. 3^6
Base 3
Exponent 6

4. 6^3
Base 6
Exponent 3

5. 8^2
Base 8
Exponent 2

6. 2^8
Base 2
Exponent 8

7. 9^1
Base 9
Exponent 1

8. 1^9
Base 1
Exponent 9

9. 4^0
Base 4
Exponent 0

10. 0^4
Base 0
Exponent 4

B Use the definition of exponents as indicating repeated multiplication to simplify each of the following expressions. [Examples 4–12]

▶ **11.** 6^2
36

12. 7^2
49

13. 2^3
8

▶ **14.** 2^4
16

15. 1^4
1

16. 5^1
5

17. 9^0
1

18. 27^0
1

19. 9^2
81

20. 8^2
64

21. 10^1
10

22. 8^1
8

23. 12^1
12

▶ **24.** 16^0
1

25. 45^0
1

26. 3^4
81

C Use the rule for the order of operations to simplify each expression. [Examples 13–16]

▶ **27.** $16 - 8 + 4$
12

28. $16 - 4 + 8$
20

29. $20 \div 2 \cdot 10$
100

30. $40 \div 4 \cdot 5$
50

31. $20 - 4 \cdot 4$
4

32. $30 - 10 \cdot 2$
10

▶ **33.** $3 + 5 \cdot 8$
43

34. $7 + 4 \cdot 9$
43

▶ **35.** $3 \cdot 6 - 2$
16

36. $5 \cdot 1 + 6$
11

▶ **37.** $6 \cdot 2 + 9 \cdot 8$
84

38. $4 \cdot 5 + 9 \cdot 7$
83

▶ **39.** $4 \cdot 5 - 3 \cdot 2$
14

40. $5 \cdot 6 - 4 \cdot 3$
18

41. $5^2 + 7^2$
74

42. $4^2 + 9^2$
97

43. $480 + 12(32)^2$
12,768

44. $360 + 14(27)^2$
10,566

▶ **45.** $3 \cdot 2^3 + 5 \cdot 4^2$
104

46. $4 \cdot 3^2 + 5 \cdot 2^3$
76

▶ Selected exercises available online at www.webassign.net/brookscole

▶ **47.** $8 \cdot 10^2 - 6 \cdot 4^3$
416

48. $5 \cdot 11^2 - 3 \cdot 2^3$
581

▶ **49.** $2(3 + 6 \cdot 5)$
66

50. $8(1 + 4 \cdot 2)$
72

▶ **51.** $19 + 50 \div 5^2$
21

52. $9 + 8 \div 2^2$
11

▶ **53.** $9 - 2(4 - 3)$
7

54. $15 - 6(9 - 7)$
3

▶ **55.** $4 \cdot 3 + 2(5 - 3)$
16

56. $6 \cdot 8 + 3(4 - 1)$
57

57. $4[2(3) + 3(5)]$
84

58. $3[2(5) + 3(4)]$
66

▶ **59.** $(7 - 3)(8 + 2)$
40

60. $(9 - 5)(9 + 5)$
56

61. $3(9 - 2) + 4(7 - 2)$
41

62. $7(4 - 2) - 2(5 - 3)$
10

▶ **63.** $18 + 12 \div 4 - 3$
18

64. $20 + 16 \div 2 - 5$
23

65. $4(10^2) + 20 \div 4$
405

66. $3(4^2) + 10 \div 5$
50

▶ **67.** $8 \cdot 2^4 + 25 \div 5 - 3^2$
124

68. $5 \cdot 3^4 + 16 \div 8 - 2^2$
403

▶ **69.** $5 + 2[9 - 2(4 - 1)]$
11

70. $6 + 3[8 - 3(1 + 1)]$
12

▶ **71.** $3 + 4[6 + 8(2 - 0)]$
91

72. $2 + 5[9 + 3(4 - 1)]$
92

73. $\dfrac{15 + 5(4)}{17 - 12}$
7

74. $\dfrac{20 + 6(2)}{11 - 7}$
8

Translate each English expression into an equivalent mathematical expression written in symbols. Then simplify.

▶ **75.** 8 times the sum of 4 and 2
$8(4 + 2) = 48$

76. 3 times the difference of 6 and 1
$3(6 - 1) = 15$

77. Twice the sum of 10 and 3
$2(10 + 3) = 26$

78. 5 times the difference of 12 and 6
$5(12 - 6) = 30$

▶ **79.** 4 added to 3 times the sum of 3 and 4
$3(3 + 4) + 4 = 25$

80. 25 added to 4 times the difference of 7 and 5
$4(7 - 5) + 25 = 33$

▶ **81.** 9 subtracted from the quotient of 20 and 2
$(20 \div 2) - 9 = 1$

82. 7 added to the quotient of 6 and 2
$(6 \div 2) + 7 = 10$

▶ **83.** The sum of 8 times 5 and 5 times 4
$(8 \cdot 5) + (5 \cdot 4) = 60$

84. The difference of 10 times 5 and 6 times 2
$(10 \cdot 5) - (6 \cdot 2) = 38$

▪ Applying the Concepts

Nutrition Labels Use the three nutrition labels below to work Problems 95–100.

SPAGHETTI

Nutrition Facts

Serving Size 2 oz. (56g/⅛ of pkg) dry
Servings Per Container: 8

Amount Per Serving

Calories 210	Calories from fat 10

	% Daily Value*
Total Fat 1g	**2%**
Saturated Fat 0g	**0%**
Poly unsaturated Fat 0.5g	
Monounsaturated Fat 0g	
Cholesterol 0mg	**0%**
Sodium 0mg	**0%**
Total Carbohydrate 42g	**14%**
Dietary Fiber 2g	**7%**
Sugars 3g	
Protein 7g	

Vitamin A 0%	•	Vitamin C 0%
Calcium 0%	•	Iron 10%

*Percent Daily Values are based on a 2,000 calorie diet

CANNED ITALIAN TOMATOES

Nutrition Facts

Serving Size 1/2 cup (121g)
Servings Per Container: about 3 1/2

Amount Per Serving

Calories 25	Calories from fat 0

	% Daily Value*
Total Fat 0g	**0%**
Saturated Fat 0g	**0%**
Cholesterol 0mg	**0%**
Sodium 300mg	**12%**
Potassium 145mg	**4%**
Total Carbohydrate 4g	**2%**
Dietary Fiber 1g	**4%**
Sugars 4g	
Protein 1g	

Vitamin A 20%	•	Vitamin C 15%
Calcium 4%	•	Iron 15%

*Percent Daily Values are based on a 2,000 calorie diet. Your daily values may be higher or lower depending on your calorie needs.

SHREDDED ROMANO CHEESE

Nutrition Facts

Serving Size 2 tsp (5g)
Servings Per Container: 34

Amount Per Serving

Calories 20	Calories from fat 10

	% Daily Value*
Total Fat 1.5g	**2%**
Saturated Fat 1g	**5%**
Cholesterol 5mg	**2%**
Sodium 70mg	**3%**
Total Carbohydrate 0g	**0%**
Fiber 0g	**0%**
Sugars 0g	
Protein 2g	

Vitamin A 0%	•	Vitamin C 0%
Calcium 4%	•	Iron 0%

*Percent Daily Values (DV) are based on a 2,000 calorie diet

Find the total number of calories in each of the following meals.

85. Spaghetti   1 serving
Tomatoes   1 serving
Cheese   1 serving

255 calories

86. Spaghetti   1 serving
Tomatoes   2 servings
Cheese   1 serving

280 calories

87. Spaghetti   2 servings
Tomatoes   1 serving
Cheese   1 serving

465 calories

88. Spaghetti   2 servings
Tomatoes   1 serving
Cheese   2 servings

485 calories

The following table lists the number of calories consumed by eating some popular fast foods. Use the table to work Problems 89 and 90.

89. Compare the total number of calories in the meal in Problem 95 with the number of calories in a McDonald's Big Mac.

Big Mac has twice the calories.

90. Compare the total number of calories in the meal in Problem 98 with the number of calories in a Burger King hamburger.

Hamburger has 225 fewer calories.

CALORIES IN FOOD	
Food	**Calories**
McDonald's hamburger	270
Burger King hamburger	260
Jack in the Box hamburger	280
McDonald's Big Mac	510
Burger King Whopper	630
Jack in the Box Colossus burger	940

■ Extending the Concepts: Number Sequences

There is a relationship between the two sequences below. The first sequence is the *sequence of odd numbers.* The second sequence is called the *sequence of squares.*

$$1, 3, 5, 7, \ldots \qquad \text{The sequence of odd numbers}$$
$$1, 4, 9, 16, \ldots \qquad \text{The sequence of squares}$$

91. Add the first two numbers in the sequence of odd numbers.

4

92. Add the first three numbers in the sequence of odd numbers.

9

93. Add the first four numbers in the sequence of odd numbers.

16

94. Add the first five numbers in the sequence of odd numbers.

25

Chapter 1 Summary

The numbers in brackets indicate the sections in which the topics were discussed.

EXAMPLES

The margins of the chapter summaries will be used for examples of the topics being reviewed, whenever convenient.

◼ Place Values for Decimal Numbers [1.1]

The place values for the digits of any base 10 number are as follows:

Trillions			Billions			Millions			Thousands			Ones		
Hundreds	Tens	Ones	Hundreds	Tens	Ones	Hundreds	Tens	Ones	Hundreds	Tens	Ones	Hundreds	Tens	Ones

1. The number 42,103,045 written in words is "forty-two million, one hundred three thousand, forty-five."

The number 5,745 written in expanded form is
$5,000 + 700 + 40 + 5$

◼ Vocabulary Associated with Addition, Subtraction, Multiplication, and Division [1.2, 1.4, 1.5, 1.6]

The word *sum* indicates addition.

The word *difference* indicates subtraction.

The word *product* indicates multiplication.

The word *quotient* indicates division.

2. The sum of 5 and 2 is $5 + 2$.
The difference of 5 and 2 is $5 - 2$.
The product of 5 and 2 is $5 \cdot 2$.
The quotient of 10 and 2 is $10 \div 2$.

◼ Properties of Addition and Multiplication [1.2, 1.5]

If a, b, and c represent any three numbers, then the properties of addition and multiplication used most often are:

Commutative property of addition: $a + b = b + a$
Commutative property of multiplication: $a \cdot b = b \cdot a$
Associative property of addition: $(a + b) + c = a + (b + c)$
Associative property of multiplication: $(a \cdot b) \cdot c = a \cdot (b \cdot c)$
Distributive property: $a(b + c) = a(b) + a(c)$

3. $3 + 2 = 2 + 3$
$3 \cdot 2 = 2 \cdot 3$
$(x + 3) + 5 = x + (3 + 5)$
$(4 \cdot 5) \cdot 6 = 4 \cdot (5 \cdot 6)$
$3(4 + 7) = 3(4) + 3(7)$

◼ Perimeter of a Polygon [1.2]

The *perimeter* of any polygon is the sum of the lengths of the sides, and it is denoted with the letter P.

4. The perimeter of the rectangle below is
$P = 37 + 37 + 24 + 24$
$\quad = 122$ feet

24 ft

37 ft

5. 5,482 to the nearest ten is 5,480.

5,482 to the nearest hundred is 5,500.

5,482 to the nearest thousand is 5,000.

Steps for Rounding Whole Numbers [1.3]

1. Locate the digit just to the right of the place you are to round to.

2. If that digit is less than 5, replace it and all digits to its right with zeros.

3. If that digit is 5 or more, replace it and all digits to its right with zeros, and add 1 to the digit to its left.

Division by 0 (Zero) [1.6]

6. Each expression below is undefined.

$5 \div 0 \quad \dfrac{7}{0} \quad 4/0$

Division by 0 is undefined. We cannot use 0 as a divisor in any division problem.

Order of Operations [1.7]

7. $4 + 6(8 - 2)$

$= 4 + 6(6)$ Inside parentheses first

$= 4 + 36$ Then multiply

$= 40$ Then add

To simplify a mathematical expression:

1. We simplify the expression inside the grouping symbols first. Grouping symbols are parentheses ( ), brackets [ ], or a fraction bar.

2. Then we evaluate any numbers with exponents.

3. We then perform all multiplications and divisions in order, starting at the left and moving right.

4. Finally, we do all the additions and subtractions, from left to right.

Exponents [1.7]

8. $2^3 = 2 \cdot 2 \cdot 2 = 8$

$5^0 = 1$

$3^1 = 3$

In the expression 2^3, 2 is the *base* and 3 is the *exponent*. An exponent is a shorthand notation for repeated multiplication. The exponent 0 is a special exponent. Any nonzero number to the 0 power is 1.

The numbers in brackets indicate the sections in which problems of a similar type can be found.

1. One of the largest Pacific blue marlins was caught near Hawaii in 1982. It weighed 1,376 pounds. Write 1,376 in words. [1.1]

one thousand, three hundred seventy-six

2. In 2003 the New York Yankees had the highest home attendance in major league baseball. The attendance that year was 3,465,600. Write 3,465,600 in words. [1.1]

three million, four hundred sixty-five thousand, six hundred

For Problems 3 and 4, write each number with digits instead of words. [1.1]

3. Five million, two hundred forty-five thousand, six hundred fifty-two

5,245,652

4. Twelve million, twelve thousand, twelve

12,012,012

5. In 2003 the Montreal Expos had the lowest attendance in major league baseball. The attendance that year was 1,025,639. Write 1,025,639 in expanded form. [1.1]

1,000,000 + 20,000 + 5,000 + 600 + 30 + 9

6. According to the American Medical Association, in 2002, there were 215,005 female physicians practicing medicine in the United States. Write 215,005 in expanded form. [1.1]

200,000 + 10,000 + 5,000 + 5

Identify each of the statements in Problems 7–14 as an example of one of the following properties. [1.2, 1.5]

a. Addition property of 0
b. Multiplication property of 0
c. Multiplication property of 1
d. Commutative property of addition

e. Commutative property of multiplication
f. Associative property of addition
g. Associative property of multiplication

7. $5 + 7 = 7 + 5$

d

8. $(4 + 3) + 2 = 4 + (3 + 2)$

f

9. $6 \cdot 1 = 6$

c

10. $8 + 0 = 8$

a

11. $5 \cdot 0 = 0$

b

12. $4 \cdot 6 = 6 \cdot 4$

e

13. $5 \cdot (3 \cdot 2) = (5 \cdot 3) \cdot 2$

g

14. $(6 + 2) + 3 = (2 + 6) + 3$

d

Find each of the following sums. (Add.) [1.2]

15.
```
  498
+ 251
-----
  749
```

16.
```
  784
+ 598
-----
1,382
```

17.
```
7,384
  251
+ 637
-----
8,272
```

18.
```
 4,901
   648
+3,592
------
 9,141
```

Find each of the following differences. (Subtract.) [1.4]

19.　789
　　　−475
　　　314

20.　792
　　　−178
　　　614

21.　5,908
　　　−2,759
　　　3,149

22.　3,527
　　　−1,789
　　　1,738

Find each of the following products. (Multiply.) [1.5]

23. 8(73)
584

24. 7(984)
6,888

25. 63(59)
3,717

26. 49(876)
42,924

Find each of the following quotients. (Divide.) [1.6]

27. 692 ÷ 4
173

28. 1,020 ÷ 15
68

29. 36)15,408
428

30. 286)21,736
76

Round the number 3,781,092 to the nearest: [1.3]

31. Ten
3,781,090

32. Hundred
3,781,100

33. Hundred thousand
3,800,000

34. Million
4,000,000

Use the rule for the order of operations to simplify each expression as much as possible. [1.7]

35. $4 + 3 \cdot 5^2$
79

36. $7(9)^2 - 6(4)^3$
183

37. $3(2 + 8 \cdot 9)$
222

38. $7 - 2(6 - 4)$
3

39. $24 \div 6 \cdot 2$
8

40. $20 \cdot 3 \div 12 \cdot 2$
10

41. $4(3 - 1)^3$
32

42. $36 \div 9 \cdot 3^2$
36

Write an expression using symbols that is equivalent to each of the following expressions; then simplify. [1.7]

43. 3 times the sum of 4 and 6
$3(4 + 6) = 30$

44. 9 times the difference of 5 and 3
$9(5 - 3) = 18$

45. Twice the difference of 17 and 5
$2(17 - 5) = 24$

46. The product of 5 and the sum of 8 and 2
$5(8 + 2) = 50$

Find the perimeter of the shapes. [1.2]

47.

6 m

5 m　4 m

$P = 22$ m

48.

7 ft

12 ft

$P = 38$ ft

Chapter 1   Test

1. Write the number 20,347 in words.

Twenty thousand, three hundred forty-seven

2. Write the number two million, forty-five thousand, six with digits instead of words.

2,045,006

3. Write the number 123,407 in expanded form.

100,000 + 20,000 + 3,000 + 400 + 7

Identify each of the statements in Problems 4–7 as an example of one of the following properties.

   a. Addition property of 0
   b. Multiplication property of 0
   c. Multiplication property of 1
   d. Commutative property of addition
   e. Commutative property of multiplication
   f. Associative property of addition
   g. Associative property of multiplication

4. $(5 + 6) + 3 = 5 + (6 + 3)$ **5.** $7 \cdot 1 = 7$

   f   c

6. $9 + 0 = 9$ **7.** $5 \cdot 6 = 6 \cdot 5$

   a   e

Find each of the following sums. (Add.)

8.   135   **9.**   5,401
    + 741   329
     876   + 10,653
                     16,383

Find each of the following differences. (Subtract.)

10.   937   **11.**   7,052
    − 413   − 3,967
     524   3,085

Find each of the following products. (Multiply.)

12. 9(186)   **13.** 62(359)

   1,674   22,258

Find each of the following quotients. (Divide.)

14. $1,105 \div 13$ **15.** $583\overline{)12,243}$

   85   21

16. Round the number 516,249 to the nearest ten thousand.

520,000

Use the rule for the order of operations to simplify each expression as much as possible.

17. $8(5)^2 - 7(3)^3$ **18.** $8 - 2(5 - 3)$

   11   4

19. $7 + 2(53 - 3)$ **20.** $3(x - 2)$

   107                 $3x - 6$

21. Twice the sum of 11 and 7

$2(11 + 7) = 36$

22. The quotient of 20 and 5 increased by 9

$(20 \div 5) + 9 = 13$

23. Find the perimeter.

$P = 46$ m

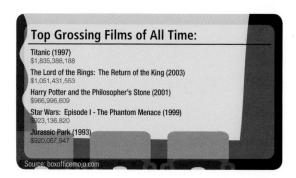

13 m

10 m   7 m

The snapshot shows the top grossing films. Use the chart to answer the following questions.

Top Grossing Films of All Time:

Titanic (1997)
$1,835,388,188

The Lord of the Rings: The Return of the King (2003)
$1,051,431,553

Harry Potter and the Philosopher's Stone (2001)
$966,996,609

Star Wars: Episode I - The Phantom Menace (1999)
$923,136,820

Jurassic Park (1993)
$920,067,947

Source: boxofficemojo.com

24. How much more did Lord of the Rings gross than Jurrasic Park?

$131,363,606

25. How much more did Titanic gross than Star Wars: Episode 1?

$912,251,368

Chapter 1 Projects

WHOLE NUMBERS

GROUP PROJECT

Egyptian Numbers

Number of People	3
Time Needed	10 minutes
Equipment	Pencil and paper

Background The Egyptians had a fully developed number system as early as 3500 B.C. They recorded very large numbers in the macehead of Narmer, which boasts of the spoils taken during wars, and the *Book of the Dead,* a collection of religious texts. The Egyptians used a base-ten system. A special pictograph was used to represent each power of ten. Here are some pictographs used.

1	10	100	1,000	10,000	100,000	1,000,000
staff	horseshoe	rope	lotus flower	bent finger	tadpole or frog	astonished person

Example Usually the direction of writing was from right to left, with the larger units first. Symbols were placed in rows to save lateral space. Writing the number 132,146 in Egyptian hieroglyphics looks like this:

132,146 =

Procedure Write each of the following Egyptian numbers in our system.

1.

2.

Express each of the given numbers in Egyptian hieroglyphics.

3. 1,842

4. 4,310,175

Students and Instructors: The end of each chapter in this book will have two projects. The group projects are intended to be done in class. The research projects are to be completed outside of class. They can be done in groups or individually.

Leopold Kronecker

Leopold Kronecker (1823–1891) was a German mathematician and logician who thought that arithmetic should be based on whole numbers. He is known for the quote, "God made the natural numbers; all else is the work of man." He was openly critical of the efforts of his contemporaries. Kronecker's primary work was in the field of algebraic number theory. Research the life of Leopold Kronecker, or discuss the work of a mathematician who was criticized by Kronecker.

Courtesy of Wolfram Research/
National Science Foundation

A Glimpse of Algebra

At the end of most chapters of this book you will find a section like this one. These sections show how some of the material in the chapter looks when it is extended to algebra. If you are planning to take an algebra course after you have finished this one, these sections will give you a head start. If you are not planning to take algebra, these sections will give you an idea of what algebra is like. Who knows? You may decide to take an algebra class after you work through a few of these sections.

In this chapter we did some work with exponents. We can use the definition of exponents, along with the commutative property of multiplication, to rewrite some expressions that contain variables and exponents.

We can expand the expression $(5x)^2$ using the definition of exponents as

$$(5x)^2 = (5x)(5x)$$

Because the expression on the right is all multiplication, we can rewrite it as

$$(5x)(5x) = 5 \cdot x \cdot 5 \cdot x$$

And because multiplication is a commutative operation, we can rearrange this last expression so that the numbers are grouped together, and the variables are grouped together:

$$5 \cdot x \cdot 5 \cdot x = (5 \cdot 5)(x \cdot x)$$

Now, because

$$5 \cdot 5 = 25 \quad \text{and} \quad x \cdot x = x^2$$

we can rewrite the expression as

$$(5 \cdot 5)(x \cdot x) = 25x^2$$

Here is what the problem looks like when the steps are shown together:

$$(5x)^2 = (5x)(5x) \qquad \text{Definition of exponents}$$
$$= (5 \cdot 5)(x \cdot x) \qquad \text{Commutative property}$$
$$= 25x^2 \qquad \text{Multiplication and definition of exponents}$$

We have shown only the important steps in this summary. We rewrite the expression by (1) applying the definition of exponents to expand it, (2) rearranging the numbers and variables by using the commutative property, and then (3) simplifying by multiplication.

Here are some more examples.

EXAMPLE 1
Expand $(7x)^2$ using the definition of exponents, and then simplify the result.

SOLUTION We begin by writing the expression as $(7x)(7x)$, then rearranging the numbers and variables, and then simplifying:

$$(7x)^2 = (7x)(7x) \qquad \text{Definition of exponents}$$
$$= (7 \cdot 7)(x \cdot x) \qquad \text{Commutative property}$$
$$= 49x^2 \qquad \text{Multiplication and definition of exponents}$$

PRACTICE PROBLEMS

1. Expand $(3x)^2$ using the definition of exponents, and then simplify the result.

Answer
1. $9x^2$

2. Expand and simplify: $(2a)^3$

EXAMPLE 2

Expand and simplify: $(5a)^3$

SOLUTION We begin by writing the expression as $(5a)(5a)(5a)$:

$$(5a)^3 = (5a)(5a)(5a) \quad \text{Definition of exponents}$$
$$= (5 \cdot 5 \cdot 5)(a \cdot a \cdot a) \quad \text{Commutative property}$$
$$= 125a^3 \quad 5 \cdot 5 \cdot 5 = 125; a \cdot a \cdot a = a^3$$

3. Expand and simplify: $(7xy)^2$

EXAMPLE 3

Expand and simplify: $(8xy)^2$

SOLUTION Proceeding as we have above, we have:

$$(8xy)^2 = (8xy)(8xy) \quad \text{Definition of exponents}$$
$$= (8 \cdot 8)(x \cdot x)(y \cdot y) \quad \text{Commutative property}$$
$$= 64x^2y^2 \quad 8 \cdot 8 = 64; x \cdot x = x^2; y \cdot y = y^2$$

4. Simplify: $(3x)^2(7xy)^2$

EXAMPLE 4

Simplify: $(7x)^2(8xy)^2$

SOLUTION We begin by applying the definition of exponents:

$$(7x)^2(8xy)^2 = (7x)(7x)(8xy)(8xy)$$
$$= (7 \cdot 7 \cdot 8 \cdot 8)(x \cdot x \cdot x \cdot x)(y \cdot y) \quad \text{Commutative property}$$
$$= 3{,}136x^4y^2$$

5. Simplify: $(5x)^3(2x)^2$

EXAMPLE 5

Simplify: $(2x)^3(4x)^2$

SOLUTION Proceeding as we have above, we have:

$$(2x)^3(4x)^2 = (2x)(2x)(2x)(4x)(4x)$$
$$= (2 \cdot 2 \cdot 2 \cdot 4 \cdot 4)(x \cdot x \cdot x \cdot x \cdot x)$$
$$= 128x^5$$

Answer
2. $8a^3$ **3.** $49x^2y^2$ **4.** $441x^4y^2$
5. $500x^5$

A Glimpse of Algebra Problems

Use the definition of exponents to expand each of the following expressions. Apply the commutative property, and simplify the result in each case.

1. $(6x)^2$
$36x^2$

2. $(9x)^2$
$81x^2$

3. $(4x)^2$
$16x^2$

4. $(10x)^2$
$100x^2$

5. $(3a)^3$
$27a^3$

6. $(6a)^3$
$216a^3$

7. $(2ab)^3$
$8a^3b^3$

8. $(5ab)^3$
$125a^3b^3$

9. $(9xy)^2$
$81x^2y^2$

10. $(5xy)^2$
$25x^2y^2$

11. $(5xyz)^2$
$25x^2y^2z^2$

12. $(7xyz)^2$
$49x^2y^2z^2$

13. $(4x)^2(9xy)^2$
$1{,}296x^4y^2$

14. $(10x)^2(5xy)^2$
$2{,}500x^4y^2$

15. $(2x)^2(3x)^2(4x)^2$
$576x^6$

16. $(5x)^2(2x)^2(10x)^2$
$10{,}000x^6$

17. $(2x)^3(5x)^2$
$200x^5$

18. $(3x)^3(4x)^2$
$432x^5$

19. $(2a)^3(3a)^2(10a)^2$
$7{,}200a^7$

20. $(3a)^3(2a)^2(10a)^2$
$10{,}800a^7$

21. $(3xy)^3(4xy)^2$
$432x^5y^5$

22. $(2xy)^4(3xy)^2$
$144x^6y^6$

23. $(5xyz)^2(2xyz)^4$
$400x^6y^6z^6$

24. $(6xyz)^2(3xyz)^3$
$972x^5y^5z^5$

25. $(xy)^3(xz)^2(yz)^4$
$x^5y^7z^6$

26. $(xy)^4(xz)^2(yz)^3$
$x^6y^7z^5$

27. $(2a^3b^2)^2(3a^2b^3)^4$
$324a^{14}b^{16}$

28. $(4a^4b^3)^2(5a^2b^4)^2$
$400a^{12}b^{14}$

29. $(5x^2y^3)(2x^3y^3)^3$
$40x^{11}y^{12}$

30. $(8x^2y^2)^2(3x^3y^4)^2$
$576x^{10}y^{12}$

Fractions and Mixed Numbers

2

Image © 2008 Jackson County GIS
Image State of Oregon

Introduction

Crater Lake, located in the Cascade Mountain range in Southern Oregon, is 594 meters deep, making it the deepest lake in the United States. Here is a chart showing the depth of Crater Lake and the location of some lakes that are deeper than Crater Lake.

Deepest Lakes in the World

Crater Lake — 594 m
Issyk Kul — 668 m
O'Higgins-San Martin — 836 m
Tanganyika — 1,470 m
Baikal — 1,637 m

As you can see from the chart, although Crater lake is the deepest lake in the United States, it is far from being the deepest lake in the world. We can use fractions to compare the depths of these lakes. For example, Crater Lake is approximately $\frac{2}{5}$ as deep as Lake Tanganyika. In this chapter, we begin our work with fractions.

The pretest below contains problems that are representative of the problems you will find in the chapter.

1. Reduce to lowest terms: $\dfrac{16}{20}$ $\dfrac{4}{5}$

2. Factor 112 into a product of prime factors. $2^4 \cdot 7$

Perform the indicated operations. Reduce all answers to lowest terms.

3. $\dfrac{3}{8} \cdot 16$ 6

4. $10 \div \left(\dfrac{5}{6}\right)$ 12

5. $\dfrac{32}{45} \div \dfrac{40}{63}$ $\dfrac{28}{25}$

6. $\dfrac{3}{4} \div 9$ $\dfrac{1}{12}$

7. $\dfrac{5}{16} + \dfrac{7}{20}$ $\dfrac{53}{80}$

8. $\dfrac{5}{8} + \dfrac{1}{6}$ $\dfrac{19}{24}$

9. Write $4\dfrac{3}{5}$ as an improper fraction. $\dfrac{23}{5}$

10. Write $\dfrac{21}{8}$ as a mixed number. $2\dfrac{5}{8}$

Perform the indicated operations. Reduce all answers to lowest terms.

11. $1\dfrac{3}{8} \cdot 2\dfrac{4}{5}$ $3\dfrac{17}{20}$

12. $12 \div 3\dfrac{1}{6}$ $3\dfrac{15}{19}$

13. $4\dfrac{1}{5} + 1\dfrac{1}{10}$ $5\dfrac{3}{10}$

14. $6\dfrac{1}{6} - 3\dfrac{1}{3}$ $2\dfrac{5}{6}$

Simplify each of the following as much as possible.

15. $\left(\dfrac{1}{4}\right)^2$ $\dfrac{1}{16}$

16. $\left(\dfrac{1}{3}\right)^2 \cdot 27 + \left(\dfrac{3}{2}\right)^2 \cdot 4$ 12

17. $12 + \dfrac{9}{10} \div \dfrac{10}{9}$ $12\dfrac{81}{100}$

18. $\left(1 - \dfrac{1}{4}\right)\left(1\dfrac{2}{3} - \dfrac{1}{3}\right)$ 1

19. $\dfrac{\dfrac{3}{5}}{\dfrac{9}{10}}$ $\dfrac{2}{3}$

20. $\dfrac{2 + \dfrac{1}{4}}{2 - \dfrac{1}{4}}$ $1\dfrac{2}{7}$

Getting Ready for Chapter 2

The problems below review material covered previously that you need to know in order to be successful in Chapter 2. If you have any difficulty with the problems here, you need to go back and review before going on to Chapter 2.

1. Place either < or > between the two numbers so that the resulting statement is true.
   a. $9 > 5$ **b.** $10 > 0$ **c.** $0 < 1$ **d.** $2001 > 201$

Simplify.

2. $2 \cdot 5$
   10

3. $5 - 3$
   2

4. $13 + 12 - 9$
   16

5. $5 \cdot 4 + 3$
   23

6. $64 \div 8 \cdot 2$
   16

7. $17 - (3 \cdot 5 + 2)$
   0

8. $(3 + 5)(2 + 1)$
   24

9. $3 + 2(3 + 4)^2$
   101

10. $32 \div 4^2 + 75 \div 5^2$
   5

The following division problems all have remainders. Divide.

11. $11 \div 4$
   $2 \text{ R } 3$

12. $208 \div 24$
   $8 \text{ R } 16$

13. $8,648 \div 43$
   $201 \text{ R } 5$

14. $14,713 \div 29$
   $507 \text{ R } 10$

15. Use the distributive property to rewrite $2 \cdot 7 + 3 \cdot 7$.
   $(2 + 3) \cdot 7$

16. Rewrite using exponents: $2 \cdot 2 \cdot 3 \cdot 3 \cdot 3$.
   $2^2 \cdot 3^3$

The Meaning and Properties of Fractions

Introduction . . .

The information in the table below was taken from the website for Cal Poly. The pie chart was created from the table. Both the table and pie chart use fractions to specify how the students at Cal Poly are distributed among the different schools within the university.

Objectives

A Identify the numerator and denominator of a fraction.

B Identify proper and improper fractions.

C Write equivalent fractions.

D Simplify fractions with division.

E Compare the size of fractions.

CAL POLY ENROLLMENT FOR FALL	
School	Fraction Of Students
Agriculture	$\frac{11}{50}$
Architecture and Environmental Design	$\frac{1}{10}$
Business	$\frac{3}{20}$
Engineering	$\frac{1}{4}$
Liberal Arts	$\frac{4}{25}$
Science and Mathematics	$\frac{3}{25}$

Cal Poly Enrollment for Fall

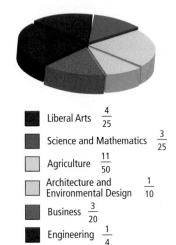

Liberal Arts $\frac{4}{25}$

Science and Mathematics $\frac{3}{25}$

Agriculture $\frac{11}{50}$

Architecture and Environmental Design $\frac{1}{10}$

Business $\frac{3}{20}$

Engineering $\frac{1}{4}$

From the table, we see that $\frac{1}{4}$ (one-fourth) of the students are enrolled in the School of Engineering. This means that one out of every four students at Cal Poly is studying engineering. The fraction $\frac{1}{4}$ tells us we have 1 part of 4 equal parts.

Figure 1 at the right shows a rectangle that has been divided into equal parts in four different ways. The shaded area for each rectangle is $\frac{1}{2}$ the total area.

Now that we have an intuitive idea of the meaning of fractions, here are the more formal definitions and vocabulary associated with fractions.

A The Numerator and Denominator

> **Definition**
>
> A **fraction** is any number that can be put in the form $\frac{a}{b}$ (also sometimes written a/b), where a and b are numbers and b is not 0.

Some examples of fractions are:

$$\frac{1}{2} \qquad \frac{3}{4} \qquad \frac{7}{8} \qquad \frac{9}{5}$$

One-half   *Three-fourths*   *Seven-eighths*   *Nine-fifths*

Note When we use a letter to represent a number, or a group of numbers, that letter is called a variable. In the definition below, we are restricting the numbers that the variable b can represent to numbers other than 0. As you will see later in the chapter, we do this to avoid writing an expression that would imply division by the number 0.

a. $\frac{1}{2}$ is shaded

b. $\frac{2}{4}$ are shaded

c. $\frac{3}{6}$ are shaded

d. $\frac{4}{8}$ are shaded

FIGURE 1 FOUR WAYS TO VISUALIZE $\frac{1}{2}$

> **Definition**
> For the fraction $\frac{a}{b}$, a and b are called the **terms** of the fraction. More specifically, a is called the **numerator,** and b is called the **denominator.**
>
> $$\text{fraction } \frac{a}{b} \begin{array}{l} \leftarrow \textbf{numerator} \\ \leftarrow \textbf{denominator} \end{array}$$

PRACTICE PROBLEMS

1. Name the terms of the fraction $\frac{5}{6}$. Which is the numerator and which is the denominator?

2. Name the numerator and the denominator of the fraction $\frac{x}{3}$.

3. Why is the number 9 considered to be a fraction?

EXAMPLE 1　The terms of the fraction $\frac{3}{4}$ are 3 and 4. The 3 is called the numerator, and the 4 is called the denominator.

EXAMPLE 2　The numerator of the fraction $\frac{a}{5}$ is a. The denominator is 5. Both a and 5 are called terms.

EXAMPLE 3　The number 7 may also be put in fraction form, because it can be written as $\frac{7}{1}$. In this case, 7 is the numerator and 1 is the denominator.

B　Proper and Improper Fractions

> **Definition**
> A **proper fraction** is a fraction in which the numerator is less than the denominator. If the numerator is greater than or equal to the denominator, the fraction is called an **improper fraction.**

4. Which of the following are proper fractions?

$$\frac{1}{6} \qquad \frac{2}{3} \qquad \frac{8}{5}$$

5. Which of the following are improper fractions?

$$\frac{5}{9} \qquad \frac{6}{5} \qquad \frac{4}{3} \qquad 7$$

EXAMPLE 4　The fractions $\frac{3}{4}$, $\frac{1}{8}$, and $\frac{9}{10}$ are all proper fractions, because in each case the numerator is less than the denominator.

EXAMPLE 5　The numbers $\frac{9}{5}$, $\frac{10}{10}$, and 6 are all improper fractions, because in each case the numerator is greater than or equal to the denominator. (Remember that 6 can be written as $\frac{6}{1}$, in which case 6 is the numerator and 1 is the denominator.)

Fractions on the Number Line

We can give meaning to the fraction $\frac{2}{3}$ by using a number line. If we take that part of the number line from 0 to 1 and divide it into *three equal parts,* we say that we have divided it into *thirds* (see Figure 2). Each of the three segments is $\frac{1}{3}$ (one third) of the whole segment from 0 to 1.

Note　There are many ways to give meaning to fractions like $\frac{2}{3}$ other than by using the number line. One popular way is to think of cutting a pie into three equal pieces, as shown below. If you take two of the pieces, you have taken $\frac{2}{3}$ of the pie.

FIGURE 2

Answers
1. Terms: 5 and 6; numerator: 5; denominator: 6
2. Numerator: x; denominator: 3
3. Because it can be written $\frac{9}{1}$
4. $\frac{1}{6}, \frac{2}{3}$　**5.** $\frac{6}{5}, \frac{4}{3}, 7$

Two of these smaller segments together are $\frac{2}{3}$ (two thirds) of the whole segment. And three of them would be $\frac{3}{3}$ (three thirds), or the whole segment, as indicated in Figure 3.

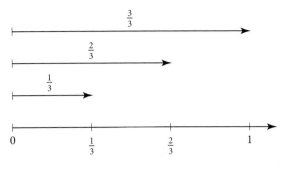

FIGURE 3

Let's do the same thing again with six and twelve equal divisions of the segment from 0 to 1 (see Figure 4).

The same point that we labeled with $\frac{1}{3}$ in Figure 3 is now labeled with $\frac{2}{6}$ and with $\frac{4}{12}$. It must be true then that

$$\frac{4}{12} = \frac{2}{6} = \frac{1}{3}$$

Although these three fractions look different, each names the same point on the number line, as shown in Figure 4. All three fractions have the same *value*, because they all represent the same number.

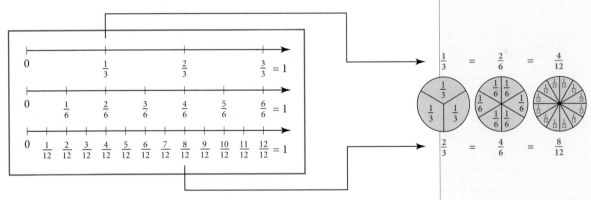

FIGURE 4

C Equivalent Fractions

Definition
Fractions that represent the same number are said to be **equivalent.**
Equivalent fractions may look different, but they must have the same value.

It is apparent that every fraction has many different representations, each of which is equivalent to the original fraction. The next two properties give us a way of changing the terms of a fraction without changing its value.

> **Property 1 for Fractions**
> If a, b, and c are numbers and b and c are not 0, then it is always true that
> $$\frac{a}{b} = \frac{a \cdot c}{b \cdot c}$$
> *In words:* If the numerator and the denominator of a fraction are multiplied by the same nonzero number, the resulting fraction is equivalent to the original fraction.

6. Write $\frac{2}{3}$ as an equivalent fraction with denominator 12.

EXAMPLE 6 Write $\frac{3}{4}$ as an equivalent fraction with denominator 20.

SOLUTION The denominator of the original fraction is 4. The fraction we are trying to find must have a denominator of 20. We know that if we multiply 4 by 5, we get 20. Property 1 indicates that we are free to multiply the denominator by 5 so long as we do the same to the numerator.

$$\frac{3}{4} = \frac{3 \cdot \mathbf{5}}{4 \cdot \mathbf{5}} = \frac{15}{20}$$

The fraction $\frac{15}{20}$ is equivalent to the fraction $\frac{3}{4}$.

7. Write $\frac{2}{3}$ as an equivalent fraction with denominator $12x$.

EXAMPLE 7 Write $\frac{3}{4}$ as an equivalent fraction with denominator $12x$.

SOLUTION If we multiply 4 by $3x$, we will have $12x$:

$$\frac{3}{4} = \frac{3 \cdot \mathbf{3x}}{4 \cdot \mathbf{3x}} = \frac{9x}{12x}$$

> **Property 2 for Fractions**
> If a, b, and c are integers and b and c are not 0, then it is always true that
> $$\frac{a}{b} = \frac{a \div c}{b \div c}$$
> *In words*: If the numerator and the denominator of a fraction are divided by the same nonzero number, the resulting fraction is equivalent to the original fraction.

8. Write $\frac{15}{20}$ as an equivalent fraction with denominator 4.

EXAMPLE 8 Write $\frac{10}{12}$ as an equivalent fraction with denominator 6.

SOLUTION If we divide the original denominator 12 by 2, we obtain 6. Property 2 indicates that if we divide both the numerator and the denominator by 2, the resulting fraction will be equal to the original fraction:

$$\frac{10}{12} = \frac{10 \div \mathbf{2}}{12 \div \mathbf{2}} = \frac{5}{6}$$

Answers

6. $\frac{8}{12}$ **7.** $\frac{8x}{12x}$ **8.** $\frac{3}{4}$

D The Number 1 and Fractions

There are two situations involving fractions and the number 1 that occur frequently in mathematics. The first is when the denominator of a fraction is 1. In this case, if we let a represent any number, then

$$\frac{a}{1} = a \qquad \text{for any number } a.$$

The second situation occurs when the numerator and the denominator of a fraction are the same nonzero number:

$$\frac{a}{a} = 1 \qquad \text{for any nonzero number } a.$$

EXAMPLE 9 Simplify each expression.

a. $\dfrac{24}{1}$ b. $\dfrac{24}{24}$ c. $\dfrac{48}{24}$ d. $\dfrac{72}{24}$

SOLUTION In each case we divide the numerator by the denominator:

a. $\dfrac{24}{1} = 24$ b. $\dfrac{24}{24} = 1$ c. $\dfrac{48}{24} = 2$ d. $\dfrac{72}{24} = 3$

E Comparing Fractions

We can compare fractions to see which is larger or smaller when they have the same denominator.

EXAMPLE 10 Write each fraction as an equivalent fraction with denominator 24. Then write them in order from smallest to largest.

$$\frac{5}{8} \quad \frac{5}{6} \quad \frac{3}{4} \quad \frac{2}{3}$$

SOLUTION We begin by writing each fraction as an equivalent fraction with denominator 24.

$$\frac{5}{8} = \frac{15}{24} \quad \frac{5}{6} = \frac{20}{24} \quad \frac{3}{4} = \frac{18}{24} \quad \frac{2}{3} = \frac{16}{24}$$

Now that they all have the same denominator, the smallest fraction is the one with the smallest numerator and the largest fraction is the one with the largest numerator. Writing them in order from smallest to largest we have:

$$\frac{15}{24} < \frac{16}{24} < \frac{18}{24} < \frac{20}{24}$$

or

$$\frac{5}{8} < \frac{2}{3} < \frac{3}{4} < \frac{5}{6}$$

STUDY SKILLS
Be Focused, Not Distracted

I have students who begin their assignments by asking themselves, "Why am I taking this class?" or, "When am I ever going to use this stuff?" If you are asking yourself similar questions, you may be distracting yourself from doing the things that will produce the results you want in this course. Don't dwell on questions and evaluations of the class that can be used as excuses for not doing well. If you want to succeed in this course, focus your energy and efforts toward success.

9. Simplify.

a. $\dfrac{18}{1}$ b. $\dfrac{18}{18}$

c. $\dfrac{36}{18}$ d. $\dfrac{72}{18}$

10. Write each fraction as an equivalent fraction with denominator 12. Then write in order from smallest to largest.

$$\frac{1}{3}, \frac{1}{6}, \frac{1}{4}, \frac{5}{12}$$

Answers
9. a. 18 b. 1 c. 2 d. 4
10. $\dfrac{2}{12}, \dfrac{3}{12}, \dfrac{4}{12}, \dfrac{5}{12}$

DESCRIPTIVE STATISTICS

Calculators

The table and bar chart give the daily gain in the price of a certain stock for one week, when stock prices were given in terms of fractions instead of decimals.

Change in Stock Price	
Day	Gain
Monday	$\frac{3}{4}$
Tuesday	$\frac{9}{16}$
Wednesday	$\frac{3}{32}$
Thursday	$\frac{7}{32}$
Friday	$\frac{1}{16}$

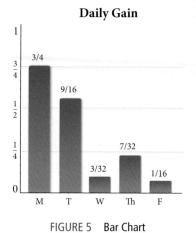

Daily Gain

FIGURE 5   Bar Chart

Figure 6 below shows another way to visualize the information in the table. It is called a scatter diagram. In the *scatter diagram,* dots are used instead of the bars shown in Figure 5 to represent the gain in stock price for each day of the week. If we connect the dots in Figure 6 with straight lines, we produce the diagram in Figure 7, which is known as a *line graph.*

FIGURE 6   Scatter Diagram

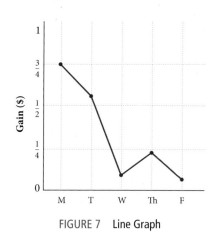

FIGURE 7   Line Graph

Getting Ready for Class

After reading through the preceding section, respond in your own words and in complete sentences. An answer of yes or no should always be accompanied by a sentence explaining why the answer is yes or no.

1. Explain what a fraction is.
2. Which term in the fraction $\frac{7}{8}$ is the numerator?
3. Is the fraction $\frac{3}{9}$ a proper fraction?
4. What word do we use to describe fractions such as $\frac{1}{5}$ and $\frac{4}{20}$, which look different, but have the same value?

Problem Set 2.1

A Name the numerator of each fraction. [Examples 1–3]

▶ **1.** $\frac{1}{3}$ **2.** $\frac{1}{4}$ **3.** $\frac{2}{3}$ **4.** $\frac{2}{4}$

1   1   2   2

▶ **5.** $\frac{x}{8}$ **6.** $\frac{y}{10}$ **7.** $\frac{a}{b}$ **8.** $\frac{x}{y}$

x   y   a   x

A Name the denominator of each fraction. [Examples 1–3]

▶ **9.** $\frac{2}{5}$ **10.** $\frac{3}{5}$ ▶ **11.** 6   **12.** 2

5   5   1   1

▶ **13.** $\frac{a}{12}$ **14.** $\frac{b}{14}$

12   14

A Complete the following tables.

15.

Numerator	Denominator	Fraction
a	b	$\frac{a}{b}$
3	5	$\frac{3}{5}$
1	7	$\frac{1}{7}$
x	y	$\frac{x}{y}$
x + 1	x	$\frac{x+1}{x}$

16.

Numerator	Denominator	Fraction
a	b	$\frac{a}{b}$
2	9	$\frac{2}{9}$
4	3	$\frac{4}{3}$
1	x	$\frac{1}{x}$
x	x + 1	$\frac{x}{x+1}$

B

▶ **17.** For the set of numbers $\left\{\frac{3}{4}, \frac{6}{5}, \frac{12}{3}, \frac{1}{2}, \frac{9}{10}, \frac{20}{10}\right\}$, list all the proper fractions.

$\frac{3}{4}, \frac{1}{2}, \frac{9}{10}$

▶ **18.** For the set of numbers $\left\{\frac{1}{8}, \frac{7}{9}, \frac{6}{3}, \frac{18}{6}, \frac{3}{5}, \frac{9}{8}\right\}$, list all the improper fractions.

$\frac{6}{3}, \frac{18}{6}, \frac{9}{8}$

Indicate whether each of the following is *True* or *False*.

19. Every whole number greater than 1 can also be expressed as an improper fraction.

True

20. Some improper fractions are also proper fractions.

False

C

21. Adding the same number to the numerator and the denominator of a fraction will not change its value.

False

▶ **22.** The fractions $\frac{3}{4}$ and $\frac{9}{16}$ are equivalent.

False

▶ Selected exercises available online at www.webassign.net/brookscole

C Divide the numerator and the denominator of each of the following fractions by 2. [Examples 6–8]

▶ **23.** $\dfrac{6}{8}$ **24.** $\dfrac{10}{12}$ **25.** $\dfrac{86}{94}$ ▶ **26.** $\dfrac{106}{142}$

$\dfrac{3}{4}$ $\dfrac{5}{6}$ $\dfrac{43}{47}$ $\dfrac{53}{71}$

C Divide the numerator and the denominator of each of the following fractions by 3. [Examples 6–8]

27. $\dfrac{12}{9}$ **28.** $\dfrac{33}{27}$ **29.** $\dfrac{39}{51}$ **30.** $\dfrac{57}{69}$

$\dfrac{4}{3}$ $\dfrac{11}{9}$ $\dfrac{13}{17}$ $\dfrac{19}{23}$

C Write each of the following fractions as an equivalent fraction with denominator 6. [Examples 6–8]

▶ **31.** $\dfrac{2}{3}$ **32.** $\dfrac{1}{2}$ ▶ **33.** $\dfrac{55}{66}$ **34.** $\dfrac{65}{78}$

$\dfrac{4}{6}$ $\dfrac{3}{6}$ $\dfrac{5}{6}$ $\dfrac{5}{6}$

C Write each of the following fractions as an equivalent fraction with denominator 12. [Examples 6–8]

35. $\dfrac{2}{3}$ **36.** $\dfrac{5}{6}$ **37.** $\dfrac{56}{84}$ **38.** $\dfrac{143}{156}$

$\dfrac{8}{12}$ $\dfrac{10}{12}$ $\dfrac{8}{12}$ $\dfrac{11}{12}$

C Write each fraction as an equivalent fraction with denominator 12x. [Example 7]

▶ **39.** $\dfrac{1}{6}$ **40.** $\dfrac{3}{4}$

$\dfrac{2x}{12x}$ $\dfrac{9x}{12x}$

C Write each number as an equivalent fraction with denominator 24a. [Example 7]

41. 2   **42.** 1   **43.** 5   ▶ **44.** 8

$\dfrac{48a}{24a}$ $\dfrac{24a}{24a}$ $\dfrac{120a}{24a}$ $\dfrac{192a}{24a}$

45. One-fourth of the first circle below is shaded. Use the other three circles to show three other ways to shade one-fourth of the circle.

Answers will vary

46. The objects below are hexagons, six-sided figures. One-third of the first hexagon is shaded. Shade the other three hexagons to show three other ways to represent one-third.

Answers will vary

D Simplify by dividing the numerator by the denominator.

▶ **47.** $\dfrac{3}{1}$ **48.** $\dfrac{3}{3}$ **49.** $\dfrac{6}{3}$ **50.** $\dfrac{12}{3}$ **51.** $\dfrac{37}{1}$ **52.** $\dfrac{37}{37}$

3   1   2   4   37   1

▶ **53.** For each square below, what fraction of the area is given by the shaded region?

a.

b.

c.

d.

$\frac{1}{2}$ $\frac{1}{2}$ $\frac{1}{4}$ $\frac{1}{4}$

54. For each square below, what fraction of the area is given by the shaded region?

a.

b.

c.

d.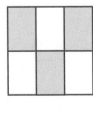

$\frac{2}{4}$ $\frac{2}{4}$ $\frac{4}{8}$ $\frac{3}{6}$

The number line below extends from 0 to 2, with the segment from 0 to 1 and the segment from 1 to 2 each divided into 8 equal parts. Locate each of the following numbers on this number line.

55. $\frac{1}{4}$ **56.** $\frac{1}{8}$ **57.** $\frac{1}{16}$ **58.** $\frac{5}{8}$ **59.** $\frac{3}{4}$

60. $\frac{15}{16}$ **61.** $\frac{3}{2}$ **62.** $\frac{5}{4}$ **63.** $\frac{31}{16}$ **64.** $\frac{15}{8}$

[number line diagram showing from 0 to 2 with labels $\frac{1}{16}$, $\frac{1}{8}$, $\frac{1}{4}$, $\frac{5}{8}$, $\frac{3}{4}$, $\frac{15}{16}$, $\frac{5}{4}$, $\frac{3}{2}$, $\frac{15}{8}$, $\frac{31}{16}$]

E [Example 10]

65. Write each fraction as an equivalent fraction with denominator 100. Then write them in order from smallest to largest.

$$\frac{3}{10} \qquad \frac{1}{20} \qquad \frac{4}{25} \qquad \frac{2}{5}$$

$$\frac{1}{20} < \frac{4}{25} < \frac{3}{10} < \frac{2}{5}$$

66. Write each fraction as an equivalent fraction with denominator 30. Then write them in order from smallest to largest.

$$\frac{1}{15} \qquad \frac{5}{6} \qquad \frac{7}{10} \qquad \frac{1}{2}$$

$$\frac{1}{15} < \frac{1}{2} < \frac{7}{10} < \frac{5}{6}$$

■ Applying the Concepts

67. Rainfall The chart shows the average rainfall for Death Valley in the given months. Write the rainfall for January as an equivalent fraction with denominator 12.

$\frac{3}{12}$ inch

68. Rainfall The chart shows the average rainfall for Death Valley in the given months. Write the rainfall for April as an equivalent fraction with denominator 75.

$\frac{9}{75}$ inch

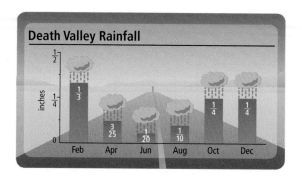

▶ **69. Sending E-mail** The pie chart below shows the fraction of workers who responded to a survey about sending non-work-related e-mail from the office. Use the pie chart to fill in the table.

Workers sending personal e-mail from the office

■ Never $\frac{4}{25}$
■ 1-5 times a day $\frac{47}{100}$
□ 5-10 times day $\frac{8}{25}$
■ >10 times a day $\frac{1}{20}$

How Often Workers Send Non-Work-Related E-Mail From the Office	Fraction of Respondents Saying Yes
never	$\frac{4}{25}$
1 to 5 times a day	$\frac{47}{100}$
5 to 10 times a day	$\frac{8}{25}$
more than 10 times a day	$\frac{1}{20}$

70. Surfing the Internet The pie chart below shows the fraction of workers who responded to a survey about viewing non-work-related sites during working hours. Use the pie chart to fill in the table.

Workers surfing the net from the office

□ Constantly $\frac{37}{100}$
■ Never $\frac{9}{100}$
■ A few times a day $\frac{8}{25}$
■ A few times a week $\frac{11}{50}$

How Often Workers View Non-Work-Related Sites From the Office	Fraction of Respondents Saying Yes
never	$\frac{9}{100}$
a few times a week	$\frac{11}{50}$
a few times a day	$\frac{8}{25}$
constantly	$\frac{37}{100}$

71. Number of Children If there are 3 girls in a family with 5 children, then we say that $\frac{3}{5}$ of the children are girls. If there are 4 girls in a family with 5 children, what fraction of the children are girls?

$\frac{4}{5}$

72. Medical School If 3 out of every 7 people who apply to medical school actually get accepted, what fraction of the people who apply get accepted?

$\frac{3}{7}$

73. Downloaded Songs The new iPod™ Shuffle will hold up to 500 songs. You load 311 of your favorite tunes onto your iPod. Represent the number of songs on your iPod as a fraction of the total number of songs it can hold.

$\frac{311}{500}$

74. Cell Phones In a survey of 1,000 cell phone subscribers it was determined that 160 subscribers owned more than one cell phone and used different carriers for each phone. Represent the number of cell phone subscribers with more than one carrier as a fraction.

$\frac{160}{1000}$ (In the next section we will reduce fractions like this to lowest terms.)

75. College Basketball Recently the men's basketball team at the University of Maryland won 19 of the 33 games they played. What fraction represents the number of games won?

$\frac{19}{33}$

76. Score on a Test Your math teacher grades on a point system. You take a test worth 75 points and score a 67 on the test. Represent your score as a fraction.

$\frac{67}{75}$

77. Circles A circle measures 360 degrees, which is commonly written as 360°. The shaded region of each of the circles below is given in degrees. Write a fraction that represents the area of the shaded region for each of these circles.

a.

$\frac{90}{360}$

b.

$\frac{45}{360}$

c.

$\frac{180}{360}$

d.

$\frac{270}{360}$

78. Carbon Dating All living things contain a small amount of carbon-14, which is radioactive and decays. The half-life of carbon-14 is 5,600 years. During the lifetime of an organism, the carbon-14 is replenished, but after its death the carbon-14 begins to disappear. By measuring the amount left, the age of the organism can be determined with surprising accuracy. The line graph below shows the fraction of carbon-14 remaining after the death of an organism. Use the line graph to complete the table.

Concentration of Carbon-14	
Years Since Death of Organism	Fraction of Carbon-14 Remaining
0	1
5,600	$\frac{1}{2}$
11,200	$\frac{1}{4}$
16,800	$\frac{1}{8}$
22,400	$\frac{1}{16}$

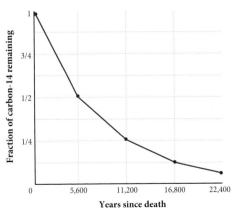

■ Estimating

▶ **79.** Which of the following fractions is closest to the number 0?

  a. $\frac{1}{2}$ **b.** $\frac{1}{3}$ **c.** $\frac{1}{4}$ **d.** $\frac{1}{5}$

  d

▶ **80.** Which of the following fractions is closest to the number 1?

  a. $\frac{1}{2}$ **b.** $\frac{1}{3}$ **c.** $\frac{1}{4}$ **d.** $\frac{1}{5}$

  a

81. Which of the following fractions is closest to the number 0?

  a. $\frac{1}{8}$ **b.** $\frac{3}{8}$ **c.** $\frac{5}{8}$ **d.** $\frac{7}{8}$

  a

82. Which of the following fractions is closest to the number 1?

  a. $\frac{1}{8}$ **b.** $\frac{3}{8}$ **c.** $\frac{5}{8}$ **d.** $\frac{7}{8}$

  d

■ Getting Ready for the Next Section

Multiply.

83. $2 \cdot 2 \cdot 3 \cdot 3 \cdot 3$
108

84. $2^2 \cdot 3^3$
108

85. $2^2 \cdot 3 \cdot 5$
60

86. $2 \cdot 3^2 \cdot 5$
90

Divide.

87. $12 \div 3$
4

88. $15 \div 3$
5

89. $20 \div 4$
5

90. $24 \div 4$
6

91. $42 \div 6$
7

92. $72 \div 8$
9

93. $102 \div 2$
51

94. $105 \div 7$
15

■ Maintaining Your Skills

The problems below review material covered previously.

Simplify.

95. $3 + 4 \cdot 5$
23

96. $20 - 8 \cdot 2$
4

97. $5 \cdot 2^4 - 3 \cdot 4^2$
32

98. $7 \cdot 8^2 + 2 \cdot 5^2$
498

99. $4 \cdot 3 + 2(5 - 3)$
16

100. $6 \cdot 8 + 3(4 - 1)$
57

101. $18 + 12 \div 4 - 3$
18

102. $20 + 16 \div 2 - 5$
23

Introduction . . .

Suppose you and a friend decide to split a medium-sized pizza for lunch. When the pizza is delivered you find that it has been cut into eight equal pieces. If you eat four pieces, you have eaten $\frac{4}{8}$ of the pizza, but you also know that you have eaten $\frac{1}{2}$ of the pizza. The fraction $\frac{4}{8}$ is equivalent to the fraction $\frac{1}{2}$; that is, they both have the same value. The mathematical process we use to rewrite $\frac{4}{8}$ as $\frac{1}{2}$ is called *reducing to lowest terms*. Before we look at that process, we need to define some new terms. Here is our first one:

A Prime Numbers

> **Definition**
>
> A **prime number** is any whole number greater than 1 that has exactly two divisors—itself and 1. (A number is a divisor of another number if it divides it without a remainder.)

$$\text{Prime numbers} = \{2, 3, 5, 7, 11, 13, 17, 19, 23, 29, 31, 37, \ldots\}$$

The list goes on indefinitely. Each number in the list has exactly two distinct divisors—itself and 1.

> **Definition**
>
> Any whole number greater than 1 that is not a prime number is called a **composite number.** A composite number always has at least one divisor other than itself and 1.

EXAMPLE 1 Identify each of the numbers below as either a prime number or a composite number. For those that are composite, give two divisors other than the number itself or 1.

    a. 43   **b.** 12

SOLUTION   **a.** 43 is a prime number, because the only numbers that divide it without a remainder are 43 and 1.

      b. 12 is a composite number, because it can be written as $12 = 4 \cdot 3$, which means that 4 and 3 are divisors of 12. (These are not the only divisors of 12; other divisors are 1, 2, 6, and 12.)

B Factoring

Every composite number can be written as the product of prime factors. Let's look at the composite number 108. We know we can write 108 as $2 \cdot 54$. The number 2 is a prime number, but 54 is not prime. Because 54 can be written as $2 \cdot 27$, we have

$$108 = 2 \cdot 54$$
$$= 2 \cdot 2 \cdot 27$$

PRACTICE PROBLEMS

1. Which of the numbers below are prime numbers, and which are composite? For those that are composite, give two divisors other than the number itself and 1.

   37, 39, 51, 59

 Note You may have already noticed that the word *divisor* as we are using it here means the same as the word *factor*. A divisor and a factor of a number are the same thing. A number can't be a divisor of another number without also being a factor of it.

Answer

1. See solutions section.

Note This process works by writing the original composite number as the product of any two of its factors and then writing any factor that is not prime as the product of any two of its factors. The process is continued until all factors are prime numbers. You do not have to start with the smallest prime factor, as shown in Example 1. No matter which factors you start with you will always end up with the same prime factorization of a number.

2. Factor into a product of prime factors.
  a. 90
  b. 900

Note There are some "shortcuts" to finding the divisors of a number. For instance, if a number ends in 0 or 5, then it is divisible by 5. If a number ends in an even number (0, 2, 4, 6, or 8), then it is divisible by 2. A number is divisible by 3 if the sum of its digits is divisible by 3. For example, 921 is divisible by 3 because the sum of its digits is $9 + 2 + 1 = 12$, which is divisible by 3.

3. Which of the following fractions are in lowest terms?
$$\frac{1}{6}, \frac{2}{8}, \frac{15}{25}, \frac{9}{13}$$

4. Reduce $\frac{12}{18}$ to lowest terms by dividing the numerator and the denominator by 6.

Answers
2. a. $2 \cdot 3^2 \cdot 5$ **b.** $2^2 \cdot 3^2 \cdot 5^2$
3. $\frac{1}{6}, \frac{9}{13}$ **4.** $\frac{2}{3}$

Now the number 27 can be written as $3 \cdot 9$ or $3 \cdot 3 \cdot 3$ (because $9 = 3 \cdot 3$), so

$$108 = 2 \cdot 54$$
$$108 = 2 \cdot 2 \cdot 27$$
$$108 = 2 \cdot 2 \cdot 3 \cdot 9$$
$$108 = 2 \cdot 2 \cdot 3 \cdot 3 \cdot 3$$

This last line is the number 108 written as the product of prime factors. We can use exponents to rewrite the last line:

$$108 = 2^2 \cdot 3^3$$

EXAMPLE 2 Factor 60 into a product of prime factors.

SOLUTION We begin by writing 60 as $6 \cdot 10$ and continue factoring until all factors are prime numbers:

$$60 = 6 \cdot 10$$
$$= 2 \cdot 3 \cdot 2 \cdot 5$$
$$= 2^2 \cdot 3 \cdot 5$$

Notice that if we had started by writing 60 as $3 \cdot 20$, we would have achieved the same result:

$$60 = 3 \cdot 20$$
$$= 3 \cdot 2 \cdot 10$$
$$= 3 \cdot 2 \cdot 2 \cdot 5$$
$$= 2^2 \cdot 3 \cdot 5$$

C Reducing Fractions

We can use the method of factoring numbers into prime factors to help reduce fractions to lowest terms. Here is the definition for lowest terms.

> **Definition**
> A fraction is said to be in **lowest terms** if the numerator and the denominator have no factors in common other than the number 1.

EXAMPLE 3 The fractions $\frac{1}{2}, \frac{1}{3}, \frac{2}{3}, \frac{1}{4}, \frac{3}{4}, \frac{1}{5}, \frac{2}{5}, \frac{3}{5}$, and $\frac{4}{5}$ are all in lowest terms, because in each case the numerator and the denominator have no factors other than 1 in common. That is, in each fraction, no number other than 1 divides both the numerator and the denominator exactly (without a remainder).

EXAMPLE 4 The fraction $\frac{6}{8}$ is not written in lowest terms, because the numerator and the denominator are both divisible by 2. To write $\frac{6}{8}$ in lowest terms, we apply Property 2 from Section 2.1 and divide both the numerator and the denominator by 2:

$$\frac{6}{8} = \frac{6 \div \mathbf{2}}{8 \div \mathbf{2}} = \frac{3}{4}$$

The fraction $\frac{3}{4}$ is in lowest terms, because 3 and 4 have no factors in common except the number 1.

Reducing a fraction to lowest terms is simply a matter of dividing the numerator and the denominator by all the factors they have in common. We know from Property 2 of Section 2.1 that this will produce an equivalent fraction.

EXAMPLE 5   Reduce the fraction $\frac{12}{15}$ to lowest terms by first factoring the numerator and the denominator into prime factors and then dividing both the numerator and the denominator by the factor they have in common.

SOLUTION   The numerator and the denominator factor as follows:

$$12 = 2 \cdot 2 \cdot 3 \quad \text{and} \quad 15 = 3 \cdot 5$$

The factor they have in common is 3. Property 2 tells us that we can divide both terms of a fraction by 3 to produce an equivalent fraction. So

$$\frac{12}{15} = \frac{2 \cdot 2 \cdot 3}{3 \cdot 5} \qquad \text{Factor the numerator and the denominator completely}$$

$$= \frac{2 \cdot 2 \cdot 3 \div \mathbf{3}}{3 \cdot 5 \div \mathbf{3}} \qquad \text{Divide by 3}$$

$$= \frac{2 \cdot 2}{5} = \frac{4}{5}$$

The fraction $\frac{4}{5}$ is equivalent to $\frac{12}{15}$ and is in lowest terms, because the numerator and the denominator have no factors other than 1 in common.

We can shorten the work involved in reducing fractions to lowest terms by using a slash to indicate division. For example, we can write the above problem as:

$$\frac{12}{15} = \frac{2 \cdot 2 \cdot \cancel{3}}{\cancel{3} \cdot 5} = \frac{4}{5}$$

So long as we understand that the slashes through the 3's indicate that we have divided both the numerator and the denominator by 3, we can use this notation.

D   Applications

EXAMPLE 6   Laura is having a party. She puts 4 six-packs of soda in a cooler for her guests. At the end of the party she finds that only 4 sodas have been consumed. What fraction of the sodas are left? Write your answer in lowest terms.

SOLUTION   She had 4 six-packs of soda, which is 4(6) = 24 sodas. Only 4 were consumed at the party, so 20 are left. The fraction of sodas left is

$$\frac{20}{24}$$

Factoring 20 and 24 completely and then dividing out both the factors they have in common gives us

$$\frac{20}{24} = \frac{\cancel{2} \cdot \cancel{2} \cdot 5}{\cancel{2} \cdot \cancel{2} \cdot 2 \cdot 3} = \frac{5}{6}$$

EXAMPLE 7   Reduce $\frac{6}{42}$ to lowest terms.

SOLUTION   We begin by factoring both terms. We then divide through by any factors common to both terms:

$$\frac{6}{42} = \frac{\cancel{2} \cdot \cancel{3}}{\cancel{2} \cdot \cancel{3} \cdot 7} = \frac{1}{7}$$

---

5. Reduce the fraction $\frac{15}{20}$ to lowest terms by first factoring the numerator and the denominator into prime factors and then dividing out the factors they have in common.

Instructor Note
I try to avoid using the word "cancel" when reducing fractions to lowest terms, because I find that students will misuse this term later. I emphasize that the slashes I put through the common factors represent division. Using the phrase "divide the numerator and the denominator by the common factor 3" reminds students of the operation, division, that is used to reduce fractions to lowest terms.

6. Reduce to lowest terms.
   a. $\frac{30}{35}$ **b.** $\frac{300}{350}$

Note   The slashes in Example 6 indicate that we have divided both the numerator and the denominator by $2 \cdot 2$, which is equal to 4. With some fractions it is apparent at the start what number divides the numerator and the denominator. For instance, you may have recognized that both 20 and 24 in Example 6 are divisible by 4. We can divide both terms by 4 without factoring first, just as we did in Section 2.1. Property 2 guarantees that dividing both terms of a fraction by 4 will produce an equivalent fraction:

$$\frac{20}{24} = \frac{20 \div \mathbf{4}}{24 \div \mathbf{4}} = \frac{5}{6}$$

7. Reduce to lowest terms.
   a. $\frac{8}{72}$ **b.** $\frac{16}{144}$

Answers

5. $\frac{3}{4}$ **6.** Both are $\frac{6}{7}$.

We must be careful in a problem like this to remember that the slashes indicate division. They are used to indicate that we have divided both the numerator and the denominator by $2 \cdot 3 = 6$. The result of dividing the numerator 6 by $2 \cdot 3$ is 1. It is a very common mistake to call the numerator 0 instead of 1 or to leave the numerator out of the answer.

Reduce each fraction to lowest terms.

8. $\dfrac{5}{50}$

9. $\dfrac{120}{25}$

EXAMPLE 8　Reduce to lowest terms: $\dfrac{4}{40} = \dfrac{\cancel{2} \cdot 2 \cdot 1}{\cancel{2} \cdot 2 \cdot 2 \cdot 5}$

$$= \dfrac{1}{10}$$

EXAMPLE 9　Reduce to lowest terms: $\dfrac{105}{30} = \dfrac{\cancel{3} \cdot \cancel{5} \cdot 7}{2 \cdot \cancel{3} \cdot \cancel{5}}$

$$= \dfrac{7}{2}$$

Getting Ready for Class

After reading through the preceding section, respond in your own words and in complete sentences.

A. What is a prime number?

B. Why is the number 22 a composite number?

C. Factor 120 into a product of prime factors.

D. What is meant by the phrase "a fraction in lowest possible terms"?

Answers

7. Both are $\frac{1}{9}$　**8.** $\frac{1}{10}$　**9.** $\frac{24}{5}$

Problem Set 2.2

A Identify each of the numbers below as either a prime number or a composite number. For those that are composite, give at least one divisor (factor) other than the number itself or the number 1. [Example 1]

1. 11
Prime

2. 23
Prime

3. 105
Composite; 3, 5, and 7 are factors

4. 41
Prime

5. 81
Composite; 3 is a factor

▶ **6.** 50
Composite; 2 and 5 are factors

7. 13
Prime

8. 219
Composite; 3 and 73 are factors

B Factor each of the following into a product of prime factors. [Example 2]

9. 12
$2^2 \cdot 3$

▶ **10.** 8
2^3

11. 81
3^4

▶ **12.** 210
$2 \cdot 3 \cdot 5 \cdot 7$

13. 215
$5 \cdot 43$

▶ **14.** 75
$3 \cdot 5^2$

15. 15
$3 \cdot 5$

▶ **16.** 42
$2 \cdot 3 \cdot 7$

C Reduce each fraction to lowest terms. [Examples 4, 5, 7–9]

▶ **17.** $\dfrac{5}{10}$
$\dfrac{1}{2}$

18. $\dfrac{3}{6}$
$\dfrac{1}{2}$

19. $\dfrac{4}{6}$
$\dfrac{2}{3}$

20. $\dfrac{4}{10}$
$\dfrac{2}{5}$

21. $\dfrac{8}{10}$
$\dfrac{4}{5}$

22. $\dfrac{6}{10}$
$\dfrac{3}{5}$

23. $\dfrac{36}{20}$
$\dfrac{9}{5}$

24. $\dfrac{32}{12}$
$\dfrac{8}{3}$

25. $\dfrac{42}{66}$
$\dfrac{7}{11}$

▶ **26.** $\dfrac{36}{60}$
$\dfrac{3}{5}$

27. $\dfrac{24}{40}$
$\dfrac{3}{5}$

28. $\dfrac{50}{75}$
$\dfrac{2}{3}$

▶ **29.** $\dfrac{14}{98}$
$\dfrac{1}{7}$

30. $\dfrac{12}{84}$
$\dfrac{1}{7}$

31. $\dfrac{70}{90}$
$\dfrac{7}{9}$

▶ **32.** $\dfrac{80}{90}$
$\dfrac{8}{9}$

33. $\dfrac{42}{30}$
$\dfrac{7}{5}$

34. $\dfrac{60}{36}$
$\dfrac{5}{3}$

35. $\dfrac{18}{90}$
$\dfrac{1}{5}$

36. $\dfrac{150}{210}$
$\dfrac{5}{7}$

37. $\dfrac{110}{70}$
$\dfrac{11}{7}$

38. $\dfrac{45}{75}$
$\dfrac{3}{5}$

39. $\dfrac{180}{108}$
$\dfrac{5}{3}$

40. $\dfrac{105}{30}$
$\dfrac{7}{2}$

41. $\dfrac{96}{108}$
$\dfrac{8}{9}$

42. $\dfrac{66}{84}$
$\dfrac{11}{14}$

▶ **43.** $\dfrac{126}{165}$
$\dfrac{42}{55}$

44. $\dfrac{210}{462}$
$\dfrac{5}{11}$

45. $\dfrac{102}{114}$
$\dfrac{17}{19}$

46. $\dfrac{255}{285}$
$\dfrac{17}{19}$

▶ **47.** $\dfrac{294}{693}$
$\dfrac{14}{33}$

48. $\dfrac{273}{385}$
$\dfrac{39}{55}$

▶ Selected exercises available online at www.webassign.net/brookscole

49. Reduce each fraction to lowest terms.

a. $\dfrac{6}{51}$ b. $\dfrac{6}{52}$ c. $\dfrac{6}{54}$ d. $\dfrac{6}{56}$ e. $\dfrac{6}{57}$

$\dfrac{2}{17}$ $\dfrac{3}{26}$ $\dfrac{1}{9}$ $\dfrac{3}{28}$ $\dfrac{2}{19}$

▶ **50.** Reduce each fraction to lowest terms.

a. $\dfrac{6}{42}$ b. $\dfrac{6}{44}$ c. $\dfrac{6}{45}$ d. $\dfrac{6}{46}$ e. $\dfrac{6}{48}$

$\dfrac{1}{7}$ $\dfrac{3}{22}$ $\dfrac{2}{15}$ $\dfrac{3}{23}$ $\dfrac{1}{8}$

51. Reduce each fraction to lowest terms.

a. $\dfrac{2}{90}$ b. $\dfrac{3}{90}$ c. $\dfrac{5}{90}$ d. $\dfrac{6}{90}$ e. $\dfrac{9}{90}$

$\dfrac{1}{45}$ $\dfrac{1}{30}$ $\dfrac{1}{18}$ $\dfrac{1}{15}$ $\dfrac{1}{10}$

▶ **52.** Reduce each fraction to lowest terms.

a. $\dfrac{3}{105}$ b. $\dfrac{5}{105}$ c. $\dfrac{7}{105}$ d. $\dfrac{15}{105}$ e. $\dfrac{21}{105}$

$\dfrac{1}{35}$ $\dfrac{1}{21}$ $\dfrac{1}{15}$ $\dfrac{1}{7}$ $\dfrac{1}{5}$

53. The answer to each problem below is wrong. Give the correct answer in lowest terms.

a. $\dfrac{5}{15} = \dfrac{5}{3 \cdot \cancel{5}} = \dfrac{0}{3}$

$\dfrac{1}{3}$

b. $\dfrac{5}{6} = \dfrac{3+2}{4+2} = \dfrac{3}{4}$

$\dfrac{5}{6}$

c. $\dfrac{6}{30} = \dfrac{2 \cdot 3}{2 \cdot 3 \cdot 5} = 5$

$\dfrac{1}{5}$

54. The answer to each problem below is wrong. Give the correct answer in lowest terms.

a. $\dfrac{10}{20} = \dfrac{7+3}{17+3} = \dfrac{7}{17}$

$\dfrac{1}{2}$

b. $\dfrac{9}{36} = \dfrac{3 \cdot 3}{2 \cdot 2 \cdot 3 \cdot 3} = \dfrac{0}{4}$

$\dfrac{1}{4}$

c. $\dfrac{4}{12} = \dfrac{2 \cdot 2}{2 \cdot 2 \cdot 3} = 3$

$\dfrac{1}{3}$

55. Which of the fractions $\dfrac{6}{8}, \dfrac{15}{20}, \dfrac{9}{16}$, and $\dfrac{21}{28}$ does not reduce to $\dfrac{3}{4}$?

$\dfrac{9}{16}$

▶ **56.** Which of the fractions $\dfrac{4}{9}, \dfrac{10}{15}, \dfrac{8}{12}$, and $\dfrac{6}{12}$ do not reduce to $\dfrac{2}{3}$?

$\dfrac{4}{9}, \dfrac{6}{12}$

The number line below extends from 0 to 2, with the segment from 0 to 1 and the segment from 1 to 2 each divided into 8 equal parts. Locate each of the following numbers on this number line.

57. $\dfrac{1}{2}, \dfrac{2}{4}, \dfrac{4}{8},$ and $\dfrac{8}{16}$

58. $\dfrac{3}{2}, \dfrac{6}{4}, \dfrac{12}{8},$ and $\dfrac{24}{16}$

59. $\dfrac{5}{4}, \dfrac{10}{8},$ and $\dfrac{20}{16}$

60. $\dfrac{1}{4}, \dfrac{2}{8},$ and $\dfrac{4}{16}$

D   Applying the Concepts   [Example 6]

61. Tower Heights The Eiffel Tower is 1,060 feet tall and the Stratosphere Tower in Las Vegas is 1,150 feet tall. Write the height of the Eiffel tower over the height of the Stratosphere Tower and then reduce to lowest terms.

$\dfrac{106}{115}$

62. Car Insurance The chart below shows the annual cost of auto insurance for some major U.S. cities. Write the price of auto insurance in Los Angeles over the price of insurance in Detroit and then reduce to lowest terms.

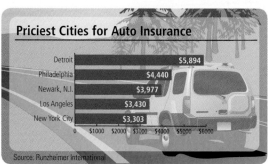

Priciest Cities for Auto Insurance

City	Cost
Detroit	$5,894
Philadelphia	$4,440
Newark, N.J.	$3,977
Los Angeles	$3,430
New York City	$3,303

Source: Runzheimer International

$\dfrac{245}{421}$

▶ **63. Hours and Minutes** There are 60 minutes in 1 hour. What fraction of an hour is 20 minutes? Write your answer in lowest terms.

$\dfrac{1}{3}$

▶ **64. Final Exam** Suppose 33 people took the final exam in a math class. If 11 people got an A on the final exam, what fraction of the students did not get an A on the exam? Write your answer in lowest terms.

$\dfrac{2}{3}$

65. Driving Distractions Many of us focus our attention on things other than driving when we are behind the wheel of our car. In a survey of 150 drivers, it was noted that 48 drivers spend time reading or writing while they are driving. Represent the number of drivers who spend time reading or writing while driving as a fraction in lowest terms.

$\dfrac{8}{25}$

66. Watching Television According to the U.S. Census Bureau, it is estimated that the average person watches 4 hours of TV each day. Represent the number of hours of TV watched each day as a fraction in lowest terms.

$\dfrac{1}{6}$

67. Hurricanes Over a recent five-year period, 9 hurricanes struck the mainland of the United States. Three of these hurricanes were classified as a category 3, 4 or 5. Represent the number of major hurricanes that struck the mainland U.S. over this time period as a fraction in lowest terms.

$\dfrac{1}{3}$

68. Gasoline Tax Suppose a gallon of regular gas costs $3.99, and 54 cents of this goes to pay state gas taxes. What fractional part of the cost of a gallon of gas goes to state taxes? Write your answer in lowest terms.

$\dfrac{18}{133}$

69. On-Time Record A random check of Delta airline flights for the past month showed that of the 350 flights scheduled 185 left on time. Represent the number of on time flights as a fraction in lowest terms.

$\dfrac{37}{70}$

70. Internet Users Based on the most recent data available, there are approximately 1,320,000,000 Internet users in the world. North America makes up about 240,000,000 of this total. Represent the number of Internet users in North America as a fraction of the total expressed in lowest terms.

$\dfrac{2}{11}$

Nutrition The nutrition labels below are from two different granola bars.

▶ 71. What fraction of the calories in Bar 1 comes from fat?

$\frac{1}{3}$

GRANOLA BAR 1

Nutrition Facts
Serving Size 2 bars (47g)
Servings Per Container: 6

Amount Per Serving		
Calories 210	Calories from fat 70	
		% Daily Value*
Total Fat 8g		12%
Saturated Fat 1g		5%
Cholesterol 0mg		0%
Sodium 150mg		6%
Total Carbohydrate 32g		11%
Fiber 2g		10%
Sugars 12g		
Protein 4g		

*Percent Daily Values are based on a 2,000 calorie diet. Your daily values may be higher or lower depending on your calorie needs.

GRANOLA BAR 2

Nutrition Facts
Serving Size 1 bar (21g)
Servings Per Container: 8

Amount Per Serving		
Calories 80	Calories from fat 15	
		% Daily Value*
Total Fat 1.5g		2%
Saturated Fat 0g		0%
Cholesterol 0mg		0%
Sodium 60mg		3%
Total Carbohydrate 16g		5%
Fiber 1g		4%
Sugars 5g		
Protein 2g		

*Percent Daily Values are based on a 2,000 calorie diet. Your daily values may be higher or lower depending on your calorie needs.

72. What fraction of the calories in Bar 2 comes from fat?

$\frac{3}{16}$

73. For Bar 1, what fraction of the total fat is from saturated fat?

$\frac{1}{8}$

▶ 74. What fraction of the total carbohydrates in Bar 1 is from sugar?

$\frac{3}{8}$

■ Getting Ready for the Next Section

Multiply.

75. $1 \cdot 3 \cdot 1$

3

76. $2 \cdot 4 \cdot 5$

40

77. $3 \cdot 5 \cdot 3$

45

78. $1 \cdot 4 \cdot 1$

4

79. $5 \cdot 5 \cdot 1$

25

80. $6 \cdot 6 \cdot 2$

72

Factor into prime factors.

81. 60

$2^2 \cdot 5 \cdot 3$

82. 72

$2^3 \cdot 3^2$

83. $15 \cdot 4$

$2^2 \cdot 5 \cdot 3$

84. $8 \cdot 9$

$2^3 \cdot 3^2$

Expand and multiply.

85. 3^2

9

86. 4^2

16

87. 5^2

25

88. 6^2

36

■ Maintaining Your Skills

Simplify.

89. $16 - 8 + 4$

12

90. $16 - 4 + 8$

20

91. $24 - 14 + 8$

18

92. $24 - 16 + 6$

14

93. $36 - 6 + 12$

42

94. $36 - 9 + 20$

47

95. $48 - 12 + 17$

53

96. $48 - 13 + 15$

50

Multiplication with Fractions, and the Area of a Triangle

Objectives

A Multiply fractions.

B Find the area of a triangle.

Introduction . . .

A recipe calls for $\frac{3}{4}$ cup of flour. If you are making only $\frac{1}{2}$ the recipe, how much flour do you use? This question can be answered by multiplying $\frac{1}{2}$ and $\frac{3}{4}$. Here is the problem written in symbols:

$$\frac{1}{2} \cdot \frac{3}{4} = \frac{3}{8}$$

As you can see from this example, to multiply two fractions, we multiply the numerators and then multiply the denominators. We begin this section with the rule for multiplication of fractions.

A Multiplying Fractions

Rule

The product of two fractions is the fraction whose numerator is the product of the two numerators and whose denominator is the product of the two denominators. We can write this rule in symbols as follows:

If a, b, c, and d represent any numbers and b and d are not zero, then

$$\frac{a}{b} \cdot \frac{c}{d} = \frac{a \cdot c}{b \cdot d}$$

Note You may wonder why we did not divide the amount needed by 2. Dividing by 2 is the same as multiplying by $\frac{1}{2}$.

EXAMPLE 1 Multiply: $\frac{3}{5} \cdot \frac{2}{7}$

SOLUTION Using our rule for multiplication, we multiply the numerators and multiply the denominators:

$$\frac{3}{5} \cdot \frac{2}{7} = \frac{3 \cdot 2}{5 \cdot 7} = \frac{6}{35}$$

The product of $\frac{3}{5}$ and $\frac{2}{7}$ is the fraction $\frac{6}{35}$. The numerator 6 is the product of 3 and 2, and the denominator 35 is the product of 5 and 7.

EXAMPLE 2 Multiply: $\frac{3}{8} \cdot 5$

SOLUTION The number 5 can be written as $\frac{5}{1}$. That is, 5 can be considered a fraction with numerator 5 and denominator 1. Writing 5 this way enables us to apply the rule for multiplying fractions.

$$\frac{3}{8} \cdot 5 = \frac{3}{8} \cdot \frac{5}{1}$$

$$= \frac{3 \cdot 5}{8 \cdot 1}$$

$$= \frac{15}{8}$$

PRACTICE PROBLEMS

1. Multiply: $\frac{2}{3} \cdot \frac{5}{9}$

2. Multiply: $\frac{2}{5} \cdot 7$

3. Multiply: $\frac{1}{3}\left(\frac{4}{5} \cdot \frac{1}{3}\right)$

EXAMPLE 3 Multiply: $\frac{1}{2}\left(\frac{3}{4} \cdot \frac{1}{5}\right)$

SOLUTION We find the product inside the parentheses first and then multiply the result by $\frac{1}{2}$:

$$\frac{1}{2}\left(\frac{3}{4} \cdot \frac{1}{5}\right) = \frac{1}{2}\left(\frac{3 \cdot 1}{4 \cdot 5}\right)$$
$$= \frac{1}{2}\left(\frac{3}{20}\right)$$
$$= \frac{1 \cdot 3}{2 \cdot 20} = \frac{3}{40}$$

The properties of multiplication that we developed in Chapter 1 for whole numbers apply to fractions as well. That is, if a, b, and c are fractions, then

$$a \cdot b = b \cdot a$$ Multiplication with fractions is commutative

$$a \cdot (b \cdot c) = (a \cdot b) \cdot c$$ Multiplication with fractions is associative

To demonstrate the associative property for fractions, let's do Example 3 again, but this time we will apply the associative property first:

$$\frac{1}{2}\left(\frac{3}{4} \cdot \frac{1}{5}\right) = \left(\frac{1}{2} \cdot \frac{3}{4}\right) \cdot \frac{1}{5}$$ Associative property
$$= \left(\frac{1 \cdot 3}{2 \cdot 4}\right) \cdot \frac{1}{5}$$
$$= \left(\frac{3}{8}\right) \cdot \frac{1}{5}$$
$$= \frac{3 \cdot 1}{8 \cdot 5} = \frac{3}{40}$$

The result is identical to that of Example 3.

Here is another example that involves the associative property. Problems like this will be useful when we solve equations.

The answers to all the examples so far in this section have been in lowest terms. Let's see what happens when we multiply two fractions to get a product that is not in lowest terms.

4. Multiply.
  a. $\frac{12}{25} \cdot \frac{5}{6}$
  b. $\frac{12}{25} \cdot \frac{50}{60}$

EXAMPLE 4 Multiply: $\frac{15}{8} \cdot \frac{4}{9}$

SOLUTION Multiplying the numerators and multiplying the denominators, we have

$$\frac{15}{8} \cdot \frac{4}{9} = \frac{15 \cdot 4}{8 \cdot 9}$$
$$= \frac{60}{72}$$

The product is $\frac{60}{72}$, which can be reduced to lowest terms by factoring 60 and 72 and then dividing out any factors they have in common:

$$\frac{60}{72} = \frac{2 \cdot 2 \cdot 3 \cdot 5}{2 \cdot 2 \cdot 2 \cdot 3 \cdot 3}$$
$$= \frac{5}{6}$$

Answers

3. $\frac{4}{45}$ **4.** Both are $\frac{2}{5}$

We can actually save ourselves some time by factoring before we multiply. Here's how it is done:

$$\frac{15}{8} \cdot \frac{4}{9} = \frac{15 \cdot 4}{8 \cdot 9}$$

$$= \frac{(3 \cdot 5) \cdot (2 \cdot 2)}{(2 \cdot 2 \cdot 2) \cdot (3 \cdot 3)}$$

$$= \frac{3 \cdot 5 \cdot 2 \cdot 2}{2 \cdot 2 \cdot 2 \cdot 3 \cdot 3}$$

$$= \frac{5}{6}$$

The result is the same in both cases. Reducing to lowest terms before we actually multiply takes less time.

Here are some additional examples.

EXAMPLE 5   Multiply: $\dfrac{9}{2}\left(\dfrac{8}{18}\right)$

SOLUTION $\dfrac{9}{2}\left(\dfrac{8}{18}\right) = \dfrac{9 \cdot 8}{2 \cdot 18}$

$$= \frac{(3 \cdot 3) \cdot (2 \cdot 2 \cdot 2)}{2 \cdot (2 \cdot 3 \cdot 3)}$$

$$= \frac{3 \cdot 3 \cdot 2 \cdot 2 \cdot 2}{2 \cdot 2 \cdot 3 \cdot 3}$$

$$= \frac{2}{1}$$

$$= 2$$

EXAMPLE 6   Multiply: $\dfrac{2}{3} \cdot \dfrac{6}{5} \cdot \dfrac{5}{8}$

SOLUTION $\dfrac{2}{3} \cdot \dfrac{6}{5} \cdot \dfrac{5}{8} = \dfrac{2 \cdot 6 \cdot 5}{3 \cdot 5 \cdot 8}$

$$= \frac{2 \cdot (2 \cdot 3) \cdot 5}{3 \cdot 5 \cdot (2 \cdot 2 \cdot 2)}$$

$$= \frac{2 \cdot 2 \cdot 3 \cdot 5}{3 \cdot 5 \cdot 2 \cdot 2 \cdot 2}$$

$$= \frac{1}{2}$$

In Chapter 1 we did some work with exponents. We can extend our work with exponents to include fractions, as the following examples indicate.

EXAMPLE 7   Expand and multiply: $\left(\dfrac{3}{4}\right)^2$

SOLUTION $\left(\dfrac{3}{4}\right)^2 = \left(\dfrac{3}{4}\right)\left(\dfrac{3}{4}\right)$

$$= \frac{3 \cdot 3}{4 \cdot 4}$$

$$= \frac{9}{16}$$

---

5. Multiply.
  a. $\dfrac{8}{3} \cdot \dfrac{9}{24}$
  b. $\dfrac{8}{30} \cdot \dfrac{90}{24}$

 Although $\frac{2}{1}$ is in lowest terms, it is still simpler to write the answer as just 2. We will always do this when the denominator is the number 1.

6. Multiply: $\dfrac{3}{4} \cdot \dfrac{8}{3} \cdot \dfrac{1}{6}$

Apply the definition of exponents, and then multiply.

7. $\left(\dfrac{2}{3}\right)^2$

Answers
5. Both are 1   **6.** $\dfrac{1}{3}$ **7.** $\dfrac{4}{9}$

8. **a.** $\left(\dfrac{3}{4}\right)^2 \cdot \dfrac{1}{2}$

   b. $\left(\dfrac{2}{3}\right)^3 \cdot \dfrac{9}{8}$

EXAMPLE 8 Expand and multiply: $\left(\dfrac{5}{6}\right)^2 \cdot \dfrac{1}{2}$

SOLUTION

$$\left(\frac{5}{6}\right)^2 \cdot \frac{1}{2} = \frac{5}{6} \cdot \frac{5}{6} \cdot \frac{1}{2}$$

$$= \frac{5 \cdot 5 \cdot 1}{6 \cdot 6 \cdot 2}$$

$$= \frac{25}{72}$$

The word *of* used in connection with fractions indicates multiplication. If we want to find $\dfrac{1}{2}$ of $\dfrac{2}{3}$, then what we do is multiply $\dfrac{1}{2}$ and $\dfrac{2}{3}$.

9. **a.** Find $\dfrac{2}{3}$ of $\dfrac{1}{2}$.

   b. Find $\dfrac{3}{5}$ of 15.

EXAMPLE 9 Find $\dfrac{1}{2}$ of $\dfrac{2}{3}$.

SOLUTION Knowing the word *of*, as used here, indicates multiplication, we have

$$\frac{1}{2} \text{ of } \frac{2}{3} = \frac{1}{2} \cdot \frac{2}{3}$$

$$= \frac{1 \cdot 2}{2 \cdot 3} = \frac{1}{3}$$

This seems to make sense. Logically, $\dfrac{1}{2}$ of $\dfrac{2}{3}$ should be $\dfrac{1}{3}$, as Figure 1 shows.

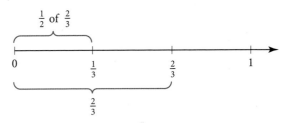

FIGURE 1

10. **a.** What is $\dfrac{2}{3}$ of 12?

   b. What is $\dfrac{2}{3}$ of 120?

EXAMPLE 10 What is $\dfrac{3}{4}$ of 12?

SOLUTION Again, *of* means multiply.

$$\frac{3}{4} \text{ of } 12 = \frac{3}{4}(12)$$

$$= \frac{3}{4}\left(\frac{12}{1}\right)$$

$$= \frac{3 \cdot 12}{4 \cdot 1}$$

$$= \frac{3 \cdot 2 \cdot 2 \cdot 3}{2 \cdot 2 \cdot 1}$$

$$= \frac{9}{1} = 9$$

> **Note** As you become familiar with multiplying fractions, you may notice shortcuts that reduce the number of steps in the problems. It's okay to use these shortcuts if you understand why they work and are consistently getting correct answers. If you are using shortcuts and not consistently getting correct answers, then go back to showing all the work until you completely understand the process.

Answers

8. **a.** $\dfrac{9}{32}$ **b.** $\dfrac{1}{3}$ 9. **a.** $\dfrac{1}{3}$ **b.** 9

10. **a.** 8 **b.** 80

B The Area of a Triangle

FACTS FROM GEOMETRY   The Area of a Triangle

The formula for the area of a triangle is one application of multiplication with fractions. Figure 2 shows a triangle with base b and height h. Below the triangle is the formula for its area. As you can see, it is a product containing the fraction $\frac{1}{2}$.

$$\text{Area} = \frac{1}{2}\,(\text{base})(\text{height})$$

$$A = \frac{1}{2}\,bh$$

FIGURE 2   The area of a triangle

EXAMPLE 11   Find the area of the triangle in Figure 3.

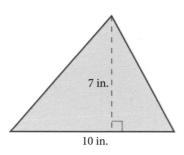

FIGURE 3   A triangle with base 10 inches and height 7 inches

SOLUTION   Applying the formula for the area of a triangle, we have

$$A = \frac{1}{2}bh = \frac{1}{2} \cdot 10 \cdot 7 = 5 \cdot 7 = 35 \text{ in}^2$$

11. Find the area of the triangle below.

Note   How did we get in² as the final units in Example 11? In this problem:

$A = \frac{1}{2}bh$

$= \frac{1}{2} \cdot 10 \text{ inches} \cdot 7 \text{ inches}$

$= 5 \text{ in.} \cdot 7 \text{ in.} = 35 \text{ in}^2$

Answers

11. 35 in²

12. Find the total area enclosed by the figure.

4 ft

4 ft

6 ft

4 ft

10 ft

EXAMPLE 12   Find the area of the figure in Figure 4.

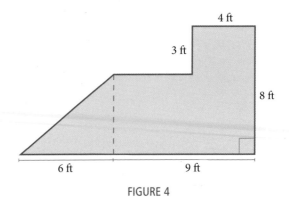

FIGURE 4

SOLUTION   We divide the figure into three parts and then find the area of each part (see Figure 5). The area of the whole figure is the sum of the areas of its parts.

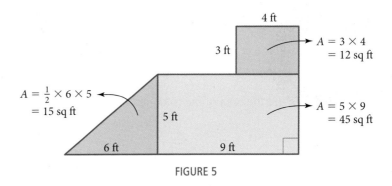

$A = \frac{1}{2} \times 6 \times 5$
$= 15$ sq ft

$A = 3 \times 4$
$= 12$ sq ft

$A = 5 \times 9$
$= 45$ sq ft

4 ft

3 ft

5 ft

6 ft

9 ft

FIGURE 5

Total area $= 12 + 45 + 15$
$= 72$ sq ft

STUDY SKILLS
Be Resilient
Don't let setbacks keep you from your goals. You want to put yourself on the road to becoming someone who can succeed in this class or any class in college. Failing a test or quiz or having a difficult time on some topics is normal. No one goes through college without some setbacks. A low grade on a test or quiz is simply a signal that some reevaluation of your study habits needs to take place.

Getting Ready for Class

After reading through the preceding section, respond in your own words and in complete sentences.

1. When we multiply the fractions $\frac{3}{5}$ and $\frac{2}{7}$, the numerator in the answer will be what number?

2. When we ask for $\frac{1}{2}$ of $\frac{2}{3}$, are we asking for an addition problem or a multiplication problem?

3. True or false? Reducing to lowest terms before you multiply two fractions will give the same answer as if you were to reduce after you multiply.

4. Write the formula for the area of a triangle with base *x* and height *y*.

Answer

12. 34 ft²

Problem Set 2.3

A Find each of the following products. (Multiply.) [Examples 1–6]

1. $\dfrac{2}{3} \cdot \dfrac{4}{5}$
   $\dfrac{8}{15}$

▶ 2. $\dfrac{5}{6} \cdot \dfrac{7}{4}$
   $\dfrac{35}{24}$

3. $\dfrac{1}{2} \cdot \dfrac{7}{4}$
   $\dfrac{7}{8}$

4. $\dfrac{3}{5} \cdot \dfrac{4}{7}$
   $\dfrac{12}{35}$

5. $\dfrac{5}{3} \cdot \dfrac{3}{5}$
   1

▶ 6. $\dfrac{4}{7} \cdot \dfrac{7}{4}$
   1

7. $\dfrac{3}{4} \cdot 9$
   $\dfrac{27}{4}$

8. $\dfrac{2}{3} \cdot 5$
   $\dfrac{10}{3}$

9. $\dfrac{6}{7}\left(\dfrac{7}{6}\right)$
   1

10. $\dfrac{2}{9}\left(\dfrac{9}{2}\right)$
   1

11. $\dfrac{1}{2} \cdot \dfrac{1}{3} \cdot \dfrac{1}{4}$
   $\dfrac{1}{24}$

12. $\dfrac{2}{3} \cdot \dfrac{4}{5} \cdot \dfrac{1}{3}$
   $\dfrac{8}{45}$

13. $\dfrac{2}{5} \cdot \dfrac{3}{5} \cdot \dfrac{4}{5}$
   $\dfrac{24}{125}$

▶ 14. $\dfrac{1}{4} \cdot \dfrac{3}{4} \cdot \dfrac{3}{4}$
   $\dfrac{9}{64}$

15. $\dfrac{3}{2} \cdot \dfrac{5}{2} \cdot \dfrac{7}{2}$
   $\dfrac{105}{8}$

16. $\dfrac{4}{3} \cdot \dfrac{5}{3} \cdot \dfrac{7}{3}$
   $\dfrac{140}{27}$

A Complete the following tables.

17.

First Number x	Second Number y	Their Product xy
$\dfrac{1}{2}$	$\dfrac{2}{3}$	$\dfrac{1}{3}$
$\dfrac{2}{3}$	$\dfrac{3}{4}$	$\dfrac{1}{2}$
$\dfrac{3}{4}$	$\dfrac{4}{5}$	$\dfrac{3}{5}$
$\dfrac{5}{a}$	$\dfrac{a}{6}$	$\dfrac{5}{6}$

18.

First Number x	Second Number y	Their Product xy
12	$\dfrac{1}{2}$	6
12	$\dfrac{1}{3}$	4
12	$\dfrac{1}{4}$	3
12	$\dfrac{1}{6}$	2

19.

First Number x	Second Number y	Their Product xy
$\dfrac{1}{2}$	30	15
$\dfrac{1}{5}$	30	6
$\dfrac{1}{6}$	30	5
$\dfrac{1}{15}$	30	2

20.

First Number x	Second Number y	Their Product xy
$\dfrac{1}{3}$	$\dfrac{3}{5}$	$\dfrac{1}{5}$
$\dfrac{3}{5}$	$\dfrac{5}{7}$	$\dfrac{3}{7}$
$\dfrac{5}{7}$	$\dfrac{7}{9}$	$\dfrac{5}{9}$
$\dfrac{7}{b}$	$\dfrac{b}{11}$	$\dfrac{7}{11}$

A Multiply each of the following. Be sure all answers are written in lowest terms. [Examples 1–6]

▶ **21.** $\dfrac{9}{20} \cdot \dfrac{4}{3}$

$\dfrac{3}{5}$

22. $\dfrac{135}{16} \cdot \dfrac{2}{45}$

$\dfrac{3}{8}$

▶ **23.** $\dfrac{3}{4} \cdot 12$

9

24. $\dfrac{3}{4} \cdot 20$

15

25. $\dfrac{1}{3}(3)$

1

26. $\dfrac{1}{5}(5)$

1

27. $\dfrac{2}{5} \cdot 20$

8

28. $\dfrac{3}{5} \cdot 15$

9

29. $\dfrac{72}{35} \cdot \dfrac{55}{108} \cdot \dfrac{7}{110}$

$\dfrac{1}{15}$

30. $\dfrac{32}{27} \cdot \dfrac{72}{49} \cdot \dfrac{1}{40}$

$\dfrac{32}{735}$

A Expand and simplify each of the following. [Examples 7, 8]

31. $\left(\dfrac{2}{3}\right)^2$

$\dfrac{4}{9}$

▶ **32.** $\left(\dfrac{3}{5}\right)^2$

$\dfrac{9}{25}$

33. $\left(\dfrac{3}{4}\right)^2$

$\dfrac{9}{16}$

34. $\left(\dfrac{2}{7}\right)^2$

$\dfrac{4}{49}$

35. $\left(\dfrac{1}{2}\right)^2$

$\dfrac{1}{4}$

36. $\left(\dfrac{1}{3}\right)^2$

$\dfrac{1}{9}$

37. $\left(\dfrac{2}{3}\right)^3$

$\dfrac{8}{27}$

38. $\left(\dfrac{3}{5}\right)^3$

$\dfrac{27}{125}$

39. $\left(\dfrac{3}{4}\right)^2 \cdot \dfrac{8}{9}$

$\dfrac{1}{2}$

40. $\left(\dfrac{5}{6}\right)^2 \cdot \dfrac{12}{15}$

$\dfrac{5}{9}$

41. $\left(\dfrac{1}{2}\right)^2 \left(\dfrac{3}{5}\right)^2$

$\dfrac{9}{100}$

▶ **42.** $\left(\dfrac{3}{8}\right)^2 \left(\dfrac{4}{3}\right)^2$

$\dfrac{1}{4}$

43. $\left(\dfrac{1}{2}\right)^2 \cdot 8 + \left(\dfrac{1}{3}\right)^2 \cdot 9$

3

▶ **44.** $\left(\dfrac{2}{3}\right)^2 \cdot 9 + \left(\dfrac{1}{2}\right)^2 \cdot 4$

5

A [Examples 9, 10]

▶ **45.** Find $\dfrac{3}{8}$ of 64.

24

46. Find $\dfrac{2}{3}$ of 18.

12

▶ **47.** What is $\dfrac{1}{3}$ of the sum of 8 and 4?

4

48. What is $\dfrac{3}{5}$ of the sum of 8 and 7?

9

▶ **49.** Find $\dfrac{1}{2}$ of $\dfrac{3}{4}$ of 24.

9

50. Find $\dfrac{3}{5}$ of $\dfrac{1}{3}$ of 15.

3

Find the mistakes in Problems 51 and 52. Correct the right-hand side of each one.

51. $\dfrac{1}{2} \cdot \dfrac{3}{5} = \dfrac{4}{10}$

$\dfrac{3}{10}$; numerator should be 3, not 4.

52. $\dfrac{2}{7} \cdot \dfrac{3}{5} = \dfrac{5}{35}$

$\dfrac{6}{35}$; numerator should be 6.

53. a. Complete the following table.

Number x	Square x^2
1	1
2	4
3	9
4	16
5	25
6	36
7	49
8	64

b. Using the results of part a, fill in the blank in the following statement:

For numbers larger than 1, the square of the number is _____ than the number.

Either *larger* or *greater* will work.

54. a. Complete the following table.

Number x	Square x^2
$\dfrac{1}{2}$	$\dfrac{1}{4}$
$\dfrac{1}{3}$	$\dfrac{1}{9}$
$\dfrac{1}{4}$	$\dfrac{1}{16}$
$\dfrac{1}{5}$	$\dfrac{1}{25}$
$\dfrac{1}{6}$	$\dfrac{1}{36}$
$\dfrac{1}{7}$	$\dfrac{1}{49}$
$\dfrac{1}{8}$	$\dfrac{1}{64}$

b. Using the results of part a, fill in the blank in the following statement:

For numbers between 0 and 1, the square of the number is _____ than the number.

Either *smaller* or *less* will work.

B [Examples 11, 12]

55. Find the area of the triangle with base 19 inches and height 14 inches.

133 in²

56. Find the area of the triangle with base 13 inches and height 8 inches.

52 in²

57. The base of a triangle is $\dfrac{4}{3}$ feet and the height is $\dfrac{2}{3}$ feet. Find the area.

$\dfrac{4}{9}$ ft²

58. The base of a triangle is $\dfrac{8}{7}$ feet and the height is $\dfrac{14}{5}$ feet. Find the area.

$\dfrac{8}{5}$ ft²

Find the area of each figure.

59.

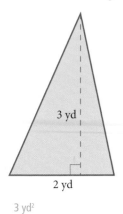

3 yd

2 yd

3 yd²

60.

7 mi

6 mi

9 mi   3 mi

57 mi²

61.

12 in.

10 in.

8 in.

5 in.

20 in.

138 in²

62.

5 in.

4 in.

6 in.

22 in²

■ Applying the Concepts

63. Rainfall The chart shows the average rainfall for Death Valley in the given months. Use this chart to answer the questions below.

a. How many inches of rain is 5 times the average for January? $\frac{5}{4}$ inches

b. How many inches of rain is 7 times the average for May? $\frac{7}{10}$ inch

c. How many inches of rain is 12 times the average for September? 3 inches

64. Rainfall The chart shows the average rainfall for Death Valley in the given months. Use this chart to answer the questions below.

a. How many inches of rain is 6 times the average for February? 2 inches

b. How many inches of rain is 5 times the average for April? $\frac{3}{5}$ inch

c. How many inches of rain is 8 times the average for October? 2 inches

65. Hot Air Balloon Aerostar International makes a hot air balloon called the Rally 105 that has a volume of 105,400 cubic feet. Another balloon, the Rally 126, was designed with a volume that is approximately $\frac{6}{5}$ the volume of the Rally 105. Find the volume of the Rally 126 to the nearest hundred cubic feet.

126,500 ft³

▶ **66. Bicycle Safety** The National Safe Kids Campaign and Bell Sports sponsored a study that surveyed 8,159 children ages 5 to 14 who were riding bicycles. Approximately $\frac{2}{5}$ of the children were wearing helmets, and of those, only $\frac{13}{20}$ were wearing the helmets correctly. About how many of the children were wearing helmets correctly?

About 2,121 children

67. Health Care According to a study reported on MSNBC, almost one-third of the people diagnosed with diabetes don't seek proper medical care. If there are 12 million Americans with diabetes, about how many of them are seeking proper medical care?

About 8 million

68. Working Students Studies indicate that approximately $\frac{3}{4}$ of all undergraduate college students work while attending school. A local community college has a student enrollment of 8,500 students. How many of these students work while attending college?

6,375 students

69. Cigarette Tax In a recent survey of 1,410 adults, it was determined that $\frac{3}{5}$ of those surveyed favored raising the tax on cigarettes as a way to discourage young people from smoking. What number of adults believes that this would reduce the number of young people who smoke?

846 adults

70. Shared Rent You and three friends decide to rent an apartment for the academic year rather than to live in the dorms. The monthly rent is $1250. If you and your friends split the rent equally, what is your share of the monthly rent?

$312.50

71. Importing Oil According to the U.S. Department of Energy, we imported approximately 8,340,000 barrels of oil in November 2007, which represents a typical month. We import a little over $\frac{1}{5}$ of our oil from Canada, approximately $\frac{3}{20}$ of our oil from Venezuela, and less than $\frac{1}{10}$ of our oil from Iraq. Determine the amount of oil we imported from each of these countries.

Canada: > 1,668,000 barrels   Venezuela: 1,251,000 barrels
Iraq: < 834,000 barrels

72. Improving Your Quantitative Literacy MSNBC reported that at least three-fourths of the 55 companies that advertise nationally on television will cut spending on commercials because of electronics that let viewers record programs and edit out commercials. Does this mean at least 41, or at least 42, of the companies will cut spending on commercials?

At least 42

Geometric Sequences Recall that a geometric sequence is a sequence in which each term comes from the previous term by multiplying by the same number each time. For example, the sequence $1, \frac{1}{2}, \frac{1}{4}, \frac{1}{8}, \ldots$ is a geometric sequence in which each term is found by multiplying the previous term by $\frac{1}{2}$. By observing this fact, we know that the next term in the sequence will be $\frac{1}{8} \cdot \frac{1}{2} = \frac{1}{16}$.

Find the next number in each of the geometric sequences below.

73. $1, \frac{1}{3}, \frac{1}{9}, \ldots$

$\frac{1}{27}$

74. $1, \frac{1}{4}, \frac{1}{16}, \ldots$

$\frac{1}{64}$

▶ **75.** $\frac{3}{2}, 1, \frac{2}{3}, \frac{4}{9}, \ldots$

$\frac{8}{27}$

76. $\frac{2}{3}, 1, \frac{3}{2}, \frac{9}{4}, \ldots$

$\frac{27}{8}$

Estimating For each problem below, mentally estimate which of the numbers 0, 1, 2, or 3 is closest to the answer. Make your estimate without using pencil and paper or a calculator.

77. $\frac{11}{5} \cdot \frac{19}{20}$

2

78. $\frac{3}{5} \cdot \frac{1}{20}$

0

79. $\frac{16}{5} \cdot \frac{23}{24}$

3

80. $\frac{9}{8} \cdot \frac{31}{32}$

1

■ Getting Ready for the Next Section

If you want your students to see the relationship between division and multiplication by the reciprocal, you will have to assign the even problems along with the odd problems in Problems 81–92. These problems are a good way to lead in to the next section.

In the next section we will do division with fractions. As you already know, division and multiplication are closely related. These review problems are intended to let you see more of the relationship between multiplication and division.

Perform the indicated operations.

81. $8 \div 4$

2

82. $8 \cdot \frac{1}{4}$

2

83. $15 \div 3$

5

84. $15 \cdot \frac{1}{3}$

5

▶ **85.** $18 \div 6$

3

86. $18 \cdot \frac{1}{6}$

3

For each number below, find a number to multiply it by to obtain 1.

87. $\frac{3}{4}$

$\frac{4}{3}$

88. $\frac{9}{5}$

$\frac{5}{9}$

▶ **89.** $\frac{1}{3}$

3

90. $\frac{1}{4}$

4

91. 7

$\frac{1}{7}$

92. 2

$\frac{1}{2}$

■ Maintaining Your Skills

Simplify.

93. $20 \div 2 \cdot 10$

100

94. $40 \div 4 \cdot 5$

50

95. $24 \div 8 \cdot 3$

9

96. $24 \div 4 \cdot 6$

36

97. $36 \div 6 \cdot 3$

18

98. $36 \div 9 \cdot 2$

8

99. $48 \div 12 \cdot 2$

8

100. $48 \div 8 \cdot 3$

18

Objectives

A Divide fractions.

B Simplify order of operation problems involving division of fractions.

C Solve application problems involving division of fractions.

Introduction . . .

A few years ago our 4-H club was making blankets to keep their lambs clean at the county fair. Each blanket required $\frac{3}{4}$ yard of material. We had 9 yards of material left over from the year before. To see how many blankets we could make, we divided 9 by $\frac{3}{4}$. The result was 12, meaning that we could make 12 lamb blankets for the fair.

Before we define division with fractions, we must first introduce the idea of *reciprocals.* Look at the following multiplication problems:

$$\frac{3}{4} \cdot \frac{4}{3} = \frac{12}{12} = 1 \qquad \frac{7}{8} \cdot \frac{8}{7} = \frac{56}{56} = 1$$

In each case the product is 1. Whenever the product of two numbers is 1, we say the two numbers are *reciprocals.*

> **Definition**
>
> Two numbers whose product is 1 are said to be **reciprocals.** In symbols, the reciprocal of $\frac{a}{b}$ is $\frac{b}{a}$, because
>
> $$\frac{a}{b} \cdot \frac{b}{a} = \frac{a \cdot b}{b \cdot a} = \frac{a \cdot b}{a \cdot b} = 1 \qquad (a \neq 0, b \neq 0)$$

Every number has a reciprocal except 0. The reason that 0 does not have a reciprocal is because the product of *any* number with 0 is 0. It can never be 1. Reciprocals of whole numbers are fractions with 1 as the numerator. For example, the reciprocal of 5 is $\frac{1}{5}$, because

$$5 \cdot \frac{1}{5} = \frac{5}{1} \cdot \frac{1}{5} = \frac{5}{5} = 1$$

Table 1 lists some numbers and their reciprocals.

TABLE 1		
Number	**Reciprocal**	**Reason**
$\frac{3}{4}$	$\frac{4}{3}$	Because $\frac{3}{4} \cdot \frac{4}{3} = \frac{12}{12} = 1$
$\frac{9}{5}$	$\frac{5}{9}$	Because $\frac{9}{5} \cdot \frac{5}{9} = \frac{45}{45} = 1$
$\frac{1}{3}$	3	Because $\frac{1}{3} \cdot 3 = \frac{1}{3} \cdot \frac{3}{1} = \frac{3}{3} = 1$
7	$\frac{1}{7}$	Because $7 \cdot \frac{1}{7} = \frac{7}{1} \cdot \frac{1}{7} = \frac{7}{7} = 1$

A Dividing Fractions

Division with fractions is accomplished by using reciprocals. More specifically, we can define division by a fraction to be the same as multiplication by its reciprocal. Here is the precise definition:

> **Definition**
>
> If a, b, c, and d are numbers and b, c, and d are all not equal to 0, then
>
> $$\frac{a}{b} \div \frac{c}{d} = \frac{a}{b} \cdot \frac{d}{c}$$

Note Defining division to be the same as multiplication by the reciprocal does make sense. If we divide 6 by 2, we get 3. On the other hand, if we multiply 6 by $\frac{1}{2}$ (the reciprocal of 2), we also get 3. Whether we divide by 2 or multiply by $\frac{1}{2}$, we get the same result.

This definition states that dividing by the fraction $\frac{c}{d}$ is exactly the same as multiplying by its reciprocal $\frac{d}{c}$. Because we developed the rule for multiplying fractions in Section 2.3, we do not need a new rule for division. We simply *replace the divisor by its reciprocal* and multiply. Here are some examples to illustrate the procedure.

PRACTICE PROBLEMS

1. Divide.

   a. $\frac{1}{3} \div \frac{1}{6}$

   b. $\frac{1}{30} \div \frac{1}{60}$

EXAMPLE 1   Divide: $\frac{1}{2} \div \frac{1}{4}$

SOLUTION   The divisor is $\frac{1}{4}$, and its reciprocal is $\frac{4}{1}$. Applying the definition of division for fractions, we have

$$\frac{1}{2} \div \frac{1}{4} = \frac{1}{2} \cdot \frac{4}{1}$$
$$= \frac{1 \cdot 4}{2 \cdot 1}$$
$$= \frac{1 \cdot 2 \cdot 2}{2 \cdot 1}$$
$$= \frac{2}{1}$$
$$= 2$$

The quotient of $\frac{1}{2}$ and $\frac{1}{4}$ is 2. Or, $\frac{1}{4}$ "goes into" $\frac{1}{2}$ two times. Logically, our definition for division of fractions seems to be giving us answers that are consistent with what we know about fractions from previous experience. Because 2 times $\frac{1}{4}$ is $\frac{2}{4}$ or $\frac{1}{2}$, it seems logical that $\frac{1}{2}$ divided by $\frac{1}{4}$ should be 2.

2. Divide: $\frac{5}{9} \div \frac{10}{3}$

EXAMPLE 2   Divide: $\frac{3}{8} \div \frac{9}{4}$

SOLUTION   Dividing by $\frac{9}{4}$ is the same as multiplying by its reciprocal, which is $\frac{4}{9}$:

$$\frac{3}{8} \div \frac{9}{4} = \frac{3}{8} \cdot \frac{4}{9}$$
$$= \frac{3 \cdot 2 \cdot 2}{2 \cdot 2 \cdot 2 \cdot 3 \cdot 3}$$
$$= \frac{1}{6}$$

The quotient of $\frac{3}{8}$ and $\frac{9}{4}$ is $\frac{1}{6}$.

3. Divide.

   a. $\frac{3}{4} \div 3$

   b. $\frac{3}{5} \div 3$

   c. $\frac{3}{7} \div 3$

EXAMPLE 3   Divide: $\frac{2}{3} \div 2$

SOLUTION   The reciprocal of 2 is $\frac{1}{2}$. Applying the definition for division of fractions, we have

$$\frac{2}{3} \div 2 = \frac{2}{3} \cdot \frac{1}{2}$$
$$= \frac{2 \cdot 1}{3 \cdot 2}$$
$$= \frac{1}{3}$$

4. Divide: $4 \div \frac{1}{5}$

EXAMPLE 4   Divide: $2 \div \left(\frac{1}{3}\right)$

SOLUTION   We replace $\frac{1}{3}$ by its reciprocal, which is 3, and multiply:

$$2 \div \left(\frac{1}{3}\right) = 2(3)$$
$$= 6$$

Answers
1. Both are 2   **2.** $\frac{1}{6}$
3. a. $\frac{1}{4}$ **b.** $\frac{1}{5}$ **c.** $\frac{1}{7}$ **4.** 20

Here are some further examples of division with fractions. Notice in each case that the first step is the only new part of the process.

EXAMPLE 5 Divide: $\dfrac{4}{27} \div \dfrac{16}{9}$

SOLUTION $\dfrac{4}{27} \div \dfrac{16}{9} = \dfrac{4}{27} \cdot \dfrac{9}{16}$

$= \dfrac{4 \cdot 9}{3 \cdot 9 \cdot 4 \cdot 4}$

$= \dfrac{1}{12}$

In Example 5 we did not factor the numerator and the denominator completely in order to reduce to lowest terms because, as you have probably already noticed, it is not necessary to do so. We need to factor only enough to show what numbers are common to the numerator and the denominator. If we factored completely in the second step, it would look like this:

$= \dfrac{2 \cdot 2 \cdot 3 \cdot 3}{3 \cdot 3 \cdot 3 \cdot 2 \cdot 2 \cdot 2 \cdot 2}$

$= \dfrac{1}{12}$

The result is the same in both cases. From now on we will factor numerators and denominators only enough to show the factors we are dividing out.

EXAMPLE 6 Divide: $\dfrac{16}{35} \div 8$

SOLUTION $\dfrac{16}{35} \div 8 = \dfrac{16}{35} \cdot \dfrac{1}{8}$

$= \dfrac{2 \cdot 8 \cdot 1}{35 \cdot 8}$

$= \dfrac{2}{35}$

EXAMPLE 7 Divide: $27 \div \left(\dfrac{3}{2}\right)$

SOLUTION $27 \div \left(\dfrac{3}{2}\right) = 27 \cdot \left(\dfrac{2}{3}\right)$

$= \dfrac{3 \cdot 9 \cdot 2}{3}$

$= 18$

B Fractions and the Order of Operations

The next two examples combine what we have learned about division of fractions with the rule for order of operations.

EXAMPLE 8 The quotient of $\dfrac{8}{3}$ and $\dfrac{1}{6}$ is increased by 5. What number results?

SOLUTION Translating to symbols, we have

$\dfrac{8}{3} \div \dfrac{1}{6} + 5 = \dfrac{8}{3} \cdot \dfrac{6}{1} + 5$

$= 16 + 5$

$= 21$

Find each quotient.

5. **a.** $\dfrac{5}{32} \div \dfrac{10}{42}$

  b. $\dfrac{15}{32} \div \dfrac{30}{42}$

6. **a.** $\dfrac{12}{25} \div 6$

  b. $\dfrac{24}{25} \div 6$

7. **a.** $12 \div \dfrac{4}{3}$

  b. $12 \div \dfrac{4}{5}$

  c. $12 \div \dfrac{4}{7}$

8. The quotient of $\dfrac{5}{4}$ and $\dfrac{1}{8}$ is increased by 8. What number results?

Answers

5. Both are $\dfrac{21}{32}$ 6. **a.** $\dfrac{2}{25}$ **b.** $\dfrac{4}{25}$

7. **a.** 9 **b.** 15 **c.** 21 8. 18

9. Simplify:

$$18 \div \left(\frac{3}{5}\right)^2 + 48 \div \left(\frac{2}{5}\right)^2$$

EXAMPLE 9 Simplify: $32 \div \left(\frac{4}{3}\right)^2 + 75 \div \left(\frac{5}{2}\right)^2$

SOLUTION According to the rule for order of operations, we must first evaluate the numbers with exponents, then divide, and finally, add.

$$32 \div \left(\frac{4}{3}\right)^2 + 75 \div \left(\frac{5}{2}\right)^2 = 32 \div \frac{16}{9} + 75 \div \frac{25}{4}$$
$$= 32 \cdot \frac{9}{16} + 75 \cdot \frac{4}{25}$$
$$= 18 + 12$$
$$= 30$$

C Applications

EXAMPLE 10 A 4-H club is making blankets to keep their lambs clean at the county fair. If each blanket requires $\frac{3}{4}$ yard of material, how many blankets can they make from 9 yards of material?

10. How many blankets can the 4-H club make with 12 yards of material?

SOLUTION To answer this question we must divide 9 by $\frac{3}{4}$.

$$9 \div \frac{3}{4} = 9 \cdot \frac{4}{3}$$
$$= 3 \cdot 4$$
$$= 12$$

They can make 12 blankets from the 9 yards of material.

Getting Ready for Class

After reading through the preceding section, respond in your own words and in complete sentences.

1. What do we call two numbers whose product is 1?
2. True or false? The quotient of $\frac{3}{5}$ and $\frac{3}{8}$ is the same as the product of $\frac{3}{5}$ and $\frac{8}{3}$.
3. How are multiplication and division of fractions related?
4. Dividing by $\frac{19}{9}$ is the same as multiplying by what number?

Answers
9. 350 **10.** 16 blankets

Problem Set 2.4

A   Find the quotient in each case by replacing the divisor by its reciprocal and multiplying. Reduce to LCD. [Examples 1–7]

▶ **1.** $\dfrac{3}{4} \div \dfrac{1}{5}$

$\dfrac{15}{4}$

2. $\dfrac{1}{3} \div \dfrac{1}{2}$

$\dfrac{2}{3}$

3. $\dfrac{2}{3} \div \dfrac{1}{2}$

$\dfrac{4}{3}$

4. $\dfrac{5}{8} \div \dfrac{1}{4}$

$\dfrac{5}{2}$

5. $6 \div \left(\dfrac{2}{3}\right)$

9

6. $8 \div \left(\dfrac{3}{4}\right)$

$\dfrac{32}{3}$

7. $20 \div \dfrac{1}{10}$

200

8. $16 \div \dfrac{1}{8}$

128

9. $\dfrac{3}{4} \div 2$

$\dfrac{3}{8}$

10. $\dfrac{3}{5} \div 2$

$\dfrac{3}{10}$

▶ **11.** $\dfrac{7}{8} \div \dfrac{7}{8}$

1

12. $\dfrac{4}{3} \div \dfrac{4}{3}$

1

13. $\dfrac{7}{8} \div \dfrac{8}{7}$

$\dfrac{49}{64}$

▶ **14.** $\dfrac{4}{3} \div \dfrac{3}{4}$

$\dfrac{16}{9}$

15. $\dfrac{9}{16} \div \dfrac{3}{4}$

$\dfrac{3}{4}$

16. $\dfrac{25}{36} \div \dfrac{5}{6}$

$\dfrac{5}{6}$

▶ **17.** $\dfrac{25}{46} \div \dfrac{40}{69}$

$\dfrac{15}{16}$

18. $\dfrac{25}{24} \div \dfrac{15}{36}$

$\dfrac{5}{2}$

19. $\dfrac{13}{28} \div \dfrac{39}{14}$

$\dfrac{1}{6}$

20. $\dfrac{28}{125} \div \dfrac{5}{2}$

$\dfrac{56}{625}$

21. $\dfrac{27}{196} \div \dfrac{9}{392}$

6

22. $\dfrac{16}{135} \div \dfrac{2}{45}$

$\dfrac{8}{3}$

23. $\dfrac{25}{18} \div 5$

$\dfrac{5}{18}$

24. $\dfrac{30}{27} \div 6$

$\dfrac{5}{27}$

25. $6 \div \dfrac{4}{3}$

$\dfrac{9}{2}$

26. $12 \div \dfrac{4}{3}$

9

27. $\dfrac{4}{3} \div 6$

$\dfrac{2}{9}$

28. $\dfrac{4}{3} \div 12$

$\dfrac{1}{9}$

29. $\dfrac{3}{4} \div \dfrac{1}{2} \cdot 6$

9

30. $12 \div \dfrac{6}{7} \cdot 7$

98

▶ **31.** $\dfrac{2}{3} \cdot \dfrac{3}{4} \div \dfrac{5}{8}$

$\dfrac{4}{5}$

32. $4 \cdot \dfrac{7}{6} \div 7$

$\dfrac{2}{3}$

33. $\dfrac{35}{110} \cdot \dfrac{80}{63} \div \dfrac{16}{27}$

$\dfrac{15}{22}$

34. $\dfrac{20}{72} \cdot \dfrac{42}{18} \div \dfrac{20}{16}$

$\dfrac{14}{27}$

B Simplify each expression as much as possible. [Examples 8, 9]

▶ **35.** $10 \div \left(\dfrac{1}{2}\right)^2$

40

36. $12 \div \left(\dfrac{1}{4}\right)^2$

192

37. $\dfrac{18}{35} \div \left(\dfrac{6}{7}\right)^2$

$\dfrac{7}{10}$

38. $\dfrac{48}{55} \div \left(\dfrac{8}{11}\right)^2$

$\dfrac{33}{20}$

▶ **39.** $\dfrac{4}{5} \div \dfrac{1}{10} + 5$

13

40. $\dfrac{3}{8} \div \dfrac{1}{16} + 4$

10

41. $10 + \dfrac{11}{12} \div \dfrac{11}{24}$

12

42. $15 + \dfrac{13}{14} \div \dfrac{13}{42}$

18

▶ **43.** $24 \div \left(\dfrac{2}{5}\right)^2 + 25 \div \left(\dfrac{5}{6}\right)^2$

186

44. $18 \div \left(\dfrac{3}{4}\right)^2 + 49 \div \left(\dfrac{7}{9}\right)^2$

113

45. $100 \div \left(\dfrac{5}{7}\right)^2 + 200 \div \left(\dfrac{2}{3}\right)^2$

646

46. $64 \div \left(\dfrac{8}{11}\right)^2 + 81 \div \left(\dfrac{9}{11}\right)^2$

242

47. What is the quotient of $\dfrac{3}{8}$ and $\dfrac{5}{8}$?

$\dfrac{3}{5}$

▶ **48.** Find the quotient of $\dfrac{4}{5}$ and $\dfrac{16}{25}$.

$\dfrac{5}{4}$

▶ **49.** If the quotient of 18 and $\dfrac{3}{5}$ is increased by 10, what number results?

40

▶ **50.** If the quotient of 50 and $\dfrac{5}{3}$ is increased by 8, what number results?

38

51. Show that multiplying 3 by 5 is the same as dividing 3 by $\dfrac{1}{5}$.

$3 \cdot 5 = 15; 3 \div \dfrac{1}{5} = 3 \cdot \dfrac{5}{1} = 15$

52. Show that multiplying 8 by $\dfrac{1}{2}$ is the same as dividing 8 by 2.

$8 \cdot \dfrac{1}{2} = 4; 8 \div 2 = 4$

c Applying the Concepts [Example 10]

53. Pyramids The Luxor Hotel in Las Vegas is $\frac{5}{7}$ the original height of the Great Pyramid of Giza. If the hotel is 350 feet tall, what was the original height of the Great Pyramid of Giza?

490 feet

54. Skyscrapers The Bloomberg tower in New York City is $\frac{3}{5}$ the height of the Sears Tower. How tall is the Bloomberg tower?

870 feet

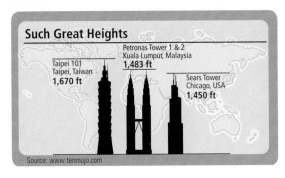

55. Sewing If $\frac{6}{7}$ yard of material is needed to make a blanket, how many blankets can be made from 12 yards of material?

14 blankets

56. Manufacturing A clothing manufacturer is making scarves that require $\frac{3}{8}$ yard of material each. How many can be made from 27 yards of material?

72 scarves

57. Cooking A man is making cookies from a recipe that calls for $\frac{3}{4}$ teaspoon of oil. If the only measuring spoon he can find is a $\frac{1}{8}$ teaspoon, how many of these will he have to fill with oil in order to have a total of $\frac{3}{4}$ teaspoon of oil?

6

58. Cooking A cake recipe calls for $\frac{1}{2}$ cup of sugar. If the only measuring cup available is a $\frac{1}{8}$ cup, how many of these will have to be filled with sugar to make a total of $\frac{1}{2}$ cup of sugar?

4

59. Cartons of Milk If a small carton of milk holds exactly $\frac{1}{2}$ pint, how many of the $\frac{1}{2}$-pint cartons can be filled from a 14-pint container?

28 cartons

60. Pieces of Pipe How many pieces of pipe that are $\frac{2}{3}$ foot long must be laid together to make a pipe 16 feet long?

24 pieces

61. Lot Size A land developer wants to subdivide 5 acres of property into lots suitable for building a home. If each lot is to be $\frac{1}{4}$ of an acre in size how many lots can be made?

20 lots

62. House Plans If $\frac{1}{8}$ inch represents 1 ft on a drawing of a new home, determine the dimensions of a bedroom that measures 2 inches by 2 inches on the drawing.

16 ft × 16 ft

▬ Getting Ready for the Next Section

Write each fraction as an equivalent fraction with denominator 6.

▶ **63.** $\frac{1}{2}$

$\frac{3}{6}$

64. $\frac{1}{3}$

$\frac{2}{6}$

65. $\frac{3}{2}$

$\frac{9}{6}$

66. $\frac{2}{3}$

$\frac{4}{6}$

Write each fraction as an equivalent fraction with denominator 12.

67. $\frac{1}{3}$

$\frac{4}{12}$

68. $\frac{1}{2}$

$\frac{6}{12}$

69. $\frac{2}{3}$

$\frac{8}{12}$

70. $\frac{3}{4}$

$\frac{9}{12}$

Write each fraction as an equivalent fraction with denominator 30.

▶ **71.** $\frac{7}{15}$

$\frac{14}{30}$

72. $\frac{3}{10}$

$\frac{9}{30}$

73. $\frac{3}{5}$

$\frac{18}{30}$

74. $\frac{1}{6}$

$\frac{5}{30}$

Write each fraction as an equivalent fraction with denominator 24.

75. $\frac{1}{2}$

$\frac{12}{24}$

76. $\frac{1}{4}$

$\frac{6}{24}$

77. $\frac{1}{6}$

$\frac{4}{24}$

78. $\frac{1}{8}$

$\frac{3}{24}$

Write each fraction as an equivalent fraction with denominator 36.

79. $\frac{5}{12}$

$\frac{15}{36}$

▶ **80.** $\frac{7}{18}$

$\frac{14}{36}$

81. $\frac{1}{4}$

$\frac{9}{36}$

82. $\frac{1}{6}$

$\frac{6}{36}$

▬ Maintaining Your Skills

83. Fill in the table by rounding the numbers.

Number	Rounded to the Nearest		
	Ten	Hundred	Thousand
74	70	100	0
747	750	700	1,000
474	470	500	0

84. Fill in the table by rounding the numbers.

Number	Rounded to the Nearest		
	Ten	Hundred	Thousand
63	60	100	0
636	640	600	1,000
363	360	400	0

85. Estimating The quotient $253 \div 24$ is closer to which of the following?

   a. 5   **b.** 10   **c.** 15   **d.** 20

  b

86. Estimating The quotient $1,000 \div 47$ is closer to which of the following?

   a. 5   **b.** 10   **c.** 15   **d.** 20

  d

Addition and Subtraction with Fractions

Introduction . . .

Adding and subtracting fractions is actually just another application of the distributive property. The distributive property looks like this:

$$a(b + c) = a(b) + a(c)$$

where a, b, and c may be whole numbers or fractions. We will want to apply this property to expressions like

$$\frac{2}{7} + \frac{3}{7}$$

But before we do, we must make one additional observation about fractions. The fraction $\frac{2}{7}$ can be written as $2 \cdot \frac{1}{7}$, because

$$2 \cdot \frac{1}{7} = \frac{2}{1} \cdot \frac{1}{7} = \frac{2}{7}$$

Likewise, the fraction $\frac{3}{7}$ can be written as $3 \cdot \frac{1}{7}$, because

$$3 \cdot \frac{1}{7} = \frac{3}{1} \cdot \frac{1}{7} = \frac{3}{7}$$

In general, we can say that the fraction $\frac{a}{b}$ can always be written as $a \cdot \frac{1}{b}$, because

$$a \cdot \frac{1}{b} = \frac{a}{1} \cdot \frac{1}{b} = \frac{a}{b}$$

To add the fractions $\frac{2}{7}$ and $\frac{3}{7}$, we simply rewrite each of them as we have done above and apply the distributive property. Here is how it works:

$$\frac{2}{7} + \frac{3}{7} = 2 \cdot \frac{1}{7} + 3 \cdot \frac{1}{7} \qquad \text{Rewrite each fraction}$$

$$= (2 + 3) \cdot \frac{1}{7} \qquad \text{Apply the distributive property}$$

$$= 5 \cdot \frac{1}{7} \qquad \text{Add 2 and 3 to get 5}$$

$$= \frac{5}{7} \qquad \text{Rewrite } 5 \cdot \frac{1}{7} \text{ as } \frac{5}{7}$$

We can visualize the process shown above by using circles that are divided into 7 equal parts:

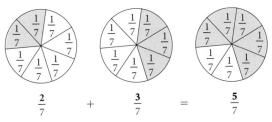

The fraction $\frac{5}{7}$ is the sum of $\frac{2}{7}$ and $\frac{3}{7}$. The steps and diagrams above show why we add numerators *but do not add denominators*. Using this example as justification, we can write a rule for adding two fractions that have the same denominator.

> **Note** Most people who have done any work with adding fractions know that you add fractions that have the same denominator by adding their numerators, but not their denominators. However, most people don't know why this works. The reason why we add numerators but not denominators is because of the distributive property. And that is what the discussion at the left is all about. If you really want to understand addition of fractions, pay close attention to this discussion.

A Combining Fractions with the Same Denominator

> **Rule**
> To add two fractions that have the same denominator, we add their numerators to get the numerator of the answer. The denominator in the answer is the same denominator as in the original fractions.

What we have here is the sum of the numerators placed over the *common denominator*. In symbols we have the following:

> **Addition and Subtraction of Fractions**
> If a, b, and c are numbers, and c is not equal to 0, then
> $$\frac{a}{c} + \frac{b}{c} = \frac{a+b}{c}$$
> This rule holds for subtraction as well. That is,
> $$\frac{a}{c} - \frac{b}{c} = \frac{a-b}{c}$$

PRACTICE PROBLEMS

Find the sum or difference. Reduce all answers to lowest terms.

1. $\frac{3}{10} + \frac{1}{10}$

2. $\frac{a+5}{12} + \frac{3}{12}$

3. $\frac{8}{7} - \frac{5}{7}$

4. $\frac{5}{9} + \frac{8}{9} + \frac{5}{9}$

Answers

1. $\frac{2}{5}$ **2.** $\frac{a+8}{12}$ **3.** $\frac{3}{7}$ **4.** 2

EXAMPLE 1 Add: $\frac{3}{8} + \frac{1}{8}$

SOLUTION $\frac{3}{8} + \frac{1}{8} = \frac{3+1}{8}$ Add numerators; keep the same denominator

$= \frac{4}{8}$ The sum of 3 and 1 is 4

$= \frac{1}{2}$ Reduce to lowest terms

EXAMPLE 2 Subtract: $\frac{a+5}{8} - \frac{3}{8}$

SOLUTION $\frac{a+5}{8} - \frac{3}{8} = \frac{a+5-3}{8}$ Combine numerators; keep the same denominator

$= \frac{a+2}{8}$ The difference of 5 and 3 is 2

EXAMPLE 3 Subtract: $\frac{9}{5} - \frac{3}{5}$

SOLUTION $\frac{9}{5} - \frac{3}{5} = \frac{9-3}{5}$ Subtract numerators; keep the same denominator

$= \frac{6}{5}$ The difference of 9 and 3 is 6

EXAMPLE 4 Add: $\frac{3}{7} + \frac{2}{7} + \frac{9}{7}$

SOLUTION $\frac{3}{7} + \frac{2}{7} + \frac{9}{7} = \frac{3+2+9}{7}$

$= \frac{14}{7}$

$= 2$

As Examples 1–4 indicate, addition and subtraction are simple, straightforward processes when all the fractions have the same denominator.

B The Least Common Denominator or LCD

We will now turn our attention to the process of adding fractions that have different denominators. In order to get started, we need the following definition.

> **Definition**
> The **least common denominator** (LCD) for a set of denominators is the smallest number that is exactly divisible by each denominator. (Note that, in some books, the least common denominator is also called the **least common multiple.**)

In other words, all the denominators of the fractions involved in a problem must divide into the least common denominator exactly. That is, they divide it without leaving a remainder.

EXAMPLE 5 Find the LCD for the fractions $\frac{5}{12}$ and $\frac{7}{18}$.

SOLUTION The least common denominator for the denominators 12 and 18 must be the smallest number divisible by both 12 and 18. We can factor 12 and 18 completely and then build the LCD from these factors. Factoring 12 and 18 completely gives us

$$12 = 2 \cdot 2 \cdot 3 \qquad 18 = 2 \cdot 3 \cdot 3$$

Now, if 12 is going to divide the LCD exactly, then the LCD must have factors of $2 \cdot 2 \cdot 3$. If 18 is to divide it exactly, it must have factors of $2 \cdot 3 \cdot 3$. We don't need to repeat the factors that 12 and 18 have in common:

$$\left.\begin{array}{l} 12 = 2 \cdot 2 \cdot 3 \\ 18 = 2 \cdot 3 \cdot 3 \end{array}\right\} \qquad \overset{\text{12 divides the LCD}}{\text{LCD}} = 2 \cdot 2 \cdot 3 \cdot 3 = 36 \atop \text{18 divides the LCD}$$

The LCD for 12 and 18 is 36. It is the smallest number that is divisible by both 12 and 18; 12 divides it exactly three times, and 18 divides it exactly two times.

We can visualize the results in Example 5 with the diagram below. It shows that 36 is the smallest number that both 12 and 18 divide evenly. As you can see, 12 divides 36 exactly 3 times, and 18 divides 36 exactly 2 times.

12	12	12

18	18

36

EXAMPLE 6 Add: $\frac{5}{12} + \frac{7}{18}$

SOLUTION We can add fractions only when they have the same denominators. In Example 5, we found the LCD for $\frac{5}{12}$ and $\frac{7}{18}$ to be 36. We change $\frac{5}{12}$ and $\frac{7}{18}$ to equivalent fractions that have 36 for a denominator by applying Property 1 for fractions:

$$\frac{5}{12} = \frac{5 \cdot \mathbf{3}}{12 \cdot \mathbf{3}} = \frac{15}{36}$$

$$\frac{7}{18} = \frac{7 \cdot \mathbf{2}}{18 \cdot \mathbf{2}} = \frac{14}{36}$$

---

5. **a.** Find the LCD for the fractions:

$$\frac{5}{18} \text{ and } \frac{3}{14}$$

b. Find the LCD for the fractions:

$$\frac{5}{36} \text{ and } \frac{3}{28}$$

 Note The ability to find least common denominators is very important in mathematics. The discussion here is a detailed explanation of how to find an LCD.

6. Add.
    a. $\frac{5}{18} + \frac{3}{14}$
    b. $\frac{5}{36} + \frac{3}{28}$

Answer
5. **a.** 126 **b.** 252

The fraction $\frac{15}{36}$ is equivalent to $\frac{5}{12}$, because it was obtained by multiplying both the numerator and the denominator by 3. Likewise, $\frac{14}{36}$ is equivalent to $\frac{7}{18}$, because it was obtained by multiplying the numerator and the denominator by 2. All we have left to do is to add numerators.

$$\frac{15}{36} + \frac{14}{36} = \frac{29}{36}$$

The sum of $\frac{5}{12}$ and $\frac{7}{18}$ is the fraction $\frac{29}{36}$. Let's write the complete problem again step by step.

$$\frac{5}{12} + \frac{7}{18} = \frac{5 \cdot \mathbf{3}}{12 \cdot \mathbf{3}} + \frac{7 \cdot \mathbf{2}}{18 \cdot \mathbf{2}}$$

Rewrite each fraction as an equivalent fraction with denominator 36

$$= \frac{15}{36} + \frac{14}{36}$$

$$= \frac{29}{36}$$

Add numerators; keep the common denominator

7. a. Find the LCD for $\frac{2}{9}$ and $\frac{4}{15}$.

b. Find the LCD for $\frac{2}{27}$ and $\frac{4}{45}$.

EXAMPLE 7 Find the LCD for $\frac{3}{4}$ and $\frac{1}{6}$.

SOLUTION We factor 4 and 6 into products of prime factors and build the LCD from these factors.

$$\left.\begin{array}{l} 4 = 2 \cdot 2 \\ 6 = 2 \cdot 3 \end{array}\right\} \text{LCD} = 2 \cdot 2 \cdot 3 = 12$$

The LCD is 12. Both denominators divide it exactly; 4 divides 12 exactly 3 times, and 6 divides 12 exactly 2 times.

8. Add.

a. $\frac{2}{9} + \frac{4}{15}$

b. $\frac{2}{27} + \frac{4}{45}$

EXAMPLE 8 Add: $\frac{3}{4} + \frac{1}{6}$

SOLUTION In Example 7, we found that the LCD for these two fractions is 12. We begin by changing $\frac{3}{4}$ and $\frac{1}{6}$ to equivalent fractions with denominator 12:

$$\frac{3}{4} = \frac{3 \cdot \mathbf{3}}{4 \cdot \mathbf{3}} = \frac{9}{12}$$

$$\frac{1}{6} = \frac{1 \cdot \mathbf{2}}{6 \cdot \mathbf{2}} = \frac{2}{12}$$

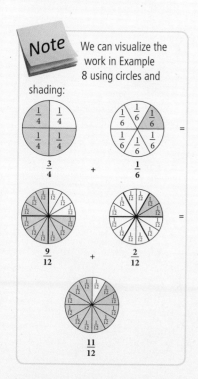

Note We can visualize the work in Example 8 using circles and shading:

The fraction $\frac{9}{12}$ is equal to the fraction $\frac{3}{4}$, because it was obtained by multiplying the numerator and the denominator of $\frac{3}{4}$ by 3. Likewise, $\frac{2}{12}$ is equivalent to $\frac{1}{6}$, because it was obtained by multiplying the numerator and the denominator of $\frac{1}{6}$ by 2. To complete the problem we add numerators:

$$\frac{9}{12} + \frac{2}{12} = \frac{11}{12}$$

The sum of $\frac{3}{4}$ and $\frac{1}{6}$ is $\frac{11}{12}$. Here is how the complete problem looks:

$$\frac{3}{4} + \frac{1}{6} = \frac{3 \cdot \mathbf{3}}{4 \cdot \mathbf{3}} + \frac{1 \cdot \mathbf{2}}{6 \cdot \mathbf{2}}$$

Rewrite each fraction as an equivalent fraction with denominator 12

$$= \frac{9}{12} + \frac{2}{12}$$

$$= \frac{11}{12}$$

Add numerators; keep the same denominator

Answers

6. a. $\frac{31}{63}$ **b.** $\frac{31}{126}$ **7. a.** 45 **b.** 135

8. a. $\frac{22}{45}$ **b.** $\frac{22}{135}$

EXAMPLE 9 Subtract: $\dfrac{7}{15} - \dfrac{3}{10}$

SOLUTION Let's factor 15 and 10 completely and use these factors to build the LCD:

15 divides the LCD

$$\left.\begin{array}{l} 15 = 3 \cdot 5 \\ 10 = 2 \cdot 5 \end{array}\right\} \; \text{LCD} = 2 \cdot 3 \cdot 5 = 30$$

10 divides the LCD

Changing to equivalent fractions and subtracting, we have

$$\frac{7}{15} - \frac{3}{10} = \frac{7 \cdot \mathbf{2}}{15 \cdot \mathbf{2}} - \frac{3 \cdot \mathbf{3}}{10 \cdot \mathbf{3}} \qquad \text{Rewrite as equivalent fractions with the LCD for the denominator}$$

$$= \frac{14}{30} - \frac{9}{30}$$

$$= \frac{5}{30} \qquad \text{Subtract numerators; keep the LCD}$$

$$= \frac{1}{6} \qquad \text{Reduce to lowest terms}$$

As a summary of what we have done so far, and as a guide to working other problems, we now list the steps involved in adding and subtracting fractions with different denominators.

Strategy Adding or Subtracting Any Two Fractions

Step 1 Factor each denominator completely, and use the factors to build the LCD. (Remember, the LCD is the smallest number divisible by each of the denominators in the problem.)

Step 2 Rewrite each fraction as an equivalent fraction that has the LCD for its denominator. This is done by multiplying both the numerator and the denominator of the fraction in question by the appropriate whole number.

Step 3 Add or subtract the numerators of the fractions produced in Step 2. This is the numerator of the sum or difference. The denominator of the sum or difference is the LCD.

Step 4 Reduce the fraction produced in Step 3 to lowest terms if it is not already in lowest terms.

The idea behind adding or subtracting fractions is really very simple. We can only add or subtract fractions that have the same denominators. If the fractions we are trying to add or subtract do not have the same denominators, we rewrite each of them as an equivalent fraction with the LCD for a denominator.

Here are some additional examples of sums and differences of fractions.

EXAMPLE 10 Subtract: $\dfrac{3}{5} - \dfrac{1}{6}$

SOLUTION The LCD for 5 and 6 is their product, 30. We begin by rewriting each fraction with this common denominator:

$$\frac{3}{5} - \frac{1}{6} = \frac{3 \cdot \mathbf{6}}{5 \cdot \mathbf{6}} - \frac{1 \cdot \mathbf{5}}{6 \cdot \mathbf{5}}$$

$$= \frac{18}{30} - \frac{5}{30}$$

$$= \frac{13}{30}$$

9. Subtract: $\dfrac{8}{25} - \dfrac{3}{20}$

10. Subtract: $\dfrac{3}{4} - \dfrac{1}{5}$

Answers

9. $\dfrac{17}{100}$ **10.** $\dfrac{11}{20}$

11. Add.

a. $\dfrac{1}{9} + \dfrac{1}{4} + \dfrac{1}{6}$

b. $\dfrac{1}{90} + \dfrac{1}{40} + \dfrac{1}{60}$

12. Subtract: $2 - \dfrac{3}{4}$

EXAMPLE 11 Add: $\dfrac{1}{6} + \dfrac{1}{8} + \dfrac{1}{4}$

SOLUTION We begin by factoring the denominators completely and building the LCD from the factors that result:

8 divides the LCD

$$6 = 2 \cdot 3$$
$$8 = 2 \cdot 2 \cdot 2$$
$$4 = 2 \cdot 2$$

$$LCD = 2 \cdot 2 \cdot 2 \cdot 3 = 24$$

4 divides the LCD   6 divides the LCD

We then change to equivalent fractions and add as usual:

$$\dfrac{1}{6} + \dfrac{1}{8} + \dfrac{1}{4} = \dfrac{1 \cdot 4}{6 \cdot 4} + \dfrac{1 \cdot 3}{8 \cdot 3} + \dfrac{1 \cdot 6}{4 \cdot 6} = \dfrac{4}{24} + \dfrac{3}{24} + \dfrac{6}{24} = \dfrac{13}{24}$$

EXAMPLE 12 Subtract: $3 - \dfrac{5}{6}$

SOLUTION The denominators are 1 (because $3 = \dfrac{3}{1}$) and 6. The smallest number divisible by both 1 and 6 is 6.

$$3 - \dfrac{5}{6} = \dfrac{3}{1} - \dfrac{5}{6} = \dfrac{3 \cdot 6}{1 \cdot 6} - \dfrac{5}{6} = \dfrac{18}{6} - \dfrac{5}{6} = \dfrac{13}{6}$$

Getting Ready for Class

After reading through the preceding section, respond in your own words and in complete sentences.

1. When adding two fractions with the same denominators, we always add their _____, but we never add their _____.
2. What does the abbreviation *LCD* stand for?
3. What is the first step when finding the LCD for the fractions $\dfrac{5}{12}$ and $\dfrac{7}{18}$?
4. When adding fractions, what is the last step?

Answers

11. a. $\dfrac{19}{36}$ **b.** $\dfrac{19}{360}$ **12.** $\dfrac{5}{4}$

Problem Set 2.5

A Find the following sums and differences, and reduce to lowest terms. (Add or subtract as indicated.) [Examples 1–4]

▶ 1. $\dfrac{3}{6} + \dfrac{1}{6}$

$\dfrac{2}{3}$

2. $\dfrac{2}{5} + \dfrac{3}{5}$

1

3. $\dfrac{5}{8} - \dfrac{3}{8}$

$\dfrac{1}{4}$

▶ 4. $\dfrac{6}{7} - \dfrac{1}{7}$

$\dfrac{5}{7}$

5. $\dfrac{3}{4} - \dfrac{1}{4}$

$\dfrac{1}{2}$

6. $\dfrac{7}{9} - \dfrac{4}{9}$

$\dfrac{1}{3}$

7. $\dfrac{2}{3} - \dfrac{1}{3}$

$\dfrac{1}{3}$

8. $\dfrac{9}{8} - \dfrac{1}{8}$

1

9. $\dfrac{1}{4} + \dfrac{2}{4} + \dfrac{3}{4}$

$\dfrac{3}{2}$

10. $\dfrac{2}{5} + \dfrac{3}{5} + \dfrac{4}{5}$

$\dfrac{9}{5}$

11. $\dfrac{x+7}{2} - \dfrac{1}{2}$

$\dfrac{x+6}{2}$

▶ 12. $\dfrac{x+5}{4} - \dfrac{3}{4}$

$\dfrac{x+2}{4}$

13. $\dfrac{1}{10} + \dfrac{3}{10} + \dfrac{4}{10}$

$\dfrac{4}{5}$

14. $\dfrac{3}{20} + \dfrac{1}{20} + \dfrac{4}{20}$

$\dfrac{2}{5}$

15. $\dfrac{1}{3} + \dfrac{4}{3} + \dfrac{5}{3}$

$\dfrac{10}{3}$

16. $\dfrac{5}{4} + \dfrac{4}{4} + \dfrac{3}{4}$

3

B Complete the following tables. [Examples 5–12]

▶ 17.

First Number a	Second Number b	The Sum of a and b $a + b$
$\dfrac{1}{2}$	$\dfrac{1}{3}$	$\dfrac{5}{6}$
$\dfrac{1}{3}$	$\dfrac{1}{4}$	$\dfrac{7}{12}$
$\dfrac{1}{4}$	$\dfrac{1}{5}$	$\dfrac{9}{20}$
$\dfrac{1}{5}$	$\dfrac{1}{6}$	$\dfrac{11}{30}$

▶ 18.

First Number a	Second Number b	The Sum of a and b $a + b$
1	$\dfrac{1}{2}$	$\dfrac{3}{2}$
1	$\dfrac{1}{3}$	$\dfrac{4}{3}$
1	$\dfrac{1}{4}$	$\dfrac{5}{4}$
1	$\dfrac{1}{5}$	$\dfrac{6}{5}$

19.

First Number a	Second Number b	The Sum of a and b $a + b$
$\dfrac{1}{12}$	$\dfrac{1}{2}$	$\dfrac{7}{12}$
$\dfrac{1}{12}$	$\dfrac{1}{3}$	$\dfrac{5}{12}$
$\dfrac{1}{12}$	$\dfrac{1}{4}$	$\dfrac{4}{12} = \dfrac{1}{3}$
$\dfrac{1}{12}$	$\dfrac{1}{6}$	$\dfrac{3}{12} = \dfrac{1}{4}$

20.

First Number a	Second Number b	The Sum of a and b $a + b$
$\dfrac{1}{8}$	$\dfrac{1}{2}$	$\dfrac{5}{8}$
$\dfrac{1}{8}$	$\dfrac{1}{4}$	$\dfrac{3}{8}$
$\dfrac{1}{8}$	$\dfrac{1}{16}$	$\dfrac{3}{16}$
$\dfrac{1}{8}$	$\dfrac{1}{24}$	$\dfrac{4}{24} = \dfrac{1}{6}$

B Find the LCD for each of the following; then use the methods developed in this section to add or subtract as indicated. [Examples 5–14]

▶ **21.** $\dfrac{4}{9} + \dfrac{1}{3}$

$\dfrac{7}{9}$

22. $\dfrac{1}{2} + \dfrac{1}{4}$

$\dfrac{3}{4}$

23. $2 + \dfrac{1}{3}$

$\dfrac{7}{3}$

24. $3 + \dfrac{1}{2}$

$\dfrac{7}{2}$

▶ **25.** $\dfrac{3}{4} + 1$

$\dfrac{7}{4}$

26. $\dfrac{3}{4} + 2$

$\dfrac{11}{4}$

27. $\dfrac{1}{2} + \dfrac{2}{3}$

$\dfrac{7}{6}$

28. $\dfrac{1}{8} + \dfrac{3}{4}$

$\dfrac{7}{8}$

29. $\dfrac{1}{4} + \dfrac{1}{5}$

$\dfrac{9}{20}$

30. $\dfrac{1}{3} + \dfrac{1}{5}$

$\dfrac{8}{15}$

31. $\dfrac{1}{2} + \dfrac{1}{5}$

$\dfrac{7}{10}$

32. $\dfrac{1}{2} - \dfrac{1}{5}$

$\dfrac{3}{10}$

33. $\dfrac{5}{12} + \dfrac{3}{8}$

$\dfrac{19}{24}$

34. $\dfrac{9}{16} + \dfrac{7}{12}$

$\dfrac{55}{48}$

35. $\dfrac{8}{30} - \dfrac{1}{20}$

$\dfrac{13}{60}$

36. $\dfrac{9}{40} - \dfrac{1}{30}$

$\dfrac{23}{120}$

37. $\dfrac{3}{10} + \dfrac{1}{100}$

$\dfrac{31}{100}$

38. $\dfrac{9}{100} + \dfrac{7}{10}$

$\dfrac{79}{100}$

39. $\dfrac{10}{36} + \dfrac{9}{48}$

$\dfrac{67}{144}$

40. $\dfrac{12}{28} + \dfrac{9}{20}$

$\dfrac{123}{140}$

Problems 41–46 are more challenging than the others.

41. $\dfrac{17}{30} + \dfrac{11}{42}$

$\dfrac{29}{35}$

42. $\dfrac{19}{42} + \dfrac{13}{70}$

$\dfrac{67}{105}$

▶ **43.** $\dfrac{25}{84} + \dfrac{41}{90}$

$\dfrac{949}{1,260}$

44. $\dfrac{23}{70} + \dfrac{29}{84}$

$\dfrac{283}{420}$

▶ **45.** $\dfrac{13}{126} - \dfrac{13}{180}$

$\frac{13}{420}$

46. $\dfrac{17}{84} - \dfrac{17}{90}$

$\frac{17}{1,260}$

47. $\dfrac{3}{4} + \dfrac{1}{8} + \dfrac{5}{6}$

$\frac{41}{24}$

48. $\dfrac{3}{8} + \dfrac{2}{5} + \dfrac{1}{4}$

$\frac{41}{40}$

49. $\dfrac{3}{10} + \dfrac{5}{12} + \dfrac{1}{6}$

$\frac{53}{60}$

50. $\dfrac{5}{21} + \dfrac{1}{7} + \dfrac{3}{14}$

$\frac{25}{42}$

▶ **51.** $\dfrac{1}{2} + \dfrac{1}{3} + \dfrac{1}{4} + \dfrac{1}{6}$

$\frac{5}{4}$

52. $\dfrac{1}{8} + \dfrac{1}{4} + \dfrac{1}{5} + \dfrac{1}{10}$

$\frac{27}{40}$

53. $10 - \dfrac{2}{9}$

$\frac{88}{9}$

54. $9 - \dfrac{3}{5}$

$\frac{42}{5}$

55. $\dfrac{1}{10} + \dfrac{4}{5} - \dfrac{3}{20}$

$\frac{3}{4}$

56. $\dfrac{1}{2} + \dfrac{3}{4} - \dfrac{5}{8}$

$\frac{5}{8}$

57. $\dfrac{1}{4} - \dfrac{1}{8} + \dfrac{1}{2} - \dfrac{3}{8}$

$\frac{1}{4}$

58. $\dfrac{7}{8} - \dfrac{3}{4} + \dfrac{5}{8} - \dfrac{1}{2}$

$\frac{1}{4}$

There are two ways to work the problems below. You can combine the fractions inside the parentheses first and then multiply, or you can apply the distributive property first, then add.

59. $15\left(\dfrac{2}{3} + \dfrac{3}{5}\right)$

19

60. $15\left(\dfrac{4}{5} - \dfrac{1}{3}\right)$

7

61. $4\left(\dfrac{1}{2} + \dfrac{1}{4}\right)$

3

62. $6\left(\dfrac{1}{3} + \dfrac{1}{2}\right)$

5

63. Find the sum of $\dfrac{3}{7}$, 2, and $\dfrac{1}{9}$.

$\frac{160}{63}$

▶ **64.** Find the sum of 6, $\dfrac{6}{11}$, and 11.

$\frac{193}{11}$

65. Give the difference of $\dfrac{7}{8}$ and $\dfrac{1}{4}$.

$\frac{5}{8}$

66. Give the difference of $\dfrac{9}{10}$ and $\dfrac{1}{100}$.

$\frac{89}{100}$

■ Applying the Concepts

Some of the application problems below involve multiplication or division, while others involve addition or subtraction.

67. Rainfall How much total rainfall did Death Valley get during the months of July and September?

$\frac{7}{20}$ inch

68. Rainfall How much more rainfall did Death Valley get in February than in December?

$\frac{1}{12}$ inch

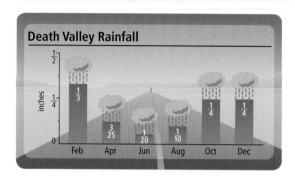

► **69. Capacity** One carton of milk contains $\frac{1}{2}$ pint while another contains 4 pints. How much milk is contained in both cartons?

$\frac{9}{2}$ pints

► **70. Baking** A recipe calls for $\frac{2}{3}$ cup of flour and $\frac{3}{4}$ cup of sugar. What is the total amount of flour and sugar called for in the recipe?

$\frac{17}{12}$ cups

71. Budgeting A student earns $2,500 a month while working in college. She sets aside $\frac{1}{20}$ of this money for gas to travel to and from campus, $\frac{1}{16}$ for food, and $\frac{1}{25}$ for savings. What fraction of her income does she plan to spend on these three items?

$\frac{61}{400}$

72. Popular Majors Enrollment figures show that the most popular programs at a local college are liberal art studies and business programs. The liberal arts studies program accounts for $\frac{1}{5}$ of the student enrollment while business programs account for $\frac{1}{10}$ of the enrollment. What fraction of student enrollment chooses one of these two areas of study?

$\frac{3}{10}$

73. Exercising According to national studies, childhood obesity is on the rise. Doctors recommend a minimum of 30 minutes of exercise three times a week to help keep us fit. Suppose during a given week you walk for $\frac{1}{4}$ hour one day, $\frac{2}{3}$ of an hour a second day and $\frac{3}{4}$ of an hour on a third day. Find the total number of hours walked as a fraction.

$\frac{5}{3}$ hours

74. Cooking You are making pancakes for breakfast and need $\frac{3}{4}$ of a cup of milk for your batter. You discover that you only have $\frac{1}{2}$ cup of milk in the refrigerator. How much more milk do you need?

$\frac{1}{4}$ cup

75. Conference Attendees At a recent mathematics confer-ence $\frac{1}{3}$ of the attendees were teachers, $\frac{1}{4}$ were soft-ware salespersons, and $\frac{1}{12}$ were representatives from various book publishing companies. The remainder of the people in the conference center were employees of the center. What fraction represents the employees of the conference center?

$\frac{1}{3}$

▶ **76. Painting** Recently you purchased $\frac{1}{2}$ gallon of paint to paint your dorm room. Once the job was finished you realized that you only used $\frac{1}{3}$ of the gallon. What frac-tional amount of the paint is left in the can?

$\frac{1}{6}$ gallon

77. Subdivision A 6-acre piece of land is subdivided into $\frac{3}{5}$-acre lots. How many lots are there?

10 lots

▶ **78. Cutting Wood** A 12-foot piece of wood is cut into shelves. If each is $\frac{3}{4}$ foot in length, how many shelves are there?

16 shelves

Find the perimeter of each figure.

79.

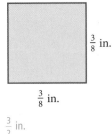

$\frac{3}{8}$ in.

$\frac{3}{8}$ in.

$\frac{3}{2}$ in.

80.

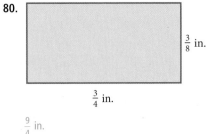

$\frac{3}{8}$ in.

$\frac{3}{4}$ in.

$\frac{9}{4}$ in.

▶ **81.**

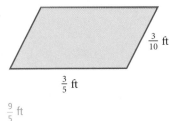

$\frac{3}{10}$ ft

$\frac{3}{5}$ ft

$\frac{9}{5}$ ft

▶ **82.**

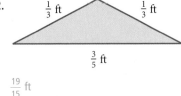

$\frac{1}{3}$ ft $\frac{1}{3}$ ft

$\frac{3}{5}$ ft

$\frac{19}{15}$ ft

Arithmetic Sequences Recall that an arithmetic sequence is a sequence in which each term comes from the previous term by adding the same number each time. For example, the sequence $1, \frac{3}{2}, 2, \frac{5}{2}, \ldots$ is an arithmetic sequence that starts with the number 1. Then each term after that is found by adding $\frac{1}{2}$ to the previous term. By observing this fact, we know that the next term in the sequence will be $\frac{5}{2} + \frac{1}{2} = \frac{6}{2} = 3$.

Find the next number in each arithmetic sequence below.

83. $1, \frac{4}{3}, \frac{5}{3}, 2, \ldots$

$\frac{7}{3}$

84. $1, \frac{5}{4}, \frac{3}{2}, \frac{7}{4}, \ldots$

2

85. $\frac{3}{2}, 2, \frac{5}{2}, \ldots$

3

86. $\frac{2}{3}, 1, \frac{4}{3}, \ldots$

$\frac{5}{3}$

■ Getting Ready for the Next Section

Simplify.

87. $9 \cdot 6 + 5$

59

88. $4 \cdot 6 + 3$

27

89. Write 2 as a fraction with denominator 8.

$\frac{16}{8}$

90. Write 2 as a fraction with denominator 4.

$\frac{8}{4}$

91. Write 1 as a fraction with denominator 8.

$\frac{8}{8}$

92. Write 5 as a fraction with denominator 4.

$\frac{20}{4}$

Add.

93. $\frac{8}{4} + \frac{3}{4}$

$\frac{11}{4}$

94. $\frac{16}{8} + \frac{1}{8}$

$\frac{17}{8}$

95. $2 + \frac{1}{8}$

$\frac{17}{8}$

96. $2 + \frac{3}{4}$

$\frac{11}{4}$

97. $1 + \frac{1}{8}$

$\frac{9}{8}$

98. $5 + \frac{3}{4}$

$\frac{23}{4}$

Divide.

99. $11 \div 4$

2 R 3

100. $10 \div 3$

3 R 1

101. $208 \div 24$

8 R 16

102. $207 \div 26$

7 R 25

■ Maintaining Your Skills

Multiply or divide as indicated.

103. $\frac{3}{4} \div \frac{5}{6}$

$\frac{9}{10}$

104. $12 \div \frac{1}{2}$

24

105. $12 \cdot \frac{2}{3}$

8

106. $12 \cdot \frac{3}{4}$

9

107. $4 \cdot \frac{3}{4}$

3

108. $4 \cdot \frac{1}{2}$

2

109. $\frac{7}{6} \div \frac{7}{12}$

2

110. $\frac{9}{10} \div \frac{7}{10}$

$\frac{9}{7}$

111. $\frac{2}{3} \cdot \frac{3}{4} \cdot \frac{4}{5} \cdot \frac{5}{6} \cdot \frac{6}{7}$

$\frac{2}{7}$

112. $\frac{11}{12} \cdot \frac{10}{11} \cdot \frac{9}{10} \cdot \frac{8}{9} \cdot \frac{7}{8}$

$\frac{7}{12}$

113. $\frac{35}{110} \cdot \frac{80}{63} \div \frac{16}{27}$

$\frac{15}{22}$

114. $\frac{20}{72} \cdot \frac{42}{18} \div \frac{20}{16}$

$\frac{14}{27}$

2.6

Objectives

A Change mixed numbers to improper fractions.

B Change improper fractions to mixed numbers.

Introduction . . .

If you are interested in the stock market, you know that, prior to the year 2000, stock prices were given in eighths. For example, at one point in 1990, one share of Intel Corporation was selling at $73\frac{5}{8}$, or seventy-three and five-eighths dollars. The number $73\frac{5}{8}$ is called a *mixed number*. It is the sum of a whole number and a proper fraction. With mixed-number notation, we leave out the addition sign.

Notation

A number such as $5\frac{3}{4}$ is called a *mixed number* and is equal to $5 + \frac{3}{4}$. It is simply the sum of the whole number 5 and the proper fraction $\frac{3}{4}$, written without a + sign. Here are some further examples:

$$2\frac{1}{8} = 2 + \frac{1}{8}, \quad 6\frac{5}{9} = 6 + \frac{5}{9}, \quad 11\frac{2}{3} = 11 + \frac{2}{3}$$

The notation used in writing mixed numbers (writing the whole number and the proper fraction next to each other) must always be interpreted as addition. It is a mistake to read $5\frac{3}{4}$ as meaning 5 times $\frac{3}{4}$. If we want to indicate multiplication, we must use parentheses or a multiplication symbol. That is:

$$5\frac{3}{4} \text{ is not the same as } 5\left(\frac{3}{4}\right)$$

This implies addition

This implies multiplication

$$5\frac{3}{4} \text{ is not the same as } 5 \cdot \frac{3}{4}$$

A Changing Mixed Numbers to Improper Fractions

To change a mixed number to an improper fraction, we write the mixed number with the + sign showing and then add the two numbers, as we did earlier.

EXAMPLE 1 Change $2\frac{3}{4}$ to an improper fraction.

SOLUTION

$$2\frac{3}{4} = 2 + \frac{3}{4}$$ Write the mixed number as a sum

$$= \frac{2}{1} + \frac{3}{4}$$ Show that the denominator of 2 is 1

$$= \frac{4 \cdot 2}{4 \cdot 1} + \frac{3}{4}$$ Multiply the numerator and the denominator of $\frac{2}{1}$ by 4 so both fractions will have the same denominator

$$= \frac{8}{4} + \frac{3}{4}$$

$$= \frac{11}{4}$$ Add the numerators; keep the common denominator

The mixed number $2\frac{3}{4}$ is equal to the improper fraction $\frac{11}{4}$. The diagram that follows further illustrates the equivalence of $2\frac{3}{4}$ and $\frac{11}{4}$.

PRACTICE PROBLEMS

1. Change $5\frac{2}{3}$ to an improper fraction.

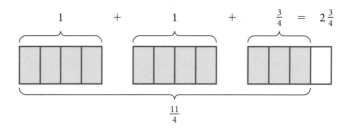

2. Change $3\frac{1}{6}$ to an improper fraction.

$$\boxed{\text{EXAMPLE 2}} \quad \text{Change } 2\frac{1}{8} \text{ to an improper fraction.}$$

SOLUTION

$$2\frac{1}{8} = 2 + \frac{1}{8} \qquad \text{Write as addition}$$

$$= \frac{2}{1} + \frac{1}{8} \qquad \text{Write the whole number 2 as a fraction}$$

$$= \frac{\mathbf{8} \cdot 2}{\mathbf{8} \cdot 1} + \frac{1}{8} \qquad \text{Change } \frac{2}{1} \text{ to a fraction with denominator 8}$$

$$= \frac{16}{8} + \frac{1}{8}$$

$$= \frac{17}{8} \qquad \text{Add the numerators}$$

If we look closely at Examples 1 and 2, we can see a shortcut that will let us change a mixed number to an improper fraction without so many steps.

> **Strategy   Changing a Mixed Number to an Improper Fraction (Shortcut)**
>
> **Step 1:** Multiply the whole number part of the mixed number by the denominator.
>
> **Step 2:** Add your answer to the numerator of the fraction.
>
> **Step 3:** Put your new number over the original denominator.

3. Use the shortcut to change $5\frac{2}{3}$ to an improper fraction.

$$\boxed{\text{EXAMPLE 3}} \quad \text{Use the shortcut to change } 5\frac{3}{4} \text{ to an improper fraction.}$$

SOLUTION   **1.** First, we multiply 4×5 to get 20.

   2. Next, we add 20 to 3 to get 23.

   3. The improper fraction equal to $5\frac{3}{4}$ is $\frac{23}{4}$.

Here is a diagram showing what we have done:

Step 1 Multiply $4 \times 5 = 20$.

$$5\frac{3}{4}$$

Step 2 Add $20 + 3 = 23$.

Mathematically, our shortcut is written like this:

$$5\frac{3}{4} = \frac{(4 \cdot 5) + 3}{4} = \frac{20 + 3}{4} = \frac{23}{4} \qquad \text{The result will always have the same denominator as the original mixed number}$$

The shortcut shown in Example 3 works because the whole-number part of a mixed number can always be written with a denominator of 1. Therefore, the LCD for a whole number and fraction will always be the denominator of the fraction. That is why we multiply the whole number by the denominator of the fraction:

$$5\frac{3}{4} = 5 + \frac{3}{4} = \frac{5}{1} + \frac{3}{4} = \frac{4 \cdot 5}{4 \cdot 1} + \frac{3}{4} = \frac{4 \cdot 5 + 3}{4} = \frac{23}{4}$$

Answers

1. $\frac{17}{3}$ **2.** $\frac{19}{6}$ **3.** $\frac{17}{3}$

EXAMPLE 4 Change $6\frac{5}{9}$ to an improper fraction.

SOLUTION Using the first method, we have

$$6\frac{5}{9} = 6 + \frac{5}{9} = \frac{6}{1} + \frac{5}{9} = \frac{\mathbf{9} \cdot 6}{\mathbf{9} \cdot 1} + \frac{5}{9} = \frac{54}{9} + \frac{5}{9} = \frac{59}{9}$$

Using the shortcut method, we have

$$6\frac{5}{9} = \frac{(9 \cdot 6) + 5}{9} = \frac{54 + 5}{9} = \frac{59}{9}$$

B Changing Improper Fractions to Mixed Numbers

To change an improper fraction to a mixed number, we divide the numerator by the denominator. The result is used to write the mixed number.

EXAMPLE 5 Change $\frac{11}{4}$ to a mixed number.

SOLUTION Dividing 11 by 4 gives us

$$\begin{array}{r} 2 \\ 4\overline{)11} \\ 8 \\ \hline 3 \end{array}$$

We see that 4 goes into 11 two times with 3 for a remainder. We write this as

$$\frac{11}{4} = 2 + \frac{3}{4} = 2\frac{3}{4}$$

The improper fraction $\frac{11}{4}$ is equivalent to the mixed number $2\frac{3}{4}$.

An easy way to visualize the results in Example 5 is to imagine having 11 quarters. Your 11 quarters are equivalent to $\frac{11}{4}$ dollars. In dollars, your quarters are worth 2 dollars plus 3 quarters, or $2\frac{3}{4}$ dollars.

EXAMPLE 6 Change $\frac{10}{3}$ to a mixed number.

SOLUTION $\frac{10}{3}$: $\begin{array}{r} 3 \\ 3\overline{)10} \\ 9 \\ \hline 1 \end{array}$ so $\frac{10}{3} = \mathbf{3} + \frac{\mathbf{1}}{3} = 3\frac{1}{3}$

EXAMPLE 7 Change $\frac{208}{24}$ to a mixed number.

SOLUTION $\frac{208}{24}$: $\begin{array}{r} 8 \\ 24\overline{)208} \\ 192 \\ \hline 16 \end{array}$ so $\frac{208}{24} = \mathbf{8} + \frac{\mathbf{16}}{24} = 8 + \frac{2}{3} = 8\frac{2}{3}$

Reduce to lowest terms

---

4. Change $6\frac{4}{9}$ to an improper fraction.

CALCULATOR NOTE

The sequence of keys to press on a calculator to obtain the numerator in Example 4 looks like this:

5. Change $\frac{11}{3}$ to a mixed number.

Note This division process shows us how many ones are in $\frac{11}{4}$ and, when the ones are taken out, how many fourths are left.

Change each improper fraction to a mixed number.

6. $\frac{14}{5}$

7. $\frac{207}{26}$

Answers

4. $\frac{58}{9}$ **5.** $3\frac{2}{3}$ **6.** $2\frac{4}{5}$ **7.** $7\frac{25}{26}$

Long Division, Remainders, and Mixed Numbers

Mixed numbers give us another way of writing the answers to long division problems that contain remainders. Here is how we divided 1,690 by 67 in Chapter 1:

$$
\begin{array}{r}
25 \text{ R } 15 \\
67\overline{)1{,}690} \\
\underline{1\ 34} \\
350 \\
\underline{335} \\
15
\end{array}
$$

The answer is 25 with a remainder of 15. Using mixed numbers, we can now write the answer as $25\frac{15}{67}$. That is,

$$\frac{1{,}690}{67} = 25\frac{15}{67}$$

The quotient of 1,690 and 67 is $25\frac{15}{67}$.

Getting Ready for Class

After reading through the preceding section, respond in your own words and in complete sentences.

1. What is a mixed number?

2. The expression $5\frac{3}{4}$ is equivalent to what addition problem?

3. The improper fraction $\frac{11}{4}$ is equivalent to what mixed number?

4. Why is $\frac{13}{5}$ an improper fraction, but $\frac{3}{5}$ is not an improper fraction?

Problem Set 2.6

A   Change each mixed number to an improper fraction. [Examples 1–4]

1. $4\frac{2}{3}$ ▶ **2.** $3\frac{5}{8}$ ▶ **3.** $5\frac{1}{4}$ ▶ **4.** $7\frac{1}{2}$ **5.** $1\frac{5}{8}$ ▶ **6.** $1\frac{6}{7}$

$\frac{14}{3}$ $\frac{29}{8}$ $\frac{21}{4}$ $\frac{15}{2}$ $\frac{13}{8}$ $\frac{13}{7}$

▶ **7.** $15\frac{2}{3}$ **8.** $17\frac{3}{4}$ ▶ **9.** $4\frac{20}{21}$ ▶ **10.** $5\frac{18}{19}$ **11.** $12\frac{31}{33}$ ▶ **12.** $14\frac{29}{31}$

$\frac{47}{3}$ $\frac{71}{4}$ $\frac{104}{21}$ $\frac{113}{19}$ $\frac{427}{33}$ $\frac{463}{31}$

B   Change each improper fraction to a mixed number. [Examples 5–7]

▶ **13.** $\frac{9}{8}$ ▶ **14.** $\frac{10}{9}$ ▶ **15.** $\frac{19}{4}$ ▶ **16.** $\frac{23}{5}$ **17.** $\frac{29}{6}$ ▶ **18.** $\frac{7}{2}$

$1\frac{1}{8}$ $1\frac{1}{9}$ $4\frac{3}{4}$ $4\frac{3}{5}$ $4\frac{5}{6}$ $3\frac{1}{2}$

19. $\frac{13}{4}$ ▶ **20.** $\frac{41}{15}$ ▶ **21.** $\frac{109}{27}$ ▶ **22.** $\frac{319}{23}$ **23.** $\frac{428}{15}$ ▶ **24.** $\frac{769}{27}$

$3\frac{1}{4}$ $2\frac{11}{15}$ $4\frac{1}{27}$ $13\frac{20}{23}$ $28\frac{8}{15}$ $28\frac{13}{27}$

▶ Selected exercises available online at www.webassign.net/brookscole

Getting Ready for the Next Section

Change to improper fractions.

25. $2\frac{3}{4}$

$\frac{11}{4}$

26. $3\frac{1}{5}$

$\frac{16}{5}$

27. $4\frac{5}{8}$

$\frac{37}{8}$

28. $1\frac{3}{5}$

$\frac{8}{5}$

29. $2\frac{4}{5}$

$\frac{14}{5}$

30. $5\frac{9}{10}$

$\frac{59}{10}$

Find the following products. (Multiply.)

31. $\frac{3}{8} \cdot \frac{3}{5}$

$\frac{9}{40}$

32. $\frac{11}{4} \cdot \frac{16}{5}$

$\frac{44}{5} = 8\frac{4}{5}$

33. $\frac{2}{3}\left(\frac{9}{16}\right)$

$\frac{3}{8}$

34. $\frac{7}{10}\left(\frac{5}{21}\right)$

$\frac{1}{6}$

Find the quotients. (Divide.)

35. $\frac{4}{5} \div \frac{7}{8}$

$\frac{32}{35}$

36. $\frac{3}{4} \div \frac{1}{2}$

$\frac{3}{2} = 1\frac{1}{2}$

37. $\frac{8}{5} \div \frac{14}{5}$

$\frac{4}{7}$

38. $\frac{59}{10} \div 2$

$\frac{59}{20} = 2\frac{19}{20}$

Maintaining Your Skills

Perform the indicated operations.

39. $\frac{2}{3} \cdot \frac{3}{4} \div \frac{5}{8}$

$\frac{4}{5}$

40. $4 \cdot \frac{7}{6} \div 7$

$\frac{2}{3}$

41. $\frac{3}{4} \div \frac{1}{2} \cdot 6$

9

42. $\frac{2}{3} \div \frac{1}{6} \cdot 12$

48

43. $12 \div \frac{6}{7} \cdot 7$

98

44. $15 \div \frac{5}{8} \cdot 16$

384

Objectives

A Multiply mixed numbers.

B Divide mixed numbers.

Introduction . . .

The figure here shows one of the nutrition labels we worked with in Chapter 1. It is from a can of Italian tomatoes. Notice toward the top of the label, the number of servings in the can is $3\frac{1}{2}$. The number $3\frac{1}{2}$ is called a *mixed number*. If we want to know how many calories are in the whole can of tomatoes, we must be able to multiply $3\frac{1}{2}$ by 25 (the number of calories per serving). Multiplication with mixed numbers is one of the topics we will cover in this section.

The procedures for multiplying and dividing mixed numbers are the same as those we used in Sections 2.3 and 2.4 to multiply and divide fractions. The only additional work involved is in changing the mixed numbers to improper fractions before we actually multiply or divide.

CANNED ITALIAN TOMATOES

Nutrition Facts

Serving Size 1/2 cup (121g)
Servings Per Container: about 3 1/2

Amount Per Serving

Calories 25	Calories from fat 0

	% Daily Value*
Total Fat 0g	0%
Saturated Fat 0g	0%
Cholesterol 0mg	0%
Sodium 300mg	12%
Potassium 145mg	4%
Total Carbohydrate 4g	2%
Dietary Fiber 1g	4%
Sugars 4g	
Protein 1g	

Vitamin A 20%	●	Vitamin C 15%
Calcium 4%	●	Iron 15%

*Percent Daily Values are based on a 2,000 calorie diet. Your daily values may be higher or lower depending on your calorie needs.

A Multiplying Mixed Numbers

EXAMPLE 1 Multiply: $2\frac{3}{4} \cdot 3\frac{1}{5}$

SOLUTION We begin by changing each mixed number to an improper fraction:

$$2\frac{3}{4} = \frac{11}{4} \quad \text{and} \quad 3\frac{1}{5} = \frac{16}{5}$$

Using the resulting improper fractions, we multiply as usual. (That is, we multiply numerators and multiply denominators.)

$$\frac{11}{4} \cdot \frac{16}{5} = \frac{11 \cdot 16}{4 \cdot 5}$$

$$= \frac{11 \cdot 4 \cdot 4}{4 \cdot 5}$$

$$= \frac{44}{5} \quad \text{or} \quad 8\frac{4}{5}$$

EXAMPLE 2 Multiply: $3 \cdot 4\frac{5}{8}$

SOLUTION Writing each number as an improper fraction, we have

$$3 = \frac{3}{1} \quad \text{and} \quad 4\frac{5}{8} = \frac{37}{8}$$

The complete problem looks like this:

$$3 \cdot 4\frac{5}{8} = \frac{3}{1} \cdot \frac{37}{8} \qquad \text{Change to improper fractions}$$

$$= \frac{111}{8} \qquad \text{Multiply numerators and multiply denominators}$$

$$= 13\frac{7}{8} \qquad \text{Write the answer as a mixed number}$$

PRACTICE PROBLEMS

1. Multiply: $2\frac{3}{4} \cdot 4\frac{1}{3}$

Instructor Note
Example 2 is a simple example, but you may find your students try to multiply the whole numbers and not the fractions. This is a good place to remind them that mixed-number notation is shorthand for the sum of a whole number and a fraction.

2. Multiply: $2 \cdot 3\frac{5}{8}$

Note As you can see, once you have changed each mixed number to an improper fraction, you multiply the resulting fractions the same way you did in Section 2.3.

Answers

1. $11\frac{11}{12}$ **2.** $7\frac{1}{4}$

3. Divide: $1\frac{3}{5} \div 3\frac{2}{5}$

B Dividing Mixed Numbers

Dividing mixed numbers also requires that we change all mixed numbers to improper fractions before we actually do the division.

EXAMPLE 3 Divide: $1\frac{3}{5} \div 2\frac{4}{5}$

SOLUTION We begin by rewriting each mixed number as an improper fraction:

$$1\frac{3}{5} = \frac{8}{5} \quad \text{and} \quad 2\frac{4}{5} = \frac{14}{5}$$

We then divide using the same method we used in Section 2.4. Remember? We multiply by the reciprocal of the divisor. Here is the complete problem:

$$1\frac{3}{5} \div 2\frac{4}{5} = \frac{8}{5} \div \frac{14}{5} \qquad \text{Change to improper fractions}$$

$$= \frac{8}{5} \cdot \frac{5}{14} \qquad \text{To divide by } \frac{14}{5}, \text{ multiply by } \frac{5}{14}$$

$$= \frac{8 \cdot 5}{5 \cdot 14} \qquad \text{Multiply numerators and multiply denominators}$$

$$= \frac{4 \cdot 2 \cdot 5}{5 \cdot 2 \cdot 7} \qquad \text{Divide out factors common to the numerator and denominator}$$

$$= \frac{4}{7} \qquad \text{Answer in lowest terms}$$

4. Divide: $4\frac{5}{8} \div 2$

EXAMPLE 4 Divide: $5\frac{9}{10} \div 2$

SOLUTION We change to improper fractions and proceed as usual:

$$5\frac{9}{10} \div 2 = \frac{59}{10} \div \frac{2}{1} \qquad \text{Write each number as an improper fraction}$$

$$= \frac{59}{10} \cdot \frac{1}{2} \qquad \text{Write division as multiplication by the reciprocal}$$

$$= \frac{59}{20} \qquad \text{Multiply numerators and multiply denominators}$$

$$= 2\frac{19}{20} \qquad \text{Change to a mixed number}$$

Getting Ready for Class

After reading through the preceding section, respond in your own words and in complete sentences.

1. What is the first step when multiplying or dividing mixed numbers?

2. What is the reciprocal of $2\frac{4}{5}$?

3. Dividing $5\frac{9}{10}$ by 2 is equivalent to multiplying $5\frac{9}{10}$ by what number?

4. Find $4\frac{5}{8}$ of 3.

Answers

3. $\frac{8}{17}$ **4.** $2\frac{5}{16}$

Problem Set 2.7

A Write your answers as proper fractions or mixed numbers, not as improper fractions. Find the following products. (Multiply.) [Examples 1, 2]

▶ **1.** $3\frac{2}{5} \cdot 1\frac{1}{2}$

$5\frac{1}{10}$

2. $2\frac{1}{3} \cdot 6\frac{3}{4}$

$15\frac{3}{4}$

▶ **3.** $5\frac{1}{8} \cdot 2\frac{2}{3}$

$13\frac{2}{3}$

4. $1\frac{5}{6} \cdot 1\frac{4}{5}$

$3\frac{3}{10}$

5. $2\frac{1}{10} \cdot 3\frac{3}{10}$

$6\frac{93}{100}$

6. $4\frac{7}{10} \cdot 3\frac{1}{10}$

$14\frac{57}{100}$

7. $1\frac{1}{4} \cdot 4\frac{2}{3}$

$5\frac{5}{6}$

8. $3\frac{1}{2} \cdot 2\frac{1}{6}$

$7\frac{7}{12}$

9. $2 \cdot 4\frac{7}{8}$

$9\frac{3}{4}$

▶ **10.** $10 \cdot 1\frac{1}{4}$

$12\frac{1}{2}$

11. $\frac{3}{5} \cdot 5\frac{1}{3}$

$3\frac{1}{5}$

12. $\frac{2}{3} \cdot 4\frac{9}{10}$

$3\frac{4}{15}$

▶ **13.** $2\frac{1}{2} \cdot 3\frac{1}{3} \cdot 1\frac{1}{2}$

$12\frac{1}{2}$

14. $3\frac{1}{5} \cdot 5\frac{1}{6} \cdot 1\frac{1}{8}$

$18\frac{3}{5}$

▶ **15.** $\frac{3}{4} \cdot 7 \cdot 1\frac{4}{5}$

$9\frac{9}{20}$

16. $\frac{7}{8} \cdot 6 \cdot 1\frac{5}{6}$

$9\frac{5}{8}$

B Find the following quotients. (Divide.) [Examples 3, 4]

17. $3\frac{1}{5} \div 4\frac{1}{2}$

$\frac{32}{45}$

▶ **18.** $1\frac{4}{5} \div 2\frac{5}{6}$

$\frac{54}{85}$

19. $6\frac{1}{4} \div 3\frac{3}{4}$

$1\frac{2}{3}$

20. $8\frac{2}{3} \div 4\frac{1}{3}$

2

▶ **21.** $10 \div 2\frac{1}{2}$

4

22. $12 \div 3\frac{1}{6}$

$3\frac{15}{19}$

▶ **23.** $8\frac{3}{5} \div 2$

$4\frac{3}{10}$

24. $12\frac{6}{7} \div 3$

$4\frac{2}{7}$

25. $\left(\frac{3}{4} \div 2\frac{1}{2}\right) \div 3$

$\frac{1}{10}$

26. $\frac{7}{8} \div \left(1\frac{1}{4} \div 4\right)$

$2\frac{4}{5}$

▶ **27.** $\left(8 \div 1\frac{1}{4}\right) \div 2$

$3\frac{1}{5}$

28. $8 \div \left(1\frac{1}{4} \div 2\right)$

$12\frac{4}{5}$

▶ **29.** $2\frac{1}{2} \cdot \left(3\frac{2}{5} \div 4\right)$

$2\frac{1}{8}$

30. $4\frac{3}{5} \cdot \left(2\frac{1}{4} \div 5\right)$

$2\frac{7}{100}$

▶ **31.** Find the product of $2\frac{1}{2}$ and 3.

$7\frac{1}{2}$

32. Find the product of $\frac{1}{5}$ and $3\frac{2}{3}$.

$\frac{11}{15}$

▶ **33.** What is the quotient of $2\frac{3}{4}$ and $3\frac{1}{4}$?

$\frac{11}{13}$

34. What is the quotient of $1\frac{1}{5}$ and $2\frac{2}{5}$?

$\frac{1}{2}$

▶ Selected exercises available online at www.webassign.net/brookscole

■ Applying the Concepts

▶ **35. Cooking** A certain recipe calls for $2\frac{3}{4}$ cups of sugar. If the recipe is to be doubled, how much sugar should be used?

$5\frac{1}{2}$ cups

▶ **36. Cooking** A recipe calls for $3\frac{1}{4}$ cups of flour. If Diane is using only half the recipe, how much flour should she use?

$1\frac{5}{8}$ cups   Problem 36 can be used to reinforce the idea that division by a number is equivalent to multiplication by its reciprocal.

▶ **37. Number Problem** Find $\frac{3}{4}$ of $1\frac{7}{9}$. (Remember that *of* means multiply.)

$1\frac{1}{3}$

38. Number Problem Find $\frac{5}{6}$ of $2\frac{4}{15}$.

$1\frac{8}{9}$

39. Cost of Gasoline If a gallon of gas costs $335\frac{9}{10}$¢, how much do 8 gallons cost?

$2{,}687\frac{1}{5}$ cents

40. Cost of Gasoline If a gallon of gas costs $353\frac{9}{10}$¢, how much does $\frac{1}{2}$ gallon cost?

$176\frac{19}{20}$¢

41. Distance Traveled If a car can travel $32\frac{3}{4}$ miles on a gallon of gas, how far will it travel on 5 gallons of gas?

$163\frac{3}{4}$ mi

▶ **42. Sewing** If it takes $1\frac{1}{2}$ yards of material to make a pillow cover, how much material will it take to make 3 pillow covers?

$4\frac{1}{2}$ yd

43. Buying Stocks Assume that you have $1000 to invest in the stock market. Because you own an iPod™ and an iPhone™, you decide to buy Apple stock. It is currently selling at a cost of $150\frac{7}{8}$ per share. At this price how many shares can you buy?

$6\frac{758}{1{,}207}$ shares

44. Subdividing Land A local developer owns $145\frac{3}{4}$ acres of land that he hopes to subdivide into $2\frac{1}{2}$ acre home site lots to sell. How many home sites can be developed from this tract of land?

$58\frac{3}{10}$ sites

▶ **45. Selling Stocks** You inherit 100 shares of Cisco stock that has a current value of $25\frac{1}{6}$ per share. How much will you receive when you sell the stock?

$\$2{,}516\frac{2}{3}$

46. Gas Mileage You won a new car and are anxious to see what kind of gas mileage you get. You travel $427\frac{1}{5}$ miles before needing to fill your tank. You purchase $13\frac{3}{4}$ gallons of gas. How many miles were you able to travel on a single gallon of gas?

$31\frac{19}{275}$ miles

47. Area Find the area of a bedroom that measures $11\frac{1}{2}$ ft by $15\frac{7}{8}$ ft.

$182\frac{9}{16}$ ft²

48. Building Shelves You are building a small bookcase. You need three shelves, each with a length of $4\frac{7}{8}$ ft. You bought a piece of wood that is 15 ft long. Will this board be long enough?

yes

49. The Google Earth image shows some fields in the mid-western part of the United States. The rectangle outlines a corn field, and gives the dimensions in miles. Find the area of the corn field written as a mixed number.

$3\frac{7}{16}$ miles²

50. Dollar Bill The size of the dollar now is $\frac{2}{3}$ of its original size. If the size now is $\frac{307}{50}$ inches long, how long was the dollar?

$\frac{921}{100}$

Nutrition The figure below shows nutrition labels for two different cans of Italian tomatoes.

CANNED TOMATOES 1

Nutrition Facts

Serving Size 1/2 cup (121g)
Servings Per Container: about 3 1/2

Amount Per Serving	
Calories 45	Calories from fat 0

	% Daily Value*
Total Fat 0g	0%
Saturated Fat 0g	0%
Cholesterol 0mg	0%
Sodium 560mg	23%
Total Carbohydrate 11g	4%
Dietary Fiber 2g	8%
Sugars 9g	
Protein 1g	

Vitamin A 10%	●	Vitamin C 25%
Calcium 2%	●	Iron 2%

*Percent Daily Values are based on a 2,000 calorie diet.

CANNED TOMATOES 2

Nutrition Facts

Serving Size 1/2 cup (121g)
Servings Per Container: about 3 1/2

Amount Per Serving	
Calories 25	Calories from fat 0

	% Daily Value*
Total Fat 0g	0%
Saturated Fat 0g	0%
Cholesterol 0mg	0%
Sodium 300mg	12%
Potassium 145mg	4%
Total Carbohydrate 4g	2%
Dietary Fiber 1g	4%
Sugars 4g	
Protein 1g	

Vitamin A 20%	●	Vitamin C 15%
Calcium 4%	●	Iron 15%

*Percent Daily Values are based on a 2,000 calorie diet. Your daily values may be higher or lower depending on your calorie needs.

51. Compare the total number of calories in the two cans of tomatoes.

Can 1 contains $157\frac{1}{2}$ calories, whereas Can 2 contains $87\frac{1}{2}$ calories. Can 1 contains 70 more calories than Can 2.

52. Compare the total amount of sugar in the two cans of tomatoes.

Can 1 contains $31\frac{1}{2}$ grams of sugar, whereas Can 2 contains 14 grams of sugar. Can 1 contains $17\frac{1}{2}$ more grams of sugar than Can 2.

53. Compare the total amount of sodium in the two cans of tomatoes.

Can 1 contains 1,960 milligrams of sodium, whereas Can 2 contains 1,050 milligrams of sodium. Can 1 contains 910 more milligrams of sodium than Can 2.

54. Compare the total amount of protein in the two cans of tomatoes.

Both cans contain $3\frac{1}{2}$ grams of protein.

■ Getting Ready for the Next Section

55. Write as equivalent fractions with denominator 15.

   a. $\dfrac{2}{3}$ $\dfrac{10}{15}$ **b.** $\dfrac{1}{5}$ $\dfrac{3}{15}$ **c.** $\dfrac{3}{5}$ $\dfrac{9}{15}$ **d.** $\dfrac{1}{3}$ $\dfrac{5}{15}$

56. Write as equivalent fractions with denominator 12.

   a. $\dfrac{3}{4}$ $\dfrac{9}{12}$ **b.** $\dfrac{1}{3}$ $\dfrac{4}{12}$ **c.** $\dfrac{5}{6}$ $\dfrac{10}{12}$ **d.** $\dfrac{1}{4}$ $\dfrac{3}{12}$

57. Write as equivalent fractions with denominator 20.

   a. $\dfrac{1}{4}$ $\dfrac{5}{20}$ **b.** $\dfrac{3}{5}$ $\dfrac{12}{20}$ **c.** $\dfrac{9}{10}$ $\dfrac{18}{20}$ **d.** $\dfrac{1}{10}$ $\dfrac{2}{20}$

58. Write as equivalent fractions with denominator 24.

   a. $\dfrac{3}{4}$ $\dfrac{18}{24}$ **b.** $\dfrac{7}{8}$ $\dfrac{21}{24}$ **c.** $\dfrac{5}{8}$ $\dfrac{15}{24}$ **d.** $\dfrac{3}{8}$ $\dfrac{9}{24}$

■ Maintaining Your Skills

Add or subtract the following fractions, as indicated.

59. $\dfrac{2}{3} + \dfrac{1}{5}$

$\dfrac{13}{15}$

60. $\dfrac{3}{4} + \dfrac{5}{6}$

$\dfrac{19}{12} = 1\dfrac{7}{12}$

61. $\dfrac{2}{3} + \dfrac{8}{9}$

$\dfrac{14}{9} = 1\dfrac{5}{9}$

▶ **62.** $\dfrac{1}{4} + \dfrac{3}{5} + \dfrac{9}{10}$

$\dfrac{7}{4} = 1\dfrac{3}{4}$

63. $\dfrac{9}{10} - \dfrac{3}{10}$

$\dfrac{3}{5}$

64. $\dfrac{7}{10} - \dfrac{3}{5}$

$\dfrac{1}{10}$

65. $\dfrac{1}{14} + \dfrac{3}{21}$

$\dfrac{3}{14}$

66. $\dfrac{5}{12} - \dfrac{1}{3}$

$\dfrac{1}{12}$

■ Extending the Concepts

To find the square of a mixed number, we first change the mixed number to an improper fraction, and then we square the result. For example:

$$\left(2\dfrac{1}{2}\right)^2 = \left(\dfrac{5}{2}\right)^2 = \dfrac{25}{4}$$

If we are asked to write our answer as a mixed number, we write it as $6\dfrac{1}{4}$.

Find each of the following squares, and write your answers as mixed numbers.

▶ **67.** $\left(1\dfrac{1}{2}\right)^2$

$2\dfrac{1}{4}$

68. $\left(3\dfrac{1}{2}\right)^2$

$12\dfrac{1}{4}$

69. $\left(1\dfrac{3}{4}\right)^2$

$3\dfrac{1}{16}$

70. $\left(2\dfrac{3}{4}\right)^2$

$7\dfrac{9}{16}$

Introduction . . .

In March 1995, rumors that Michael Jordan would return to basketball sent stock prices for the companies whose products he endorsed higher. The price of one share of General Mills, the maker of Wheaties, which Michael Jordan endorses, went from $60\frac{1}{2}$ to $63\frac{3}{8}$. To find the increase in the price of this stock, we must be able to subtract mixed numbers.

The notation we use for mixed numbers is especially useful for addition and subtraction. When adding and subtracting mixed numbers, we will assume you recall how to go about finding a least common denominator (LCD). (If you don't remember, then review Section 2.5.)

A Combining Mixed Numbers

PRACTICE PROBLEMS

1. Add: $3\frac{2}{3} + 2\frac{1}{4}$

EXAMPLE 1 Add: $3\frac{2}{3} + 4\frac{1}{5}$

SOLUTION **Method 1:** We begin by writing each mixed number showing the + sign. We then apply the commutative and associative properties to rearrange the order and grouping:

$$3\frac{2}{3} + 4\frac{1}{5} = 3 + \frac{2}{3} + 4 + \frac{1}{5} \quad \text{Expand each number to show the + sign}$$

$$= 3 + 4 + \frac{2}{3} + \frac{1}{5} \quad \text{Commutative property}$$

$$= (3 + 4) + \left(\frac{2}{3} + \frac{1}{5}\right) \quad \text{Associative property}$$

$$= 7 + \left(\frac{\mathbf{5} \cdot 2}{\mathbf{5} \cdot 3} + \frac{\mathbf{3} \cdot 1}{\mathbf{3} \cdot 5}\right) \quad \text{Add } 3 + 4 = 7; \text{ then multiply to get the LCD}$$

$$= 7 + \left(\frac{10}{15} + \frac{3}{15}\right) \quad \text{Write each fraction with the LCD}$$

$$= 7 + \frac{13}{15} \quad \text{Add the numerators}$$

$$= 7\frac{13}{15} \quad \text{Write the answer in mixed-number notation}$$

Method 2: As you can see, we obtain our result by adding the whole-number parts $(3 + 4 = 7)$ and the fraction parts $\left(\frac{2}{3} + \frac{1}{5} = \frac{13}{15}\right)$ of each mixed number. Knowing this, we can save ourselves some writing by doing the same problem in columns:

$$3\frac{2}{3} = 3\frac{2 \cdot \mathbf{5}}{3 \cdot \mathbf{5}} = 3\frac{10}{15} \quad \text{Add whole numbers}$$

$$+ 4\frac{1}{5} = 4\frac{1 \cdot \mathbf{3}}{5 \cdot \mathbf{3}} = 4\frac{3}{15} \quad \text{Then add fractions}$$

$$\overline{\qquad\qquad 7\frac{13}{15}}$$

Write each fraction with LCD 15

Note You should try both methods given in Example 1 on Practice Problem 1.

The second method shown above requires less writing and lends itself to mixed-number notation. We will use this method for the rest of this section.

Answer

1. $5\frac{11}{12}$

2. Add: $5\dfrac{3}{4} + 6\dfrac{4}{5}$

3. Add: $6\dfrac{3}{4} + 2\dfrac{7}{8}$

4. Add: $2\dfrac{1}{3} + 1\dfrac{1}{4} + 3\dfrac{11}{12}$

Answers

2. $12\dfrac{11}{20}$ **3.** $9\dfrac{5}{8}$ **4.** $7\dfrac{1}{2}$

EXAMPLE 2 Add: $5\dfrac{3}{4} + 9\dfrac{5}{6}$

SOLUTION The LCD for 4 and 6 is 12. Writing the mixed numbers in a column and then adding looks like this:

$$5\dfrac{3}{4} = 5\dfrac{3 \cdot 3}{4 \cdot 3} = 5\dfrac{9}{12}$$
$$+ 9\dfrac{5}{6} = 9\dfrac{5 \cdot 2}{6 \cdot 2} = 9\dfrac{10}{12}$$
$$\overline{\phantom{+ 9\dfrac{5}{6} = 9\dfrac{5 \cdot 2}{6 \cdot 2} = } 14\dfrac{19}{12}}$$

The fraction part of the answer is an improper fraction. We rewrite it as a whole number and a proper fraction:

$$14\dfrac{19}{12} = 14 + \dfrac{19}{12} \qquad \text{Write the mixed number with a + sign}$$
$$= 14 + 1\dfrac{7}{12} \qquad \text{Write } \dfrac{19}{12} \text{ as a mixed number}$$
$$= 15\dfrac{7}{12} \qquad \text{Add 14 and 1}$$

EXAMPLE 3 Add: $5\dfrac{2}{3} + 6\dfrac{8}{9}$

SOLUTION
$$5\dfrac{2}{3} = 5\dfrac{2 \cdot 3}{3 \cdot 3} = 5\dfrac{6}{9}$$
$$+ 6\dfrac{8}{9} = 6\dfrac{8}{9} = 6\dfrac{8}{9}$$
$$\overline{\phantom{+ 6\dfrac{8}{9} = 6\dfrac{8}{9} = } 11\dfrac{14}{9} = 12\dfrac{5}{9}}$$

The last step involves writing $\dfrac{14}{9}$ as $1\dfrac{5}{9}$ and then adding 11 and 1 to get 12.

EXAMPLE 4 Add: $3\dfrac{1}{4} + 2\dfrac{3}{5} + 1\dfrac{9}{10}$

SOLUTION The LCD is 20. We rewrite each fraction as an equivalent fraction with denominator 20 and add:

$$3\dfrac{1}{4} = 3\dfrac{1 \cdot 5}{4 \cdot 5} = 3\dfrac{5}{20}$$
$$2\dfrac{3}{5} = 2\dfrac{3 \cdot 4}{5 \cdot 4} = 2\dfrac{12}{20}$$
$$+ 1\dfrac{9}{10} = 1\dfrac{9 \cdot 2}{10 \cdot 2} = 1\dfrac{18}{20}$$
$$\overline{\phantom{+ 1\dfrac{9}{10} = 1\dfrac{9 \cdot 2}{10 \cdot 2} = } 6\dfrac{35}{20} = 7\dfrac{15}{20} = 7\dfrac{3}{4}} \qquad \text{Reduce to lowest terms}$$
$$\dfrac{35}{20} = 1\dfrac{15}{20}$$

Change to a mixed number

We should note here that we could have worked each of the first four examples in this section by first changing each mixed number to an improper fraction and then adding as we did in Section 2.5. To illustrate, if we were to work Example 4 this way, it would look like this:

$$3\frac{1}{4} + 2\frac{3}{5} + 1\frac{9}{10} = \frac{13}{4} + \frac{13}{5} + \frac{19}{10}$$ Change to improper fractions

$$= \frac{13 \cdot 5}{4 \cdot 5} + \frac{13 \cdot 4}{5 \cdot 4} + \frac{19 \cdot 2}{10 \cdot 2}$$ LCD is 20

$$= \frac{65}{20} + \frac{52}{20} + \frac{38}{20}$$ Equivalent fractions

$$= \frac{155}{20}$$ Add numerators

$$= 7\frac{15}{20} = 7\frac{3}{4}$$ Change to a mixed number, and reduce

As you can see, the result is the same as the result we obtained in Example 4.

There are advantages to both methods. The method just shown works well when the whole-number parts of the mixed numbers are small. The vertical method shown in Examples 1–4 works well when the whole-number parts of the mixed numbers are large.

Subtraction with mixed numbers is very similar to addition with mixed numbers.

EXAMPLE 5 Subtract: $3\frac{9}{10} - 1\frac{3}{10}$

SOLUTION Because the denominators are the same, we simply subtract the whole numbers and subtract the fractions:

$$3\frac{9}{10}$$
$$- 1\frac{3}{10}$$
$$\overline{\quad 2\frac{6}{10} = 2\frac{3}{5}}$$

Reduce to lowest terms

An easy way to visualize the results in Example 5 is to imagine 3 dollar bills and 9 dimes in your pocket. If you spend 1 dollar and 3 dimes, you will have 2 dollars and 6 dimes left.

EXAMPLE 6 Subtract: $12\frac{7}{10} - 8\frac{3}{5}$

SOLUTION The common denominator is 10. We must rewrite $\frac{3}{5}$ as an equivalent fraction with denominator 10:

$$12\frac{7}{10} = 12\frac{7}{10} = 12\frac{7}{10}$$
$$-8\frac{3}{5} = -8\frac{3 \cdot 2}{5 \cdot 2} = -8\frac{6}{10}$$
$$\overline{\qquad\qquad\qquad\qquad 4\frac{1}{10}}$$

5. Subtract: $4\frac{7}{8} - 1\frac{5}{8}$

6. Subtract: $12\frac{7}{10} - 7\frac{2}{5}$

Answers

5. $3\frac{1}{4}$ **6.** $5\frac{3}{10}$

7. Subtract: $10 - 5\frac{4}{7}$

> **Note** Convince yourself that 10 is the same as $9\frac{7}{7}$. The reason we choose to write the 1 we borrowed as $\frac{7}{7}$ is that the fraction we eventually subtracted from $\frac{7}{7}$ was $\frac{2}{7}$. Both fractions must have the same denominator, 7, so that we can subtract.

8. Subtract: $6\frac{1}{3} - 2\frac{2}{3}$

9. Subtract: $6\frac{3}{4} - 2\frac{5}{6}$

B   Borrowing with Mixed Numbers

EXAMPLE 7   Subtract: $10 - 5\frac{2}{7}$

SOLUTION   In order to have a fraction from which to subtract $\frac{2}{7}$, we borrow 1 from 10 and rewrite the 1 we borrow as $\frac{7}{7}$. The process looks like this:

$$10 = \quad 9\frac{7}{7} \quad \longleftarrow \text{We rewrite 10 as } 9 + 1, \text{ which is } 9 + \frac{7}{7} = 9\frac{7}{7}$$
$$-\ 5\frac{2}{7} = -\ 5\frac{2}{7} \quad \text{Then we can subtract as usual}$$
$$\overline{\qquad\qquad 4\frac{5}{7}}$$

EXAMPLE 8   Subtract: $8\frac{1}{4} - 3\frac{3}{4}$

SOLUTION   Because $\frac{3}{4}$ is larger than $\frac{1}{4}$, we again need to borrow 1 from the whole number. The 1 that we borrow from the 8 is rewritten as $\frac{4}{4}$, because 4 is the denominator of both fractions:

$$8\frac{1}{4} = \quad 7\frac{5}{4} \quad \longleftarrow \quad \text{Borrow 1 in the form } \frac{4}{4};$$
$$-\ 3\frac{3}{4} = -\ 3\frac{3}{4} \qquad\qquad \text{then } \frac{4}{4} + \frac{1}{4} = \frac{5}{4}$$
$$\overline{\qquad\qquad 4\frac{2}{4} = 4\frac{1}{2}} \quad \text{Reduce to lowest terms}$$

EXAMPLE 9   Subtract: $4\frac{3}{4} - 1\frac{5}{6}$

SOLUTION   This is about as complicated as it gets with subtraction of mixed numbers. We begin by rewriting each fraction with the common denominator 12:

$$4\frac{3}{4} = \quad 4\frac{3 \cdot 3}{4 \cdot 3} = \quad 4\frac{9}{12}$$
$$-\ 1\frac{5}{6} = -\ 1\frac{5 \cdot 2}{6 \cdot 2} = -\ 1\frac{10}{12}$$

Because $\frac{10}{12}$ is larger than $\frac{9}{12}$, we must borrow 1 from 4 in the form $\frac{12}{12}$ before we subtract:

$$4\frac{9}{12} = \quad 3\frac{21}{12} \quad \longleftarrow 4 = 3 + 1 = 3 + \frac{12}{12}, \text{ so } 4\frac{9}{12} = \left(3 + \frac{12}{12}\right) + \frac{9}{12}$$
$$-\ 1\frac{10}{12} = -\ 1\frac{10}{12} \qquad\qquad\qquad\qquad = 3 + \left(\frac{12}{12} + \frac{9}{12}\right)$$
$$\overline{\qquad\qquad 2\frac{11}{12}} \qquad\qquad\qquad\qquad\qquad = 3 + \frac{21}{12}$$
$$\qquad\qquad\qquad\qquad\qquad\qquad\qquad\qquad = 3\frac{21}{12}$$

Getting Ready for Class

After reading through the preceding section, respond in your own words and in complete sentences.

1. Is it necessary to "borrow" when subtracting $1\frac{3}{10}$ from $3\frac{9}{10}$?
2. To subtract $1\frac{2}{7}$ from 10, it is necessary to rewrite 10 as what mixed number?
3. To subtract $11\frac{20}{30}$ from $15\frac{3}{30}$ it is necessary to rewrite $15\frac{3}{30}$ as what mixed number?
4. Rewrite $14\frac{19}{12}$ so that the fraction part is a proper fraction instead of an improper fraction.

Answers

7. $4\frac{3}{7}$ **8.** $3\frac{2}{3}$ **9.** $3\frac{11}{12}$

Problem Set 2.8

A Add and subtract the following mixed numbers as indicated. [Examples 1–6]

▶ **1.** $2\frac{1}{5} + 3\frac{3}{5}$

$5\frac{4}{5}$

2. $8\frac{2}{9} + 1\frac{5}{9}$

$9\frac{7}{9}$

3. $4\frac{3}{10} + 8\frac{1}{10}$

$12\frac{2}{5}$

4. $5\frac{2}{7} + 3\frac{3}{7}$

$8\frac{5}{7}$

5. $6\frac{8}{9} - 3\frac{4}{9}$

$3\frac{4}{9}$

6. $12\frac{5}{12} - 7\frac{1}{12}$

$5\frac{1}{3}$

▶ **7.** $9\frac{1}{6} + 2\frac{5}{6}$

12

8. $9\frac{1}{4} + 5\frac{3}{4}$

15

▶ **9.** $3\frac{5}{8} - 2\frac{1}{4}$

$1\frac{3}{8}$

10. $7\frac{9}{10} - 6\frac{3}{5}$

$1\frac{3}{10}$

11. $11\frac{1}{3} + 2\frac{5}{6}$

$14\frac{1}{6}$

12. $1\frac{5}{8} + 2\frac{1}{2}$

$4\frac{1}{8}$

13. $7\frac{5}{12} - 3\frac{1}{3}$

$4\frac{1}{12}$

14. $7\frac{3}{4} - 3\frac{5}{12}$

$4\frac{1}{3}$

15. $6\frac{1}{3} - 4\frac{1}{4}$

$2\frac{1}{12}$

▶ **16.** $5\frac{4}{5} - 3\frac{1}{3}$

$2\frac{7}{15}$

17. $10\frac{5}{6} + 15\frac{3}{4}$

$26\frac{7}{12}$

18. $11\frac{7}{8} + 9\frac{1}{6}$

$21\frac{1}{24}$

19. $5\frac{2}{3} + 6\frac{1}{3}$

12

20. $8\frac{5}{6} + 9\frac{5}{6}$

$18\frac{2}{3}$

▶ **21.** $\begin{array}{r} 10\frac{13}{16} \\ -\ 8\frac{5}{16} \\ \hline 2\frac{1}{2} \end{array}$

22. $\begin{array}{r} 17\frac{7}{12} \\ -\ 9\frac{5}{12} \\ \hline 8\frac{1}{6} \end{array}$

23. $\begin{array}{r} 6\frac{1}{2} \\ +\ 2\frac{5}{14} \\ \hline 8\frac{6}{7} \end{array}$

24. $\begin{array}{r} 9\frac{11}{12} \\ +\ 4\frac{1}{6} \\ \hline 14\frac{1}{12} \end{array}$

25. $\begin{array}{r} 1\frac{5}{8} \\ +\ 1\frac{3}{4} \\ \hline 3\frac{3}{8} \end{array}$

▶ **26.** $\begin{array}{r} 7\frac{6}{7} \\ +\ 2\frac{3}{14} \\ \hline 10\frac{1}{14} \end{array}$

27. $\begin{array}{r} 4\frac{2}{3} \\ +\ 5\frac{3}{5} \\ \hline 10\frac{4}{15} \end{array}$

28. $\begin{array}{r} 9\frac{4}{9} \\ +\ 1\frac{1}{6} \\ \hline 10\frac{11}{18} \end{array}$

29. $\begin{array}{r} 5\frac{4}{10} \\ -\ 3\frac{1}{3} \\ \hline 2\frac{1}{15} \end{array}$

▶ **30.** $\begin{array}{r} 12\frac{7}{8} \\ -\ 3\frac{5}{6} \\ \hline 9\frac{1}{24} \end{array}$

31. $\begin{array}{r} 10\frac{1}{20} \\ +\ 11\frac{4}{5} \\ \hline 21\frac{17}{20} \end{array}$

32. $\begin{array}{r} 18\frac{7}{8} \\ +\ 19\frac{1}{12} \\ \hline 37\frac{23}{24} \end{array}$

▶ Selected exercises available online at www.webassign.net/brookscole

A Find the following sums. (Add.) [Examples 1–4]

▶ **33.** $1\frac{1}{4} + 2\frac{3}{4} + 5$

9

34. $6 + 5\frac{3}{5} + 8\frac{2}{5}$

20

35. $7\frac{1}{10} + 8\frac{3}{10} + 2\frac{7}{10}$

$18\frac{1}{10}$

36. $5\frac{2}{7} + 8\frac{1}{7} + 3\frac{5}{7}$

$17\frac{1}{7}$

37. $\frac{3}{4} + 8\frac{1}{4} + 5$

14

38. $\frac{5}{8} + 1\frac{1}{8} + 7$

$8\frac{3}{4}$

▶ **39.** $3\frac{1}{2} + 8\frac{1}{3} + 5\frac{1}{6}$

17

40. $4\frac{1}{5} + 7\frac{1}{3} + 8\frac{1}{15}$

$19\frac{3}{5}$

▶ **41.** $8\frac{2}{3}$
$9\frac{1}{8}$
$+ 6\frac{1}{4}$
——
$24\frac{1}{24}$

42. $7\frac{3}{5}$
$8\frac{2}{3}$
$+ 1\frac{1}{5}$
——
$17\frac{7}{15}$

43. $6\frac{1}{7}$
$9\frac{3}{14}$
$+ 12\frac{1}{2}$
——
$27\frac{6}{7}$

44. $1\frac{5}{6}$
$2\frac{3}{4}$
$+ 5\frac{1}{2}$
——
$10\frac{1}{12}$

B The following problems all involve the concept of borrowing. Subtract in each case. [Examples 7–9]

▶ **45.** $8 - 1\frac{3}{4}$

$6\frac{1}{4}$

46. $5 - 3\frac{1}{3}$

$1\frac{2}{3}$

47. $15 - 5\frac{3}{10}$

$9\frac{7}{10}$

48. $24 - 10\frac{5}{12}$

$13\frac{7}{12}$

▶ **49.** $8\frac{1}{4} - 2\frac{3}{4}$

$5\frac{1}{2}$

50. $12\frac{3}{10} - 5\frac{7}{10}$

$6\frac{3}{5}$

51. $9\frac{1}{3} - 8\frac{2}{3}$

$\frac{2}{3}$

52. $7\frac{1}{6} - 6\frac{5}{6}$

$\frac{1}{3}$

53. $4\frac{1}{4} - 2\frac{1}{3}$

$1\frac{11}{12}$

▶ **54.** $6\frac{1}{5} - 1\frac{2}{3}$

$4\frac{8}{15}$

55. $9\frac{2}{3} - 5\frac{3}{4}$

$3\frac{11}{12}$

56. $12\frac{5}{6} - 8\frac{7}{8}$

$3\frac{23}{24}$

57. $16\frac{3}{4} - 10\frac{4}{5}$

$5\frac{19}{20}$

58. $18\frac{5}{12} - 9\frac{3}{4}$

$8\frac{2}{3}$

59. $10\frac{3}{10} - 4\frac{4}{5}$

$5\frac{1}{2}$

60. $9\frac{4}{7} - 7\frac{2}{3}$

$1\frac{19}{21}$

61. $13\frac{1}{6} - 12\frac{5}{8}$

$\frac{13}{24}$

▶ **62.** $21\frac{2}{5} - 20\frac{5}{6}$

$\frac{17}{30}$

63. $15\frac{3}{10} - 11\frac{4}{5}$

$3\frac{1}{2}$

64. $19\frac{3}{15} - 10\frac{2}{3}$

$8\frac{8}{15}$

■ Applying the Concepts

Stock Prices As we mentioned in the introduction to this section, in March 1995, rumors that Michael Jordan would return to basketball sent stock prices for the companies whose products he endorses higher. The table at the right gives some of the details of those increases. Use the table to work Problems 65–70.

		Stock Prices for Companies with Michael Jordan Endorsements		
			Stock Price (Dollars)	
Company	**Product Endorsed**		**3/8/95**	**3/13/95**
Nike	Air Jordans		$74\frac{7}{8}$	$77\frac{3}{8}$
Quaker Oats	Gatorade		$32\frac{1}{4}$	$32\frac{5}{8}$
General Mills	Wheaties		$60\frac{1}{2}$	$63\frac{3}{8}$
McDonald's			$32\frac{7}{8}$	$34\frac{3}{8}$

65. Find the difference in the price of Nike stock between March 13 and March 8.
$2\frac{1}{2}$

66. Find the difference in price of General Mills stock between March 13 and March 8.
$2\frac{7}{8}$

67. If you owned 100 shares of Nike stock, how much more are the 100 shares worth on March 13 than on March 8?
$250

68. If you owned 1,000 shares of General Mills stock on March 8, how much more would they be worth on March 13?
$2,875

69. If you owned 200 shares of McDonald's stock on March 8, how much more would they be worth on March 13?
$300

70. If you owned 100 shares of McDonald's stock on March 8, how much more would they be worth on March 13?
$150

71. Area and Perimeter The diagrams below show the dimensions of playing fields for the National Football League (NFL), the Canadian Football League, and Arena Football.

Football Fields

NFL — 100 yd, $53\frac{1}{3}$ yd   Canadian — 110 yd, 65 yd   Arena — 50 yd, $28\frac{1}{3}$ yd

    a. Find the perimeter of each football field.

NFL: $P = 306\frac{2}{3}$ yd   Canadian: $P = 350$ yd   Arena: $P = 156\frac{2}{3}$ yd

    b. Find the area of each football field.

NFL: $A = 5,333\frac{1}{3}$ sq yd   Canadian: $A = 7,150$ sq yd
Arena: $A = 1,416\frac{2}{3}$ sq yd

72. Triple Crown The three races that constitute the Triple Crown in horse racing are shown in the table. The information comes from the ESPN website.

    a. Write the distances in order from smallest to largest.

$1\frac{3}{16}, 1\frac{1}{4}, 1\frac{1}{2}$

    b. How much longer is the Belmont Stakes race than the Preakness Stakes?

$\frac{5}{16}$ mi

Race	Distance (miles)
Kentucky Derby	$1\frac{1}{4}$
Preakness Stakes	$1\frac{3}{16}$
Belmont Stakes	$1\frac{1}{2}$

73. Length of Jeans A pair of jeans is $32\frac{1}{2}$ inches long. How long are the jeans after they have been washed if they shrink $1\frac{1}{3}$ inches?

$31\frac{1}{6}$ in.

74. Manufacturing A clothing manufacturer has two rolls of cloth. One roll is $35\frac{1}{2}$ yards, and the other is $62\frac{5}{8}$ yards. What is the total number of yards in the two rolls?

$98\frac{1}{8}$ yd

■ Getting Ready for the Next Section

Multiply or divide as indicated.

75. $\dfrac{11}{8} \cdot \dfrac{29}{8}$

$4\frac{63}{64}$

76. $\dfrac{3}{4} \div \dfrac{5}{6}$

$\frac{9}{10}$

77. $\dfrac{7}{6} \cdot \dfrac{12}{7}$

2

78. $10\dfrac{1}{3} \div 8\dfrac{2}{3}$

$1\frac{5}{26}$

Combine.

79. $\dfrac{3}{4} + \dfrac{5}{8}$

$\frac{11}{8} = 1\frac{3}{8}$

80. $\dfrac{1}{2} + \dfrac{2}{3}$

$\frac{7}{6} = 1\frac{1}{6}$

81. $2\dfrac{3}{8} + 1\dfrac{1}{4}$

$3\frac{5}{8}$

82. $3\dfrac{2}{3} + 4\dfrac{1}{3}$

8

■ Maintaining Your Skills

Use the rule for order of operations to combine the following.

83. $3 + 2 \cdot 7$

17

84. $8 \cdot 3 - 2$

22

85. $4 \cdot 5 - 3 \cdot 2$

14

86. $9 \cdot 7 + 6 \cdot 5$

93

87. $3 \cdot 2^3 + 5 \cdot 4^2$

104

88. $6 \cdot 5^2 + 2 \cdot 3^3$

204

89. $3[2 + 5(6)]$

96

90. $4[2(3) + 3(5)]$

84

91. $(7 - 3)(8 + 2)$

40

92. $(9 - 5)(9 + 5)$

56

■ Extending the Concepts

▶ **93.** Find the difference between $6\dfrac{1}{5}$ and $2\dfrac{7}{10}$.

$3\frac{1}{2}$

94. Give the difference between $5\dfrac{1}{3}$ and $1\dfrac{5}{6}$.

$3\frac{1}{2}$

95. Find the sum of $3\dfrac{1}{8}$ and $2\dfrac{3}{5}$.

$5\frac{29}{40}$

▶ **96.** Find the sum of $1\dfrac{5}{6}$ and $3\dfrac{4}{9}$.

$5\frac{5}{18}$

97. Improving Your Quantitative Literacy A column on horse racing in the *Daily News* in Los Angeles reported that the horse Action This Day ran 3 furlongs in $35\dfrac{1}{5}$ seconds and another horse, Halfbridled, went two-fifths of a second faster. How many seconds did it take Halfbridled to run 3 furlongs?

$34\frac{4}{5}$ sec

Introduction . . .

Now that we have developed skills with both fractions and mixed numbers, we can simplify expressions that contain both types of numbers.

A Simplifying Expressions Involving Fractions and Mixed Numbers

PRACTICE PROBLEMS

1. Simplify the expression:
$$4 + \left(1\frac{1}{2}\right)\left(2\frac{3}{4}\right)$$

EXAMPLE 1 Simplify the expression: $5 + \left(2\frac{1}{2}\right)\left(3\frac{2}{3}\right)$

SOLUTION The rule for order of operations indicates that we should multiply $2\frac{1}{2}$ times $3\frac{2}{3}$ and then add 5 to the result:

$$5 + \left(2\frac{1}{2}\right)\left(3\frac{2}{3}\right) = 5 + \left(\frac{5}{2}\right)\left(\frac{11}{3}\right)$$ Change the mixed numbers to improper fractions

$$= 5 + \frac{55}{6}$$ Multiply the improper fractions

$$= \frac{30}{6} + \frac{55}{6}$$ Write 5 as $\frac{30}{6}$ so both numbers have the same denominator

$$= \frac{85}{6}$$ Add fractions by adding their numerators

$$= 14\frac{1}{6}$$ Write the answer as a mixed number

EXAMPLE 2 Simplify: $\left(\frac{3}{4} + \frac{5}{8}\right)\left(2\frac{3}{8} + 1\frac{1}{4}\right)$

2. Simplify:
$$\left(\frac{2}{3} + \frac{1}{6}\right)\left(2\frac{5}{6} + 1\frac{1}{3}\right)$$

SOLUTION We begin by combining the numbers inside the parentheses:

$$\frac{3}{4} + \frac{5}{8} = \frac{3 \cdot 2}{4 \cdot 2} + \frac{5}{8} \quad \text{and} \quad 2\frac{3}{8} = \quad 2\frac{3}{8} = \quad 2\frac{3}{8}$$

$$= \frac{6}{8} + \frac{5}{8} \qquad\qquad\qquad + 1\frac{1}{4} = + 1\frac{1 \cdot 2}{4 \cdot 2} = + 1\frac{2}{8}$$

$$= \frac{11}{8} \qquad\qquad\qquad\qquad\qquad\qquad\qquad 3\frac{5}{8}$$

Now that we have combined the expressions inside the parentheses, we can complete the problem by multiplying the results:

$$\left(\frac{3}{4} + \frac{5}{8}\right)\left(2\frac{3}{8} + 1\frac{1}{4}\right) = \left(\frac{11}{8}\right)\left(3\frac{5}{8}\right)$$

$$= \frac{11}{8} \cdot \frac{29}{8}$$ Change $3\frac{5}{8}$ to an improper fraction

$$= \frac{319}{64}$$ Multiply fractions

$$= 4\frac{63}{64}$$ Write the answer as a mixed number

3. Simplify:

$$\frac{3}{7} + \frac{1}{3}\left(1\frac{1}{2} + 4\frac{1}{2}\right)^2$$

EXAMPLE 3 Simplify: $\dfrac{3}{5} + \dfrac{1}{2}\left(3\dfrac{2}{3} + 4\dfrac{1}{3}\right)^2$

SOLUTION We begin by combining the expressions inside the parentheses:

$$\frac{3}{5} + \frac{1}{2}\left(3\frac{2}{3} + 4\frac{1}{3}\right)^2 = \frac{3}{5} + \frac{1}{2}(8)^2 \qquad \text{The sum inside the parentheses is 8}$$

$$= \frac{3}{5} + \frac{1}{2}(64) \qquad \text{The square of 8 is 64}$$

$$= \frac{3}{5} + 32 \qquad \frac{1}{2} \text{ of 64 is 32}$$

$$= 32\frac{3}{5} \qquad \text{The result is a mixed number}$$

B Complex Fractions

> **Definition**
> A **complex fraction** is a fraction in which the numerator and/or the denominator are themselves fractions or combinations of fractions.

Each of the following is a complex fraction:

$$\frac{\dfrac{3}{4}}{\dfrac{5}{6}}, \quad \frac{3 + \dfrac{1}{2}}{2 - \dfrac{3}{4}}, \quad \frac{\dfrac{1}{2} + \dfrac{2}{3}}{\dfrac{3}{4} - \dfrac{1}{6}}$$

4. Simplify:

$$\frac{\dfrac{2}{3}}{\dfrac{5}{9}}$$

EXAMPLE 4 Simplify: $\dfrac{\dfrac{3}{4}}{\dfrac{5}{6}}$

SOLUTION This is actually the same as the problem $\frac{3}{4} \div \frac{5}{6}$, because the bar between $\frac{3}{4}$ and $\frac{5}{6}$ indicates division. Therefore, it must be true that

$$\frac{\dfrac{3}{4}}{\dfrac{5}{6}} = \frac{3}{4} \div \frac{5}{6}$$

$$= \frac{3}{4} \cdot \frac{6}{5}$$

$$= \frac{18}{20}$$

$$= \frac{9}{10}$$

As you can see, we continue to use properties we have developed previously when we encounter new situations. In Example 4 we use the fact that division by a number and multiplication by its reciprocal produce the same result. We are taking a new problem, simplifying a complex fraction, and thinking of it in terms of a problem we have done previously, division by a fraction.

Answers

3. $12\frac{3}{7}$ **4.** $1\frac{1}{5}$

EXAMPLE 5 Simplify: $\dfrac{\frac{1}{2} + \frac{2}{3}}{\frac{3}{4} - \frac{1}{6}}$

SOLUTION Let's decide to call the numerator of this complex fraction the *top* of the fraction and its denominator the *bottom* of the complex fraction. It will be less confusing if we name them this way. The LCD for all the denominators on the top and bottom is 12, so we can multiply the top and bottom of this complex fraction by 12 and be sure all the denominators will divide it exactly. This will leave us with only whole numbers on the top and bottom:

$$\frac{\frac{1}{2} + \frac{2}{3}}{\frac{3}{4} - \frac{1}{6}} = \frac{12\left(\frac{1}{2} + \frac{2}{3}\right)}{12\left(\frac{3}{4} - \frac{1}{6}\right)}$$ Multiply the top and bottom by the LCD

$$= \frac{12 \cdot \frac{1}{2} + 12 \cdot \frac{2}{3}}{12 \cdot \frac{3}{4} - 12 \cdot \frac{1}{6}}$$ Distributive property

$$= \frac{6 + 8}{9 - 2}$$ Multiply each fraction by 12

$$= \frac{14}{7}$$ Add on top and subtract on bottom

$$= 2$$ Reduce to lowest terms

The problem can be worked in another way also. We can simplify the top and bottom of the complex fraction separately. Simplifying the top, we have

$$\frac{1}{2} + \frac{2}{3} = \frac{1 \cdot 3}{2 \cdot 3} + \frac{2 \cdot 2}{3 \cdot 2} = \frac{3}{6} + \frac{4}{6} = \frac{7}{6}$$

Simplifying the bottom, we have

$$\frac{3}{4} - \frac{1}{6} = \frac{3 \cdot 3}{4 \cdot 3} - \frac{1 \cdot 2}{6 \cdot 2} = \frac{9}{12} - \frac{2}{12} = \frac{7}{12}$$

We now write the original complex fraction again using the simplified expressions for the top and bottom. Then we proceed as we did in Example 4.

$$\frac{\frac{1}{2} + \frac{2}{3}}{\frac{3}{4} - \frac{1}{6}} = \frac{\frac{7}{6}}{\frac{7}{12}}$$

$$= \frac{7}{6} \div \frac{7}{12}$$ The divisor is $\frac{7}{12}$

$$= \frac{7}{6} \cdot \frac{12}{7}$$ Replace $\frac{7}{12}$ by its reciprocal and multiply

$$= \frac{7 \cdot 2 \cdot 6}{6 \cdot 7}$$ Divide out common factors

$$= 2$$

STUDY SKILLS
Review with the Exam in Mind

Each day you should review material that will be covered on the next exam. Your review should consist of working problems. Preferably, the problems you work should be problems from your list of difficult problems.

5. Simplify: $\dfrac{\frac{1}{2} + \frac{3}{4}}{\frac{2}{3} - \frac{1}{4}}$

Note We are going to simplify this complex fraction by two different methods. This is the first method.

Note The fraction bar that separates the numerator of the complex fraction from its denominator works like parentheses. If we were to rewrite this problem without it, we would write it like this:

$$\left(\frac{1}{2} + \frac{2}{3}\right) \div \left(\frac{3}{4} - \frac{1}{6}\right)$$

That is why we simplify the top and bottom of the complex fraction separately and then divide.

Answer

5. 3

6. Simplify: $\dfrac{4 + \dfrac{2}{3}}{3 - \dfrac{1}{4}}$

EXAMPLE 6 Simplify: $\dfrac{3 + \dfrac{1}{2}}{2 - \dfrac{3}{4}}$

SOLUTION The simplest approach here is to multiply both the top and bottom by the LCD for all fractions, which is 4:

$$\frac{3 + \dfrac{1}{2}}{2 - \dfrac{3}{4}} = \frac{4\left(3 + \dfrac{1}{2}\right)}{4\left(2 - \dfrac{3}{4}\right)} \qquad \text{Multiply the top and bottom by 4}$$

$$= \frac{4 \cdot 3 + 4 \cdot \dfrac{1}{2}}{4 \cdot 2 - 4 \cdot \dfrac{3}{4}} \qquad \text{Distributive property}$$

$$= \frac{12 + 2}{8 - 3} \qquad \text{Multiply each number by 4}$$

$$= \frac{14}{5} \qquad \text{Add on top and subtract on bottom}$$

$$= 2\frac{4}{5}$$

7. Simplify: $\dfrac{12\dfrac{1}{3}}{6\dfrac{2}{3}}$

EXAMPLE 7 Simplify: $\dfrac{10\dfrac{1}{3}}{8\dfrac{2}{3}}$

SOLUTION The simplest way to simplify this complex fraction is to think of it as a division problem.

$$\frac{10\dfrac{1}{3}}{8\dfrac{2}{3}} = 10\frac{1}{3} \div 8\frac{2}{3} \qquad \text{Write with a} \div \text{symbol}$$

$$= \frac{31}{3} \div \frac{26}{3} \qquad \text{Change to improper fractions}$$

$$= \frac{31}{3} \cdot \frac{3}{26} \qquad \text{Write in terms of multiplication}$$

$$= \frac{31 \cdot 3}{3 \cdot 26} \qquad \text{Divide out the common factor 3}$$

$$= \frac{31}{26} = 1\frac{5}{26} \qquad \text{Answer as a mixed number}$$

Getting Ready for Class

After reading through the preceding section, respond in your own words and in complete sentences.

1. What is a complex fraction?

2. Rewrite $\dfrac{\dfrac{5}{6}}{\dfrac{1}{3}}$ as a multiplication problem.

3. True or false? The rules for order of operations tell us to work inside parentheses first.

4. True or false? We find the LCD when we add or subtract fractions, but not when we multiply them.

Answers

6. $1\frac{23}{33}$ 7. $1\frac{17}{20}$

Problem Set 2.9

A Use the rule for order of operations to simplify each of the following. [Examples 1–3]

1. $3 + \left(1\frac{1}{2}\right)\left(2\frac{2}{3}\right)$
7

2. $7 - \left(1\frac{3}{5}\right)\left(2\frac{1}{2}\right)$
3

▶ **3.** $8 - \left(\frac{6}{11}\right)\left(1\frac{5}{6}\right)$
7

4. $10 + \left(2\frac{4}{5}\right)\left(\frac{5}{7}\right)$
12

5. $\frac{2}{3}\left(1\frac{1}{2}\right) + \frac{3}{4}\left(1\frac{1}{3}\right)$
2

6. $\frac{2}{5}\left(2\frac{1}{2}\right) + \frac{5}{8}\left(3\frac{1}{5}\right)$
3

▶ **7.** $2\left(1\frac{1}{2}\right) + 5\left(6\frac{2}{5}\right)$
35

8. $4\left(5\frac{3}{4}\right) + 6\left(3\frac{5}{6}\right)$
46

▶ **9.** $\left(\frac{3}{5} + \frac{1}{10}\right)\left(\frac{1}{2} + \frac{3}{4}\right)$
$\frac{7}{8}$

10. $\left(\frac{2}{9} + \frac{1}{3}\right)\left(\frac{1}{5} + \frac{1}{10}\right)$
$\frac{1}{6}$

11. $\left(2 + \frac{2}{3}\right)\left(3 + \frac{1}{8}\right)$
$8\frac{1}{3}$

12. $\left(3 - \frac{3}{4}\right)\left(3 + \frac{1}{3}\right)$
$7\frac{1}{2}$

▶ **13.** $\left(1 + \frac{5}{6}\right)\left(1 - \frac{5}{6}\right)$
$\frac{11}{36}$

14. $\left(2 - \frac{1}{4}\right)\left(2 + \frac{1}{4}\right)$
$3\frac{15}{16}$

▶ **15.** $\frac{2}{3} + \frac{1}{3}\left(2\frac{1}{2} + \frac{1}{2}\right)^2$
$3\frac{2}{3}$

16. $\frac{3}{5} + \frac{1}{4}\left(2\frac{1}{2} - \frac{1}{2}\right)^3$
$2\frac{3}{5}$

17. $2\frac{3}{8} + \frac{1}{2}\left(\frac{1}{3} + \frac{5}{3}\right)^3$
$6\frac{3}{8}$

18. $8\frac{2}{3} + \frac{1}{3}\left(\frac{8}{5} + \frac{7}{5}\right)^2$
$11\frac{2}{3}$

19. $2\left(\frac{1}{2} + \frac{1}{3}\right) + 3\left(\frac{2}{3} + \frac{1}{4}\right)$
$4\frac{5}{12}$

▶ **20.** $5\left(\frac{1}{5} + \frac{3}{10}\right) + 2\left(\frac{1}{10} + \frac{1}{2}\right)$
$3\frac{7}{10}$

B Simplify each complex fraction as much as possible. [Examples 4–7]

21. $\dfrac{\frac{2}{3}}{\frac{3}{4}}$

$\frac{8}{9}$

22. $\dfrac{\frac{5}{6}}{\frac{3}{12}}$

$3\frac{1}{3}$

▶ **23.** $\dfrac{\frac{2}{3}}{\frac{4}{3}}$

$\frac{1}{2}$

24. $\dfrac{\frac{7}{9}}{\frac{5}{9}}$

$1\frac{2}{5}$

25. $\dfrac{\frac{11}{20}}{\frac{5}{10}}$

$1\frac{1}{10}$

▶ **26.** $\dfrac{\frac{9}{16}}{\frac{3}{4}}$

$\frac{3}{4}$

27. $\dfrac{\frac{1}{2}+\frac{1}{3}}{\frac{1}{2}-\frac{1}{3}}$

5

▶ **28.** $\dfrac{\frac{1}{4}+\frac{1}{5}}{\frac{1}{4}-\frac{1}{5}}$

9

29. $\dfrac{\frac{5}{8}-\frac{1}{4}}{\frac{1}{8}+\frac{1}{2}}$

$\frac{3}{5}$

30. $\dfrac{\frac{3}{4}+\frac{1}{3}}{\frac{2}{3}+\frac{1}{6}}$

$1\frac{3}{10}$

▶ **31.** $\dfrac{\frac{9}{20}-\frac{1}{10}}{\frac{1}{10}+\frac{9}{20}}$

$\frac{7}{11}$

32. $\dfrac{\frac{1}{2}+\frac{2}{3}}{\frac{3}{4}+\frac{5}{6}}$

$\frac{14}{19}$

33. $\dfrac{1+\frac{2}{3}}{1-\frac{2}{3}}$

5

34. $\dfrac{5-\frac{3}{4}}{2+\frac{3}{4}}$

$1\frac{6}{11}$

▶ **35.** $\dfrac{2+\frac{5}{6}}{5-\frac{1}{3}}$

$\frac{17}{28}$

36. $\dfrac{9-\frac{11}{5}}{3+\frac{13}{10}}$

$1\frac{25}{43}$

37. $\dfrac{3+\frac{5}{6}}{1+\frac{5}{3}}$

$1\frac{7}{16}$

38. $\dfrac{10+\frac{9}{10}}{5+\frac{4}{5}}$

$1\frac{51}{58}$

39. $\dfrac{\frac{1}{3}+\frac{3}{4}}{2-\frac{1}{6}}$

$\frac{13}{22}$

40. $\dfrac{3+\frac{5}{2}}{\frac{5}{6}+\frac{1}{4}}$

$5\frac{1}{13}$

41. $\dfrac{\frac{5}{6}}{3+\frac{2}{3}}$

$\frac{5}{22}$

▶ **42.** $\dfrac{9-\frac{3}{2}}{\frac{7}{4}}$

$4\frac{2}{7}$

B Simplify each of the following complex fractions. [Examples 5–7]

43. $\dfrac{2\frac{1}{2} + \frac{1}{2}}{3\frac{3}{5} - \frac{2}{5}}$

$\frac{15}{16}$

▶ 44. $\dfrac{5\frac{3}{8} + \frac{5}{8}}{4\frac{1}{4} + 1\frac{3}{4}}$

1

45. $\dfrac{2 + 1\frac{2}{3}}{3\frac{5}{6} - 1}$

$1\frac{5}{17}$

▶ 46. $\dfrac{5 + 8\frac{3}{5}}{2\frac{3}{10} + 4}$

$2\frac{10}{63}$

47. $\dfrac{3\frac{1}{4} - 2\frac{1}{2}}{5\frac{3}{4} + 1\frac{1}{2}}$

$\frac{3}{29}$

48. $\dfrac{9\frac{3}{8} + 2\frac{5}{8}}{6\frac{1}{2} + 7\frac{1}{2}}$

$\frac{6}{7}$

▶ 49. $\dfrac{3\frac{1}{4} + 5\frac{1}{6}}{2\frac{1}{3} + 3\frac{1}{4}}$

$1\frac{34}{67}$

50. $\dfrac{8\frac{5}{6} + 1\frac{2}{3}}{7\frac{1}{3} + 2\frac{1}{4}}$

$1\frac{11}{115}$

51. $\dfrac{6\frac{2}{3} + 7\frac{3}{4}}{8\frac{1}{2} + 9\frac{7}{8}}$

$\frac{346}{441}$

52. $\dfrac{3\frac{4}{5} - 1\frac{9}{10}}{6\frac{5}{6} - 2\frac{3}{4}}$

$\frac{114}{245}$

53. What is twice the sum of $2\frac{1}{5}$ and $\frac{3}{6}$?

$5\frac{2}{5}$

▶ 54. Find 3 times the difference of $1\frac{7}{9}$ and $\frac{2}{9}$.

$\frac{14}{3} = 4\frac{2}{3}$

55. Add $5\frac{1}{4}$ to the sum of $\frac{3}{4}$ and 2.

8

▶ 56. Subtract $\frac{7}{8}$ from the product of 2 and $3\frac{1}{2}$.

$6\frac{1}{8}$

◼ Applying the Concepts

57. Tri-cities The Google Earth image shows a right triangle between three cities in Colorado. If the distance between Edgewater and Denver is 4 miles, and the distance between Denver and North Washington is $2\frac{1}{2}$ miles, what is the area of the triangle created by the three cities?

5 miles²

58. Tri-cities The Google Earth image shows a right triangle between three cities in California. If the distance between Pomona and Ontario is $5\frac{7}{10}$ miles, and the distance between Ontario and Upland is $3\frac{3}{5}$ miles, what is the area of the triangle created by the three cities?

$10\frac{13}{50}$ miles²

▶ **59. Manufacturing** A dress manufacturer usually buys two rolls of cloth, one of $32\frac{1}{2}$ yards and the other of $25\frac{1}{3}$ yards, to fill his weekly orders. If his orders double one week, how much of the cloth should he order? (Give the total yardage.)

$115\frac{2}{3}$ yd

▶ **60. Body Temperature** Suppose your normal body temperature is $98\frac{3}{5}°$ Fahrenheit. If your temperature goes up $3\frac{1}{5}°$ on Monday and then down $1\frac{4}{5}°$ on Tuesday, what is your temperature on Tuesday?

100°F

◼ Maintaining Your Skills

These problems review the four basic operations with fractions from this chapter.

Perform the indicated operations.

61. $\frac{3}{4} \cdot \frac{8}{9}$

$\frac{2}{3}$

62. $8 \cdot \frac{5}{6}$

$\frac{20}{3} = 6\frac{2}{3}$

63. $\frac{2}{3} \div 4$

$\frac{1}{6}$

64. $\frac{7}{8} \div \frac{14}{24}$

$\frac{3}{2} = 1\frac{1}{2}$

65. $\frac{3}{7} - \frac{2}{7}$

$\frac{1}{7}$

66. $\frac{6}{7} + \frac{9}{14}$

$\frac{3}{2} = 1\frac{1}{2}$

67. $10 - \frac{2}{9}$

$9\frac{7}{9}$

68. $\frac{2}{3} - \frac{3}{5}$

$\frac{1}{15}$

Chapter 2 Summary

◼ Definition of Fractions [2.1]

A fraction is any number that can be written in the form $\frac{a}{b}$, where a and b are numbers and b is not 0. The number a is called the *numerator*, and the number b is called the *denominator*.

1. Each of the following is a fraction:

$$\frac{1}{2}, \quad \frac{3}{4}, \quad \frac{8}{1}, \quad \frac{7}{3}$$

◼ Properties of Fractions [2.1]

Multiplying the numerator and the denominator of a fraction by the same non-zero number will produce an equivalent fraction. The same is true for dividing the numerator and denominator by the same nonzero number. In symbols the properties look like this: If a, b, and c are numbers and b and c are not 0, then

Property 1 $\quad \frac{a}{b} = \frac{a \cdot c}{b \cdot c}$ **Property 2** $\quad \frac{a}{b} = \frac{a \div c}{b \div c}$

2. Change $\frac{3}{4}$ to an equivalent fraction with denominator 12.

$$\frac{3}{4} = \frac{3 \cdot 3}{4 \cdot 3} = \frac{9}{12}$$

◼ Fractions and the Number 1 [2.1]

If a represents any number, then

$$\frac{a}{1} = a \quad \text{and} \quad \frac{a}{a} = 1 \quad \text{(where } a \text{ is not 0)}$$

3. $\frac{5}{1} = 5$, $\frac{5}{5} = 1$

◼ Reducing Fractions to Lowest Terms [2.2]

To reduce a fraction to lowest terms, factor the numerator and the denominator, and then divide both the numerator and denominator by any factors they have in common.

4. $\frac{90}{588} = \frac{2 \cdot 3 \cdot 3 \cdot 5}{2 \cdot 2 \cdot 3 \cdot 7 \cdot 7}$
$$= \frac{3 \cdot 5}{2 \cdot 7 \cdot 7}$$
$$= \frac{15}{98}$$

◼ Multiplying Fractions [2.3]

To multiply fractions, multiply numerators and multiply denominators.

5. $\frac{3}{5} \cdot \frac{4}{7} = \frac{3 \cdot 4}{5 \cdot 7} = \frac{12}{35}$

◼ The Area of a Triangle [2.3]

The formula for the area of a triangle with base b and height h is

$$A = \frac{1}{2}bh$$

6. If the base of a triangle is 10 inches and the height is 7 inches, then the area is
$$A = \frac{1}{2}bh$$
$$= \frac{1}{2} \cdot 10 \cdot 7$$
$$= 5 \cdot 7$$
$$= 35 \text{ square inches}$$

Reciprocals [2.4]

Any two numbers whose product is 1 are called *reciprocals*. The numbers $\frac{2}{3}$ and $\frac{3}{2}$ are reciprocals, because their product is 1.

Division with Fractions [2.4]

7. $\dfrac{3}{8} \div \dfrac{1}{3} = \dfrac{3}{8} \cdot \dfrac{3}{1} = \dfrac{9}{8}$

To divide by a fraction, multiply by its reciprocal. That is, the quotient of two fractions is defined to be the product of the first fraction with the reciprocal of the second fraction (the divisor).

Least Common Denominator (LCD) [2.5]

The *least common denominator* (LCD) for a set of denominators is the smallest number that is exactly divisible by each denominator.

Addition and Subtraction of Fractions [2.5]

8. $\dfrac{1}{8} + \dfrac{3}{8} = \dfrac{1+3}{8}$

$= \dfrac{4}{8}$

$= \dfrac{1}{2}$

To add (or subtract) two fractions with a common denominator, add (or subtract) numerators and use the common denominator. In symbols: If a, b, and c are numbers with c not equal to 0, then

$$\frac{a}{c} + \frac{b}{c} = \frac{a+b}{c} \quad \text{and} \quad \frac{a}{c} - \frac{b}{c} = \frac{a-b}{c}$$

Additional Facts about Fractions

1. In some books fractions are called *rational numbers*.
2. Every whole number can be written as a fraction with a denominator of 1.
3. The commutative, associative, and distributive properties are true for fractions.
4. The word *of* as used in the expression "$\frac{2}{3}$ *of* 12" indicates that we are to multiply $\frac{2}{3}$ and 12.
5. Two fractions with the same value are called *equivalent fractions*.

Mixed-Number Notation [2.6]

A mixed number is the sum of a whole number and a fraction. The + sign is not shown when we write mixed numbers; it is implied. The mixed number $4\frac{2}{3}$ is actually the sum $4 + \frac{2}{3}$.

Changing Mixed Numbers to Improper Fractions [2.6]

To change a mixed number to an improper fraction, we write the mixed number showing the + sign and add as usual. The result is the same if we multiply the denominator of the fraction by the whole number and add what we get to the numerator of the fraction, putting this result over the denominator of the fraction.

9. $4\frac{2}{3} = \frac{3 \cdot 4 + 2}{3} = \frac{14}{3}$

Mixed number Improper fraction

Changing an Improper Fraction to a Mixed Number [2.6]

To change an improper fraction to a mixed number, divide the denominator into the numerator. The quotient is the whole-number part of the mixed number. The fraction part is the remainder over the divisor.

10. Change $\frac{14}{3}$ to a mixed number.

Quotient

$$3\overline{)14} \qquad \frac{14}{3} = 4\frac{2}{3}$$
$$\underline{12}$$
$$2 \qquad \text{Divisor}$$

Remainder

Multiplication and Division with Mixed Numbers [2.7]

To multiply or divide two mixed numbers, change each to an improper fraction and multiply or divide as usual.

11. $2\frac{1}{3} \cdot 1\frac{3}{4} = \frac{7}{3} \cdot \frac{7}{4} = \frac{49}{12} = 4\frac{1}{12}$

Addition and Subtraction with Mixed Numbers [2.8]

To add or subtract two mixed numbers, add or subtract the whole-number parts and the fraction parts separately. This is best done with the numbers written in columns.

12.
$$3\frac{4}{9} = 3\frac{4}{9} = 3\frac{4}{9}$$
$$+2\frac{2}{3} = +2\frac{2 \cdot 3}{3 \cdot 3} = +2\frac{6}{9}$$
$$\overline{} \qquad \qquad 5\frac{10}{9} = 6\frac{1}{9}$$

Common
denominator

Add whole numbers

Add fractions

Borrowing in Subtraction with Mixed Numbers [2.8]

It is sometimes necessary to borrow when doing subtraction with mixed numbers. We always change to a common denominator before we actually borrow.

13.
$$4\frac{1}{3} = 4\frac{2}{6} = 3\frac{8}{6}$$
$$-1\frac{5}{6} = -1\frac{5}{6} = -1\frac{5}{6}$$
$$\overline{} \qquad 2\frac{3}{6} = 2\frac{1}{2}$$

Complex Fractions [2.9]

A fraction that contains a fraction in its numerator or denominator is called a *complex fraction*.

14.
$$\frac{4 + \frac{1}{3}}{2 - \frac{5}{6}} = \frac{6\left(4 + \frac{1}{3}\right)}{6\left(2 - \frac{5}{6}\right)}$$

$$= \frac{6 \cdot 4 + 6 \cdot \frac{1}{3}}{6 \cdot 2 - 6 \cdot \frac{5}{6}}$$

$$= \frac{24 + 2}{12 - 5}$$

$$= \frac{26}{7} = 3\frac{5}{7}$$

⊘ COMMON MISTAKES

1. The most common mistake when working with fractions occurs when we try to add two fractions without using a common denominator. For example,

$$\frac{2}{3} + \frac{4}{5} \neq \frac{2+4}{3+5}$$

If the two fractions we are trying to add don't have the same denominators, then we must rewrite each one as an equivalent fraction with a common denominator. *We never add denominators when adding fractions.*

Note: We do *not* need a common denominator when multiplying fractions.

2. A common mistake made with division of fractions occurs when we multiply by the reciprocal of the first fraction instead of the reciprocal of the divisor. For example,

$$\frac{2}{3} \div \frac{5}{6} \neq \frac{3}{2} \cdot \frac{5}{6}$$

Remember, we perform division by multiplying by the reciprocal of the divisor (the fraction to the right of the division symbol).

3. If the answer to a problem turns out to be a fraction, that fraction should always be written in lowest terms. It is a mistake not to reduce to lowest terms.

4. A common mistake when working with mixed numbers is to confuse mixed-number notation for multiplication of fractions. The notation $3\frac{2}{5}$ does *not* mean 3 *times* $\frac{2}{5}$. It means 3 *plus* $\frac{2}{5}$.

5. Another mistake occurs when multiplying mixed numbers. The mistake occurs when we don't change the mixed number to an improper fraction before multiplying and instead try to multiply the whole numbers and fractions separately. Like this:

$$2\frac{1}{2} \cdot 3\frac{1}{3} = (2 \cdot 3) + \left(\frac{1}{2} \cdot \frac{1}{3}\right) \quad \text{Mistake}$$
$$= 6 + \frac{1}{6}$$
$$= 6\frac{1}{6}$$

Remember, the correct way to multiply mixed numbers is to first change to improper fractions and then multiply numerators and multiply denominators. This is correct:

$$2\frac{1}{2} \cdot 3\frac{1}{3} = \frac{5}{2} \cdot \frac{10}{3} = \frac{50}{6} = 8\frac{2}{6} = 8\frac{1}{3} \quad \text{Correct}$$

Reduce each of the following fractions to lowest terms. [2.2]

1. $\dfrac{6}{8}$

$\dfrac{3}{4}$

2. $\dfrac{12}{36}$

$\dfrac{1}{3}$

3. $\dfrac{110}{70}$

$\dfrac{11}{7}$

4. $\dfrac{45}{75}$

$\dfrac{3}{5}$

Multiply the following fractions. (That is, find the product in each case, and reduce to lowest terms.) [2.3]

5. $\dfrac{1}{5}(5)$

1

6. $\dfrac{80}{27}\left(\dfrac{3}{20}\right)$

$\dfrac{4}{9}$

7. $\dfrac{96}{25}\cdot\dfrac{15}{98}\cdot\dfrac{35}{54}$

$\dfrac{8}{21}$

8. $\dfrac{3}{5}\cdot 75\cdot\dfrac{2}{3}$

30

Find the following quotients. (That is, divide and reduce to lowest terms.) [2.4]

9. $\dfrac{8}{9}\div\dfrac{4}{3}$

$\dfrac{2}{3}$

10. $\dfrac{9}{10}\div 3$

$\dfrac{3}{10}$

11. $\dfrac{15}{36}\div\dfrac{10}{9}$

$\dfrac{3}{8}$

12. $\dfrac{18}{49}\div\dfrac{36}{28}$

$\dfrac{2}{7}$

Perform the indicated operations. Reduce all answers to lowest terms. [2.5]

13. $\dfrac{6}{8}-\dfrac{2}{8}$

$\dfrac{1}{2}$

14. $\dfrac{9}{10}+\dfrac{11}{10}$

2

15. $3+\dfrac{1}{2}$

$\dfrac{7}{2}$

16. $\dfrac{9}{52}+\dfrac{5}{78}$

$\dfrac{37}{156}$

17. $\dfrac{11}{126}-\dfrac{5}{84}$

$\dfrac{1}{36}$

18. $\dfrac{3}{10}+\dfrac{7}{25}+\dfrac{3}{4}$

$1\dfrac{33}{100}$

Change to improper fractions. [2.6]

19. $3\dfrac{5}{8}$

$\dfrac{29}{8}$

20. $7\dfrac{2}{3}$

$\dfrac{23}{3}$

Change to mixed numbers. [2.6]

21. $\dfrac{15}{4}$

$3\dfrac{3}{4}$

22. $\dfrac{110}{8}$

$13\dfrac{3}{4}$

Perform the indicated operations. [2.7, 2.8]

23. $2\div 3\dfrac{1}{4}$

$\dfrac{8}{13}$

24. $4\dfrac{7}{8}\div 2\dfrac{3}{5}$

$1\dfrac{7}{8}$

25. $6\cdot 2\dfrac{1}{2}\cdot\dfrac{4}{5}$

12

26. $3\dfrac{1}{5}+4\dfrac{2}{5}$

$7\dfrac{3}{5}$

27. $8\dfrac{2}{3}+9\dfrac{1}{4}$

$17\dfrac{11}{12}$

28. $5\dfrac{1}{3}-2\dfrac{8}{9}$

$2\dfrac{4}{9}$

Simplify each of the following as much as possible. [2.9]

29. $3+2\left(4\dfrac{1}{3}\right)$

$11\dfrac{2}{3}$

30. $\left(2\dfrac{1}{2}+\dfrac{3}{4}\right)\left(2\dfrac{1}{2}-\dfrac{3}{4}\right)$

$5\dfrac{11}{16}$

Simplify each complex fraction as much as possible. [2.9]

31. $\dfrac{1 + \dfrac{2}{3}}{1 - \dfrac{2}{3}}$ 5

32. $\dfrac{3 - \dfrac{3}{4}}{3 + \dfrac{3}{4}}$ $\dfrac{3}{5}$

33. $\dfrac{\dfrac{7}{8} - \dfrac{1}{2}}{\dfrac{1}{4} + \dfrac{1}{2}}$ $\dfrac{1}{2}$

34. $\dfrac{2\dfrac{1}{8} + 3\dfrac{1}{3}}{1\dfrac{1}{6} + 5\dfrac{1}{4}}$ $\dfrac{131}{154}$

35. Defective Parts If $\dfrac{1}{10}$ of the items in a shipment of 200 items are defective, how many are defective? [2.3]

20 items

36. Number of Students If 80 students took a math test and $\dfrac{3}{4}$ of them passed, then how many students passed the test? [2.3]

60 students

37. Translating What is 3 times the sum of $2\dfrac{1}{4}$ and $\dfrac{3}{4}$? [2.9]

9

38. Translating Subtract $\dfrac{5}{6}$ from the product of $1\dfrac{1}{2}$ and $\dfrac{2}{3}$. [2.9]

$\dfrac{1}{6}$

39. Cooking If a recipe that calls for $2\dfrac{1}{2}$ cups of flour will make 48 cookies, how much flour is needed to make 36 cookies? [2.7]

$1\dfrac{7}{8}$ cups

40. Length of Wood A piece of wood $10\dfrac{3}{4}$ inches long is divided into 6 equal pieces. How long is each piece? [2.7]

$1\dfrac{19}{24}$ in.

41. Cooking A recipe that calls for $3\dfrac{1}{2}$ tablespoons of oil is tripled. How much oil must be used in the tripled recipe? [2.7]

$10\dfrac{1}{2}$ tablespoons

42. Sheep Feed A rancher fed his sheep $10\dfrac{1}{2}$ pounds of feed on Monday, $9\dfrac{3}{4}$ pounds on Tuesday, and $12\dfrac{1}{4}$ pounds on Wednesday. How many pounds of feed did he use on these 3 days? [2.8]

$32\dfrac{1}{2}$ lb

43. Find the area and the perimeter of the triangle below. [2.7, 2.8]

Area = $25\dfrac{1}{5}$ ft²; perimeter = 28 ft

$10\dfrac{2}{5}$ ft   5 ft   4 ft $12\dfrac{3}{5}$ ft

44. Comparing Area On April 3, 2000, *USA TODAY* changed the size of its paper. Previous to this date, each page of the paper was $13\dfrac{1}{2}$ inches wide and $22\dfrac{1}{4}$ inches long. The new paper size is $1\dfrac{1}{4}$ inches narrower and $\dfrac{1}{2}$ inch longer. [2.7, 2.8]

a. What was the area of a page previous to April 3, 2000?

$300\dfrac{3}{8}$ in²

b. What is the area of a page after April 3, 2000?

$278\dfrac{11}{16}$ in²

c. What is the difference in the areas of the two page sizes?

$21\dfrac{11}{16}$ in²

Old size

New size

Chapter 2   Cumulative Review

Simplify.

1.
$$\begin{array}{r} 172 \\ 6{,}050 \\ +\ \ 95 \\ \hline 6{,}317 \end{array}$$

2.
$$\begin{array}{r} 4{,}320 \\ \times\ \ \ \ 17 \\ \hline 73{,}440 \end{array}$$

3. $\left(\dfrac{9}{13}\right)^2$

$\dfrac{81}{169}$

4. $17 - (11 - 4)$

10

5. $\dfrac{5}{8} - \dfrac{3}{8}$

$\dfrac{1}{4}$

6. $17\dfrac{13}{16} - 9\dfrac{5}{12}$

$8\dfrac{19}{48}$

7. $\dfrac{2}{3} \cdot \dfrac{6}{11}$

$\dfrac{4}{11}$

8. $4^3 - 2^2$

60

9. $4 \div \dfrac{1}{6}$

24

10. $196 \div 14 \div 7$

2

11. $\dfrac{92}{21}$

$4\dfrac{8}{21}$

12. $\dfrac{180}{252}$

$\dfrac{5}{7}$

13. 25^2

625

14. $(7 + 4) - (8 - 3)$

6

15. $\dfrac{2}{3} + \dfrac{1}{4}$

$\dfrac{11}{12}$

16. $1{,}030(604)$

$622{,}120$

17. $\dfrac{3}{12} \div \dfrac{9}{16}$

$\dfrac{4}{9}$

18. $4 + 5^2 - 2 \cdot 6 + 3$

20

19. $12 \cdot \dfrac{3}{4}$

9

20. $\left(\dfrac{2}{3}\right)^2 \cdot \left(\dfrac{1}{2}\right)^3$

$\dfrac{1}{18}$

21. $2{,}639 - 365$

$2{,}274$

22. $\dfrac{7\dfrac{1}{9}}{2\dfrac{2}{3}}$

$\dfrac{8}{3} = 2\dfrac{2}{3}$

23. $\left(\dfrac{3}{5} + \dfrac{2}{25}\right) - \dfrac{4}{125}$

$\dfrac{81}{125}$

24. $6 + \dfrac{3}{11} \div \dfrac{1}{2}$

$6\dfrac{6}{11}$

25. Round the following numbers to the nearest ten, then add.

$$\begin{array}{r} 747 \\ 116 \\ +\ 222 \\ \hline 1090 \end{array}$$

26. Find the sum of $\dfrac{2}{3}$, $\dfrac{1}{9}$, and $\dfrac{3}{4}$.

$\dfrac{55}{36} = 1\dfrac{19}{36}$

27. Write the fraction $\dfrac{3}{13}$ as an equivalent fraction with a denominator of $39x$.

$\dfrac{9x}{39x}$

28. Reduce $\dfrac{14}{49}$ to lowest terms.

$\dfrac{2}{7}$

29. Add $\dfrac{4}{5}$ to half of $\dfrac{4}{9}$.

$\dfrac{46}{45} = 1\dfrac{1}{45}$

30. Neptune's Diameter The planet Neptune has an equatorial diameter of about 30,760 miles. Write out Neptune's diameter in words and expanded form.

Thirty thousand, seven hundred sixty; 30,000 + 700 + 60

The chart shows the number of babies born to different age groups of women.

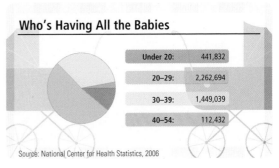

Who's Having All the Babies

Under 20:	441,832
20–29:	2,262,694
30–39:	1,449,039
40–54:	112,432

Source: National Center for Health Statistics, 2006

31. Babies How many babies were born to mothers between the ages of 30 and 54?

1,561,471 babies

Perform the indicated operations. Reduce all answers to lowest terms.

1. $\dfrac{3}{10} + \dfrac{1}{10}$

$\dfrac{2}{5}$

2. $\dfrac{5}{8} - \dfrac{2}{8}$

$\dfrac{3}{8}$

3. $4 + \dfrac{3}{5}$

$\dfrac{23}{5}$

4. $\dfrac{3}{10} + \dfrac{2}{5}$

$\dfrac{7}{10}$

5. $\dfrac{5}{6} + \dfrac{2}{9} + \dfrac{1}{4}$

$\dfrac{47}{36} = 1\dfrac{11}{36}$

6. $7\dfrac{1}{3} + 2\dfrac{3}{8}$

$9\dfrac{17}{24}$

7. $5\dfrac{1}{6} - 1\dfrac{1}{2}$

$3\dfrac{2}{3}$

8. $6 - \dfrac{3}{5}$

$5\dfrac{2}{5}$

9. $\dfrac{3}{5} - \dfrac{4}{15}$

$\dfrac{1}{3}$

10. $\dfrac{4}{9} + \dfrac{2}{3} - 1$

$\dfrac{1}{9}$

11. $\dfrac{9}{16} - \dfrac{1}{4}$

$\dfrac{5}{16}$

12. $2\dfrac{2}{3} - 1\dfrac{5}{6}$

$\dfrac{5}{6}$

13. $3\dfrac{1}{5} - \dfrac{7}{10}$

$2\dfrac{1}{2}$

14. $\dfrac{7}{12} - \dfrac{1}{3}$

$\dfrac{1}{4}$

15. $2\dfrac{5}{8} - 2\dfrac{1}{4}$

$\dfrac{3}{8}$

16. $3\dfrac{2}{3} + \dfrac{5}{6}$

$4\dfrac{1}{2}$

17. $4\dfrac{3}{5} + 2\dfrac{1}{15}$

$6\dfrac{2}{3}$

18. $1\dfrac{8}{9} + 1\dfrac{7}{12} - \dfrac{3}{4}$

$2\dfrac{13}{18}$

Simplify each of the following as much as possible.

19. $4 + 3\left(4\dfrac{1}{4}\right)$ $16\dfrac{3}{4}$

20. $\left(2\dfrac{1}{3} + \dfrac{1}{2}\right)\left(3\dfrac{2}{3} - \dfrac{1}{6}\right)$

$9\dfrac{11}{12}$

21. $\dfrac{\dfrac{11}{12} - \dfrac{2}{3}}{\dfrac{1}{6} + \dfrac{1}{3}}$ $\dfrac{1}{2}$

22. $5 - 2\left(1\dfrac{2}{3}\right)$ $1\dfrac{2}{3}$

23. $\left(5\dfrac{1}{3} - \dfrac{5}{6}\right)\left(2\dfrac{1}{2} + \dfrac{1}{4}\right)$

$12\dfrac{3}{8}$

24. $\left(\dfrac{9}{2}\right)^2 - \dfrac{7}{2}$ $16\dfrac{3}{4}$

25. $\left(\dfrac{1}{3}\right)\left(2\dfrac{1}{2}\right) - \dfrac{2}{3}$ $\dfrac{1}{6}$

26. $\dfrac{4\dfrac{1}{6}}{1\dfrac{1}{9}}$ $3\dfrac{3}{4}$

27. $\dfrac{\dfrac{8}{15}}{5\dfrac{1}{3}}$ $\dfrac{1}{10}$

28. $\dfrac{\left(1\dfrac{7}{8} + \dfrac{3}{4}\right)}{\left(4\dfrac{1}{4} - \dfrac{1}{2}\right)}$ $\dfrac{7}{10}$

29. Sewing A dress that is $31\dfrac{1}{6}$ inches long is shortened by $3\dfrac{2}{3}$ inches. What is the new length of the dress?

$27\dfrac{1}{2}$ in.

30. Find the perimeter of the triangle below.

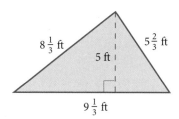

$8\dfrac{1}{3}$ ft   5 ft $5\dfrac{2}{3}$ ft

$9\dfrac{1}{3}$ ft

Perimeter $= 23\dfrac{1}{3}$ ft

The chart shows the monthly average rainfall in Honolulu.

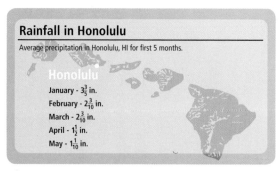

Rainfall in Honolulu

Average precipitation in Honolulu, HI for first 5 months.

Honolulu

January - $3\dfrac{3}{5}$ in.
February - $2\dfrac{3}{10}$ in.
March - $2\dfrac{3}{10}$ in.
April - $1\dfrac{1}{2}$ in.
May - $1\dfrac{1}{10}$ in.

31. How much rain does Honolulu get during the first three months of the year?

$8\dfrac{1}{5}$ in.

Chapter 2 Projects

FRACTIONS AND MIXED NUMBERS

Recipe

Number of People	2
Time Needed	5 minutes
Equipment	Pencil and paper
Background	Here is Martha Stewart's recipe for chocolate chip cookies.

Chocolate Chip Cookies

Makes 2 dozen
You can substitute bittersweet chocolate for half of the semisweet chocolate chips.

1 cup (2 sticks) unsalted butter, room temperature
1 1/2 cups packed light-brown sugar
1/2 cup granulated sugar
1 teaspoon pure vanilla extract
1 large egg, room temperature
2 cups all-purpose flour
1/2 teaspoon baking soda
1/2 teaspoon salt
12 ounces semisweet chocolate, coarsely chopped, or one 12-ounce bag semisweet chocolate chips

1. Heat oven to 375°. Line several baking sheets with parchment paper, and set aside.

2. Combine butter and both sugars in the bowl of an electric mixer fitted with the paddle attachment, and beat until light and fluffy. Add vanilla, and mix to combine. Add egg, and continue beating until well combined.

3. In a medium bowl, whisk together the flour, baking soda, and salt. Slowly add the dry ingredients to the butter mixture. Mix on low speed until just combined. Stir in chocolate chips.

4. Scoop out 2 tablespoons of dough, and place on a prepared baking sheet. Repeat with remaining dough, placing scoops 3 inches apart. Bake until just brown around the edges, 16 to 18 minutes, rotating the pans between the oven shelves halfway through baking. Remove from the oven, and let cool slightly before removing cookies from the baking sheets. Store in an airtight container at room temperature for up to 1 week.

Procedure   Rewrite the recipe to make 3 dozen cookies by multiplying the quantities by $1\frac{1}{2}$.

_____ cups (_____ sticks) unsalted butter, room temperature

_____ cups packed light-brown sugar

_____ cups granulated sugar

_____ teaspoons pure vanilla extract

_____ large eggs, room temperature

_____ cups all-purpose flour

_____ teaspoons baking soda

_____ teaspoons salt

_____ ounces semisweet chocolate, coarsely chopped, or _____ 12-ounce bags semisweet chocolate chips

Sophie Germain

The photograph at the right shows the street sign in Paris named for the French mathematician Sophie Germain (1776-1831). Among her contributions to mathematics is her work with prime numbers. In this chapter we had an introductory look at some of the classifications for numbers, including the prime numbers. Within the prime numbers themselves, there are still further classifications. In fact, a Sophie Germain prime is a prime number P, for which both P and $2P + 1$ are primes. For example, the prime number 2 is the first Sophie Germain prime because both 2 and $2 \cdot 2 + 1 = 5$ are prime numbers. The next Germain prime is 3 because both 3 and $2 \cdot 3 + 1 = 7$ are primes.

Cheryl Slaughter

Sophie Germain was born on April 1, 1776, in Paris, France. She taught herself mathematics by reading the books in her father's library at home. Today she is recognized most for her work in number theory, which includes her work with prime numbers. Research the life of Sophie Germain. Write a short essay that includes information on her work with prime numbers and how her results contributed to solving Fermat's Theorem almost 200 years later.

A Glimpse of Algebra

In algebra, we add and subtract fractions in the same way that we have added and subtracted fractions in this chapter. For example, consider the expression

$$\frac{x}{3} + \frac{2}{3}$$

The two fractions have the same denominator. So to add these fractions, all we have to do is add the numerators to get $x + 2$. The denominator of the sum is the common denominator 3:

$$\frac{x}{3} + \frac{2}{3} = \frac{x + 2}{3}$$

Here are some further examples.

EXAMPLE 1   Add or subtract as indicated.

a. $\dfrac{x}{5} + \dfrac{4}{5}$ **b.** $\dfrac{x + 5}{8} - \dfrac{3}{8}$ **c.** $\dfrac{4x}{10} + \dfrac{3x}{10}$ **d.** $\dfrac{5}{x} + \dfrac{3}{x}$

SOLUTION   In each case the denominators are the same. We add or subtract the numerators and write the sum or difference over the common denominator.

a. $\dfrac{x}{5} + \dfrac{4}{5} = \dfrac{x + 4}{5}$

b. $\dfrac{x + 5}{8} - \dfrac{3}{8} = \dfrac{x + 5 - 3}{8} = \dfrac{x + 2}{8}$

c. $\dfrac{4x}{10} + \dfrac{3x}{10} = \dfrac{4x + 3x}{10} = \dfrac{7x}{10}$

d. $\dfrac{5}{x} + \dfrac{3}{x} = \dfrac{5 + 3}{x} = \dfrac{8}{x}$

To add or subtract fractions that do not have the same denominator, we must first find the LCD. We then change each fraction to an equivalent fraction that has the LCD for its denominator. Finally, when all that has been done, we add or subtract the numerators and put the result over the common denominator.

EXAMPLE 2   Add: $\dfrac{x}{3} + \dfrac{1}{2}$

SOLUTION   The LCD for 3 and 2 is 6. We multiply the numerator and the denominator of the first fraction by 2, and the numerator and the denominator of the second fraction by 3, to change each fraction to an equivalent fraction with the LCD for a denominator. We then add the numerators as usual. Here is how it looks:

$$\frac{x}{3} + \frac{1}{2} = \frac{x \cdot \mathbf{2}}{3 \cdot \mathbf{2}} + \frac{1 \cdot \mathbf{3}}{2 \cdot \mathbf{3}}$$ Change to equivalent fractions. Also, $x \cdot 2$ is the same as $2x$, because multiplication is commutative.

$$= \frac{2x}{6} + \frac{3}{6}$$

$$= \frac{2x + 3}{6}$$ Add the numerators

PRACTICE PROBLEMS

1. Add or subtract as indicated:

   a. $\dfrac{x}{6} + \dfrac{5}{6}$

   b. $\dfrac{x + 3}{7} - \dfrac{1}{7}$

   c. $\dfrac{9x}{4} + \dfrac{4x}{4}$

   d. $\dfrac{9}{x} + \dfrac{3}{x}$

Note   Remember, the LCD is the least common denominator. It is the smallest expression that is divisible by each of the denominators.

2. Add: $\dfrac{x}{3} + \dfrac{1}{5}$

Answers

1. **a.** $\dfrac{x + 5}{6}$ **b.** $\dfrac{x + 2}{7}$ **c.** $\dfrac{13x}{4}$ **d.** $\dfrac{12}{x}$

2. $\dfrac{5x + 3}{15}$

3. Add: $\dfrac{5}{x} + \dfrac{2}{3}$

Note In Examples 3 and 4, it is understood that x cannot be 0. Do you know why?

4. Add: $\dfrac{1}{2} + \dfrac{3}{x} + \dfrac{1}{5}$

5. Add or subtract as indicated.

a. $3 + \dfrac{x}{8}$

b. $1 - \dfrac{a}{4}$

c. $6 + \dfrac{2}{x}$

d. $x + \dfrac{2}{3}$

EXAMPLE 3   Add: $\dfrac{4}{x} + \dfrac{2}{3}$

SOLUTION   The LCD for x and 3 is $3x$. We multiply the numerator and the denominator of the first fraction by 3, and the numerator and the denominator of the second fraction by x, to get two fractions with the same denominator. We then add the numerators:

$$\dfrac{4}{x} + \dfrac{2}{3} = \dfrac{4 \cdot \mathbf{3}}{x \cdot \mathbf{3}} + \dfrac{2 \cdot \mathbf{x}}{3 \cdot \mathbf{x}} \qquad \text{Change to equivalent fractions}$$

$$= \dfrac{12}{3x} + \dfrac{2x}{3x}$$

$$= \dfrac{12 + 2x}{3x} \qquad \text{Add the numerators}$$

EXAMPLE 4   Add: $\dfrac{1}{2} + \dfrac{5}{x} + \dfrac{1}{3}$

SOLUTION   The LCD for 2, x, and 3 is $6x$.

$$\dfrac{1}{2} + \dfrac{5}{x} + \dfrac{1}{3} = \dfrac{1 \cdot \mathbf{3x}}{2 \cdot \mathbf{3x}} + \dfrac{5 \cdot \mathbf{6}}{x \cdot \mathbf{6}} + \dfrac{1 \cdot \mathbf{2x}}{3 \cdot \mathbf{2x}} \qquad \text{Change to equivalent fractions}$$

$$= \dfrac{3x}{6x} + \dfrac{30}{6x} + \dfrac{2x}{6x}$$

$$= \dfrac{5x + 30}{6x} \qquad \text{Add the numerators}$$

In this chapter we changed mixed numbers to improper fractions. For example, the mixed number $3\dfrac{4}{5}$ can be changed to an improper fraction as follows:

$$3\dfrac{4}{5} = 3 + \dfrac{4}{5} = \dfrac{3 \cdot \mathbf{5}}{1 \cdot \mathbf{5}} + \dfrac{4}{5} = \dfrac{15}{5} + \dfrac{4}{5} = \dfrac{19}{5}$$

A similar kind of problem in algebra would be to add 2 and $\dfrac{x}{8}$.

EXAMPLE 5   Add or subtract as indicated.

a. $2 + \dfrac{x}{8}$ **b.** $1 - \dfrac{a}{2}$ **c.** $5 + \dfrac{3}{x}$ **d.** $x + \dfrac{3}{5}$

SOLUTION   We can think of each whole number and the letter x in part (d) as a fraction with denominator 1. In each case we multiply the numerator and the denominator of the first number by the denominator of the fraction.

a. $2 + \dfrac{x}{8} = \dfrac{2 \cdot \mathbf{8}}{1 \cdot \mathbf{8}} + \dfrac{x}{8} = \dfrac{16}{8} + \dfrac{x}{8} = \dfrac{16 + x}{8}$

b. $1 - \dfrac{a}{2} = \dfrac{1 \cdot \mathbf{2}}{1 \cdot \mathbf{2}} - \dfrac{a}{2} = \dfrac{2}{2} - \dfrac{a}{2} = \dfrac{2 - a}{2}$

c. $5 + \dfrac{3}{x} = \dfrac{5 \cdot \mathbf{x}}{1 \cdot \mathbf{x}} + \dfrac{3}{x} = \dfrac{5x}{x} + \dfrac{3}{x} = \dfrac{5x + 3}{x}$

d. $x + \dfrac{3}{5} = \dfrac{x \cdot \mathbf{5}}{x \cdot \mathbf{5}} + \dfrac{3}{5} = \dfrac{5x}{5} + \dfrac{3}{5} = \dfrac{5x + 3}{5}$

Answers

3. $\dfrac{15 + 2x}{3x}$ **4.** $\dfrac{7x + 30}{10x}$

5. a. $\dfrac{24 + x}{8}$ **b.** $\dfrac{4 - a}{4}$

c. $\dfrac{6x + 2}{x}$ **d.** $\dfrac{3x + 2}{3}$

A Glimpse of Algebra Problems

Add or subtract as indicated.

1. $\dfrac{x}{4} + \dfrac{3}{4}$

$\dfrac{x+3}{4}$

2. $\dfrac{x}{8} - \dfrac{5}{8}$

$\dfrac{x-5}{8}$

3. $\dfrac{x+6}{5} - \dfrac{4}{5}$

$\dfrac{x+2}{5}$

4. $\dfrac{x+1}{3} + \dfrac{2}{3}$

$\dfrac{x+3}{3}$

5. $\dfrac{5x}{8} + \dfrac{2x}{8}$

$\dfrac{7x}{8}$

6. $\dfrac{9x}{7} - \dfrac{3x}{7}$

$\dfrac{6x}{7}$

7. $\dfrac{6}{x} - \dfrac{4}{x}$

$\dfrac{2}{x}$

8. $\dfrac{3}{x} + \dfrac{7}{x}$

$\dfrac{10}{x}$

For each sum or difference, find the LCD, change to equivalent fractions, and then add or subtract numerators as indicated.

9. $\dfrac{x}{2} + \dfrac{1}{3}$

$\dfrac{3x+2}{6}$

10. $\dfrac{x}{6} - \dfrac{3}{4}$

$\dfrac{2x-9}{12}$

11. $\dfrac{x}{2} - \dfrac{1}{4}$

$\dfrac{2x-1}{4}$

12. $\dfrac{x}{3} - \dfrac{1}{6}$

$\dfrac{2x-1}{6}$

13. $\dfrac{3}{x} + \dfrac{3}{4}$

$\dfrac{12+3x}{4x}$

14. $\dfrac{2}{x} - \dfrac{1}{3}$

$\dfrac{6-x}{3x}$

15. $\dfrac{4}{5} - \dfrac{1}{x}$

$\dfrac{4x-5}{5x}$

16. $\dfrac{3}{4} - \dfrac{1}{x}$

$\dfrac{3x-4}{4x}$

17. $\dfrac{1}{3} + \dfrac{2}{x} + \dfrac{1}{4}$

$\dfrac{7x+24}{12x}$

18. $\dfrac{1}{5} + \dfrac{1}{x} + \dfrac{1}{3}$

$\dfrac{8x+15}{15x}$

19. $\dfrac{1}{2} + \dfrac{1}{x} + \dfrac{1}{4}$

$\dfrac{3x+4}{4x}$

20. $\dfrac{1}{3} + \dfrac{1}{x} + \dfrac{1}{6}$

$\dfrac{x+2}{2x}$

Add or subtract as indicated.

21. $3 + \dfrac{x}{4}$

$\dfrac{12 + x}{4}$

22. $2 + \dfrac{x}{7}$

$\dfrac{14 + x}{7}$

23. $5 - \dfrac{x}{2}$

$\dfrac{10 - x}{2}$

24. $6 - \dfrac{x}{8}$

$\dfrac{48 - x}{8}$

25. $4 - \dfrac{a}{7}$

$\dfrac{28 - a}{7}$

26. $6 - \dfrac{a}{4}$

$\dfrac{24 - a}{4}$

27. $1 + \dfrac{2a}{5}$

$\dfrac{5 + 2a}{5}$

28. $3 + \dfrac{4a}{9}$

$\dfrac{27 + 4a}{9}$

29. $8 + \dfrac{3}{x}$

$\dfrac{8x + 3}{x}$

30. $7 + \dfrac{9}{x}$

$\dfrac{7x + 9}{x}$

31. $2 - \dfrac{5}{x}$

$\dfrac{2x - 5}{x}$

32. $3 - \dfrac{1}{x}$

$\dfrac{3x - 1}{x}$

33. $x + \dfrac{3}{4}$

$\dfrac{4x + 3}{4}$

34. $x + \dfrac{5}{6}$

$\dfrac{6x + 5}{6}$

35. $x + \dfrac{2x}{9}$

$\dfrac{11x}{9}$

36. $x + \dfrac{3x}{5}$

$\dfrac{8x}{5}$

37. $a - \dfrac{4a}{7}$

$\dfrac{3a}{7}$

38. $a - \dfrac{3a}{5}$

$\dfrac{2a}{5}$

39. $2x - \dfrac{3x}{4}$

$\dfrac{5x}{4}$

40. $3x - \dfrac{2x}{5}$

$\dfrac{13x}{5}$

Decimals

3

Introduction

The 2000 Summer Olympic Games in Sydney, Australia, featured more than 10,000 athletes competing from 199 countries. The image above shows many of the venues as they appeared in Google Earth in 2008, almost eight years after the 2000 Olympics. The chart below shows the top four finishes in the 400-meter Freestyle swimming event in Sydney.

400-meter Freestyle Swimming
Final times for the 400-meter freestyle swim

Ian Thorpe	3:40.59
Massimiliano Rosolino	3:43.40
Klete Keller	3:47.00
Emiliano Brembilla	3:47.01

Source: espn.com

The times in the chart are in minutes and seconds, accurate to the nearest hundredth of a second. In this chapter we work with numbers like these to obtain a good working knowledge of the decimal numbers we see everywhere around us.

The pretest below contains problems that are representative of the problems you will find in the chapter.

1. Write the number 4.013 in words.
Four and thirteen thousandths

2. Write 12.09 as a mixed number.
$12\frac{9}{100}$

3. Write *thirty-four hundredths* as a decimal number.
0.34

4. Write $\frac{21}{50}$ as a decimal
0.42

5. Write the following numbers in order from smallest to largest.
0.04, 0.4, 0.51, 0.5, 0.45, 0.41
0.04, 0.4, 0.41, 0.45, 0.5, 0.51

6. Change 0.85 to a fraction, and then reduce to lowest terms.
$\frac{17}{20}$

Perform the indicated operations.

7. $7.36 + 8.05$ 15.41

8. $20.3 - 15.09$ 5.21

9. 3.6×2.7 9.72

10. $56.78(10)$ 567.8

11. $32\overline{)131.84}$ 4.12

12. $1.04 \div 0.12$ 8.7

Getting Ready for Chapter 3

The problems below review material covered previously that you need to know in order to be successful in Chapter 3. If you have any difficulty with the problems here, you need to go back and review before going on to Chapter 3.

Simplify.

1. $25,430 + 2,897 + 379,600$
407,927

2. $39,812 - 14,236$
25,576

3. $2,000 - 1,564$
436

4. $800 - 137$
663

5. 305×436
132,980

6. $13(56)$
728

7. $480 + 12(32)^2$
12,768

8. $384 \div 4$
96

9. $49,896 \div 27$
1,848

10. $5,974 \div 20$
298 R 14

11. $5^2 + 7^2$
74

12. $\left(\frac{1}{4}\right)^2$
$\frac{1}{16}$

13. $\frac{3}{4}\left(\frac{2}{5}\right)$
$\frac{3}{10}$

14. $\frac{1}{2}\left(2\frac{5}{8}\right)\left(1\frac{1}{4}\right)$
$1\frac{41}{64}$

15. Round 9,235 to the nearest hundred.
9,200

16. Reduce: $\frac{38}{100}$
$\frac{19}{50}$

Factor into a product of prime factors.

17. 48
$2^4 \cdot 3$

18. 180
$2^2 \cdot 3^2 \cdot 5$

3.1

Objectives

A Understand place value for decimal numbers.

B Write decimal numbers in words and with digits.

C Convert decimals to fractions and fractions to decimals.

D Round a decimal number.

E Solve applications involving decimals.

Introduction . . .

In this chapter we will focus our attention on *decimals*. Anyone who has used money in the United States has worked with decimals already. For example, if you have been paid an hourly wage, such as

$6.25 per hour

⌐—— Decimal point

you have had experience with decimals. What is interesting and useful about decimals is their relationship to fractions and to powers of ten. The work we have done up to now—especially our work with fractions—can be used to develop the properties of decimal numbers.

A Place Value

In Chapter 1 we developed the idea of place value for the digits in a whole number. At that time we gave the name and the place value of each of the first seven columns in our number system, as follows:

Millions Column	Hundred Thousands Column	Ten Thousands Column	Thousands Column	Hundreds Column	Tens Column	Ones Column
1,000,000	100,000	10,000	1,000	100	10	1

As we move from right to left, we multiply by 10 each time. The value of each column is 10 times the value of the column on its right, with the rightmost column being 1. Up until now we have always looked at place value as increasing by a factor of 10 each time we move one column to the left:

Ten Thousands	Thousands	Hundreds	Tens	Ones
10,000 ←	1,000 ←	100 ←	10 ←	1
Multiply by 10	Multiply by 10	Multiply by 10	Multiply by 10	

To understand the idea behind decimal numbers, we notice that moving in the opposite direction, from left to right, we *divide* by 10 each time:

Ten Thousands	Thousands	Hundreds	Tens	Ones
10,000 →	1,000 →	100 →	10 →	1
Divide by 10	Divide by 10	Divide by 10	Divide by 10	

If we keep going to the right, the next column will have to be

$$1 \div 10 = \frac{1}{10} \qquad \text{Tenths}$$

The next one after that will be

$$\frac{1}{10} \div 10 = \frac{1}{10} \cdot \frac{1}{10} = \frac{1}{100} \qquad \text{Hundredths}$$

After that, we have

$$\frac{1}{100} \div 10 = \frac{1}{100} \cdot \frac{1}{10} = \frac{1}{1,000} \qquad \text{Thousandths}$$

We could continue this pattern as long as we wanted. We simply divide by 10 to move one column to the right. (And remember, dividing by 10 gives the same result as multiplying by $\frac{1}{10}$.)

To show where the ones column is, we use a *decimal point* between the ones column and the tenths column.

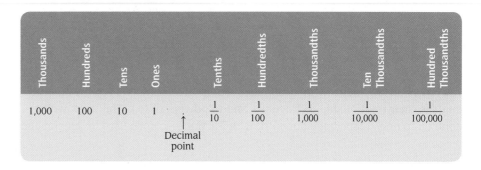

Thousands	Hundreds	Tens	Ones		Tenths	Hundredths	Thousandths	Ten Thousandths	Hundred Thousandths
1,000	100	10	1	$\uparrow$ Decimal point	$\frac{1}{10}$	$\frac{1}{100}$	$\frac{1}{1,000}$	$\frac{1}{10,000}$	$\frac{1}{100,000}$

The ones column can be thought of as the middle column, with columns larger than 1 to the left and columns smaller than 1 to the right. The first column to the right of the ones column is the tenths column, the next column to the right is the hundredths column, the next is the thousandths column, and so on. The decimal point is always written between the ones column and the tenths column.

We can use the place value of decimal fractions to write them in expanded form.

EXAMPLE 1 Write 423.576 in expanded form.

SOLUTION $423.576 = 400 + 20 + 3 + \dfrac{5}{10} + \dfrac{7}{100} + \dfrac{6}{1,000}$

B Writing Decimals with Words

EXAMPLE 2 Write each number in words.
   a. 0.4
   b. 0.04
   c. 0.004

SOLUTION **a.** 0.4 is "four tenths."
   b. 0.04 is "four hundredths."
   c. 0.004 is "four thousandths."

When a decimal fraction contains digits to the left of the decimal point, we use the word "and" to indicate where the decimal point is when writing the number in words.

EXAMPLE 3 Write each number in words.
   a. 5.4
   b. 5.04
   c. 5.004

SOLUTION **a.** 5.4 is "five and four tenths."
   b. 5.04 is "five and four hundredths."
   c. 5.004 is "five and four thousandths."

Note Because the digits to the right of the decimal point have fractional place values, numbers with digits to the right of the decimal point are called decimal fractions. In this book we will also call them decimal numbers, or simply decimals for short.

PRACTICE PROBLEMS

1. Write 785.462 in expanded form.

2. Write in words.
   a. 0.06
   b. 0.7
   c. 0.008

3. Write in words.
   a. 5.06
   b. 4.7
   c. 3.008

Note Sometimes we name decimal fractions by simply reading the digits from left to right and using the word "point" to indicate where the decimal point is. For example, using this method the number 5.04 is read "five point zero four."

Answers
1–3. See solutions section.

EXAMPLE 4 Write 3.64 in words.

SOLUTION The number 3.64 is read "three and sixty-four hundredths." The place values of the digits are as follows:

$$
\begin{array}{ccc}
3 & 6 & 4 \\
\uparrow & \uparrow & \uparrow \\
\text{3 ones} & \text{6 tenths} & \text{4 hundredths}
\end{array}
$$

We read the decimal part as "sixty-four hundredths" because

$$6 \text{ tenths} + 4 \text{ hundredths} = \frac{6}{10} + \frac{4}{100} = \frac{60}{100} + \frac{4}{100} = \frac{64}{100}$$

EXAMPLE 5 Write 25.4936 in words.

SOLUTION Using the idea given in Example 4, we write 25.4936 in words as "twenty-five and four thousand, nine hundred thirty-six ten thousandths."

C Converting Between Fractions and Decimals

In order to understand addition and subtraction of decimals in the next section, we need to be able to convert decimal numbers to fractions or mixed numbers.

EXAMPLE 6 Write each number as a fraction or a mixed number. Do not reduce to lowest terms.

    a. 0.004   **b.** 3.64   **c.** 25.4936

SOLUTION   **a.** Because 0.004 is 4 thousandths, we write

$$0.004 = \frac{4}{1{,}000}$$

Three digits after the decimal point   Three zeros

    b. Looking over the work in Example 4, we can write

$$3.64 = 3\frac{64}{100}$$

Two digits after the decimal point   Two zeros

    c. From the way in which we wrote 25.4936 in words in Example 5, we have

$$25.4936 = 25\frac{4936}{10{,}000}$$

Four digits after the decimal point   Four zeros

D Rounding Decimal Numbers

The rule for rounding decimal numbers is similar to the rule for rounding whole numbers. If the digit in the column to the right of the one we are rounding to is 5 or more, we add 1 to the digit in the column we are rounding to; otherwise, we leave it alone. We then replace all digits to the right of the column we are rounding to with zeros if they are to the left of the decimal point; otherwise, we simply delete them. Table 1 illustrates the procedure.

4. Write in words.
    a. 5.98
    b. 5.098

5. Write 305.406 in words.

6. Write each number as a fraction or a mixed number. Do not reduce to lowest terms.
    a. 0.06
    b. 5.98
    c. 305.406

Answers
4–5. See solutions section.

6. a. $\frac{6}{100}$ **b.** $5\frac{98}{100}$ **c.** $305\frac{406}{1{,}000}$

TABLE 1			
	Rounded to the Nearest		
Number	Whole Number	Tenth	Hundredth
24.785	25	24.8	24.79
2.3914	2	2.4	2.39
0.98243	1	1.0	0.98
14.0942	14	14.1	14.09
0.545	1	0.5	0.55

7. Round 8,935.042 to the nearest:
   a. hundred
   b. hundredth

EXAMPLE 7   Round 9,235.492 to the nearest hundred.

SOLUTION   The number next to the hundreds column is 3, which is less than 5. We change all digits to the right to 0, and we can drop all digits to the right of the decimal point, so we write

  9,200

8. Round 0.05067 to the nearest:
   a. ten thousandth
   b. tenth

EXAMPLE 8   Round 0.00346 to the nearest ten thousandth.

SOLUTION   Because the number to the right of the ten thousandths column is more than 5, we add 1 to the 4 and get

  0.0035

E   Applications with Decimals

9. Round each number in the bar chart to the nearest tenth of a dollar

EXAMPLE 9   The bar chart below shows some ticket prices for a recent major league baseball season. Round each ticket price to the nearest dollar.

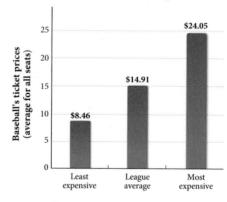

SOLUTION   Using our rule for rounding decimal numbers, we have the following results:

  Least expensive: $8.46 rounds to $8
  League average: $14.91 rounds to $15
  Most expensive: $24.05 rounds to $24

Getting Ready for Class

After reading through the preceding section, respond in your own words and in complete sentences.

1. Write 754.326 in expanded form.

2. Write $400 + 70 + 5 + \frac{1}{10} + \frac{3}{100} + \frac{7}{1,000}$ in decimal form.

3. Write seventy-two and three tenths in decimal form.

Answers
7. a. 8,900 **b.** 8,935.04
8. a. 0.0507 **b.** 0.1
9. Least expensive, $8.50;
   league average, $14.90;
   most expensive, $24.10

Problem Set 3.1

B Write out the name of each number in words. [Examples 2–5]

▶ **1.** 0.3
Three tenths

2. 0.03
Three hundredths

3. 0.015
Fifteen thousandths

▶ **4.** 0.0015
Fifteen ten thousandths

▶ **5.** 3.4
Three and four tenths

6. 2.04
Two and four hundredths

7. 52.7
Fifty-two and seven tenths

▶ **8.** 46.8
Forty-six and eight tenths

C Write each number as a fraction or a mixed number. Do not reduce your answers. [Example 6]

▶ **9.** 405.36
$405\frac{36}{100}$

10. 362.78
$362\frac{78}{100}$

▶ **11.** 9.009
$9\frac{9}{1,000}$

▶ **12.** 60.06
$60\frac{6}{100}$

13. 1.234
$1\frac{234}{1,000}$

14. 12.045
$12\frac{45}{1,000}$

▶ **15.** 0.00305
$\frac{305}{100,000}$

16. 2.00106
$2\frac{106}{100,000}$

A Give the place value of the 5 in each of the following numbers. [Examples 2–5]

▶ **17.** 458.327
Tens

18. 327.458
Hundredths

19. 29.52
Tenths

20. 25.92
Ones

21. 0.00375
Hundred thousandths

22. 0.00532
Thousandths

23. 275.01
Ones

24. 0.356
Hundredths

25. 539.76
Hundreds

26. 0.123456
Hundred thousandths

B Write each of the following as a decimal number.

▶ **27.** Fifty-five hundredths
0.55

28. Two hundred thirty-five ten thousandths
0.0235

▶ **29.** Six and nine tenths
6.9

30. Forty-five thousand and six hundred twenty-one thousandths
45,000.621

31. Eleven and eleven hundredths
11.11

▶ **32.** Twenty-six thousand, two hundred forty-five and sixteen hundredths
26,245.16

33. One hundred and two hundredths
100.02

34. Seventy-five and seventy-five hundred thousandths
75.00075

35. Three thousand and three thousandths
3,000.003

36. One thousand, one hundred eleven and one hundred eleven thousandths
1,111.111

For each pair of numbers, place the correct symbol, < or >, between the numbers.

37. a. 0.02 < 0.2

b. 0.3 > 0.032

38. a. 0.45 < 0.5

b. 0.5 < 0.56

▶ **39.** Write the following numbers in order from smallest to largest.

0.02   0.05   0.025   0.052   0.005   0.002

0.002   0.005   0.02   0.025   0.05   0.052

40. Write the following numbers in order from smallest to largest.

0.2   0.02   0.4   0.04   0.42   0.24

0.02   0.04   0.2   0.24   0.4   0.42

▶ **41.** Which of the following numbers will round to 7.5?

7.451   7.449   7.54   7.56

7.451   7.54

42. Which of the following numbers will round to 3.2?

3.14999   3.24999   3.279   3.16111

3.24999   3.16111

C Change each decimal to a fraction, and then reduce to lowest terms.

▶ **43.** 0.25

$\frac{1}{4}$

44. 0.75

$\frac{3}{4}$

▶ **45.** 0.125

$\frac{1}{8}$

46. 0.375

$\frac{3}{8}$

47. 0.625

$\frac{5}{8}$

▶ **48.** 0.0625

$\frac{1}{16}$

▶ **49.** 0.875

$\frac{7}{8}$

50. 0.1875

$\frac{3}{16}$

Estimating For each pair of numbers, choose the number that is closest to 10.

▶ **51.** 9.9 and 9.99

9.99

52. 8.5 and 8.05

8.5

▶ **53.** 10.5 and 10.05

10.05

54. 10.9 and 10.99

10.9

Estimating For each pair of numbers, choose the number that is closest to 0.

▶ **55.** 0.5 and 0.05

0.05

56. 0.10 and 0.05

0.05

▶ **57.** 0.01 and 0.02

0.01

58. 0.1 and 0.01

0.01

D Complete the following table. [Examples 7, 8]

| | Number | Whole Number | Rounded to the Nearest | | |
			Tenth	Hundredth	Thousandth
▶ **59.**	47.5479	48	47.5	47.55	47.548
60.	100.9256	101	100.9	100.93	100.926
▶ **61.**	0.8175	1	0.8	0.82	0.818
62.	29.9876	30	30.0	29.99	29.988
63.	0.1562	0	0.2	0.16	0.156
64.	128.9115	129	128.9	128.91	128.912
65.	2,789.3241	2,789	2,789.3	2,789.32	2,789.324
66.	0.8743	1	0.9	0.87	0.874
▶ **67.**	99.9999	100	100.0	100.00	100.000
68.	71.7634	72	71.8	71.76	71.763

E Applying the Concepts [Example 9]

100 Meters At the 1928 Olympic Games in Amsterdam, the winning time for the women's 100 meters was 12.2 seconds. Since then, the time has continued to get faster. The chart shows the fastest times for the women's 100 meters in competetion. Use the chart to answer Problems 69 and 70.

69. What is the place value of the 3 in Christine Arron's time in 1998?

Hundredths

Faster Than...

Florence Griffith Joyner, 1988	10.49 sec
Marion Jones, 1998	10.65 sec
Christine Arron, 1998	10.73 sec
Merlene Ottey, 1996	10.74 sec

Source: www.tenmojo.com

70. Write Christine Arron's time using words.

ten and seventy-three hundredths seconds

71. Gasoline Prices The bar chart below was created from a survey by the U.S. Department of Energy's Energy Information Administration during the month of May 2008. It gives the average price of regular gasoline for the state of California on each Monday of the month. Use the information in the chart to fill in the table.

PRICE OF 1 GALLON OF REGULAR GASOLINE	
Date	**Price (Dollars)**
5/5/08	3.903
5/12/08	3.919
5/19/08	3.952
5/26/08	4.099

72. Speed and Time The bar chart below was created from data given by *Car and Driver* magazine. It gives the minimum time in seconds for a Toyota Echo to reach various speeds from a complete stop. Use the information in the chart to fill in the table.

Speed (Miles per Hour)	Time (Seconds)
30	2.7
40	4.2
50	6.2
60	8.5
70	11.6
80	15.4
90	20.6

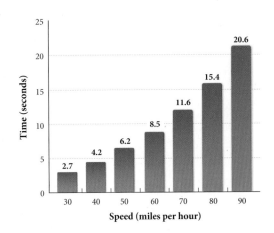

73. Penny Weight If you have a penny dated anytime from 1959 through 1982, its original weight was 3.11 grams. If the penny has a date of 1983 or later, the original weight was 2.5 grams. Write the two weights in words.

Three and eleven hundredths grams; two and five tenths grams

1959-1982   1983 - present

74. Halley's Comet Halley's comet was seen from the earth during 1986. It will be another 76.1 years before it returns. Write 76.1 in words.

Seventy-six and one tenth

NASA

75. Nutrition A 50-gram egg contains 0.15 milligram of riboflavin. Write 0.15 in words.

Fifteen hundredths

76. Nutrition One medium banana contains 0.64 milligram of B$_6$. Write 0.64 in words.

Sixty-four hundredths

■ Getting Ready for the Next Section

In the next section we will do addition and subtraction with decimals. To understand the process of addition and subtraction, we need to understand the process of addition and subtraction with mixed numbers.

Find each of the following sums and differences. (Add or subtract.)

77. $4\frac{3}{10} + 2\frac{1}{100}$

$6\frac{31}{100}$

78. $5\frac{35}{100} + 2\frac{3}{10}$

$7\frac{13}{20}$

79. $8\frac{5}{10} - 2\frac{4}{100}$

$6\frac{23}{50}$

80. $6\frac{3}{100} - 2\frac{125}{1,000}$

$3\frac{181}{200}$

81. $5\frac{1}{10} + 6\frac{2}{100} + 7\frac{3}{1,000}$

$18\frac{123}{1,000}$

82. $4\frac{3}{1,000} + 6\frac{3}{10} + 7\frac{123}{1,000}$

$17\frac{213}{500}$

■ Maintaining Your Skills

Write the fractions in order from smallest to largest.

83. $\frac{3}{8}$ $\frac{3}{16}$ $\frac{3}{4}$ $\frac{3}{10}$

$\frac{3}{16} < \frac{3}{10} < \frac{3}{8} < \frac{3}{4}$

84. $\frac{3}{4}$ $\frac{1}{4}$ $\frac{5}{4}$ $\frac{1}{2}$

$\frac{1}{4} < \frac{1}{2} < \frac{3}{4} < \frac{5}{4}$

Place the correct inequality symbol, $<$ or $>$ between each pair of numbers.

85. $\frac{3}{8}$ $<$ $\frac{5}{6}$

86. $\frac{9}{10}$ $<$ $\frac{10}{11}$

87. $\frac{1}{12}$ $>$ $\frac{1}{13}$

88. $\frac{3}{4}$ $>$ $\frac{5}{8}$

Introduction . . .

The chart shows the top finishing times for the women's 400-meter race during the Sydney Olympics in 2000. In order to analyze the different finishing times, it is important that you are able to add and subtract decimals, and that is what we will cover in this section.

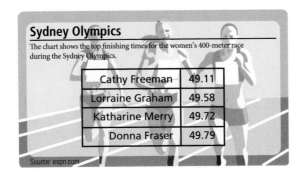

Sydney Olympics

The chart shows the top finishing times for the women's 400-meter race during the Sydney Olympics.

Cathy Freeman	49.11
Lorraine Graham	49.58
Katharine Merry	49.72
Donna Fraser	49.79

Source: espn.com

A Combining Decimals

Suppose you are earning $8.50 an hour and you receive a raise of $1.25 an hour. Your new hourly rate of pay is

$$
\begin{array}{r}
\$8.50 \\
+ \ \$1.25 \\
\hline
\$9.75
\end{array}
$$

To add the two rates of pay, we align the decimal points, and then add in columns.

To see why this is true in general, we can use mixed-number notation:

$$8.50 = 8\frac{50}{100}$$

$$+ \ 1.25 = 1\frac{25}{100}$$

$$\rule{3cm}{0.4pt}$$

$$9\frac{75}{100} = 9.75$$

We can visualize the mathematics above by thinking in terms of money:

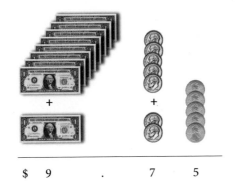

$$
\begin{array}{ccccc}
\$ & 9 & . & 7 & 5
\end{array}
$$

Instructor Note
Most of my students can add decimal numbers without much trouble. I like to show the justification for aligning decimal points by converting to mixed numbers. That way, we continue to develop and justify our rules, instead of just stating them.

PRACTICE PROBLEMS

1. Change each decimal to a fraction, and then add. Write your answer as a decimal.
   a. 38.45 + 456.073
   b. 38.045 + 456.73

Add by first changing to fractions: 25.43 + 2.897 + 379.6

SOLUTION   We first change each decimal to a mixed number. We then write each fraction using the least common denominator and add as usual:

$$25.43 = 25\frac{43}{100} = 25\frac{430}{1,000}$$

$$2.897 = 2\frac{897}{1,000} = 2\frac{897}{1,000}$$

$$+\ 379.6 = 379\frac{6}{10} = 379\frac{600}{1,000}$$

$$406\frac{1,927}{1,000} = 407\frac{927}{1,000} = 407.927$$

Again, the result is the same if we just line up the decimal points and add as if we were adding whole numbers:

$$
\begin{array}{r}
25.430 \\
2.897 \\
+\ 379.600 \\
\hline
407.927
\end{array}
$$

Notice that we can fill in zeros on the right to help keep the numbers in the correct columns. Doing this does not change the value of any of the numbers.

Note: The decimal point in the answer is directly below the decimal points in the problem

The same thing would happen if we were to subtract two decimal numbers. We can use these facts to write a rule for addition and subtraction of decimal numbers.

Rule

To add (or subtract) decimal numbers, we line up the decimal points and add (or subtract) as usual. The decimal point in the result is written directly below the decimal points in the problem.

We will use this rule for the rest of the examples in this section.

2. Subtract: 78.674 − 23.431

Subtract: 39.812 − 14.236

SOLUTION   We write the numbers vertically, with the decimal points lined up, and subtract as usual.

$$
\begin{array}{r}
39.812 \\
-\ 14.236 \\
\hline
25.576
\end{array}
$$

3. Add: 16 + 0.033 + 4.6 + 0.08

Add: 8 + 0.002 + 3.1 + 0.04

SOLUTION   To make sure we keep the digits in the correct columns, we can write zeros to the right of the rightmost digits.

$$
\begin{array}{r}
8 = 8.000 \\
3.1 = 3.100 \\
0.04 = 0.040
\end{array}
$$

Writing the extra zeros here is really equivalent to finding a common denominator for the fractional parts of the original four numbers—now we have a thousandths column in all the numbers

Answers
1. a. 494.523 **b.** 494.775
2. 55.243 **3.** 20.713

This doesn't change the value of any of the numbers, and it makes our task easier. Now we have

```
  8.000
  0.002
  3.100
+ 0.040
-------
 11.142
```

Subtract: 5.9 − 3.0814

SOLUTION In this case it is very helpful to write 5.9 as 5.9000, since we will have to borrow in order to subtract.

```
  5.9000
− 3.0814
--------
  2.8186
```

Subtract 3.09 from the sum of 9 and 5.472.

SOLUTION Writing the problem in symbols, we have

$$(9 + 5.472) − 3.09 = 14.472 − 3.09$$
$$= 11.382$$

B Applications

While I was writing this section of the book, I stopped to have lunch with a friend at a coffee shop near my office. The bill for lunch was $15.64. I gave the person at the cash register a $20 bill. For change, I received four $1 bills, a quarter, a nickel, and a penny. Was my change correct?

SOLUTION To find the total amount of money I received in change, we add:

```
Four $1 bills  =  $4.00
One quarter    =   0.25
One nickel     =   0.05
One penny      =   0.01
                 -------
Total          =  $4.31
```

To find out if this is the correct amount, we subtract the amount of the bill from $20.00.

```
 $20.00
− 15.64
-------
 $ 4.36
```

The change was not correct. It is off by 5 cents. Instead of the nickel, I should have been given a dime.

4. Subtract:
   a. 6.7 − 2.05
   b. 6.7 − 2.0563

5. Subtract 5.89 from the sum of 7 and 3.567.

6. If you pay for a purchase of $9.56 with a $10 bill, how much money should you receive in change? What will you do if the change that is given to you is one quarter, two dimes, and four pennies?

Answers
4. a. 4.65 **b.** 4.6437 **5.** 4.677
6. $0.44; Tell the clerk that you have been given too much change. Instead of two dimes, you should have received one dime and one nickel.

7. Find the perimeter of each stamp in Example 9 from the dimensions given below.
   a. Each side is 1.38 inches

b. Base = 6.6 centimeters, other two sides = 4.7 centimeters

EXAMPLE 7 Find the perimeter of each of the following stamps. Write your answer as a decimal, rounded to the nearest tenth, if necessary.

a.

Each side is 3.5 centimeters

b.

Base = 2.625 inches
Other two sides = 1.875 inches

SOLUTION To find the perimeter, we add the lengths of all the sides together.
   a. $P = 3.5 + 3.5 + 3.5 + 3.5 = 14.0$ cm
   b. $P = 2.625 + 1.875 + 1.875 = 6.4$ in.

STUDY SKILLS
Begin to Develop Confidence with Word Problems

The main difference between people who are good at working word problems and those who are not seems to be confidence. People with confidence know that no matter how long it takes them, they will eventually be able to solve the problem they are working on. Those without confidence begin by saying to themselves, "I'll never be able to work this problem." If you are in this second group, then instead of telling yourself that you can't do word problems, that you don't like them, or that they're not good for anything anyway, decide to do whatever it takes to master them.

Getting Ready for Class

After reading through the preceding section, respond in your own words and in complete sentences.

1. When adding numbers with decimals, why is it important to line up the decimal points?

2. Write 379.6 in mixed-number notation.

3. Look at Example 6 in this section of your book. If I had given the person at the cash register a $20 bill and four pennies, how much change should I then have received?

4. How many quarters does the decimal 0.75 represent?

Answers
7. a. 5.52 in. **b.** 16.0 cm

Problem Set 3.2

A Find each of the following sums. (Add.) [Examples 1, 3]

▶ **1.** 2.91 + 3.28
6.19

2. 8.97 + 2.04
11.01

▶ **3.** 0.04 + 0.31 + 0.78
1.13

4. 0.06 + 0.92 + 0.65
1.63

5. 3.89 + 2.4
6.29

▶ **6.** 7.65 + 3.8
11.45

▶ **7.** 4.532 + 1.81 + 2.7
9.042

8. 9.679 + 3.49 + 6.5
19.669

▶ **9.** 0.081 + 5 + 2.94
8.021

10. 0.396 + 7 + 3.96
11.356

11. 5.0003 + 6.78 + 0.004
11.7843

▶ **12.** 27.0179 + 7.89 + 0.009
34.9169

13.   7.123
        8.12
      + 9.1
      ‾‾‾‾‾‾
       24.343

▶ **14.**   5.432
         4.32
       + 3.2
       ‾‾‾‾‾‾
        12.952

15.   9.001
         8.01
       + 7.1
       ‾‾‾‾‾‾
        24.111

16.   6.003
         5.02
       + 4.1
       ‾‾‾‾‾‾
        15.123

▶ **17.**   89.7854
           3.4
          65.35
        + 100.006
        ‾‾‾‾‾‾‾‾‾‾
         258.5414

▶ **18.**   57.4698
            9.89
           32.032
         + 572.0079
         ‾‾‾‾‾‾‾‾‾‾‾
          671.3997

19.   543.21
         + 123.45
         ‾‾‾‾‾‾‾‾
          666.66

▶ **20.**   987.654
           + 456.789
           ‾‾‾‾‾‾‾‾‾
            1,444.443

A Find each of the following differences. (Subtract.) [Examples 2, 4]

21. 99.34 − 88.23
11.11

22. 47.69 − 36.58
11.11

23. 5.97 − 2.4
3.57

24. 9.87 − 1.04
8.83

▶ **25.** 6.3 − 2.08
4.22

26. 7.5 − 3.04
4.46

▶ **27.** 149.37 − 28.96
120.41

28. 796.45 − 32.68
763.77

29. 45 − 0.067
44.933

▶ **30.** 48 − 0.075
47.925

▶ **31.** 8 − 0.327
7.673

32. 12 − 0.962
11.038

▶ **33.** 765.432 − 234.567
530.865

34. 654.321 − 123.456
530.865

A Subtract. [Example 4]

35. 34.07
− 6.18
27.89

36. 25.008
− 3.119
21.889

▶ **37.** 40.04
− 4.4
35.64

38. 50.05
− 5.5
44.55

39. 768.436
−356.998
411.438

▶ **40.** 495.237
− 247.668
247.569

A Add and subtract as indicated. [Examples 1–7]

41. (7.8 − 4.3) + 2.5
6

42. (8.3 − 1.2) + 3.4
10.5

▶ **43.** 7.8 − (4.3 + 2.5)
1

44. 8.3 − (1.2 + 3.4)
3.7

▶ **45.** (9.7 − 5.2) − 1.4
3.1

46. (7.8 − 3.2) − 1.5
3.1

47. 9.7 − (5.2 − 1.4)
5.9

▶ **48.** 7.8 − (3.2 − 1.5)
6.1

▶ **49.** Subtract 5 from the sum of 8.2 and 0.072.
3.272

50. Subtract 8 from the sum of 9.37 and 2.5.
3.87

▶ **51.** What number is added to 0.035 to obtain 4.036?
4.001

52. What number is added to 0.043 to obtain 6.054?
6.011

B **Applying the Concepts** [Examples 6, 7]

53. 100 Meters At the 1928 Olympic Games in Amsterdam, the winning time for the women's 100 meters was 12.2 seconds. The chart shows the fastest times for the women's 100 meters. How much faster was Christine Arron's time than the first time recorded in 1928?
1.47 seconds

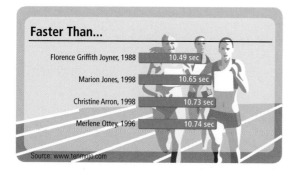

54. Computers The chart shows how many computers can be found in the countries containing the most computers. What is the total number of computers that can be found in these three countries?
372.9 million computers

55. Take-Home Pay A college professor making $2,105.96 per month has deducted from her check $311.93 for federal income tax, $158.21 for retirement, and $64.72 for state income tax. How much does the professor take home after the deductions have been taken from her monthly income?
$1,571.10

56. Take-Home Pay A cook making $1,504.75 a month has deductions of $157.32 for federal income tax, $58.52 for Social Security, and $45.12 for state income tax. How much does the cook take home after the deductions have been taken from his check?
$1,243.79

57. Perimeter of a Stamp This stamp shows the Mexican artist Frida Kahlo. The stamp was issued in 2001 and is the first U.S. stamp to honor a Hispanic woman. The image area of the stamp has a width of 0.84 inches and a length of 1.41 inches. Find the perimeter of the image.

4.5 in.

© 2004 Banco de México

58. Perimeter of a Stamp This stamp was issued in 2001 to honor the Italian scientist Enrico Fermi. The stamp caused some discussion because some of the mathematics in the upper left corner of the stamp is incorrect. The image area of the stamp has a width of 21.4 millimeters and a length of 35.8 millimeters. Find the perimeter of the image.

114.4 mm

▶ **59. Change** A person buys $4.57 worth of candy. If he pays for the candy with a $10 bill, how much change should he receive?

$5.43

▶ **60. Checking Account** A checking account contains $342.38. If checks are written for $25.04, $36.71, and $210, how much money is left in the account?

$70.63

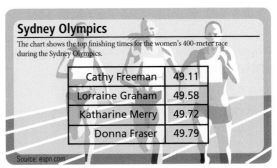

		RECORD ALL CHARGES OR CREDITS THAT AFFECT YOUR ACCOUNT			
NUMBER	DATE	DESCRIPTION OF TRANSACTION	PAYMENT/DEBIT (-)	DEPOSIT/CREDIT (+)	BALANCE
	2/8	Deposit		$342 38	$342 38
1457	2/8	Woolworths	$25 04		
1458	2/9	Walgreens	$36 71		
1459	2/11	Electric Company	$210 00		?

61. Sydney Olympics The chart show the top finishing times for the mens' 400-meter freestyle swim during Sydney's Olympics. How much faster was Ian Thorpe than Emiliano Brembilla?

6.42 seconds

400-meter Freestyle Swimming
Final times for the 400-meter freestyle swim.

Ian Thorpe	3:40.59
Massimiliano Rosolino	3:43.40
Klete Keller	3:47.00
Emiliano Brembilla	3:47.01

Source: espn.com

62. Sydney Olympics The chart shows the top finishing times for the women's 400-meter race during the Sydney Olympics. How much faster was Lorraine Graham than Katharine Merry?

0.14 seconds

Sydney Olympics
The chart shows the top finishing times for the women's 400-meter race during the Sydney Olympics.

Cathy Freeman	49.11
Lorraine Graham	49.58
Katharine Merry	49.72
Donna Fraser	49.79

Source: espn.com

▶ **63. Geometry** A rectangle has a perimeter of 9.5 inches. If the length is 2.75 inches, find the width.

2 in.

64. Geometry A rectangle has a perimeter of 11 inches. If the width is 2.5 inches, find the length.

3 in.

65. Change Suppose you eat dinner in a restaurant and the bill comes to $16.76. If you give the cashier a $20 bill and a penny, how much change should you receive? List the bills and coins you should receive for change.

$3.25; three $1 bills and a quarter

66. Change Suppose you buy some tools at the hardware store and the bill comes to $37.87. If you give the cashier two $20 bills and 2 pennies, how much change should you receive? List the bills and coins you should receive for change.

$2.15; two $1 bills, one dime, one nickel

Sequences Find the next number in each sequence.

67. 2.5, 2.75, 3, . . .

3.25

68. 3.125, 3.375, 3.625, . . .

3.875

Getting Ready for the Next Section

To understand how to multiply decimals, we need to understand multiplication with whole numbers, fractions, and mixed numbers. The following problems review these concepts.

69. $\dfrac{1}{10} \cdot \dfrac{3}{10}$

$\dfrac{3}{100}$

70. $\dfrac{5}{10} \cdot \dfrac{6}{10}$

$\dfrac{3}{10}$

71. $\dfrac{3}{100} \cdot \dfrac{17}{100}$

$\dfrac{51}{10,000}$

72. $\dfrac{7}{100} \cdot \dfrac{31}{100}$

$\dfrac{217}{10,000}$

73. $5\left(\dfrac{3}{10}\right)$

$1\dfrac{1}{2}$

74. $7 \cdot \dfrac{7}{10}$

$4\dfrac{9}{10}$

75. $56 \cdot 25$

1,400

76. $39(48)$

1,872

77. $\dfrac{5}{10} \times \dfrac{3}{10}$

$\dfrac{3}{20}$

78. $\dfrac{5}{100} \times \dfrac{3}{1,000}$

$\dfrac{3}{20,000}$

79. $2\dfrac{1}{10} \times \dfrac{7}{100}$

$\dfrac{147}{1,000}$

80. $3\dfrac{5}{10} \times \dfrac{4}{100}$

$\dfrac{7}{50}$

81. $305(436)$

132,980

82. $403(522)$

210,366

83. $5(420 + 3)$

2,115

84. $3(550 + 2)$

1656

Maintaining Your Skills

Use the rule for order of operations to simplify each expression.

85. $30 \div 5 \cdot 2$

12

86. $60 \div 3 \cdot 10$

200

87. $22 - 2 \cdot 3$

16

88. $37 - 7 \cdot 2$

23

89. $12 + 18 \div 2 - 1$

20

90. $15 + 10 \div 5 - 4$

13

91. $3 \cdot 5^2 - 75 \div 5 + 2^3$

68

92. $2 \cdot 3^2 - 18 \div 3 + 2^4$

28

Introduction . . .

The distance around a circle is called the circumference. If you know the circumference of a bicycle wheel, and you ride the bicycle for one mile, you can calculate how many times the wheel has turned through one complete revolution. In this section we learn how to multiply decimal numbers, and this gives us the information we need to work with circles and their circumferences.

A Multiplying with Decimals

Before we introduce circumference, we need to back up and discuss multiplication with decimals. Suppose that during a half-price sale a calendar that usually sells for $6.42 is priced at $3.21. Therefore it must be true that

$$\frac{1}{2} \text{ of } 6.42 \text{ is } 3.21$$

But, because $\frac{1}{2}$ can be written as 0.5 and *of* translates to *multiply*, we can write this problem again as

$$0.5 \times 6.42 = 3.21$$

If we were to ignore the decimal points in this problem and simply multiply 5 and 642, the result would be 3,210. So, multiplication with decimal numbers is similar to multiplication with whole numbers. The difference lies in deciding where to place the decimal point in the answer. To find out how this is done, we can use fraction notation.

EXAMPLE 1 Change each decimal to a fraction and multiply:

0.5 × 0.3   To indicate multiplication we are using a × sign here instead of a dot so we won't confuse the decimal points with the multiplication symbol.

SOLUTION Changing each decimal to a fraction and multiplying, we have

$$0.5 \times 0.3 = \frac{5}{10} \times \frac{3}{10} \qquad \text{Change to fractions}$$

$$= \frac{15}{100} \qquad \text{Multiply numerators and multiply denominators}$$

$$= 0.15 \qquad \text{Write the answer in decimal form}$$

The result is 0.15, which has two digits to the right of the decimal point.

What we want to do now is find a shortcut that will allow us to multiply decimals without first having to change each decimal number to a fraction. Let's look at another example.

PRACTICE PROBLEMS

1. Change each decimal to a fraction and multiply. Write your answer as a decimal.
   a. 0.4 × 0.6
   b. 0.04 × 0.06

Instructor Note
When students read through the first three examples here, you may find that some will complain that we are making things harder than they need to be. I simply remind them that we are developing the rule for multiplication with decimals. Once we have the rule, we will not convert to fractions to multiply.

Answer
1. a. 0.24 **b.** 0.0024

2. Change each decimal to a fraction and multiply. Write your answer as a decimal.
   a. 0.5×0.007
   b. 0.05×0.07

EXAMPLE 2 Change each decimal to a fraction and multiply: 0.05×0.003

SOLUTION

$$0.05 \times 0.003 = \frac{5}{100} \times \frac{3}{1,000}$$ Change to fractions

$$= \frac{15}{100,000}$$ Multiply numerators and multiply denominators

$$= 0.00015$$ Write the answer in decimal form

The result is 0.00015, which has a total of five digits to the right of the decimal point.

Looking over these first two examples, we can see that the digits in the result are just what we would get if we simply forgot about the decimal points and multiplied; that is, $3 \times 5 = 15$. The decimal point in the result is placed so that the total number of digits to its right is the same as the total number of digits to the right of both decimal points in the original two numbers. The reason this is true becomes clear when we look at the denominators after we have changed from decimals to fractions.

3. Change each decimal to a fraction and multiply. Write your answer as a decimal.
   a. 3.5×0.04
   b. 0.35×0.4

EXAMPLE 3 Multiply: 2.1×0.07

SOLUTION

$$2.1 \times 0.07 = 2\frac{1}{10} \times \frac{7}{100}$$ Change to fractions

$$= \frac{21}{10} \times \frac{7}{100}$$

$$= \frac{147}{1,000}$$ Multiply numerators and multiply denominators

$$= 0.147$$ Write the answer as a decimal

Again, the digits in the answer come from multiplying $21 \times 7 = 147$. The decimal point is placed so that there are three digits to its right, because that is the total number of digits to the right of the decimal points in 2.1 and 0.07.

We summarize this discussion with a rule.

> **Rule**
>
> To multiply two decimal numbers:
>
> **1.** Multiply as you would if the decimal points were not there.
>
> **2.** Place the decimal point in the answer so that the number of digits to its right is equal to the total number of digits to the right of the decimal points in the original two numbers in the problem.

4. How many digits will be to the right of the decimal point in the following products?
   a. 3.706×55.88
   b. 37.06×0.5588

EXAMPLE 4 How many digits will be to the right of the decimal point in the following product?

$$2.987 \times 24.82$$

SOLUTION There are three digits to the right of the decimal point in 2.987 and two digits to the right in 24.82. Therefore, there will be $3 + 2 = 5$ digits to the right of the decimal point in their product.

Answers
2. Both are 0.0035
3. Both are 0.14   **4. a.** 5   **b.** 6

EXAMPLE 5 Multiply: 3.05×4.36

SOLUTION We can set this up as if it were a multiplication problem with whole numbers. We multiply and then place the decimal point in the correct position in the answer.

$$
\begin{array}{r}
3.05 \quad \longleftarrow \text{2 digits to the right of decimal point} \\
\times\ 4.36 \quad \longleftarrow \text{2 digits to the right of decimal point} \\
\hline
1830 \\
915 \\
12\ 20 \\
\hline
13.2980
\end{array}
$$

The decimal point is placed so that there are $2 + 2 = 4$ digits to its right

As you can see, multiplying decimal numbers is just like multiplying whole numbers, except that we must place the decimal point in the result in the correct position.

Estimating

Look back to Example 5. We could have placed the decimal point in the answer by rounding the two numbers to the nearest whole number and then multiplying them. Because 3.05 rounds to 3 and 4.36 rounds to 4, and the product of 3 and 4 is 12, we estimate that the answer to 3.05×4.36 will be close to 12. We then place the decimal point in the product 132980 between the 3 and the 2 in order to make it into a number close to 12.

EXAMPLE 6 Estimate the answer to each of the following products.
    a. 29.4×8.2 **b.** 68.5×172 **c.** $(6.32)^2$

SOLUTION   **a.** Because 29.4 is approximately 30 and 8.2 is approximately 8, we estimate this product to be about $30 \times 8 = 240$. (If we were to multiply 29.4 and 8.2, we would find the product to be exactly 241.08.)

    b. Rounding 68.5 to 70 and 172 to 170, we estimate this product to be $70 \times 170 = 11,900$. (The exact answer is 11,782.) Note here that we do not always round the numbers to the nearest whole number when making estimates. The idea is to round to numbers that will be easy to multiply.

    c. Because 6.32 is approximately 6 and $6^2 = 36$, we estimate our answer to be close to 36. (The actual answer is 39.9424.)

5. Multiply.
  a. 4.03×5.22
  b. 40.3×0.522

6. Estimate the answer to each product.
  a. 82.3×5.8
  b. 37.5×178
  c. $(8.21)^2$

Answers
5. Both are 21.0366
6. a. 480 **b.** 7,200 **c.** 64

Combined Operations

We can use the rule for order of operations to simplify expressions involving decimal numbers and addition, subtraction, and multiplication.

EXAMPLE 7 Perform the indicated operations: $0.05(4.2 + 0.03)$

SOLUTION We begin by adding inside the parentheses:

$$0.05(4.2 + 0.03) = 0.05(4.23) \quad \text{Add}$$
$$= 0.2115 \quad \text{Multiply}$$

Notice that we could also have used the distributive property first, and the result would be unchanged:

$$0.05(4.2 + 0.03) = 0.05(4.2) + 0.05(0.03) \quad \text{Distributive property}$$
$$= 0.210 + 0.0015 \quad \text{Multiply}$$
$$= 0.2115 \quad \text{Add}$$

EXAMPLE 8 Simplify: $4.8 + 12(3.2)^2$

SOLUTION According to the rule for order of operations, we must first evaluate the number with an exponent, then multiply, and finally add.

$$4.8 + 12(3.2)^2 = 4.8 + 12(10.24) \quad (3.2)^2 = 10.24$$
$$= 4.8 + 122.88 \quad \text{Multiply}$$
$$= 127.68 \quad \text{Add}$$

B Applications

EXAMPLE 9 Find the area of each of the following stamps.

a. Each side is 35.0 millimeters

b. Round to the nearest hundredth.

Length = 1.56 inches
Width = 0.99 inches

Peanuts: © United Feature Syndicate, Inc.

SOLUTION Applying our formulas for area we have

a. $A = s^2 = (35 \text{ mm})^2 = 1,225 \text{ mm}^2$

b. $A = lw = (1.56 \text{ in.})(0.99 \text{ in.}) = 1.54 \text{ in}^2$

---

7. Perform the indicated operations.
  a. $0.03(5.5 + 0.02)$
  b. $0.03(0.55 + 0.002)$

8. Simplify.
  a. $5.7 + 14(2.4)^2$
  b. $0.57 + 1.4(2.4)^2$

9. Find the area of each stamp in Example 9 from the dimensions given below. Round answers to the nearest hundredth.
  a. Each side is 1.38 inches
  b. Length = 39.6 millimeters, width = 25.1 millimeters

Answers
7. a. 0.1656 **b.** 0.01656
8. a. 86.34 **b.** 8.634
9. a. 1.90 in² **b.** 993.96 mm²

EXAMPLE 10   Sally earns $6.82 for each of the first 36 hours she works in one week and $10.23 in overtime pay for each additional hour she works in the same week. How much money will she make if she works 42 hours in one week?

SOLUTION   The difference between 42 and 36 is 6 hours of overtime pay. The total amount of money she will make is

Pay for the first   Pay for the
36 hours   next 6 hours

$$6.82(36) + 10.23(6) = 245.52 + 61.38$$
$$= 306.90$$

She will make $306.90 for working 42 hours in one week.

10. How much will Sally make if she works 50 hours in one week?

Note   To estimate the answer to Example 10 before doing the actual calculations, we would do the following: $6(40) + 10(6) = 240 + 60 = 300$

C Circumference

FACTS FROM GEOMETRY   The Circumference of a Circle

The *circumference* of a circle is the distance around the outside, just as the perimeter of a polygon is the distance around the outside. The circumference of a circle can be found by measuring its radius or diameter and then using the appropriate formula. The *radius* of a circle is the distance from the center of the circle to the circle itself. The radius is denoted by the letter r. The *diameter* of a circle is the distance from one side to the other, through the center. The diameter is denoted by the letter d. In Figure 1 we can see that the diameter is twice the radius, or

$$d = 2r$$

The relationship between the circumference and the diameter or radius is not as obvious. As a matter of fact, it takes some fairly complicated mathematics to show just what the relationship between the circumference and the diameter is.

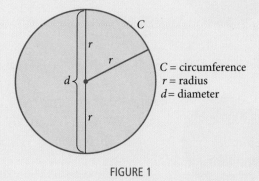

C = circumference
r = radius
d = diameter

FIGURE 1

If you took a string and actually measured the circumference of a circle by wrapping the string around the circle and then measured the diameter of the same circle, you would find that the ratio of the circumference to the diameter, C/d, would be approximately equal to 3.14. The actual ratio of C to d in any circle is an irrational number. It can't be written in decimal form. We use the symbol π (Greek pi) to represent this ratio. In symbols the relationship between the circumference and the diameter in any circle is

$$\frac{C}{d} = \pi$$

Answer
10. $388.74

Knowing what we do about the relationship between division and multiplication, we can rewrite this formula as

$$C = \pi d$$

This is the formula for the circumference of a circle. When we do the actual calculations, we will use the approximation 3.14 for π.

Because $d = 2r$, the same formula written in terms of the radius is

$$C = 2\pi r$$

Here are some examples that show how we use the formulas given above to find the circumference of a circle.

EXAMPLE 11 Find the circumference of a circle with a diameter of 5 feet.

SOLUTION Substituting 5 for d in the formula $C = \pi d$, and using 3.14 for π, we have

$$C = 3.14(5)$$
$$= 15.7 \text{ feet}$$

11. Find the circumference of a circle with a diameter of 3 centimeters.

EXAMPLE 12 Find the circumference of each coin.

a. 1 Euro coin (Round to the nearest whole number.)

Diameter = 23.25 millimeters

12. Find the circumference for each coin in Example 12 from the dimensions given below. Round answers to the nearest hundredth.
a. Diameter = 0.92 inches

b. Susan B. Anthony dollar (Round to the nearest hundredth.)

Radius = 0.52 inch

b. Radius = 13.20 millimeters

SOLUTION Applying our formulas for circumference we have:

a. $C = \pi d \approx (3.14)(23.25) \approx 73$ mm
b. $C = 2\pi r \approx 2(3.14)(0.52) \approx 3.27$ in.

Answers
11. 9.42 cm
12. a. 2.89 in. **b.** 82.90 mm

FACTS FROM GEOMETRY   Other Formulas Involving π

Two figures are presented here, along with some important formulas that are associated with each figure. As you can see, each of the formulas contains the number π. When we do the actual calculations, we will use the approximation 3.14 for π.

Area = π(radius)^2
$A = \pi r^2$

FIGURE 2   Circle

Volume = π(radius)^2(height)
$V = \pi r^2 h$

FIGURE 3   Right circular cylinder

EXAMPLE 13   Find the area of a circle with a diameter of 10 feet.

SOLUTION   The formula for the area of a circle is $A = \pi r^2$. Because the radius r is half the diameter and the diameter is 10 feet, the radius is 5 feet. Therefore,

$$A = \pi r^2 = (3.14)(5)^2 = (3.14)(25) = 78.5 \text{ ft}^2$$

EXAMPLE 14   The drinking straw shown in Figure 4 has a radius of 0.125 inch and a length of 6 inches. To the nearest thousandth, find the volume of liquid that it will hold.

0.125 in.

6 in.

FIGURE 4

SOLUTION   The total volume is found from the formula for the volume of a right circular cylinder. In this case, the radius is $r = 0.125$, and the height is $h = 6$. We approximate π with 3.14.

$$V = \pi r^2 h$$
$$= (3.14)(0.125)^2(6)$$
$$= (3.14)(0.015625)(6)$$
$$= 0.294 \text{ in}^3 \text{ to the nearest thousandth}$$

13. Find the area of a circle with a diameter of 20 feet.

14. Find the volume of the straw in Example 14, if the radius is doubled. Round your answer to the nearest thousandth.

STUDY SKILLS
Increase Effectiveness

You want to become more and more effective with the time you spend on your homework. You want to increase the amount of learning you obtain in the time you have set aside. Increase those activities that you feel are the most beneficial and decrease those that have not given you the results you want.

Getting Ready for Class

After reading through the preceding section, respond in your own words and in complete sentences.

1. If you multiply 34.76 and 0.072, how many digits will be to the right of the decimal point in your answer?

2. To simplify the expression 0.053(9) + 67.42, what would be the first step according to the rule for order of operations?

3. What is the purpose of estimating?

4. What are some applications of decimals that we use in our everyday lives?

Problem Set 3.3

A   Find each of the following products. (Multiply.) [Examples 1–3, 5]

1. 0.7 $\times\, 0.4$ 0.28	▶ **2.** 0.8 $\times\, 0.3$ 0.24	**3.** 0.07 $\times\, 0.4$ 0.028	**4.** 0.8 $\times\, 0.03$ 0.024	**5.** 0.03 $\times\, 0.09$ 0.0027	▶ **6.** 0.07 $\times\, 0.002$ 0.00014

▶ **7.** 2.6(0.3) 0.78	**8.** 8.9(0.2) 1.78	**9.** 0.9 $\times\, 0.88$ 0.792	**10.** 0.8 $\times\, 0.99$ 0.792	▶ **11.** 3.12 $\times\, 0.005$ 0.0156	**12.** 4.69 $\times\, 0.006$ 0.02814

13. 4.003 $\times\, 6.07$ 24.29821	▶ **14.** 7.0001 $\times\, 3.04$ 21.280304	**15.** 5(0.006) 0.03	▶ **16.** 7(0.005) 0.035	**17.** 75.14 $\times\, 2.5$ 187.85	**18.** 963.8 $\times\, 0.24$ 231.312

▶ **19.** 0.1 $\times\, 0.02$ 0.002	**20.** 0.3 $\times\, 0.02$ 0.006	**21.** 2.796(10) 27.96	**22.** 97.531(100) 9,753.1	▶ **23.** 0.0043 $\times\, 100$ 0.43	▶ **24.** 12.345 $\times\, 1,000$ 12,345

25. 49.94 $\times\, 1,000$ 49,940	▶ **26.** 157.02 $\times\, 10,000$ 1,570,200	**27.** 987.654 $\times\, 10,000$ 9,876,540	▶ **28.** 1.23 $\times\, 100,000$ 123,000	

A   Perform the following operations according to the rule for order of operations. [Examples 6, 7, 9, 10]

29. $2.1(3.5 - 2.6)$ 1.89	▶ **30.** $5.4(9.9 - 6.6)$ 17.82	**31.** $0.05(0.02 + 0.03)$ 0.0025	**32.** $0.04(0.07 + 0.09)$ 0.0064

33. $2.02(0.03 + 2.5)$ 5.1106	▶ **34.** $4.04(0.05 + 6.6)$ 26.866	**35.** $(2.1 + 0.03)(3.4 + 0.05)$ 7.3485	**36.** $(9.2 + 0.01)(3.5 + 0.03)$ 32.5113

▶ **37.** $(2.1 - 0.1)(2.1 + 0.1)$ 4.4	▶ **38.** $(9.6 - 0.5)(9.6 + 0.5)$ 91.91	**39.** $3.08 - 0.2(5 + 0.03)$ 2.074	**40.** $4.09 + 0.5(6 + 0.02)$ 7.1

41. $4.23 - 5(0.04 + 0.09)$ 3.58	▶ **42.** $7.89 - 2(0.31 + 0.76)$ 5.75	▶ **43.** $2.5 + 10(4.3)^2$ 187.4	▶ **44.** $3.6 + 15(2.1)^2$ 69.75

45. $100(1 + 0.08)^2$ 116.64	▶ **46.** $500(1 + 0.12)^2$ 627.2	▶ **47.** $(1.5)^2 + (2.5)^2 + (3.5)^2$ 20.75	**48.** $(1.1)^2 + (2.1)^2 + (3.1)^2$ 15.23

B **Applying the Concepts** [Examples 11–16]

Solve each of the following word problems. Note that not all of the problems are solved by simply multiplying the numbers in the problems. Many of the problems involve addition and subtraction as well as multiplication.

49. **Google Earth** This Google Earth image shows an aerial view of a crop circle found near Wroughton, England. If the crop circle has a radius of 59.13 meters, what is its circumference? Use the approximation 3.14 for π. Round to the nearest hundredth.

371.34 meters

50. **Google Earth** This is a 3D model of the Louvre Museum in Paris, France. The pyramid that dominates the Napoleon Courtyard has a height of 21.65 meters and a square base with sides of 35.50 meters. What is the volume of the pyramid to the nearest whole number? Hint: The volume of a pyramid can be found by the equation $V = \left(\frac{1}{3}\right)$(area of the base)(height).

9,095 meters^3

51. **Number Problem** What is the product of 6 and the sum of 0.001 and 0.02?

0.126

52. **Number Problem** Find the product of 8 and the sum of 0.03 and 0.002.

0.256

53. **Number Problem** What does multiplying a decimal number by 100 do to the decimal point?

Moves it two places to the right

54. **Number Problem** What does multiplying a decimal number by 1,000 do to the decimal point?

Moves it three places to the right

55. **Home Mortgage** On a certain home mortgage, there is a monthly payment of $9.66 for every $1,000 that is borrowed. What is the monthly payment on this type of loan if $143,000 is borrowed?

$1381.38

56. **Caffeine Content** If 1 cup of regular coffee contains 105 milligrams of caffeine, how much caffeine is contained in 3.5 cups of coffee?

367.5 mg

57. **Geometry of a Coin** The $1 coin shown here depicts Sacagawea and her infant son. The diameter of the coin is 26.5 mm, and the thickness is 2.00 mm. Find the following, rounding your answers to the nearest hundredth. Use 3.14 for π.

a. The circumference of the coin.
83.21 mm

b. The area of one face of the coin.
551.27 mm^2

c. The volume of the coin.
1,102.53 mm^3

58. **Geometry of a Coin** The Susan B. Anthony dollar shown here has a radius of 0.52 inches and a thickness of 0.0079 inches. Find the following, rounding your answers to the nearest ten thousandth, if necessary. Use 3.14 for π.

a. The circumference of the coin.
3.2656 in.

b. The area of one face of the coin.
0.8491 in^2

c. The volume of the coin.
0.0067 in^3

59. Area of a Stamp This stamp shows the Mexican artist Frida Kahlo. The image area of the stamp has a width of 0.84 inches and a length of 1.41 inches. Find the area of the image. Round to the nearest hundredth.

1.18 in²

© 2004 Banco de México

60. Area of a Stamp This stamp was issued in 2001 to honor the Italian scientist Enrico Fermi. The image area of the stamp has a width of 21.4 millimeters and a length of 35.8 millimeters. Find the area of the image. Round to the nearest whole number.

766 mm²

C Circumference Find the circumference and the area of each circle. Use 3.14 for π. [Examples 13–16]

61.

4 in.

$C = 25.12$ in.; $A = 50.24$ in²

62.

2 in.

$C = 12.56$ in.; $A = 12.56$ in²

▶ **63. Circumference** The radius of the earth is approximately 3,900 miles. Find the circumference of the earth at the equator. (The equator is a circle around the earth that divides the earth into two equal halves.)

$C = 24,492$ mi

64. Circumference The radius of the moon is approximately 1,100 miles. Find the circumference of the moon around its equator.

$C = 6,908$ mi

65. Bicycle Wheel The wheel on a 26-inch bicycle is such that the distance from the center of the wheel to the outside of the tire is 26.75 inches. If you walk the bicycle so that the wheel turns through one complete revolution, how many inches did you walk? Round to the nearest inch.

168 in.

66. Model Plane A model plane is flying in a circle with a radius of 40 feet. To the nearest foot, how far does it fly in one complete trip around the circle?

251 ft

Find the volume of each right circular cylinder.

67.

8 ft

2 ft

100.48 ft³

68.

8 ft

4 ft

401.92 ft³

69.

4 ft

2 ft

50.24 ft³

70.

4 ft

4 ft

200.96 ft³

■ Getting Ready for the Next Section

To get ready for the next section, which covers division with decimals, we will review division with whole numbers and fractions.

Simplify each of the following.

71. $3,758 \div 2$

1,879

72. $9,900 \div 22$

450

73. $50,032 \div 33$

1,516 R 4

74. $90,902 \div 5$

18,180 R 2

75. $20\overline{)5,960}$

298

76. $30\overline{)4,620}$

154

77. 4×8.7

34.8

78. 5×6.7

33.5

79. 27×1.848

49.896

80. 35×32.54

1,138.90

81. $38\overline{)31,350}$

825

82. $25\overline{)377,800}$

15,112

■ Maintaining Your Skills

83. Write the fractions in order from smallest to largest.

$$\frac{2}{5} \qquad \frac{4}{5} \qquad \frac{3}{10} \qquad \frac{1}{2}$$

$$\frac{3}{10} < \frac{2}{5} < \frac{1}{2} < \frac{4}{5}$$

84. Write the fractions in order from smallest to largest.

$$\frac{4}{5} \qquad \frac{1}{4} \qquad \frac{1}{10} \qquad \frac{17}{100}$$

$$\frac{1}{10} < \frac{17}{100} < \frac{1}{4} < \frac{4}{5}$$

85. Write the numbers in order from smallest to largest.

$$1\frac{5}{6} \qquad \frac{3}{2} \qquad 1\frac{2}{3} \qquad \frac{25}{12}$$

$$\frac{3}{2} < 1\frac{2}{3} < 1\frac{5}{6} < \frac{25}{12}$$

86. Write the numbers in order from smallest to largest.

$$1\frac{11}{12} \qquad \frac{19}{12} \qquad \frac{4}{3} \qquad 1\frac{1}{6}$$

$$1\frac{1}{6} < \frac{4}{3} < \frac{19}{12} < 1\frac{11}{12}$$

■ Extending the Concepts

87. Containment System Holding tanks for hazardous liquids are often surrounded by containment tanks that will hold the hazardous liquid if the main tank begins to leak. We see that the center tank has a height of 16 feet and a radius of 6 feet. The outside containment tank has a height of 4 feet and a radius of 8 feet. If the center tank is full of heating fuel and develops a leak at the bottom, will the containment tank be able to hold all the heating fuel that leaks out?

No

16 ft   6 ft

4 ft   8 ft

3.4

Objectives

A Divide decimal numbers.

B Solve application problems involving decimals.

Introduction . . .

The chart shows the top finishing times for the men's 400-meter freestyle swim during Sydney's Olympics. An Olympic pool is 50 meters long, so each swimmer will have to complete 8 lengths during a 400-meter race.

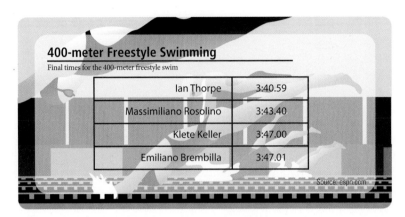

400-meter Freestyle Swimming

Final times for the 400-meter freestyle swim

Ian Thorpe	3:40.59
Massimiliano Rosolino	3:43.40
Klete Keller	3:47.00
Emiliano Brembilla	3:47.01

Source: espn.com

During the race, each swimmer keeps track of how long it takes him to complete each length. To find the time of a swimmer's average lap, we need to be able to divide with decimal numbers, which we will learn in this section.

A Dividing with Decimals

EXAMPLE 1 Divide: $5,974 \div 20$

SOLUTION

$$
\begin{array}{r}
298 \\
20\overline{)5,974} \\
\underline{4\,0} \\
1\,97 \\
\underline{1\,80} \\
174 \\
\underline{160} \\
14
\end{array}
$$

In the past we have written this answer as $298\frac{14}{20}$ or, after reducing the fraction, $298\frac{7}{10}$. Because $\frac{7}{10}$ can be written as 0.7, we could also write our answer as 298.7. This last form of our answer is exactly the same result we obtain if we write 5,974 as 5,974.0 and continue the division until we have no remainder. Here is how it looks:

$$
\begin{array}{r}
298.7 \\
20\overline{)5,974.0} \\
\underline{4\,0} \\
1\,97 \\
\underline{1\,80} \\
174 \\
\underline{160} \\
14\,0 \\
\underline{14\,0} \\
0
\end{array}
$$

Notice that we place the decimal point in the answer directly above the decimal point in the problem

Let's try another division problem. This time one of the numbers in the problem will be a decimal.

PRACTICE PROBLEMS

1. Divide: $4,626 \div 30$

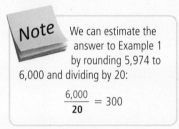

Note We can estimate the answer to Example 1 by rounding 5,974 to 6,000 and dividing by 20:

$$\frac{6,000}{20} = 300$$

Note We never need to make a mistake with division, because we can always check our results with multiplication.

Answer
1. 154.2

2. Divide.
  a. 33.5 ÷ 5
  b. 34.5 ÷ 5
  c. 35.5 ÷ 5

EXAMPLE 2 Divide: 34.8 ÷ 4

SOLUTION We can use the ideas from Example 1 and divide as usual. The decimal point in the answer will be placed directly above the decimal point in the problem.

```
      8.7        Check:    8.7
  4)34.8                 ×   4
    32 ↓                  34.8
    2 8
    2 8
      0
```

The answer is 8.7.

We can use these facts to write a rule for dividing decimal numbers.

> **Rule**
>
> To divide a decimal by a whole number, we do the usual long division as if there were no decimal point involved. The decimal point in the answer is placed directly above the decimal point in the problem.

Here are some more examples to illustrate the procedure.

EXAMPLE 3 Divide: 49.896 ÷ 27

3. Divide.
  a. 47.448 ÷ 18
  b. 474.48 ÷ 18

SOLUTION
```
        1.848
  27)49.896         Check this result by multiplication:
     27 ↓││
     22 8│                        1.848
     21 6↓                      ×    27
      1 29                      12 936
      1 08↓                     36 96
       216                      49.896
       216
         0
```

We can write as many zeros as we choose after the rightmost digit in a decimal number without changing the value of the number. For example,

$$6.91 = 6.910 = 6.9100 = 6.91000$$

There are times when this can be very useful, as Example 4 shows.

EXAMPLE 4 Divide: 1,138.9 ÷ 35

4. Divide.
  a. 1,138.5 ÷ 25
  b. 113.85 ÷ 25

SOLUTION
```
         32.54
  35)1,138.90      Write 0 after the 9. It doesn't
     1 05↓││       change the original number,
        88│        but it gives us another digit
        70↓        to bring down.
        18 9│      Check:     32.54
        17 5↓               ×    35
         1 40              162 70
         1 40              976 2
            0            1,138.90
```

Until now we have considered only division by whole numbers. Extending division to include division by decimal numbers is a matter of knowing what to do about the decimal point in the divisor.

EXAMPLE 5   Divide: $31.35 \div 3.8$

SOLUTION   In fraction form, this problem is equivalent to

$$\frac{31.35}{3.8}$$

If we want to write the divisor as a whole number, we can multiply the numerator and the denominator of this fraction by 10:

$$\frac{31.35 \times \mathbf{10}}{3.8 \times \mathbf{10}} = \frac{313.5}{38}$$

So, since this fraction is equivalent to the original fraction, our original division problem is equivalent to

$$
\begin{array}{r}
8.25 \\
38\overline{)313.50} \quad \text{Put 0 after the last digit} \\
\underline{304}\downarrow\downarrow \\
9\,5 \\
\underline{7\,6}\downarrow \\
1\,90 \\
\underline{1\,90} \\
0
\end{array}
$$

We can summarize division with decimal numbers by listing the following points, as illustrated by the first five examples.

> **Summary of Division with Decimals**
> **1.** We divide decimal numbers by the same process used in Chapter 1 to divide whole numbers. The decimal point in the answer is placed directly above the decimal point in the dividend.
>
> **2.** We are free to write as many zeros after the last digit in a decimal number as we need.
>
> **3.** If the divisor is a decimal, we can change it to a whole number by moving the decimal point to the right as many places as necessary so long as we move the decimal point in the dividend the same number of places.

EXAMPLE 6   Divide, and round the answer to the nearest hundredth:

$$0.3778 \div 0.25$$

SOLUTION   First, we move the decimal point two places to the right:

$$0.25.\overline{)\,37.78}$$

5. Divide.
  a. $13.23 \div 4.2$
  b. $13.23 \div 0.42$

> **Note**   We do not always use the rules for rounding numbers to make estimates. For example, to estimate the answer to Example 5, $31.35 \div 3.8$, we can get a rough estimate of the answer by reasoning that 3.8 is close to 4 and 31.35 is close to 32. Therefore, our answer will be approximately $32 \div 4 = 8$.

6. Divide, and round your answer to the nearest hundredth:
  $0.4553 \div 0.32$

> **Note**   Moving the decimal point two places in both the divisor and the dividend is justified like this:
> $$\frac{0.3778 \times \mathbf{100}}{0.25 \times \mathbf{100}} = \frac{37.78}{25}$$

Answers
5. a. 3.15 **b.** 31.5

Then we divide, using long division:

$$
\begin{array}{r}
1.5112 \\
25\overline{)37.7800} \\
\underline{25} \\
12\ 7 \\
\underline{12\ 5} \\
28 \\
\underline{25} \\
30 \\
\underline{25} \\
50 \\
\underline{50} \\
0
\end{array}
$$

Rounding to the nearest hundredth, we have 1.51. We actually did not need to have this many digits to round to the hundredths column. We could have stopped at the thousandths column and rounded off.

EXAMPLE 7   Divide, and round to the nearest tenth: $17 \div 0.03$

SOLUTION   Because we are rounding to the nearest tenth, we will continue dividing until we have a digit in the hundredths column. We don't have to go any further to round to the tenths column.

$$
\begin{array}{r}
5\ 66.66 \\
0.03.\overline{)17.00.00} \\
\underline{15} \\
2\ 0 \\
\underline{1\ 8} \\
20 \\
\underline{18} \\
2\ 0 \\
\underline{1\ 8} \\
20 \\
\underline{18} \\
2
\end{array}
$$

Rounding to the nearest tenth, we have 566.7.

B Applications

EXAMPLE 8   If a man earning $7.26 an hour receives a paycheck for $235.95, how many hours did he work?

SOLUTION   To find the number of hours the man worked, we divide $235.95 by $7.26.

$$
\begin{array}{r}
32.5 \\
7.26.\overline{)235.95.0} \\
\underline{217\ 8} \\
18\ 15 \\
\underline{14\ 52} \\
3\ 63\ 0 \\
\underline{3\ 63\ 0} \\
0
\end{array}
$$

The man worked 32.5 hours.

7. Divide, and round to the nearest tenth.
   a. $19 \div 0.06$
   b. $1.9 \div 0.06$

8. A woman earning $6.54 an hour receives a paycheck for $186.39. How many hours did the woman work?

Answers
6. 1.42   **7. a.** 316.7   **b.** 31.7
8. 28.5 hours

EXAMPLE 9 A telephone company charges $0.43 for the first minute and then $0.33 for each additional minute for a long-distance call. If a long-distance call costs $3.07, how many minutes was the call?

SOLUTION To solve this problem we need to find the number of additional minutes for the call. To do so, we first subtract the cost of the first minute from the total cost, and then we divide the result by the cost of each additional minute. Without showing the actual arithmetic involved, the solution looks like this:

$$\text{The number of additional minutes} = \frac{\overset{\text{Total cost of the call}}{3.07} - \overset{\text{Cost of the first minute}}{0.43}}{\underset{\text{Cost of each additional minute}}{0.33}} = \frac{2.64}{0.33} = 8$$

The call was 9 minutes long. (The number 8 is the number of additional minutes past the first minute.)

DESCRIPTIVE STATISTICS

Grade Point Average

I have always been surprised by the number of my students who have difficulty calculating their grade point average (GPA). During her first semester in college, my daughter, Amy, earned the following grades:

Class	Units	Grade
Algebra	5	B
Chemistry	4	C
English	3	A
History	3	B

When her grades arrived in the mail, she told me she had a 3.0 grade point average, because the A and C grades averaged to a B. I told her that her GPA was a little less than a 3.0. What do you think? Can you calculate her GPA? If not, you will be able to after you finish this section.

When you calculate your grade point average (GPA), you are calculating what is called a *weighted average*. To calculate your grade point average, you must first calculate the number of grade points you have earned in each class that you have completed. The number of grade points for a class is the product of the number of units the class is worth times the value of the grade received. The table below shows the value that is assigned to each grade.

Grade	Value
A	4
B	3
C	2
D	1
F	0

If you earn a B in a 4-unit class, you earn $4 \times 3 = 12$ grade points. A grade of C in the same class gives you $4 \times 2 = 8$ grade points. To find your grade point average for one term (a semester or quarter), you must add your grade points and divide that total by the number of units. Round your answer to the nearest hundredth.

9. If the phone company in Example 9 charged $4.39 for a call, how long was the call?

Instructor Note
From this point on, the examples are all application problems. We stop showing the steps in the long-division process and give only the result. In my classes, students can use calculators for these problems so long as they show the set-up on each problem.

10. If Amy had earned a B in chemistry, instead of a C, what grade point average would she have?

EXAMPLE 10
Calculate Amy's grade point average using the information above.

SOLUTION We begin by writing in two more columns, one for the value of each grade (4 for an A, 3 for a B, 2 for a C, 1 for a D, and 0 for an F), and another for the grade points earned for each class. To fill in the grade points column, we multiply the number of units by the value of the grade:

Class	Units	Grade	Value	Grade Points
Algebra	5	B	3	$5 \times 3 = 15$
Chemistry	4	C	2	$4 \times 2 = 8$
English	3	A	4	$3 \times 4 = 12$
History	3	B	3	$3 \times 3 = 9$
Total Units	15		Total Grade Points:	44

To find her grade point average, we divide 44 by 15 and round (if necessary) to the nearest hundredth:

$$\text{Grade point average} = \frac{44}{15} = 2.93$$

STUDY SKILLS
Pay Attention to Instructions

Taking a test is not like doing homework. On a test, the problems will be varied. When you do your homework, you usually work a number of similar problems. I have some students who do very well on their homework but become confused when they see the same problems on a test. The reason for their confusion is that they have not paid attention to the instructions on their homework. If a test problem asks for the *mean* of some numbers, then you must know the definition of the word *mean*. Likewise, if a test problem asks you to find a *sum* and then to *round* your answer to the nearest hundred, then you must know that the word *sum* indicates addition, and after you have added, you must round your answer as indicated.

Getting Ready for Class

After reading through the preceding section, respond in your own words and in complete sentences.

1. The answer to the division problem in Example 1 is $298 \frac{14}{20}$. Write this number in decimal notation.

2. In Example 4 we place a 0 at the end of a number without changing the value of the number. Why is the placement of this 0 helpful?

3. The expression $0.3778 \div 0.25$ is equivalent to the expression $37.78 \div 25$ because each number was multiplied by what?

4. Round 372.1675 to the nearest tenth.

Answer
10. 3.20

Problem Set 3.4

A Perform each of the following divisions. [Examples 1–5]

▶ **1.** 394 ÷ 20
19.7

2. 486 ÷ 30
16.2

3. 248 ÷ 40
6.2

▶ **4.** 372 ÷ 80
4.65

▶ **5.** 5)26
5.2

6. 8)36
4.5

7. 25)276
11.04

8. 50)276
5.52

▶ **9.** 28.8 ÷ 6
4.8

▶ **10.** 15.5 ÷ 5
3.1

11. 77.6 ÷ 8
9.7

12. 31.48 ÷ 4
7.87

▶ **13.** 35)92.05
2.63

14. 26)146.38
5.63

15. 45)190.8
4.24

▶ **16.** 55)342.1
6.22

17. $86.7 \div 34$
2.55

▶ **18.** $411.4 \div 44$
9.35

19. $29.7 \div 22$
1.35

20. $488.4 \div 88$
5.55

▶ **21.** $4.5)\overline{29.25}$
6.5

22. $3.3)\overline{21.978}$
6.66

23. $0.11)\overline{1.089}$
9.9

▶ **24.** $0.75)\overline{2.40}$
3.2

▶ **25.** $2.3)\overline{0.115}$
0.05

26. $6.6)\overline{0.198}$
0.03

27. $0.012)\overline{1.068}$
89

28. $0.052)\overline{0.23712}$
4.56

▶ **29.** $1.1)\overline{2.42}$
2.2

▶ **30.** $2.2)\overline{7.26}$
3.3

Carry out each of the following divisions only so far as needed to round the results to the nearest hundredth. [Examples 6, 7]

▶ **31.** $26\overline{)35}$
1.35

32. $18\overline{)47}$
2.61

33. $3.3\overline{)56}$
16.97

34. $4.4\overline{)75}$
17.05

▶ **35.** $0.1234 \div 0.5$
0.25

36. $0.543 \div 2.1$
0.26

37. $19 \div 7$
2.71

▶ **38.** $16 \div 6$
2.67

39. $0.059\overline{)0.69}$
11.69

▶ **40.** $0.048\overline{)0.49}$
10.21

41. $1.99 \div 0.5$
3.98

42. $0.99 \div 0.5$
1.98

▶ **43.** $2.99 \div 0.5$
5.98

44. $3.99 \div 0.5$
7.98

Calculator Problems   Work each of the following problems on your calculator. If rounding is necessary, round to the nearest hundred thousandth.

▶ **45.** 7 ÷ 9
0.77778

46. 11 ÷ 13
0.84615

▶ **47.** 243 ÷ 0.791
307.20607

48. 67.8 ÷ 37.92
1.78797

▶ **49.** 0.0503 ÷ 0.0709
0.70945

▶ **50.** 429.87 ÷ 16.925
25.39852

B **Applying the Concepts** [Examples 8–10]

51. Google Earth The Google Earth map shows Yellowstone National Park. There is an average of 2.3 moose per square mile. If there are about 7,986 moose in Yellowstone, how many square miles does Yellowstone cover? Round to the nearest square mile.
3,472 square miles

52. Google Earth The Google Earth image shows a corn field. A farmer harvests 29,952 bushels of corn. If the farmer harvested 130 bushels per acre, how many acres does the field cover?
230.4 acres

53. Hot Air Balloon Since the pilot of a hot air balloon can only control the balloon's altitude, he relies on the winds for travel. To ride on the jet streams, a hot air balloon must rise as high as 12 kilometers. Convert this to miles by dividing by 1.61. Round your answer to the nearest tenth of a mile.
7.5 mi

54. Hot Air Balloon December and January are the best times for traveling in a hot-air balloon because the jet streams in the Northern Hemisphere are the strongest. They reach speeds of 400 kilometers per hour. Convert this to miles per hour by dividing by 1.61. Round to the nearest whole number.
248 mph

55. Wages If a woman earns $39.90 for working 6 hours, how much does she earn per hour?
$6.65/hr

56. Wages How many hours does a person making $6.78 per hour have to work in order to earn $257.64?
38 hr

▶ **57. Gas Mileage** If a car travels 336 miles on 15 gallons of gas, how far will the car travel on 1 gallon of gas?
22.4 mi

58. Gas Mileage If a car travels 392 miles on 16 gallons of gas, how far will the car travel on 1 gallon of gas?
24.5 mi

▶ **59. Wages** Suppose a woman earns $6.78 an hour for the first 36 hours she works in a week and then $10.17 an hour in overtime pay for each additional hour she works in the same week. If she makes $294.93 in one week, how many hours did she work overtime?

5 hr

60. Wages Suppose a woman makes $286.08 in one week. If she is paid $5.96 an hour for the first 36 hours she works and then $8.94 an hour in overtime pay for each additional hour she works in the same week, how many hours did she work overtime that week?

8 hr

▶ **61. Phone Bill** Suppose a telephone company charges $0.41 for the first minute and then $0.32 for each additional minute for a long-distance call. If a long-distance call costs $2.33, how many minutes was the call?

7 min

62. Phone Bill Suppose a telephone company charges $0.45 for the first three minutes and then $0.29 for each additional minute for a long-distance call. If a long-distance call costs $2.77, how many minutes was the call?

11 min

63. Women's Golf The table gives the top five money earners for the Ladies' Professional Golf Association (LPGA) in 2008, through June 1. Fill in the last column of the table by finding the average earnings per event for each golfer. Round your answers to the nearest dollar.

Rank	Name	Number of Events	Total Earnings	Average per Event
1.	Lorena Ochoa	25	$1,838,616	$73,545
2.	Annika Sorenstam	13	$1,295,585	$99,660
3.	Paula Creamer	24	$891,804	$37,159
4.	Seon Hwa Lee	28	$656,313	$23,440
5.	Jeong Jang	27	$642,320	$23,790

64. Men's Golf The table gives the top five money earners for the men's Professional Golf Association (PGA) in 2008, through June 1. Fill in the last column of the table by finding the average earnings per event for each golfer. Round your answers to the nearest dollar.

Rank	Name	Number of Events	Total Earnings	Average per Event
1.	Tiger Woods	5	$4,425,000	$885,000
2.	Phil Mickelson	13	$3,872,270	$297,867
3.	Geoff Ogilvy	13	$2,584,685	$198,822
4.	Stewart Cink	13	$2,516,512	$193,578
5.	Kenny Perry	15	$2,437,655	$162,510

Grade Point Average The following grades were earned by Steve during his first term in college. Use these data to answer Problems 65–68.

Class	Units	Grade
Basic mathematics	3	A
Health	2	B
History	3	B
English	3	C
Chemistry	4	C

65. Calculate Steve's GPA.

2.73

66. If his grade in chemistry had been a B instead of a C, by how much would his GPA have increased?

0.27

67. If his grade in health had been a C instead of a B, by how much would his grade point average have dropped?

0.13

68. If his grades in both English and chemistry had been B's, what would his GPA have been?

3.2

■ Getting Ready for the Next Section

In the next section we will consider the relationship between fractions and decimals in more detail. The problems below review some of the material that is necessary to make a successful start in the next section.

Reduce to lowest terms.

69. $\dfrac{75}{100}$ $\frac{3}{4}$

70. $\dfrac{220}{1,000}$ $\frac{11}{50}$

71. $\dfrac{12}{18}$ $\frac{2}{3}$

72. $\dfrac{15}{30}$ $\frac{1}{2}$

73. $\dfrac{75}{200}$ $\frac{3}{8}$

74. $\dfrac{220}{2,000}$ $\frac{11}{100}$

75. $\dfrac{38}{100}$ $\frac{19}{50}$

76. $\dfrac{75}{1,000}$ $\frac{3}{40}$

Write each fraction as an equivalent fraction with denominator 10.

77. $\dfrac{3}{5}$ $\frac{6}{10}$

78. $\dfrac{1}{2}$ $\frac{5}{10}$

Write each fraction as an equivalent fraction with denominator 100.

79. $\dfrac{3}{5}$ $\frac{60}{100}$

80. $\dfrac{17}{20}$ $\frac{85}{100}$

Write each fraction as an equivalent fraction with denominator 15.

81. $\dfrac{4}{5}$ $\frac{12}{15}$

82. $\dfrac{2}{3}$ $\frac{10}{15}$

83. $\dfrac{4}{1}$ $\frac{60}{15}$

84. $\dfrac{2}{1}$ $\frac{30}{15}$

85. $\dfrac{6}{5}$ $\frac{18}{15}$

86. $\dfrac{7}{3}$ $\frac{35}{15}$

Divide.

87. $3 \div 4$
0.75

88. $3 \div 5$
0.6

89. $7 \div 8$
0.875

90. $3 \div 8$
0.375

■ Maintaining Your Skills

Simplify.

91. $15\left(\dfrac{2}{3} + \dfrac{3}{5}\right)$
19

92. $15\left(\dfrac{4}{5} - \dfrac{1}{3}\right)$
7

93. $4\left(\dfrac{1}{2} + \dfrac{1}{4}\right)$
3

94. $6\left(\dfrac{1}{3} + \dfrac{1}{2}\right)$
5

Introduction . . .

If you are shopping for clothes and a store has a sale advertising $\frac{1}{3}$ off the regular price, how much can you expect to pay for a pair of pants that normally sells for $31.95? If the sale price of the pants is $22.30, have they really been marked down by $\frac{1}{3}$? To answer questions like these, we need to know how to solve problems that involve fractions and decimals together.

We begin this section by showing how to convert back and forth between fractions and decimals.

A Converting Fractions to Decimals

You may recall that the notation we use for fractions can be interpreted as implying division. That is, the fraction $\frac{3}{4}$ can be thought of as meaning "3 divided by 4." We can use this idea to convert fractions to decimals.

PRACTICE PROBLEMS

EXAMPLE 1 Write $\frac{3}{4}$ as a decimal.

SOLUTION Dividing 3 by 4, we have

$$
\begin{array}{r}
.75 \\
4\overline{)3.00} \\
\underline{2\ 8}\downarrow \\
20 \\
\underline{20} \\
0
\end{array}
$$

The fraction $\frac{3}{4}$ is equal to the decimal 0.75.

1. Write as a decimal.

 a. $\frac{2}{5}$

 b. $\frac{3}{5}$

 c. $\frac{4}{5}$

EXAMPLE 2 Write $\frac{7}{12}$ as a decimal correct to the thousandths column.

SOLUTION Because we want the decimal to be rounded to the thousandths column, we divide to the ten thousandths column and round off to the thousandths column:

$$
\begin{array}{r}
.5833 \\
12\overline{)7.0000} \\
\underline{6\ 0}\downarrow \\
1\ 00 \\
\underline{96}\downarrow \\
40 \\
\underline{36}\downarrow \\
40 \\
\underline{36} \\
4
\end{array}
$$

Rounding off to the thousandths column, we have 0.583. Because $\frac{7}{12}$ is not exactly the same as 0.583, we write

$$
\frac{7}{12} \approx 0.583
$$

where the symbol $\approx$ is read "is approximately."

2. Write as a decimal correct to the thousandths column.

 a. $\frac{11}{12}$

 b. $\frac{12}{13}$

If we wrote more zeros after 7.0000 in Example 2, the pattern of 3's would continue for as many places as we could want. When we get a sequence of digits that repeat like this, 0.58333 . . . , we can indicate the repetition by writing

$$0.58\overline{3}$$ The bar over the 3 indicates that the 3 repeats from there on

3. Write $\frac{5}{11}$ as a decimal.

EXAMPLE 3   Write $\frac{3}{11}$ as a decimal.

SOLUTION   Dividing 3 by 11, we have

```
        .272727
    11)3.000000
        2 2
         80
         77
          30
          22
          80
          77
           30
           22
           80
           77
            3
```

No matter how long we continue the division, the remainder will never be 0, and the pattern will continue. We write the decimal form of $\frac{3}{11}$ as $0.\overline{27}$, where

$$0.\overline{27} = 0.272727\ldots$$ The dots mean "and so on"

Note   The bar over the 2 and the 7 in $0.\overline{27}$ is used to indicate that the pattern repeats itself indefinitely.

B Converting Decimals to Fractions

To convert decimals to fractions, we take advantage of the place values we assigned to the digits to the right of the decimal point.

EXAMPLE 4   Write 0.38 as a fraction in lowest terms.

SOLUTION   0.38 is 38 hundredths, or

$$0.38 = \frac{38}{100}$$

$$= \frac{19}{50}$$ Divide the numerator and the denominator by 2 to reduce to lowest terms

The decimal 0.38 is equal to the fraction $\frac{19}{50}$.

We could check our work here by converting $\frac{19}{50}$ back to a decimal. We do this by dividing 19 by 50. That is,

```
       .38
   50)19.00
      15 0
       4 00
       4 00
          0
```

4. Write as a fraction in lowest terms.
   a. 0.48
   b. 0.048

EXAMPLE 5 Convert 0.075 to a fraction.

SOLUTION We have 75 thousandths, or

$$0.075 = \frac{75}{1,000}$$

$$= \frac{3}{40}$$ Divide the numerator and the denominator by 25 to reduce to lowest terms

EXAMPLE 6 Write 15.6 as a mixed number.

SOLUTION Converting 0.6 to a fraction, we have

$$0.6 = \frac{6}{10} = \frac{3}{5}$$ Reduce to lowest terms

Since $0.6 = \frac{3}{5}$, we have $15.6 = 15\frac{3}{5}$.

C Problems Containing Both Fractions and Decimals

We continue this section by working some problems that involve both fractions and decimals.

EXAMPLE 7 Simplify: $\frac{19}{50}(1.32 + 0.48)$

SOLUTION In Example 4, we found that $0.38 = \frac{19}{50}$. Therefore we can rewrite the problem as

$$\frac{19}{50}(1.32 + 0.48) = 0.38(1.32 + 0.48)$$ Convert all numbers to decimals
$$= 0.38(1.80)$$ Add: 1.32 + 0.48
$$= 0.684$$ Multiply: 0.38 × 1.80

EXAMPLE 8 Simplify: $\frac{1}{2} + (0.75)\left(\frac{2}{5}\right)$

SOLUTION We could do this problem one of two different ways. First, we could convert all fractions to decimals and then simplify:

$$\frac{1}{2} + (0.75)\left(\frac{2}{5}\right) = 0.5 + 0.75(0.4)$$ Convert to decimals
$$= 0.5 + 0.300$$ Multiply: 0.75 × 0.4
$$= 0.8$$ Add

Or, we could convert 0.75 to $\frac{3}{4}$ and then simplify:

$$\frac{1}{2} + 0.75\left(\frac{2}{5}\right) = \frac{1}{2} + \frac{3}{4}\left(\frac{2}{5}\right)$$ Convert decimals to fractions
$$= \frac{1}{2} + \frac{3}{10}$$ Multiply: $\frac{3}{4} \times \frac{2}{5}$
$$= \frac{5}{10} + \frac{3}{10}$$ The common denominator is 10
$$= \frac{8}{10}$$ Add numerators
$$= \frac{4}{5}$$ Reduce to lowest terms

The answers are equivalent. That is, $0.8 = \frac{8}{10} = \frac{4}{5}$. Either method can be used with problems of this type.

5. Convert 0.025 to a fraction.

6. Write 12.8 as a mixed number.

7. Simplify: $\frac{14}{25}(2.43 + 0.27)$

8. Simplify: $\frac{1}{4} + 0.25\left(\frac{3}{5}\right)$

Answers

5. $\frac{1}{40}$ 6. $12\frac{4}{5}$ 7. 1.512

8. $\frac{2}{5}$, or 0.4

9. Simplify: $\left(\frac{1}{3}\right)^3(5.4) + \left(\frac{1}{5}\right)^2(2.5)$

EXAMPLE 9 Simplify: $\left(\frac{1}{2}\right)^3(2.4) + \left(\frac{1}{4}\right)^2(3.2)$

SOLUTION This expression can be simplified without any conversions between fractions and decimals. To begin, we evaluate all numbers that contain exponents. Then we multiply. After that, we add.

$$\left(\frac{1}{2}\right)^3(2.4) + \left(\frac{1}{4}\right)^2(3.2) = \frac{1}{8}(2.4) + \frac{1}{16}(3.2) \quad \text{Evaluate exponents}$$

$$= 0.3 + 0.2 \quad \text{Multiply by } \frac{1}{8} \text{ and } \frac{1}{16}$$
$$= 0.5 \quad \text{Add}$$

D Applications

10. A shirt that normally sells for $35.50 is on sale for $\frac{1}{4}$ off. What is the sale price of the shirt? (Round to the nearest cent.)

EXAMPLE 10 If a shirt that normally sells for $27.99 is on sale for $\frac{1}{3}$ off, what is the sale price of the shirt?

SOLUTION To find out how much the shirt is marked down, we must find $\frac{1}{3}$ of 27.99. That is, we multiply $\frac{1}{3}$ and 27.99, which is the same as dividing 27.99 by 3.

$$\frac{1}{3}(27.99) = \frac{27.99}{3} = 9.33$$

The shirt is marked down $9.33. The sale price is the original price less the amount it is marked down:

$$\text{Sale price} = 27.99 - 9.33 = 18.66$$

The sale price is $18.66. We also could have solved this problem by simply multiplying the original price by $\frac{2}{3}$, since, if the shirt is marked $\frac{1}{3}$ off, then the sale price must be $\frac{2}{3}$ of the original price. Multiplying by $\frac{2}{3}$ is the same as dividing by 3 and then multiplying by 2. The answer would be the same.

11. Find the area of the stamp in Example 11 if

Base = 6.6 centimeters, height = 3.3 centimeters

EXAMPLE 11 Find the area of the stamp.

Write your answer as a decimal, rounded to the nearest hundredth.

Base = $2\frac{5}{8}$ inches

Height = $1\frac{1}{4}$ inches

SOLUTION We can work the problem using fractions and then convert the answer to a decimal.

$$A = \frac{1}{2}bh = \frac{1}{2}\left(2\frac{5}{8}\right)\left(1\frac{1}{4}\right) = \frac{1}{2} \cdot \frac{21}{8} \cdot \frac{5}{4} = \frac{105}{64} \approx 1.64 \text{ in}^2$$

Or, we can convert the fractions to decimals and then work the problem.

$$A = \frac{1}{2}bh = .5(2.625)(1.25) \approx 1.64 \text{ in}^2$$

Answers
9. 0.3 **10.** $26.63 **11.** 10.89 cm²

FACTS FROM GEOMETRY   The Volume of a Sphere

Figure 1 shows a sphere and the formula for its volume. Because the formula contains both the fraction $\frac{4}{3}$ and the number π, and we have been using 3.14 for π, we can think of the formula as containing both a fraction and a decimal.

$$\text{Volume} = \tfrac{4}{3}\pi(\text{radius})^3$$
$$= \tfrac{4}{3}\pi r^3$$

FIGURE 1   Sphere

EXAMPLE 12   Figure 2 is composed of a right circular cylinder with half a sphere on top. (A half-sphere is called a *hemisphere*.) To the nearest tenth, find the total volume enclosed by the figure.

10 in.

5 in.

FIGURE 2

12. If the radius in Figure 2 is doubled so that it becomes 10 inches instead of 5 inches, what is the new volume of the figure? Round your answer to the nearest tenth.

SOLUTION   The total volume is found by adding the volume of the cylinder to the volume of the hemisphere.

V = volume of cylinder + volume of hemisphere

$$= \pi r^2 h + \frac{1}{2} \cdot \frac{4}{3}\pi r^3$$

$$= (3.14)(5)^2(10) + \frac{1}{2} \cdot \frac{4}{3}(3.14)(5)^3$$

$$= (3.14)(25)(10) + \frac{1}{2} \cdot \frac{4}{3}(3.14)(125)$$

$$= 785 + \frac{2}{3}(392.5) \qquad \text{Multiply: } \frac{1}{2} \cdot \frac{4}{3} = \frac{4}{6} = \frac{2}{3}$$

$$= 785 + \frac{785}{3} \qquad \text{Multiply: } 2(392.5) = 785$$

$$\approx 785 + 261.7 \qquad \text{Divide 785 by 3, and round to the nearest tenth}$$

$$= 1{,}046.7 \text{ in}^3$$

Answer

12. 5,233.3 in³

Getting Ready for Class

After reading through the preceding section, respond in your own words and in complete sentences.

1. To convert fractions to decimals, do we multiply or divide the numerator by the denominator?

2. The decimal 0.13 is equivalent to what fraction?

3. Write 36 thousandths in decimal form and in fraction form.

4. Explain how to write the fraction $\dfrac{84}{1,000}$ in lowest terms.

Problem Set 3.5

A Each circle below is divided into 8 equal parts. The number below each circle indicates what fraction of the circle is shaded. Convert each fraction to a decimal. [Examples 1–3]

1.

$\dfrac{1}{8}$

0.125

2.

$\dfrac{3}{8}$

0.375

3.

$\dfrac{5}{8}$

0.625

4.

$\dfrac{7}{8}$

0.875

A Complete the following tables by converting each fraction to a decimal. [Examples 1–3]

5.

Fraction	$\frac{1}{4}$	$\frac{2}{4}$	$\frac{3}{4}$	$\frac{4}{4}$
Decimal	0.25	0.5	0.75	1

6.

Fraction	$\frac{1}{5}$	$\frac{2}{5}$	$\frac{3}{5}$	$\frac{4}{5}$	$\frac{5}{5}$
Decimal	0.2	0.4	0.6	0.8	1

7.

Fraction	$\frac{1}{6}$	$\frac{2}{6}$	$\frac{3}{6}$	$\frac{4}{6}$	$\frac{5}{6}$	$\frac{6}{6}$
Decimal	$0.1\overline{6}$	$0.\overline{3}$	0.5	$0.\overline{6}$	$0.8\overline{3}$	1

A Convert each of the following fractions to a decimal. [Examples 1–3]

8. $\dfrac{1}{2}$

0.5

9. $\dfrac{12}{25}$

0.48

10. $\dfrac{14}{25}$

0.56

11. $\dfrac{14}{32}$

0.4375

12. $\dfrac{18}{32}$

0.5625

A Write each fraction as a decimal correct to the hundredths column. [Examples 1–3]

13. $\dfrac{12}{13}$

0.92

14. $\dfrac{17}{19}$

0.89

15. $\dfrac{3}{11}$

0.27

16. $\dfrac{5}{11}$

0.45

17. $\dfrac{2}{23}$

0.09

18. $\dfrac{3}{28}$

0.11

19. $\dfrac{12}{43}$

0.28

20. $\dfrac{15}{51}$

0.29

B Complete the following table by converting each decimal to a fraction.

21.

Decimal	0.125	0.250	0.375	0.500	0.625	0.750	0.875
Fraction	$\frac{1}{8}$	$\frac{1}{4}$	$\frac{3}{8}$	$\frac{1}{2}$	$\frac{5}{8}$	$\frac{3}{4}$	$\frac{7}{8}$

22.

Decimal	0.1	0.2	0.3	0.4	0.5	0.6	0.7	0.8	0.9
Fraction	$\frac{1}{10}$	$\frac{1}{5}$	$\frac{3}{10}$	$\frac{2}{5}$	$\frac{1}{2}$	$\frac{3}{5}$	$\frac{7}{10}$	$\frac{4}{5}$	$\frac{9}{10}$

▶ Selected exercises available online at www.webassign.net/brookscole

B Write each decimal as a fraction in lowest terms. [Examples 4–6]

23. 0.15   **24.** 0.45   ▶ **25.** 0.08   **26.** 0.06   **27.** 0.375   ▶ **28.** 0.475

$\frac{3}{20}$ $\frac{9}{20}$ $\frac{2}{25}$ $\frac{3}{50}$ $\frac{3}{8}$ $\frac{19}{40}$

B Write each decimal as a mixed number. [Examples 6]

29. 5.6   ▶ **30.** 8.4   **31.** 5.06   ▶ **32.** 8.04   **33.** 1.22   **34.** 2.11

$5\frac{3}{5}$ $8\frac{2}{5}$ $5\frac{3}{50}$ $8\frac{1}{25}$ $1\frac{11}{50}$ $2\frac{11}{100}$

C Simplify each of the following as much as possible, and write all answers as decimals. [Examples 7–9]

▶ **35.** $\frac{1}{2}(2.3 + 2.5)$ **36.** $\frac{3}{4}(1.8 + 7.6)$ ▶ **37.** $\dfrac{1.99}{\frac{1}{2}}$ **38.** $\dfrac{2.99}{\frac{1}{2}}$

2.4   7.05   3.98   5.98

▶ **39.** $3.4 - \frac{1}{2}(0.76)$ **40.** $6.7 - \frac{1}{5}(0.45)$ ▶ **41.** $\frac{2}{5}(0.3) + \frac{3}{5}(0.3)$ **42.** $\frac{1}{8}(0.7) + \frac{3}{8}(0.7)$

3.02   6.61   0.3   0.35

▶ **43.** $6\left(\frac{3}{5}\right)(0.02)$ **44.** $8\left(\frac{4}{5}\right)(0.03)$ **45.** $\frac{5}{8} + 0.35\left(\frac{1}{2}\right)$ ▶ **46.** $\frac{7}{8} + 0.45\left(\frac{3}{4}\right)$

0.072   0.192   0.8   1.2125

47. $\left(\frac{1}{3}\right)^2(5.4) + \left(\frac{1}{2}\right)^3(3.2)$ ▶ **48.** $\left(\frac{1}{5}\right)^2(7.5) + \left(\frac{1}{4}\right)^2(6.4)$ ▶ **49.** $(0.25)^2 + \left(\frac{1}{4}\right)^2(3)$ **50.** $(0.75)^2 + \left(\frac{1}{4}\right)^2(7)$

1   0.7   0.25   1

D **Applying the Concepts** [Examples 10–12]

51. **Commuting** The map shows the average number of days spent commuting per year in the United States' largest cities. Change the data for Houston to a mixed number.

$4\frac{4}{10} = 4\frac{2}{5}$ days

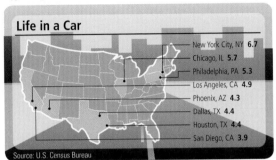

Life in a Car

New York City, NY **6.7**
Chicago, IL **5.7**
Philadelphia, PA **5.3**
Los Angeles, CA **4.9**
Phoenix, AZ **4.3**
Dallas, TX **4.4**
Houston, TX **4.4**
San Diego, CA **3.9**

Source: U.S. Census Bureau

52. **Pitchers** The chart shows the major league pitchers with the most career strikeouts. To compute the number of strikeouts per nine-inning game, divide by the total innings pitched and then multiply by 9. If Pedro Martinez had pitched 2,783 innings, write his strikeouts per game as a mixed number.

$10\frac{2}{25}$

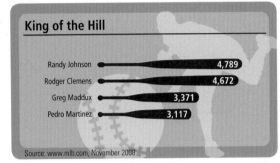

King of the Hill

Randy Johnson **4,789**
Rodger Clemens **4,672**
Greg Maddux **3,371**
Pedro Martinez **3,117**

Source: www.mlb.com, November 2008

In Problems 53–56, students have to round to the nearest cent.

▶ 53. **Price of Beef** If each pound of beef costs $4.99, how much does $3\frac{1}{4}$ pounds cost?

$16.22

54. **Price of Gasoline** What does it cost to fill a $15\frac{1}{2}$-gallon gas tank if the gasoline is priced at 429.9¢ per gallon?

$66.63

▶ 55. **Sale Price** A dress that costs $78.99 is on sale for $\frac{1}{3}$ off. What is the sale price of the dress?

$52.66

56. **Sale Price** A suit that normally sells for $221 is on sale for $\frac{1}{4}$ off. What is the sale price of the suit?

$165.75

57. **Perimeter of the Sierpinski Triangle** The diagram below shows one stage of what is known as the Sierpinski triangle. Each triangle in the diagram has three equal sides. The large triangle is made up of 4 smaller triangles. If each side of the large triangle is 2 inches, and each side of the smaller triangles is 1 inch, what is the perimeter of the shaded region?

9 in.

58. **Perimeter of the Sierpinski Triangle** The diagram below shows another stage of the Sierpinski triangle. Each triangle in the diagram has three equal sides. The largest triangle is made up of a number of smaller triangles. If each side of the large triangle is 2 inches, and each side of the smallest triangles is 0.5 inch, what is the perimeter of the shaded region?

13.5 in.

59. **Average Gain in Stock Price** The table below shows the amount of gain each day of one week in 2008 for the price of an Internet company specializing in distance learning for college students. Complete the table by converting each fraction to a decimal, rounding to the nearest hundredth if necessary.

CHANGE IN STOCK PRICE		
Date	Gain ($)	As a Decimal ($) (To the Nearest hundredth)
Monday, March 6, 2008	$\frac{3}{4}$	0.75
Tuesday, March 7, 2008	$\frac{9}{16}$	0.56
Wednesday, March 8, 2008	$\frac{3}{32}$	0.09
Thursday, March 9, 2008	$\frac{7}{32}$	0.22
Friday, March 10, 2008	$\frac{1}{16}$	0.06

60. **Average Gain in Stock Price** The table below shows the amount of gain each day of one week in 2008 for the stock price of amazon.com, an online bookstore. Complete the table by converting each fraction to a decimal, rounding to the nearest hundredth, if necessary.

CHANGE IN STOCK PRICE		
Date	Gain	As a Decimal ($) (To the Nearest Hundredth)
Monday, March 6, 2008	$\frac{1}{16}$	0.06
Tuesday, March 7, 2008	$1\frac{3}{8}$	1.38
Wednesday, March 8, 2008	$\frac{3}{8}$	0.38
Thursday, March 9, 2008	$5\frac{13}{16}$	5.81
Friday, March 10, 2008	$\frac{3}{8}$	0.38

61. **Nutrition** If 1 ounce of ground beef contains 50.75 calories and 1 ounce of halibut contains 27.5 calories, what is the difference in calories between a $4\frac{1}{2}$-ounce serving of ground beef and a $4\frac{1}{2}$-ounce serving of halibut?

104.625 calories

▶ 62. **Nutrition** If a 1-ounce serving of baked potato contains 48.3 calories and a 1-ounce serving of chicken contains 24.6 calories, how many calories are in a meal of $5\frac{1}{4}$ ounces of chicken and a $3\frac{1}{3}$-ounce baked potato?

290.15 calories

Taxi Ride Recently, the Texas Junior College Teachers Association annual conference was held in Austin. At that time a taxi ride in Austin was $1.25 for the first $\frac{1}{5}$ of a mile and $0.25 for each additional $\frac{1}{5}$ of a mile. The charge for a taxi to wait is $12.00 per hour. Use this information for Problems 63 through 66.

63. If the distance from one of the convention hotels to the airport is 7.5 miles, how much will it cost to take a taxi from that hotel to the airport?

$10.38

64. If you were to tip the driver of the taxi in Problem 63 $1.50, how much would it cost to take a taxi from the hotel to the airport?

$11.88

65. Suppose the distance from one of the hotels to one of the western dance clubs in Austin is 12.4 miles. If the fare meter in the taxi gives the charge for that trip as $16.50, is the meter working correctly?

Yes

66. Suppose that the distance from a hotel to the airport is 8.2 miles, and the ride takes 20 minutes. Is it more expensive to take a taxi to the airport or to just sit in the taxi?

It is more expensive to take a taxi to the airport.

Volume Find the volume of each sphere. Round to the nearest hundredth. Use 3.14 for π. [Example 12]

67.

2 m

33.49 m³

68.

3 m

113.04 m³

Volume Find the volume of each figure. Round to the nearest tenth. Use 3.14 for π. [Example 12]

69.

Hemisphere

6 ft

3 ft

226.1 ft³

70.

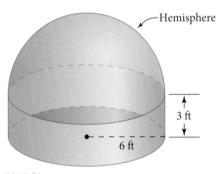

Hemisphere

3 ft

6 ft

791.3 ft³

Area Find the total area enclosed by each figure below. Use 3.14 for π.

71.

Half circle

4 in.

4 in.

22.28 in²

72.

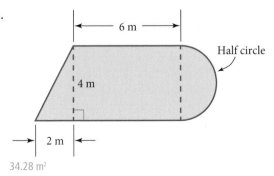

6 m

Half circle

4 m

2 m

34.28 m²

■ Maintaining Your Skills

73. Find the sum of 827 and 25.

852

74. Find the difference of 827 and 25.

802

75. Find the product of 827 and 25.

20,675

76. Find the quotient of 827 and 25.

33.08

Chapter 3 Summary

◼ Place Value [3.1]

The place values for the first five places to the right of the decimal point are

Decimal Point	Tenths	Hundredths	Thousandths	Ten Thousandths	Hundred Thousandths
.	$\frac{1}{10}$	$\frac{1}{100}$	$\frac{1}{1,000}$	$\frac{1}{10,000}$	$\frac{1}{100,000}$

EXAMPLES

1. The number 4.123 in words is "four and one hundred twenty-three thousandths."

◼ Rounding Decimals [3.1]

If the digit in the column to the right of the one we are rounding to is 5 or more, we add 1 to the digit in the column we are rounding to; otherwise, we leave it alone. We then replace all digits to the right of the column we are rounding to with zeros if they are to the left of the decimal point; otherwise, we simply delete them.

2. 357.753 rounded to the nearest
   Tenth: 357.8
   Ten: 360

◼ Addition and Subtraction with Decimals [3.2]

To add (or subtract) decimal numbers, we align the decimal points and add (or subtract) as if we were adding (or subtracting) whole numbers. The decimal point in the answer goes directly below the decimal points in the problem.

3.
```
   3.400
  25.060
+  0.347
  28.807
```

◼ Multiplication with Decimals [3.3]

To multiply two decimal numbers, we multiply as if the decimal points were not there. The decimal point in the product has as many digits to the right as there are total digits to the right of the decimal points in the two original numbers.

4. If we multiply 3.49 × 5.863, there will be a total of 2 + 3 = 5 digits to the right of the decimal point in the answer.

◼ Division with Decimals [3.4]

To begin a division problem with decimals, we make sure that the divisor is a whole number. If it is not, we move the decimal point in the divisor to the right as many places as it takes to make it a whole number. We must then be sure to move the decimal point in the dividend the same number of places to the right. Once the divisor is a whole number, we divide as usual. The decimal point in the answer is placed directly above the decimal point in the dividend.

5.
```
        1.39
2.5,)3.4,75
      2 5
        9 7
        7 5
        2 25
        2 25
           0
```

Changing Fractions to Decimals [3.5]

To change a fraction to a decimal, we divide the numerator by the denominator.

6. $\frac{4}{15} = 0.2\overline{6}$ because

```
       .266
  15)4.000
      3 0
      1 00
        90
        100
         90
         10
```

Changing Decimals to Fractions [3.5]

To change a decimal to a fraction, we write the digits to the right of the decimal point over the appropriate power of 10.

7. $0.781 = \frac{781}{1,000}$

Give the place value of the 7 in each of the following numbers. [3.1]

1. 36.007

Thousandths

2. 121.379

Hundredths

Write each of the following as a decimal number. [3.1]

3. Thirty-seven and forty-two ten thousandths

37.0042

4. One hundred and two hundred two hundred thousandths

100.00202

Round 98.7654 to the nearest: [3.1]

5. hundredth

98.77

6. hundred

100

Perform the following operations. [3.2, 3.3, 3.4]

7. $3.78 + 2.036$

5.816

8. $11.076 - 3.297$

7.779

9. 6.7×5.43

36.381

10. $0.89(24.24)$

21.5736

11. $29.07 \div 3.8$

7.65

12. $0.7134 \div 0.58$

1.23

13. $65)\overline{460.85}$

7.09

14. $(0.25)^3$

0.015625

15. $13.27 - 7.541$

5.729

16. $8.52 + 5.4$

13.92

17. $0.24(4.2)$

1.008

18. $42.5 \div 3.4$

12.5

19. $6.5)\overline{221.65}$

34.1

20. $(0.42)^2$

0.1764

21. 2.6×1.6

4.16

22. $5.7 \div 0.15$

38

Write as a decimal. [3.5]

23. $\frac{7}{8}$

0.875

24. $\frac{3}{16}$

0.1875

Write as a fraction in lowest terms. [3.5]

25. 0.705

$\frac{141}{200}$

26. 0.246

$\frac{123}{500}$

Write as a mixed number. [3.5]

27. 14.125

$14\frac{1}{8}$

28. 5.05

$5\frac{1}{20}$

Simplify each of the following expressions as much as possible. [3.5]

29. $3.3 - 4(0.22)$

2.42

30. $54.987 - 2(3.05 + 0.151)$

48.585

31. $125\left(\dfrac{3}{5}\right) + 4$

79

32. $\dfrac{3}{5}(0.9) + \dfrac{2}{5}(0.4)$

0.7

33. $0.3(1.7)(2.4)$

1.224

34. $3.6(1.4 - 0.5)$

3.24

35. $4(1.2 - 0.7) - 1.6$

0.4

Simplify.

1. $3{,}781 + 298$ 4,079

2. $903 - 576$ 327

3. $56(287)$ 16,072

4. $2.106 - 1.79$ 0.316

5. $24\overline{)149.28}$ 6.22

6. $\dfrac{2}{7} + \dfrac{3}{5}$ $\frac{31}{35}$

7. $4.3(12.96)$ 55.728

8. $1{,}292 \div 17$ 76

9. $\dfrac{5}{14} \div \dfrac{15}{21}$ $\frac{1}{2}$

10. Round 463,612 to the nearest thousand.   464,000

11. Change $\dfrac{63}{4}$ to a mixed number. $15\frac{3}{4}$

12. Change $2\dfrac{1}{5}$ to an improper fraction. $\frac{11}{5}$

13. Find the product of $2\dfrac{1}{2}$ and 8.   20

14. Change each decimal into a fraction.

Decimal	Fraction
0.125	$\frac{1}{8}$
0.250	$\frac{1}{4}$
0.375	$\frac{3}{8}$
0.500	$\frac{1}{2}$
0.625	$\frac{5}{8}$
0.750	$\frac{3}{4}$
0.875	$\frac{7}{8}$
1	$\frac{8}{8}$

15. Give the quotient of 72 and 8.

9

16. Identify the property or properties used in the following: $2 \cdot (x \cdot 3) = (2 \cdot 3) \cdot x$

Commutative and associative properties of multiplication

17. Translate into symbols, then simplify: Three times the sum of 13 and 4 is 51.

$3(13 + 4) = 51$

18. Reduce $\dfrac{120}{70}$.

$\frac{12}{7}$

19. True or False? Adding the same number to the numerator and denominator of a fraction produces an equivalent fraction.

False

Simplify.

20. $6(4)^2 - 8(2)^3$ 32

21. $\dfrac{6 + 2(4)}{8 + 10}$ $\frac{7}{9}$

22. $10\left(\dfrac{1}{2}\right) + 6\left(\dfrac{2}{3}\right)$ 9

23. $\dfrac{2}{3}(0.45) + \dfrac{4}{5}(0.8)$ 0.94

24. $\left(\dfrac{1}{2}\right)^3 + \left(\dfrac{1}{4}\right)^2$ $\frac{3}{16}$

25. $\left(3\dfrac{1}{3} - \dfrac{1}{2}\right)\left(4\dfrac{1}{2} + \dfrac{3}{4}\right)$ $14\frac{7}{8}$

26. Average Score Lorena has scores of 83, 85, 79, 93, and 80 on her first five math tests. What is her average score for these five tests?

84

27. Recipe A muffin recipe calls for $2\dfrac{3}{4}$ cups of flour. If the recipe is tripled, how many cups of flour will be needed?

$8\frac{1}{4}$ cups

28. Hourly Wage If you earn $384 for working 40 hours, what is your hourly wage?

$9.60

Use the following illustration to answer problem 29.

U.S. Open

The longest 18-hole golf courses to hold the U.S. Open

7,214 yds	Bethpage State Park (NY) Black Course (2002)
7,214 yds	Pinehurst (NC) No. 2 Course (2005)
7,213 yds	Congressional C.C. (MD) Blue Course (1997)
7,195 yds	Medinah C.C. (IL)
7,191 yds	Bellerive C.C. (MO) (1965)

29. If each U.S. Open golf course has 18 holes, how long is the average hole for the Bellerive golf course?

399.5 yds

1. Write the decimal number 5.053 in words.
Five and fifty-three thousandths

2. Give the place value of the 4 in the number 53.0543.
Thousandths

3. Write seventeen and four hundred six ten thousandths as a decimal number.
17.0406

4. Round 46.7549 to the nearest hundredth.
46.75

Perform the following operations.

5. 7 + 0.6 + 0.58
8.18

6. 12.032 − 5.976
6.056

7. 5.7(6.24)
35.568

8. 22.672 ÷ (2.6)
8.72

9. 4.3 + 7.06
11.36

10. 14.32 − 5.413
8.907

11. 0.4(2.8)(1.4)
1.568

12. 10.224 ÷ 42.6
0.24

13. Write $\frac{23}{25}$ as a decimal.
0.92

14. Write 0.56 as a fraction in lowest terms.
$\frac{14}{25}$

15. 5.2(2.8 + 0.02)
14.664

16. 5.2 − 3(0.17)
4.69

17. 23.852 − 3(2.01 + 0.231)
17.129

18. $\frac{3}{5}(0.6) - \frac{2}{3}(0.15)$
0.26

19. 14.2 − 4(4.03 − 2.1)
6.48

20. $\frac{4}{5}(0.23) + 5(4.02 - 1.9)$
10.784

21. A person purchases $8.47 worth of goods at a drug-store. If a $20 bill is used to pay for the purchases, how much change is received?
$11.53

22. If coffee sells for $6.99 per pound, how much will 3.5 pounds of coffee cost?
$24.47

23. If a person earns $262 for working 40 hours, what is the person's hourly wage?
$6.55

The following illustration shows the average annual premiums for auto insurance in several U.S. cities. Use the data to answer problem 24.

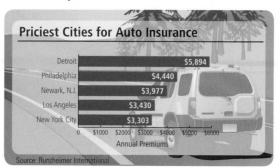

Priciest Cities for Auto Insurance

Detroit	$5,894
Philadelphia	$4,440
Newark, N.J.	$3,977
Los Angeles	$3,430
New York City	$3,303

Annual Premiums
Source: Runzheimer International

24. What is the monthly premium for someone living in Los Angeles? Round to the nearest cent. $285.83

Chapter 3 Projects

DECIMALS

Unwinding the Spiral of Roots

Number of People 2–3

Time Needed 8–12 minutes

Equipment Pencil, ruler, graph paper, scissors, and tape

Background The diagram below is called the Spiral of Roots. We can use the Spiral of Roots to visualize square roots of whole numbers.

PhotoDisc/Getty Images

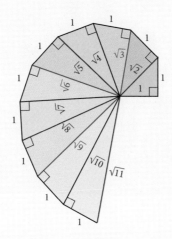

Procedure **1.** Carefully cut out each triangle from the Spiral of Roots above.

2. Line up the triangles horizontally on the coordinate system shown here so that the side of length 1 is on the x-axis and the hypotenuse is on the left. Note that the first triangle is shown in place, and the outline of the second triangle is next to it. The 1-unit side of each triangle should fit in each of the 1-unit spaces on the x-axis.

3. On the coordinate system, plot a point at the tip of each triangle. Then, connect these points to create a line graph. Each vertical line has a length that is represented by the square root of one of the first 10 counting numbers.

The Wizard of Oz

In the 1939 movie *The Wizard of Oz,* the Scarecrow (played by Ray Bolger) sings "If I only had a brain." Upon receiving a diploma from the great Oz, he rapidly recites a math theorem in an attempt to display his new knowledge. Unfortunately, the Scarecrow's inability to recite the Pythagorean Theorem might lead one to doubt the effectiveness of his diploma. Watch this scene in the movie. Write down the Scarecrow's speech and explain the errors.

The Kobal Collection

A Glimpse of Algebra

In the beginning of this chapter and in Chapter 1, we wrote numbers in expanded form. If we were to write the number 345 in expanded form and then in terms of powers of 10, it would look like this:

$$345 = 300 + 40 + 5$$
$$= 3 \cdot 100 + 4 \cdot 10 + 5$$
$$= 3 \cdot 10^2 + 4 \cdot 10 + 5$$

If we replace the 10's with x's in this last expression, we get what is called a *polynomial*. It looks like this:

$$3x^2 + 4x + 5$$

Polynomials are to algebra what whole numbers written in expanded form in terms of powers of 10 are to arithmetic. As in other expressions in algebra, we can use any variable we choose. Here are some other examples of polynomials:

$$4x - 5 \qquad a^2 + 5a + 6 \qquad y^3 + 3y^2 + 3y + 1$$

When we add two whole numbers, we add in columns. That is, if we add 345 and 234, we write one number under the other and add the numbers in the ones column, then the numbers in the tens column, and finally the numbers in the hundreds column. Here is how it looks.

$$
\begin{array}{r}
345 \\
\underline{234} \\
579
\end{array}
\quad \text{or} \quad
\begin{array}{r}
3 \cdot 10^2 + 4 \cdot 10 + 5 \\
\underline{2 \cdot 10^2 + 3 \cdot 10 + 4} \\
5 \cdot 10^2 + 7 \cdot 10 + 9
\end{array}
$$

We add polynomials in the same manner. If we want to add $3x^2 + 4x + 5$ and $2x^2 + 3x + 4$, we write one polynomial under the other, and then add in columns:

$$
\begin{array}{r}
3x^2 + 4x + 5 \\
\underline{2x^2 + 3x + 4} \\
5x^2 + 7x + 9
\end{array}
$$

The sum of the two polynomials is the polynomial $5x^2 + 7x + 9$. We add only the digits. Notice that the variable parts (the letters) stay the same (just as the powers of 10 did when we added 345 and 234).

Here are some more examples.

EXAMPLE 1   Add $3x^2 + 2x + 6$ and $4x^2 + 7x + 3$.

SOLUTION   We write one polynomial under the other and add in columns:

$$
\begin{array}{r}
3x^2 + 2x + 6 \\
\underline{4x^2 + 7x + 3} \\
7x^2 + 9x + 9
\end{array}
$$

The sum of the two polynomials is $7x^2 + 9x + 9$.

2. Add $3a + 7$ and $2a + 6$.

3. Add $2x^3 + 5x^2 + 3x + 6$,
$3x^3 + 4x^2 + 9x + 8$, and
$4x^3 + 2x^2 + 3x + 2$.

4. Add $3y^2 + 4y + 6$ and $6y^2 + 2$.

5. Add $5x^3 + 7x^2 + 3x + 1$ and
$2x^2 + 4x + 1$.

EXAMPLE 2   Add $4a + 2$ and $5a + 9$.

SOLUTION   We write one polynomial under the other and add in columns:

$$
\begin{array}{r}
4a +\ \ 2 \\
\underline{5a +\ \ 9} \\
9a + 11
\end{array}
$$

EXAMPLE 3   Add $4x^3 + 2x^2 + 4x + 1$, $2x^3 + 3x^2 + 9x + 6$,
and $2x^3 + 2x^2 + 2x + 2$.

SOLUTION   We add three polynomials the same way we add two of them. We write them one under the other and add in columns:

$$
\begin{array}{r}
4x^3 + 2x^2 +\ \ 4x + 1 \\
2x^3 + 3x^2 +\ \ 9x + 6 \\
\underline{2x^3 + 2x^2 +\ \ 2x + 2} \\
8x^3 + 7x^2 + 15x + 9
\end{array}
$$

EXAMPLE 4   Add $5y^2 + 3y + 6$ and $2y^2 + 3$.

SOLUTION   We write one polynomial under the other, so that the terms with y^2 line up, and the terms without any y's line up:

$$
\begin{array}{r}
5y^2 + 3y + 6 \\
\underline{2y^2 \quad\ \ \ + 3} \\
7y^2 + 3y + 9
\end{array}
$$

EXAMPLE 5   Add $2x^3 + 4x^2 + 2x + 6$ and $3x^2 + 2x + 1$.

SOLUTION   Again, we line up terms with the same variable part and add:

$$
\begin{array}{r}
2x^3 + 4x^2 + 2x + 6 \\
\underline{\quad\ \ \ 3x^2 + 2x + 1} \\
2x^3 + 7x^2 + 4x + 7
\end{array}
$$

Answers
2. $5a + 13$
3. $9x^3 + 11x^2 + 15x + 16$
4. $9y^2 + 4y + 8$
5. $5x^3 + 9x^2 + 7x + 2$

A Glimpse of Algebra Problems

In each case, add the polynomials.

1. $4x^2 + 2x + 3$
$\underline{2x^2 + 7x + 5}$
$6x^2 + 9x + 8$

2. $3x^2 + 4x + 5$
$\underline{5x^2 + 4x + 3}$
$8x^2 + 8x + 8$

3. $2a + 3$
$\underline{3a + 5}$
$5a + 8$

4. $5a + 2$
$\underline{2a + 1}$
$7a + 3$

5. $3x + 4$
$2x + 1$
$\underline{4x + 1}$
$9x + 6$

6. $2x + 1$
$3x + 2$
$\underline{4x + 3}$
$9x + 6$

7. $2y^3 + 3y^2 + 4y + 5$
$\underline{3y^3 + 2y^2 + 5y + 2}$
$5y^3 + 5y^2 + 9y + 7$

8. $4y^3 + 2y^2 + 6y + 7$
$\underline{5y^3 + 6y^2 + 2y + 8}$
$9y^3 + 8y^2 + 8y + 15$

9. Add $3x^2 + 4x + 3$ and $3x^2 + 2$.
$6x^2 + 4x + 5$

10. Add $5x^2 + 6x + 7$ and $4x^2 + 2$.
$9x^2 + 6x + 9$

11. Add $3a^2 + 4$ and $7a + 2$.
$3a^2 + 7a + 6$

12. Add $2a^2 + 5$ and $4a + 3$.
$2a^2 + 4a + 8$

13. Add $5x^3 + 4x^2 + 7x + 3$ and $3x^2 + 9x + 10$.
$5x^3 + 7x^2 + 16x + 13$

14. Add $2x^3 + 7x^2 + 3x + 1$ and $4x^2 + 3x + 8$.
$2x^3 + 11x^2 + 6x + 9$

Ratio and Proportion

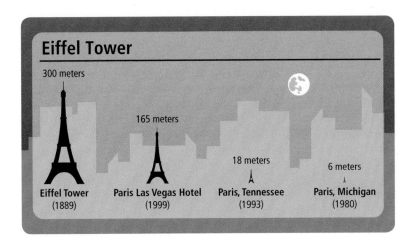

4

Introduction

The Eiffel Tower in Paris, France, is one of the most recognizable structures in the world. It was built in 1889 on the Champ de Mars beside the Seine River and named after its designer, engineer Gustave Eiffel. At that time it was the world's tallest tower, measuring 300 meters. Today it remains the tallest building in Paris.

This structure has inspired many reproductions, that is, towers built as replicas of the original Eiffel tower. The chart below shows the location and heights of some of these towers:

As you can see, these replicas are all different sizes. In mathematics, we can use ratios to compare those different size towers. For instance, we say the largest height and smallest height in the chart are in a ratio of 50 to 1. In this chapter, we study ratios like this one. As you will see, ratios are very closely related to fractions and decimals, which we have already studied.

The Pretest below contains problems that are representative of the problems you will find in the chapter.

Express each ratio as a fraction in lowest terms.

1. 15 to 25 $\frac{3}{5}$

2. 400 to 150 $\frac{8}{3}$

3. $\frac{5}{4}$ to $\frac{7}{4}$ $\frac{5}{7}$

4. 3.2 to 4.6 $\frac{16}{23}$

5. A car travels 434 miles in 7 hours. What is the rate of the car in miles per hour?   62 mi/hr

6. A 16-ounce container of heavy whipping cream costs $2.40. Find the price per ounce.   15¢

Solve each proportion.

7. $\frac{5}{6} = \frac{x}{12}$ 10

8. $\frac{2}{y} = \frac{4}{10}$ 5

9. $\frac{9}{7} = \frac{6}{x}$ $\frac{14}{3}$

10. $\frac{n}{8} = \frac{\frac{1}{6}}{\frac{1}{9}}$ 12

11. A trucker drives his rig 480 miles in 8 hours. At this rate, how far will he travel in 12 hours?   720 mi

12. A company reimburses its employees 36.5¢ for every mile of business travel. If an employee drives 150 miles, how much will she be reimbursed? $54.75

Assume the figures presented are similar.

13. Find length x.
   8

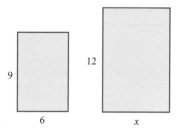

14. Find length BC.
   50

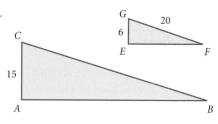

Getting Ready for Chapter 4

The problems below review material covered previously that you need to know in order to be successful in Chapter 4.

Reduce to lowest terms.

1. $\frac{16}{48}$ $\frac{1}{3}$

2. $\frac{320}{160}$ 2

Write as a decimal.

3. $\frac{1}{4}$ 0.25

4. $\frac{1}{8}$ 0.125

Multiply or divide as indicated.

5. $5 \cdot 13$ 65

6. $3(0.4)$ 1.2

7. $3.5(85)$ 297.5

8. $\frac{2}{3} \cdot 6$ 4

9. 0.08×100 8

10. 0.12×100 12

11. $125 \div 2$ 62.5

12. $1.39 \div 2$ 0.695

13. $\frac{1.99}{\frac{1}{2}}$ 3.98

14. $\frac{\frac{2}{3}}{\frac{4}{9}}$ $\frac{3}{2}$

Divide. Round answers to the nearest tenth.

15. $48 \div 5.5$ 8.7

16. $75 \div 11.5$ 6.5

4.1

A Express ratios as fractions in lowest terms.

B Use ratios to solve application problems.

Introduction

The *ratio* of two numbers is a way of comparing them. If we say that the ratio of two numbers is 2 to 1, then the first number is twice as large as the second number. For example, if there are 10 men and 5 women enrolled in a math class, then the ratio of men to women is 10 to 5. Because 10 is twice as large as 5, we can also say that the ratio of men to women is 2 to 1.

We can define the ratio of two numbers in terms of fractions.

A Express Ratios as Fractions in Lowest Terms

Definition

A **ratio** is a comparison between two numbers and is represented as a fraction, where the first number in the ratio is the numerator and the second number in the ratio is the denominator. *In symbols:*

If a and b are any two numbers,

then the ratio of a to b is $\dfrac{a}{b}$. $(b \neq 0)$

We handle ratios the same way we handle fractions. For example, when we said that the ratio of 10 men to 5 women was the same as the ratio 2 to 1, we were actually saying

$$\frac{10}{5} = \frac{2}{1} \qquad \text{Reducing to lowest terms}$$

Because we have already studied fractions in detail, much of the introductory material on ratios will seem like review.

EXAMPLE 1 Express the ratio of 16 to 48 as a fraction in lowest terms.

SOLUTION Because the ratio is 16 to 48, the numerator of the fraction is 16 and the denominator is 48:

$$\frac{16}{48} = \frac{1}{3} \qquad \text{In lowest terms}$$

Notice that the first number in the ratio becomes the numerator of the fraction, and the second number in the ratio becomes the denominator.

STUDY SKILLS
Continue to Set and Keep a Schedule

Sometimes I find students do well at first and then become overconfident. They begin to put in less time with their homework. Don't do it. Keep to the same schedule.

PRACTICE PROBLEMS

1. **a.** Express the ratio of 32 to 48 as a fraction in lowest terms.
   b. Express the ratio of 3.2 to 4.8 as a fraction in lowest terms.
   c. Express the ratio of 0.32 to 0.48 as a fraction in lowest terms.

Answer

1. All are $\frac{2}{3}$

2. a. Give the ratio of $\frac{3}{5}$ to $\frac{9}{10}$ as a fraction in lowest terms.
   b. Give the ratio of 0.6 to 0.9 as a fraction in lowest terms.

EXAMPLE 2   Give the ratio of $\frac{2}{3}$ to $\frac{4}{9}$ as a fraction in lowest terms.

SOLUTION   We begin by writing the ratio of $\frac{2}{3}$ to $\frac{4}{9}$ as a complex fraction. The numerator is $\frac{2}{3}$, and the denominator is $\frac{4}{9}$. Then we simplify.

$$\frac{\frac{2}{3}}{\frac{4}{9}} = \frac{2}{3} \cdot \frac{9}{4} \qquad \text{Division by } \frac{4}{9} \text{ is the same as multiplication by } \frac{9}{4}$$

$$= \frac{18}{12} \qquad \text{Multiply}$$

$$= \frac{3}{2} \qquad \text{Reduce to lowest terms}$$

3. a. Write the ratio of 0.06 to 0.12 as a fraction in lowest terms.
   b. Write the ratio of 600 to 1200 as a fraction in lowest terms.

EXAMPLE 3   Write the ratio of 0.08 to 0.12 as a fraction in lowest terms.

SOLUTION   When the ratio is in reduced form, it is customary to write it with whole numbers and not decimals. For this reason we multiply the numerator and the denominator of the ratio by 100 to clear it of decimals. Then we reduce to lowest terms.

$$\frac{0.08}{0.12} = \frac{0.08 \times 100}{0.12 \times 100} \qquad \begin{array}{l}\text{Multiply the numerator and the denominator}\\\text{by 100 to clear the ratio of decimals}\end{array}$$

$$= \frac{8}{12} \qquad \text{Multiply}$$

$$= \frac{2}{3} \qquad \text{Reduce to lowest terms}$$

Note   Another symbol used to denote ratio is the colon (:). The ratio of, say, 5 to 4 can be written as 5:4. Although we will not use it here, this notation is fairly common.

Table 1 shows several more ratios and their fractional equivalents. Notice that in each case the fraction has been reduced to lowest terms. Also, the ratio that contains decimals has been rewritten as a fraction that does not contain decimals.

TABLE 1		
Ratio	Fraction	Fraction In Lowest Terms
25 to 35	$\frac{25}{35}$	$\frac{5}{7}$
35 to 25	$\frac{35}{25}$	$\frac{7}{5}$
8 to 2	$\frac{8}{2}$	$\frac{4}{1}$ We can also write this as just 4.
$\frac{1}{4}$ to $\frac{3}{4}$	$\frac{\frac{1}{4}}{\frac{3}{4}}$	$\frac{1}{3}$ because $\frac{\frac{1}{4}}{\frac{3}{4}} = \frac{1}{4} \cdot \frac{4}{3} = \frac{1}{3}$
0.6 to 1.7	$\frac{0.6}{1.7}$	$\frac{6}{17}$ because $\frac{0.6 \times 10}{1.7 \times 10} = \frac{6}{17}$

B   Applications of Ratios

4. Suppose the basketball player in Example 4 makes 12 out of 16 free throws. Write the ratio again using these new numbers.

EXAMPLE 4   During a game, a basketball player makes 12 out of the 18 free throws he attempts. Write the ratio of the number of free throws he makes to the number of free throws he attempts as a fraction in lowest terms.

SOLUTION   Because he makes 12 out of 18, we want the ratio 12 to 18, or

$$\frac{12}{18} = \frac{2}{3}$$

Because the ratio is 2 to 3, we can say that, in this particular game, he made 2 out of every 3 free throws he attempted.

Answers

2. Both are $\frac{2}{3}$ **3.** Both are $\frac{1}{2}$

4. $\frac{3}{4}$

EXAMPLE 5 A solution of alcohol and water contains 15 milliliters of water and 5 milliliters of alcohol. Find the ratio of alcohol to water, water to alcohol, water to total solution, and alcohol to total solution. Write each ratio as a fraction and reduce to lowest terms.

SOLUTION There are 5 milliliters of alcohol and 15 milliliters of water, so there are 20 milliliters of solution (alcohol + water). The ratios are as follows:

The ratio of alcohol to water is 5 to 15, or

$$\frac{5}{15} = \frac{1}{3} \quad \text{In lowest terms}$$

The ratio of water to alcohol is 15 to 5, or

$$\frac{15}{5} = \frac{3}{1} \quad \text{In lowest terms}$$

— 5 mL

The ratio of water to total solution is 15 to 20, or

$$\frac{15}{20} = \frac{3}{4} \quad \text{In lowest terms}$$

The ratio of alcohol to total solution is 5 to 20, or

$$\frac{5}{20} = \frac{1}{4} \quad \text{In lowest terms}$$

Getting Ready for Class

After reading through the preceding section, respond in your own words and in complete sentences.

1. In your own words, write a definition for the ratio of two numbers.
2. What does a ratio compare?
3. What are some different ways of using mathematics to write the ratio of *a* to *b*?
4. When will the ratio of two numbers be a complex fraction?

---

5. A solution of alcohol and water contains 12 milliliters of water and 4 milliliters of alcohol. Find the ratio of alcohol to water, water to alcohol, and water to total solution. Write each ratio as a fraction and reduce to lowest terms.

Answer
5. $\frac{1}{3}, \frac{3}{1}, \frac{3}{4}$

Problem Set 4.1

A Write each of the following ratios as a fraction in lowest terms. None of the answers should contain decimals. [Examples 1–3]

1. 8 to 6

$\frac{4}{3}$

2. 6 to 8

$\frac{3}{4}$

3. 64 to 12

$\frac{16}{3}$

4. 12 to 64

$\frac{3}{16}$

5. 100 to 250

$\frac{2}{5}$

6. 250 to 100

$\frac{5}{2}$

7. 13 to 26

$\frac{1}{2}$

8. 36 to 18

$\frac{2}{1}$

9. $\frac{3}{4}$ to $\frac{1}{4}$

$\frac{3}{1}$

10. $\frac{5}{8}$ to $\frac{3}{8}$

$\frac{5}{3}$

11. $\frac{7}{3}$ to $\frac{6}{3}$

$\frac{7}{6}$

12. $\frac{9}{5}$ to $\frac{11}{5}$

$\frac{9}{11}$

13. $\frac{6}{5}$ to $\frac{6}{7}$

$\frac{7}{5}$

14. $\frac{5}{3}$ to $\frac{1}{3}$

$\frac{5}{1}$

15. $2\frac{1}{2}$ to $3\frac{1}{2}$

$\frac{5}{7}$

16. $5\frac{1}{4}$ to $1\frac{3}{4}$

$\frac{3}{1}$

17. $2\frac{2}{3}$ to $\frac{5}{3}$

$\frac{8}{5}$

18. $\frac{1}{2}$ to $3\frac{1}{2}$

$\frac{1}{7}$

19. 0.05 to 0.15

$\frac{1}{3}$

20. 0.21 to 0.03

$\frac{7}{1}$

21. 0.3 to 3

$\frac{1}{10}$

22. 0.5 to 10

$\frac{1}{20}$

23. 1.2 to 10

$\frac{3}{25}$

24. 6.4 to 0.8

$\frac{8}{1}$

25. a. What is the ratio of shaded squares to nonshaded squares?

$\frac{1}{2}$

b. What is the ratio of shaded squares to total squares?

$\frac{1}{3}$

c. What is the ratio of nonshaded squares to total squares?

$\frac{2}{3}$

26. a. What is the ratio of shaded squares to nonshaded squares?

$\frac{2}{3}$

b. What is the ratio of shaded squares to total squares?

$\frac{2}{5}$

c. What is the ratio of nonshaded squares to total squares?

$\frac{3}{5}$

B **Applying the Concepts** [Examples 4, 5]

27. Biggest Hits The chart shows the number of hits for the three best charting artists in the United States. Use the information to find the ratio of hits the Beach Boys had to hits the Beatles had.

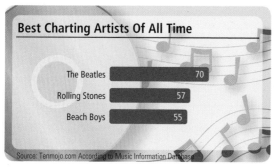

$\frac{11}{14}$

28. Google Earth The Google Earth image shows Crater Lake National Park in Oregon. The park covers 266 square miles and the lake covers 20 square miles. What is the ratio of the park's area to the lake's area?

$\frac{133}{10}$

Write each of the following ratios as a fraction in lowest terms. None of the answers should contain decimals.

29. 100 mg to 5 mL

$\frac{20 \text{ mg}}{1 \text{ mL}}$

30. 25 g to 1 L

$\frac{25 \text{ g}}{1 \text{ L}}$

31. 375 mg to 10 mL

$\frac{75 \text{ mg}}{2 \text{ mL}}$

32. 450 mg to 20 mL

$\frac{45 \text{ mg}}{2 \text{ mL}}$

▶ **33. Family Budget** A family of four budgeted the following amounts for some of their monthly bills:

- Food bill $400
- Gas bill $100
- Utilities bill $150
- Rent $650

a. What is the ratio of the rent to the food bill?

$\frac{13}{8}$

b. What is the ratio of the gas bill to the food bill?

$\frac{1}{4}$

c. What is the ratio of the utilities bill to the food bill?

$\frac{3}{8}$

d. What is the ratio of the rent to the utilities bill?

$\frac{13}{3}$

▶ **34. Nutrition** One cup of breakfast cereal was found to contain the following nutrients:

a. Find the ratio of water to protein.

$\frac{1}{2}$

b. Find the ratio of carbohydrates to protein.

$\frac{21}{2}$

c. Find the ratio of vitamins to minerals.

$\frac{3}{22}$

d. Find the ratio of protein to vitamins and minerals.

$\frac{2}{5}$

▶ **35. Profit and Revenue** The following bar chart shows the profit and revenue of the Baby Steps Shoe Company each quarter for one year.

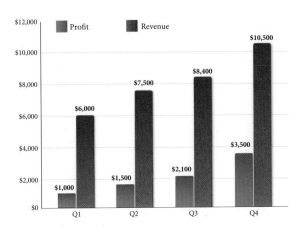

Find the ratio of revenue to profit for each of the following quarters. Write your answer in lowest terms.

a. Q1 $\frac{6}{1}$ b. Q2 $\frac{5}{1}$ c. Q3 $\frac{4}{1}$ d. Q4 $\frac{3}{1}$

e. Find the ratio of revenue to profit for the entire year. $\frac{4}{1}$

▶ **36. Geometry** Regarding the diagram below, AC represents the length of the line segment that starts at A and ends at C. From the diagram we see that AC = 8.

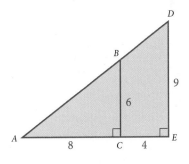

a. Find the ratio of BC to AC.

$\frac{3}{4}$

b. What is the length AE?

12

c. Find the ratio of DE to AE.

$\frac{3}{4}$

▶ **37. Major League Baseball** The following table shows the number of games won during the 2007 baseball season by several National League teams.

Team	Number of Wins
New York Mets	88
Atlanta Braves	84
Washington Nationals	73
St. Louis Cardinals	78
Houston Astros	73
Arizona Diamondbacks	90
Cincinnati Reds	72

a. What is the ratio of wins of the New York Mets to the St. Louis Cardinals?   44 to 39

b. What is the ratio of wins of the Washington Nationals to the Houston Astros?   1 to 1

c. What is the ratio of wins of the Cincinnati Reds to the Atlanta Braves?   6 to 7

38. Buying an iPod™ The hard drive of an Apple iPod determines how many songs you will be able to store and carry around with you. The table below compares the size of the hard-drive, song capacity and cost of three popular iPods.

iPod Type	Hard-Drive Size	Number of Songs	Cost
Shuffle	2 GB	500 songs	$69.00
Nano	4 GB	1000 songs	$149.00
Classic	80 GB	20,000 songs	$249.00

a. What is the ratio of hard-drive size between the Shuffle and the Nano? Between the Shuffle and the Classic?   1 to 2; 1 to 40

b. What is the ratio of number of songs between the Shuffle and the Nano? Between the Shuffle and the Classic?   1 to 2; 1 to 40

◼ Getting Ready for the Next Section

The following problems review material from a previous section. Reviewing these problems will help you with the next section.

Write as a decimal.

39. $\dfrac{90}{5}$

18

40. $\dfrac{120}{3}$

40

41. $\dfrac{125}{2}$

62.5

42. $\dfrac{2}{10}$

0.2

43. $\dfrac{1.23}{2}$

0.615

44. $\dfrac{1.39}{2}$

0.695

45. $\dfrac{88}{0.5}$

176

46. $\dfrac{1.99}{0.5}$

3.98

47. $\dfrac{46}{0.25}$

184

48. $\dfrac{92}{0.25}$

368

Divide. Round answers to the nearest thousandth.

49. $0.48 \div 5.5$

0.087

50. $0.75 \div 11.5$

0.065

51. $2.19 \div 46$

0.048

52. $1.25 \div 50$

0.025

◼ Maintaining Your Skills

Multiply and divide as indicated.

53. $\dfrac{3}{4} \cdot \dfrac{5}{6}$

$\dfrac{5}{8}$

54. $\dfrac{7}{8} \cdot 32$

28

55. $\dfrac{11}{16} \div \dfrac{1}{8}$

$\dfrac{11}{2} = 5\dfrac{1}{2}$

56. $13 \div \dfrac{1}{3}$

39

57. $\dfrac{65}{72} \cdot \dfrac{108}{273}$

$\dfrac{5}{14}$

58. $\dfrac{165}{84} \cdot \dfrac{24}{195}$

$\dfrac{22}{91}$

59. $\dfrac{3}{4} \div \dfrac{1}{8} \cdot 16$

96

60. $\dfrac{1}{4} \div \dfrac{1}{12} \cdot 6$

18

Rates and Unit Pricing

Objectives

A Express rates as ratios.

B Use ratios to write a unit price.

Here is the first paragraph of an article that appeared in *USA Today* in 2003.

Culture Clash

Dannon recently shrank its 8-ounce cup of yogurt by 25% to 6 ounces—but cut its suggested retail price by only 20% from 89 cents to 71 cents, which would raise the unit price a penny an ounce—9%—to 12 cents. At the Hoboken store, which charges more than Dannon's suggested prices, the unit price went from 12 cents to 13 cents with the size change.

DANNON YOGURT		
	Old	New
Size	8 ounces	6 ounces
Container cost	89 cents	71 cents
Price per ounce	11 cents	12 cents
Price difference per ounce: 9%		

In this section we cover material that will give you a better understanding of the information in this article. We start this section with a discussion of rates, then we move on to unit pricing.

A Rates

Whenever a ratio compares two quantities that have different units (and neither unit can be converted to the other), then the ratio is called a *rate*. For example, if we were to travel 120 miles in 3 hours, then our average rate of speed expressed as the ratio of miles to hours would be

$$\frac{120 \text{ miles}}{3 \text{ hours}} = \frac{40 \text{ miles}}{1 \text{ hour}}$$ Divide the numerator and the denominator by 3 to reduce to lowest terms

The ratio $\frac{40 \text{ miles}}{1 \text{ hour}}$ can be expressed as

$$40 \frac{\text{miles}}{\text{hour}} \quad \text{or} \quad 40 \text{ miles/hour} \quad \text{or} \quad 40 \text{ miles per hour}$$

A rate is expressed in simplest form when the numerical part of the denominator is 1. To accomplish this we use division.

EXAMPLE 1 A train travels 125 miles in 2 hours. What is the train's rate in miles per hour?

SOLUTION The ratio of miles to hours is

$$\frac{125 \text{ miles}}{2 \text{ hours}} = 62.5 \frac{\text{miles}}{\text{hour}}$$ Divide 125 by 2

$$= 62.5 \text{ miles per hour}$$

If the train travels 125 miles in 2 hours, then its average rate of speed is 62.5 miles per hour.

EXAMPLE 2 A car travels 90 miles on 5 gallons of gas. Give the ratio of miles to gallons as a rate in miles per gallon.

SOLUTION The ratio of miles to gallons is

$$\frac{90 \text{ miles}}{5 \text{ gallons}} = 18 \frac{\text{miles}}{\text{gallon}}$$ Divide 90 by 5

$$= 18 \text{ miles/gallon}$$

The gas mileage of the car is 18 miles per gallon.

PRACTICE PROBLEMS

1. A car travels 107 miles in 2 hours. What is the car's rate in miles per hour?

2. A car travels 192 miles on 6 gallons of gas. Give the ratio of miles to gallons as a rate in miles per gallon.

Answers
1. 53.5 miles/hour
2. 32 miles/gallon

B Unit Pricing

One kind of rate that is very common is *unit pricing*. Unit pricing is the ratio of price to quantity when the quantity is one unit. Suppose a 1-liter bottle of a certain soft drink costs $1.19, whereas a 2-liter bottle of the same drink costs $1.39. Which is the better buy? That is, which has the lower price per liter?

$$\frac{\$1.19}{1 \text{ liter}} = \$1.19 \text{ per liter}$$

$$\frac{\$1.39}{2 \text{ liter}} = \$0.695 \text{ per liter}$$

The unit price for the 1-liter bottle is $1.19 per liter, whereas the unit price for the 2-liter bottle is 69.5¢ per liter. The 2-liter bottle is a better buy.

EXAMPLE 3 A supermarket sells low-fat milk in three different containers at the following prices:

1 gallon $3.59
$\frac{1}{2}$ gallon $1.99
1 quart $1.29   (1 quart = $\frac{1}{4}$ gallon)

$3.59 $1.99 $1.29

Give the unit price in dollars per gallon for each one.

SOLUTION Because 1 quart = $\frac{1}{4}$ gallon, we have

1-gallon container $\dfrac{\$3.59}{1 \text{ gallon}} = \dfrac{\$3.59}{1 \text{ gallon}} = \$3.59$ per gallon

$\frac{1}{2}$-gallon container $\dfrac{\$1.99}{\frac{1}{2} \text{ gallon}} = \dfrac{\$1.99}{0.5 \text{ gallon}} = \$3.98$ per gallon

1-quart container $\dfrac{\$1.29}{1 \text{ quart}} = \dfrac{\$1.29}{0.25 \text{ gallon}} = \$5.16$ per gallon

The 1-gallon container has the lowest unit price, whereas the 1-quart container has the highest unit price.

Getting Ready for Class

After reading through the preceding section, respond in your own words and in complete sentences.

1. A rate is a special type of ratio. In your own words, explain what a rate is.
2. When is a rate written in simplest terms?
3. What is *unit pricing*?
4. Give some examples of rates *not* found in your textbook.

---

3. A supermarket sells vegetable juice in three different containers at the following prices:
  5.5 ounces, 48¢
  11.5 ounces, 75¢
   46 ounces, $2.19
Give the unit price in cents per ounce for each one. Round to the nearest tenth of a cent, if necessary.

Answer
3. 8.7¢/ounce, 6.5¢/ounce, 4.8¢/ounce

Problem Set 4.2

A Express each of the following rates as a ratio with the given units. [Examples 1, 2]

▶ 1. **Miles/Hour** A car travels 220 miles in 4 hours. What is the rate of the car in miles per hour?

55 mi/hr

▶ 2. **Miles/Hour** A train travels 360 miles in 5 hours. What is the rate of the train in miles per hour?

72 mi/hr

▶ 3. **Kilometers/Hour** It takes a car 3 hours to travel 252 kilometers. What is the rate in kilometers per hour?

84 km/hr

▶ 4. **Kilometers/Hour** In 6 hours an airplane travels 4,200 kilometers. What is the rate of the airplane in kilometers per hour?

700 km/hr

▶ 5. **Gallons/Second** The flow of water from a water faucet can fill a 3-gallon container in 15 seconds. Give the ratio of gallons to seconds as a rate in gallons per second.

0.2 gal/sec

▶ 6. **Gallons/Minute** A 225-gallon drum is filled in 3 minutes. What is the rate in gallons per minute?

75 gal/min

▶ 7. **Liters/Minute** It takes 4 minutes to fill a 56-liter gas tank. What is the rate in liters per minute?

14 L/min

▶ 8. **Liters/Hour** The gas tank on a car holds 60 liters of gas. At the beginning of a 6-hour trip, the tank is full. At the end of the trip, it contains only 12 liters. What is the rate at which the car uses gas in liters per hour?

8 L/hr

▶ 9. **Miles/Gallon** A car travels 95 miles on 5 gallons of gas. Give the ratio of miles to gallons as a rate in miles per gallon.

19 mi/gal

▶ 10. **Miles/Gallon** On a 384-mile trip, an economy car uses 8 gallons of gas. Give this as a rate in miles per gallon.

48 mi/gal

▶ 11. **Miles/Liter** The gas tank on a car has a capacity of 75 liters. On a full tank of gas, the car travels 325 miles. What is the gas mileage in miles per liter?

4.3̄ mi/L

▶ 12. **Miles/Liter** A car pulling a trailer can travel 105 miles on 70 liters of gas. What is the gas mileage in miles per liter?

1.5 mi/L

▶ Selected exercises available online at www.webassign.net/brookscole

13. Gas Prices The snapshot shows the gas prices for the different regions of the United States. If a man bought 12 gallons of gas for $48.72, where might he live?

The Midwest

Average Price per Gallon of Gasoline, July 2008

ROCKY MOUNTAINS
MIDWEST
WEST COAST
EAST COAST
GULF COAST

$4.44
$4.10
$4.06
$3.96
$4.07

Source: http://www.fueleconomy.gov

14. Pitchers The chart shows the major league pitchers with the most career strikeouts. If Pedro Martinez pitched 2,783 innings, how many strikeouts does he throw per inning? Round to the nearest hundredth.

1.12 strikeouts per inning

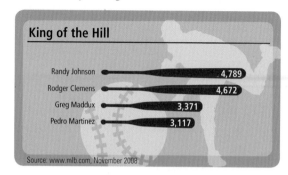

King of the Hill

Randy Johnson — 4,789
Rodger Clemens — 4,672
Greg Maddux — 3,371
Pedro Martinez — 3,117

Source: www.mlb.com, November 2008

Nursing Intravenous (IV) infusions are often ordered in either milliliters per hour or milliliters per minute.

15. What was the infusion rate in milliliters per hour if it took 5 hours to administer 2,400 mL?

480 mL/hr

16. What was the infusion rate in milliliters per minute if 42 milliliters were administered in 6 minutes?

7 mL/min

A Unit Pricing [Example 3]

▶ **17. Cents/Ounce** A 20-ounce package of frozen peas is priced at 99¢. Give the unit price in cents per ounce.

4.95¢ per ounce

▶ **18. Dollars/Pound** A 4-pound bag of cat food costs $8.12. Give the unit price in dollars per pound.

$2.03 per pound

19. Best Buy Find the unit price in cents per diaper for each of the packages shown here. Which is the better buy? Round to the nearest tenth of a cent.

36 disposable diapers
$12.49

34.7 cents/diaper

38 disposable diapers
$11.99

31.6 cents/diaper
Happy Baby is a better buy.

20. Best Buy Find the unit price in cents per pill for each of the packages shown here. Which is the better buy? Round to the nearest tenth of a cent.

100 pills
$5.99

6.0 cents/pill
Relief is a better buy.

225 pills
$13.96

6.2 cents/pill

Currency Conversions There are a number of online calculators that will show what the money in one country is worth in another country. One such converter, the XE Universal Currency Converter®, uses live, up-to-the-minute currency rates. Use the information shown here to determine what the equivalent to one U.S. dollar for each of the following denominations. Round to the nearest thousandth, where necessary.

21. $100.00 U.S. dollars are equivalent to 64.582 euros

$1.00 = 0.646 euros

22. $50.00 U.S. dollars are equivalent to $51.0775 Canadian dollars

$1.00 = 1.022 Canadian dollars

23. $40.00 U.S. dollars are equivalent to 20.3765 British pounds

$1.00 = 0.509 pounds

24. $25.00 U.S. dollars are equivalent to 2704.0125 Japanese yen

$1.00 = 108.161 yen

25. Food Prices Using unit rates is a way to compare prices of different sized packages to see which price is really the best deal. Suppose we compare the cost of a box of Cheerios sold at three different stores for the following prices:

Store	Size	Cost
A	11.3 ounce box	$4.00
B	18 ounce box	$4.99
C	180 ounce case	$52.90

Which size is the best buy? Give the cost per ounce for that size.

The 18 oz box is the best buy at $0.277 per ounce.

26. Cell Phone Plans All cell phone plans are not created equal. The number of minutes and the monthly charges can vary greatly. The table shows four plans presented by four different cell phone providers.

Carrier	AT&T	Sprint	T-Mobile	Verizon
Plan name	Nation 450	Sprint Basic	Individual Value	Nationwide Basic
Monthly minutes	450	200	600	450
Monthly cost	$39.99	$29.99	$39.99	$39.99
Plan cost per minute	$0.089	$0.15	$0.067	$0.089

Find the cost per minute for each plan. Based on your results, which plan should you go with?

T-Mobile Individual Value.

▶ **27. Miles/Hour** A car travels 675.4 miles in $12\frac{1}{2}$ hours. Give the rate in miles per hour to the nearest hundredth.

54.03 mi/hr

▶ **28. Miles/Hour** At the beginning of a trip, the odometer on a car read 32,567.2 miles. At the end of the trip, it read 32,741.8 miles. If the trip took $4\frac{1}{4}$ hours, what was the rate of the car in miles per hour to the nearest tenth?

41.1 mi/hr

▶ **29. Miles/Gallon** If a truck travels 128.4 miles on 13.8 gallons of gas, what is the gas mileage in miles per gallon? (Round to the nearest tenth.)

9.3 mi/gal

▶ **30. Cents/Day** If a 15-day supply of vitamins costs $1.62, what is the price in cents per day?

10.8¢ per day

Hourly Wages Jane has a job at the local Marcy's department store. The graph shows how much Jane earns for working 8 hours per day for 5 days.

31. What is her daily rate of pay? (Assume she works 8 hours per day.)

$64

32. What is her weekly rate of pay? (Assume she works 5 days per week.)

$320

▶ **33.** What is her annual rate of pay? (Assume she works 50 weeks per year.)

$16,000

▶ **34.** What is her hourly rate of pay? (Assume she works 8 hours per day.)

$8

Department Store Rate of Pay

Getting Ready for the Next Section

Solve each equation by finding a number to replace *n* that will make the equation a true statement.

35. $2 \cdot n = 12$

$n = 6$

36. $3 \cdot n = 27$

$n = 9$

37. $6 \cdot n = 24$

$n = 4$

38. $8 \cdot n = 16$

$n = 2$

39. $20 = 5 \cdot n$

$n = 4$

40. $35 = 7 \cdot n$

$n = 5$

41. $650 = 10 \cdot n$

$n = 65$

42. $630 = 7 \cdot n$

$n = 90$

Maintaining Your Skills

Add and subtract as indicated.

43. $\dfrac{1}{2} + \dfrac{3}{8}$

$\dfrac{7}{8}$

44. $\dfrac{7}{6} - \dfrac{1}{3}$

$\dfrac{5}{6}$

45. $\dfrac{2}{5} - \dfrac{3}{8}$

$\dfrac{1}{40}$

46. $\dfrac{5}{8} + \dfrac{3}{4}$

$\dfrac{11}{8} = 1\dfrac{3}{8}$

47. $\dfrac{11}{12} - \dfrac{9}{10}$

$\dfrac{1}{60}$

48. $\dfrac{13}{15} + \dfrac{1}{10}$

$\dfrac{29}{30}$

49. $\dfrac{5}{6} - \dfrac{1}{3} + \dfrac{4}{3}$

$\dfrac{11}{6} = 1\dfrac{5}{6}$

50. $\dfrac{7}{8} + \dfrac{1}{8} - \dfrac{1}{16}$

$\dfrac{15}{16}$

Extending the Concepts

51. Unit Pricing The makers of Wisk liquid detergent cut the size of its popular midsize jug from 100 ounces (3.125 quarts) to 80 ounces (2.5 quarts). At the same time it lowered the price from $6.99 to $5.75. Fill in the table below and use your results to decide which of the two sizes is the better buy.

100 oz is the better value.

WISK LAUNDRY DETERGENT		
	Old	New
Size	100 ounces	80 ounces
Container cost	$6.99	$5.75
Price per quart	$2.24	$2.30

Solving Equations by Division

In Chapter 1 we solved equations like $3 \cdot n = 12$ by finding a number with which to replace n that would make the equation a true statement. The solution for the equation $3 \cdot n = 12$ is $n = 4$, because

when	$n = 4$
the equation	$3 \cdot n = 12$
becomes	$3 \cdot 4 = 12$
or	$12 = 12$ A true statement

The problem with this method of solving equations is that we have to guess at the solution and then check it in the equation to see if it works. In this section we will develop a method of solving equations like $3 \cdot n = 12$ that does not require any guessing.

In Chapter 2 we simplified expressions such as

$$\frac{2 \cdot 2 \cdot 3 \cdot 5 \cdot 7}{2 \cdot 5}$$

by dividing out any factors common to the numerator and the denominator. For example:

$$\frac{2 \cdot 2 \cdot 3 \cdot 5 \cdot 7}{2 \cdot 5} = 2 \cdot 3 \cdot 7 = 42$$

The same process works with expressions that have variables for some of their factors. For example, the expression

$$\frac{2 \cdot n \cdot 7 \cdot 11}{n \cdot 11}$$

can be simplified by dividing out the factors common to the numerator and the denominator—namely, n and 11:

$$\frac{2 \cdot n \cdot 7 \cdot 11}{n \cdot 11} = 2 \cdot 7 = 14$$

A Dividing Expressions Containing a Variable

EXAMPLE 1 Divide the expression $5 \cdot n$ by 5.

SOLUTION Applying the method above, we have:

$$5 \cdot n \text{ divided by } 5 \text{ is } \frac{5 \cdot n}{5} = n$$

If you are having trouble understanding this process because there is a variable involved, consider what happens when we divide 6 by 2 and when we divide 6 by 3. Because $6 = 2 \cdot 3$, when we divide by 2 we get 3. Like this:

$$\frac{6}{2} = \frac{2 \cdot 3}{2} = 3$$

When we divide by 3, we get 2:

$$\frac{6}{3} = \frac{2 \cdot 3}{3} = 2$$

EXAMPLE 2 Divide $7 \cdot y$ by 7.

SOLUTION Dividing by 7, we have:

$$7 \cdot y \text{ divided by } 7 \text{ is } \frac{7 \cdot y}{7} = y$$

PRACTICE PROBLEMS

1. Divide the expression $8 \cdot n$ by 8.

2. Divide $3 \cdot y$ by 3.

Answers
1. n **2.** y

Note The choice of the letter we use for the variable is not important. The process works just as well with y as it does with n. The letters used for variables in equations are most often the letters a, n, x, y, or z.

 Note In the last chapter of this book, we will devote a lot of time to solving equations. For now, we are concerned only with equations that can be solved by division.

We can use division to solve equations such as $3 \cdot n = 12$. Notice that the left side of the equation is $3 \cdot n$. The equation is solved when we have just n, instead of $3 \cdot n$, on the left side and a number on the right side. That is, we have solved the equation when we have rewritten it as

$$n = \text{a number}$$

We can accomplish this by dividing *both* sides of the equation by 3:

$$\frac{3 \cdot n}{3} = \frac{12}{3} \qquad \text{Divide both sides by 3}$$
$$n = 4$$

Because 12 divided by 3 is 4, the solution to the equation is $n = 4$, which we know to be correct from our discussion at the beginning of this section. Notice that it would be incorrect to divide just the left side by 3 and not the right side also. *Whenever we divide one side of an equation by a number, we must also divide the other side by the same number.*

B Solving Equations

3. Solve the equation $8 \cdot n = 40$ by dividing both sides by 8.

EXAMPLE 3 Solve the equation $7 \cdot y = 42$ for y by dividing both sides by 7.

SOLUTION Dividing both sides by 7, we have:

$$\frac{7 \cdot y}{7} = \frac{42}{7}$$
$$y = 6$$

We can check our solution by replacing y with 6 in the original equation:

when $y = 6$

the equation $7 \cdot y = 42$

becomes $7 \cdot 6 = 42$

or $42 = 42$ A true statement

4. Solve for a: $35 = 7 \cdot a$

EXAMPLE 4 Solve for a: $30 = 5 \cdot a$

SOLUTION Our method of solving equations by division works regardless of which side the variable is on. In this case, the right side is $5 \cdot a$, and we would like it to be just a. Dividing both sides by 5, we have:

$$\frac{30}{5} = \frac{5 \cdot a}{5}$$
$$6 = a$$

The solution is $a = 6$. (If 6 is a, then a is 6.)

We can write our solutions as improper fractions, mixed numbers, or decimals. Let's agree to write our answers as either whole numbers, proper fractions, or mixed numbers unless otherwise stated.

Getting Ready for Class

After reading through the preceding section, respond in your own words and in complete sentences.

1. In your own words, explain what a solution to an equation is.

2. What number results when you simplify $\dfrac{2 \cdot n \cdot 7 \cdot 11}{n \cdot 11}$?

3. What is the result of dividing $7 \cdot y$ by 7?

4. Explain how division is used to solve the equation $30 = 5 \cdot a$.

Answers
3. 5 **4.** 5

Problem Set 4.3

A Simplify each of the following expressions by dividing out any factors common to the numerator and the denominator and then simplifying the result.

1. $\dfrac{3 \cdot 5 \cdot 5 \cdot 7}{3 \cdot 5}$

35

2. $\dfrac{2 \cdot 2 \cdot 3 \cdot 5 \cdot 7}{2 \cdot 5 \cdot 7}$

6

3. $\dfrac{2 \cdot n \cdot 3 \cdot 3 \cdot 5}{n \cdot 5}$

18

4. $\dfrac{3 \cdot 5 \cdot n \cdot 7 \cdot 7}{3 \cdot n \cdot 7}$

35

5. $\dfrac{2 \cdot 2 \cdot n \cdot 7 \cdot 11}{2 \cdot n \cdot 11}$

14

6. $\dfrac{3 \cdot n \cdot 7 \cdot 13 \cdot 17}{n \cdot 13 \cdot 17}$

21

7. $\dfrac{9 \cdot n}{9}$

n

8. $\dfrac{8 \cdot a}{8}$

a

9. $\dfrac{4 \cdot y}{4}$

y

10. $\dfrac{7 \cdot x}{7}$

x

B Solve each of the following equations by dividing both sides by the appropriate number. Be sure to show the division in each case.

11. $4 \cdot n = 8$

$n = 2$

12. $2 \cdot n = 8$

$n = 4$

13. $5 \cdot x = 35$

$x = 7$

14. $7 \cdot x = 35$

$x = 5$

15. $3 \cdot y = 21$

$y = 7$

16. $7 \cdot y = 21$

$y = 3$

17. $6 \cdot n = 48$

$n = 8$

18. $16 \cdot n = 48$

$n = 3$

19. $5 \cdot a = 40$

$a = 8$

20. $10 \cdot a = 40$

$a = 4$

21. $3 \cdot x = 6$

$x = 2$

22. $8 \cdot x = 40$

$x = 5$

23. $2 \cdot y = 2$

$y = 1$

24. $2 \cdot y = 12$

$y = 6$

25. $3 \cdot a = 18$

$a = 6$

26. $4 \cdot a = 4$

$a = 1$

27. $5 \cdot n = 25$

$n = 5$

28. $9 \cdot n = 18$

$n = 2$

29. $6 = 2 \cdot x$

$x = 3$

30. $56 = 7 \cdot x$

$x = 8$

31. $42 = 6 \cdot n$

$n = 7$

32. $30 = 5 \cdot n$

$n = 6$

33. $4 = 4 \cdot y$

$y = 1$

34. $90 = 9 \cdot y$

$y = 10$

35. $63 = 7 \cdot y$

$y = 9$

36. $3 = 3 \cdot y$

$y = 1$

37. $2 \cdot n = 7$

$n = 3\frac{1}{2}$

38. $4 \cdot n = 10$

$n = 2\frac{1}{2}$

39. $6 \cdot x = 21$
$x = 3\frac{1}{2}$

▶ **40.** $7 \cdot x = 8$
$x = 1\frac{1}{7}$

41. $5 \cdot a = 12$
$a = 2\frac{2}{5}$

42. $8 \cdot a = 13$
$a = 1\frac{5}{8}$

▶ **43.** $4 = 7 \cdot y$
$y = \frac{4}{7}$

44. $3 = 9 \cdot y$
$y = \frac{1}{3}$

▶ **45.** $10 = 13 \cdot y$
$y = \frac{10}{13}$

46. $9 = 11 \cdot y$
$y = \frac{9}{11}$

▶ **47.** $12 \cdot x = 30$
$x = 2\frac{1}{2}$

48. $16 \cdot x = 56$
$x = 3\frac{1}{2}$

49. $21 = 14 \cdot n$
$n = 1\frac{1}{2}$

▶ **50.** $48 = 20 \cdot n$
$n = 2\frac{2}{5}$

▬ Getting Ready for the Next Section

Reduce.

51. $\frac{6}{8}$

$\frac{3}{4}$

52. $\frac{17}{34}$

$\frac{1}{2}$

Multiply.

53. $3(0.4)$

1.2

54. $\frac{2}{3} \cdot 6$

4

Divide.

55. $65 \div 10$

6.5

56. $1.2 \div 8$

0.15

▬ Maintaining Your Skills

Write each fraction or mixed number as an equivalent decimal number.

57. $\frac{3}{4}$
0.75

58. $\frac{2}{5}$
0.4

59. $5\frac{1}{2}$
5.5

60. $8\frac{1}{4}$
8.25

61. $\frac{3}{100}$
0.03

62. $\frac{2}{50}$
0.04

63. $\frac{3}{8}$
0.375

64. $\frac{5}{8}$
0.625

Write each decimal as an equivalent proper fraction or mixed number.

65. 0.34
$\frac{17}{50}$

66. 0.08
$\frac{2}{25}$

67. 2.4
$2\frac{2}{5}$

68. 5.05
$5\frac{1}{20}$

69. 1.75
$1\frac{3}{4}$

70. 3.125
$3\frac{1}{8}$

71. 0.875
$\frac{7}{8}$

72. 0.375
$\frac{3}{8}$

4.4

Objectives

A Name the terms in a proportion.

B Use the fundamental property of proportions to solve a proportion.

Millions of people are turning to the Internet to view music videos of their favorite musician. Many Web sites offer different sizes of video based on the speed of a user's Internet connection. Even though the figures below are not the same size, their sides are proportional. Later in this chapter we will use proportions to find the unknown height in the larger figure.

120

160

h

400

Image © Sint, 2010. Used under license from Shutterstock.com

In this section we will solve problems using proportions. As you will see later in this chapter, proportions can model a number of everyday applications.

Definition

A statement that two ratios are equal is called a **proportion**. If $\frac{a}{b}$ and $\frac{c}{d}$ are two equal ratios, then the statement

$$\frac{a}{b} = \frac{c}{d}$$

is called a proportion.

A Terms of a Proportion

Each of the four numbers in a proportion is called a *term* of the proportion. We number the terms of a proportion as follows:

First term ⟶ $\frac{a}{b} = \frac{c}{d}$ ⟵ Third term
Second term ⟶ $\quad\quad$ ⟵ Fourth term

The first and fourth terms of a proportion are called the *extremes,* and the second and third terms of a proportion are called the *means.*

Means ⟶ $\frac{a}{b} = \frac{c}{d}$ ⟵ Extremes

EXAMPLE 1 In the proportion $\frac{3}{4} = \frac{6}{8}$, name the four terms, the means, and the extremes.

SOLUTION The terms are numbered as follows:

First term = 3 $\quad\quad$ Third term = 6
Second term = 4 $\quad\quad$ Fourth term = 8

The means are 4 and 6; the extremes are 3 and 8.

PRACTICE PROBLEMS

1. In the proportion $\frac{2}{3} = \frac{6}{9}$, name the four terms, the means, and the extremes.

Answer
1. See solutions section.

The final thing we need to know about proportions is expressed in the following property.

B The Fundamental Property of Proportions

Fundamental Property of Proportions
In any proportion, the product of the extremes is equal to the product of the means. This property is also referred to as the means/extremes property, and in symbols, it looks like this:

$$\text{If } \frac{a}{b} = \frac{c}{d} \quad \text{then} \quad ad = bc$$

2. Verify the fundamental property of proportions for the following proportions.

a. $\dfrac{5}{6} = \dfrac{15}{18}$

b. $\dfrac{13}{39} = \dfrac{1}{3}$

c. $\dfrac{\frac{2}{3}}{\frac{5}{3}} = \dfrac{2}{5}$

d. $\dfrac{0.12}{0.18} = \dfrac{2}{3}$

EXAMPLE 2 Verify the fundamental property of proportions for the following proportions.

a. $\dfrac{3}{4} = \dfrac{6}{8}$ b. $\dfrac{17}{34} = \dfrac{1}{2}$

SOLUTION We verify the fundamental property by finding the product of the means and the product of the extremes in each case.

Proportion	Product of the Means	Product of the Extremes
a. $\frac{3}{4} = \frac{6}{8}$	$4 \cdot 6 = 24$	$3 \cdot 8 = 24$
b. $\frac{17}{34} = \frac{1}{2}$	$34 \cdot 1 = 34$	$17 \cdot 2 = 34$

For each proportion the product of the means is equal to the product of the extremes.

We can use the fundamental property of proportions to solve an equation that has the form of a proportion.

A NOTE ON MULTIPLICATION Previously, we have used a multiplication dot to indicate multiplication, both with whole numbers and with variables. A more compact form for multiplication involving variables is simply to leave out the dot.
That is, $5 \cdot y = 5y$ and $10 \cdot x \cdot y = 10xy$.

3. Find the missing term:

a. $\dfrac{3}{4} = \dfrac{9}{x}$

b. $\dfrac{5}{8} = \dfrac{3}{x}$

EXAMPLE 3 Solve for x.

$$\frac{2}{3} = \frac{4}{x}$$

SOLUTION Applying the fundamental property of proportions, we have

$$\text{If } \quad \frac{2}{3} = \frac{4}{x}$$

$$\text{then} \quad 2 \cdot x = 3 \cdot 4 \quad \text{The product of the extremes equals the product of the means}$$

$$2x = 12 \quad \text{Multiply}$$

The result is an equation. We know from Section 4.3 that we can divide both sides of an equation by the same nonzero number without changing the solution to the equation. In this case we divide both sides by 2 to solve for x:

Note In some of these problems you will be able to see what the solution is just by looking the problem over. In those cases it is still best to show all the work involved in solving the proportion. It is good practice for the more difficult problems.

Answers
2. See solutions section.

$$2x = 12$$

$$\frac{2x}{2} = \frac{12}{2} \qquad \text{Divide both sides by 2}$$

$$x = 6 \qquad \text{Simplify each side}$$

The solution is 6. We can check our work by using the fundamental property of proportions:

$$\begin{array}{cc} 12 & 12 \\ \text{Product of} & \text{Product of} \\ \text{the means} & \text{the extremes} \end{array}$$

Because the product of the means and the product of the extremes are equal, our work is correct.

EXAMPLE 4 Solve for y: $\dfrac{5}{y} = \dfrac{10}{13}$

SOLUTION We apply the fundamental property and solve as we did in Example 3:

$$\text{If} \qquad \frac{5}{y} = \frac{10}{13}$$

$$\text{then} \qquad 5 \cdot 13 = y \cdot 10 \qquad \begin{array}{l}\text{The product of the extremes equals} \\ \text{the product of the means}\end{array}$$

$$65 = 10y \qquad \text{Multiply } 5 \cdot 13$$

$$\frac{65}{10} = \frac{10y}{10} \qquad \text{Divide both sides by 10}$$

$$6.5 = y \qquad 65 \div 10 = 6.5$$

The solution is 6.5. We could check our result by substituting 6.5 for y in the original proportion and then finding the product of the means and the product of the extremes.

EXAMPLE 5 Find n if $\dfrac{n}{3} = \dfrac{0.4}{8}$.

SOLUTION We proceed as we did in the previous two examples:

$$\text{If} \qquad \frac{n}{3} = \frac{0.4}{8}$$

$$\text{then} \qquad n \cdot 8 = 3(0.4) \qquad \begin{array}{l}\text{The product of the extremes equals} \\ \text{the product of the means}\end{array}$$

$$8n = 1.2 \qquad 3(0.4) = 1.2$$

$$\frac{8n}{8} = \frac{1.2}{8} \qquad \text{Divide both sides by 8}$$

$$n = 0.15 \qquad 1.2 \div 8 = 0.15$$

The missing term is 0.15.

4. Solve for y: $\dfrac{2}{y} = \dfrac{8}{19}$

5. Find n

a. $\dfrac{n}{6} = \dfrac{0.3}{15}$

b. $\dfrac{0.35}{n} = \dfrac{7}{100}$

Answers
3. a. 12 **b.** 4.8 **4.** 4.75
5. a. 0.12 **b.** 5

6. Solve for x:

a. $\dfrac{\frac{3}{4}}{7} = \dfrac{x}{8}$

b. $\dfrac{6}{\frac{3}{5}} = \dfrac{15}{x}$

EXAMPLE 6 Solve for x: $\dfrac{\frac{2}{3}}{5} = \dfrac{x}{6}$

SOLUTION We begin by multiplying the means and multiplying the extremes:

$$\text{If} \qquad \dfrac{\frac{2}{3}}{5} = \dfrac{x}{6}$$

$$\text{then} \qquad \dfrac{2}{3} \cdot 6 = 5 \cdot x \qquad \text{The product of the extremes equals the product of the means}$$

$$4 = 5 \cdot x \qquad \dfrac{2}{3} \cdot 6 = 4$$

$$\dfrac{4}{5} = \dfrac{5 \cdot x}{5} \qquad \text{Divide both sides by 5}$$

$$\dfrac{4}{5} = x$$

The missing term is $\dfrac{4}{5}$, or 0.8.

7. Solve $\dfrac{b}{18} = 0.5$

EXAMPLE 7 Solve $\dfrac{b}{15} = 2$.

SOLUTION Since the number 2 can be written as the ratio of 2 to 1, we can write this equation as a proportion, and then solve as we have in the examples above.

$$\dfrac{b}{15} = 2$$

$$\dfrac{b}{15} = \dfrac{2}{1} \qquad \text{Write 2 as a ratio}$$

$$b \cdot 1 = 15 \cdot 2 \qquad \text{Product of the extremes equals Product of the means}$$

$$b = 30$$

The procedure for finding a missing term in a proportion is always the same. We first apply the fundamental property of proportions to find the product of the extremes and the product of the means. Then we solve the resulting equation.

STUDY SKILLS

Continue to List Difficult problems

You should continue to list and rework the problems that give you the most difficulty. It is this list that you will use to study for the next exam. Your goal is to go into the next exam knowing that you can successfully work any problem from your list of difficult problems.

Getting Ready for Class

After reading through the preceding section, respond in your own words and in complete sentences.

1. In your own words, give a definition of a *proportion*.

2. In the proportion $\dfrac{2}{5} = \dfrac{4}{x}$, name the means and the extremes.

3. State the Fundamental Property of Proportions in words and in symbols.

4. For the proportion $\dfrac{2}{5} = \dfrac{4}{x}$, find the product of the means and the product of the extremes.

Answers

6. a. $\dfrac{6}{7}$ **b.** $\dfrac{3}{2}$ **7.** 9

Problem Set 4.4

A For each of the following proportions, name the means, name the extremes, and show that the product of the means is equal to the product of the extremes. [Examples 1, 2]

▶ **1.** $\dfrac{1}{3} = \dfrac{5}{15}$

Means: 3, 5; extremes: 1, 15; products: 15

2. $\dfrac{6}{12} = \dfrac{1}{2}$

Means: 12, 1; extremes: 6, 2; products: 12

▶ **3.** $\dfrac{10}{25} = \dfrac{2}{5}$

Means: 25, 2; extremes: 10, 5; products: 50

4. $\dfrac{5}{8} = \dfrac{10}{16}$

Means: 8, 10; extremes: 5, 16; products: 80

▶ **5.** $\dfrac{\frac{1}{3}}{\frac{1}{2}} = \dfrac{4}{6}$

Means: $\frac{1}{2}$, 4; extremes: $\frac{1}{3}$, 6; products: 2

6. $\dfrac{2}{\frac{1}{4}} = \dfrac{4}{\frac{1}{2}}$

Means: $\frac{1}{4}$, 4; extremes: 2, $\frac{1}{2}$; products: 1

7. $\dfrac{0.5}{5} = \dfrac{1}{10}$

Means: 5, 1; extremes: 0.5, 10; products: 5

▶ **8.** $\dfrac{0.3}{1.2} = \dfrac{1}{4}$

Means: 1.2, 1; extremes: 0.3, 4; products: 1.2

B Find the missing term in each of the following proportions. Set up each problem like the examples in this section. Write your answers as fractions in lowest terms. [Examples 3–7]

▶ **9.** $\dfrac{2}{5} = \dfrac{4}{x}$

10

10. $\dfrac{3}{8} = \dfrac{9}{x}$

24

11. $\dfrac{1}{y} = \dfrac{5}{12}$

$\frac{12}{5}$

▶ **12.** $\dfrac{2}{y} = \dfrac{6}{10}$

$\frac{10}{3}$

13. $\dfrac{x}{4} = \dfrac{3}{8}$

$\frac{3}{2}$

▶ **14.** $\dfrac{x}{5} = \dfrac{7}{10}$

$\frac{7}{2}$

▶ **15.** $\dfrac{5}{9} = \dfrac{x}{2}$

$\frac{10}{9}$

16. $\dfrac{3}{7} = \dfrac{x}{3}$

$\frac{9}{7}$

17. $\dfrac{3}{7} = \dfrac{3}{x}$

7

18. $\dfrac{2}{9} = \dfrac{2}{x}$

9

▶ **19.** $\dfrac{x}{2} = 7$

14

20. $\dfrac{x}{3} = 10$

30

21. $\dfrac{\frac{1}{2}}{y} = \dfrac{\frac{1}{3}}{12}$

18

▶ **22.** $\dfrac{\frac{2}{3}}{y} = \dfrac{\frac{1}{3}}{5}$

10

23. $\dfrac{n}{12} = \dfrac{\frac{1}{4}}{\frac{1}{2}}$

6

▶ **24.** $\dfrac{n}{10} = \dfrac{\frac{3}{5}}{\frac{3}{8}}$

16

25. $\dfrac{10}{20} = \dfrac{20}{n}$

40

▶ **26.** $\dfrac{8}{4} = \dfrac{4}{n}$

2

▶ Selected exercises available online at www.webassign.net/brookscole

▶ **27.** $\dfrac{x}{10} = \dfrac{10}{2}$
50

28. $\dfrac{x}{12} = \dfrac{12}{48}$
3

29. $\dfrac{y}{12} = 9$
108

30. $\dfrac{y}{16} = 0.75$
12

▶ **31.** $\dfrac{0.4}{1.2} = \dfrac{1}{x}$
3

32. $\dfrac{5}{0.5} = \dfrac{20}{x}$
2

▶ **33.** $\dfrac{0.3}{0.12} = \dfrac{n}{0.16}$
$\dfrac{2}{5}$

34. $\dfrac{0.01}{0.1} = \dfrac{n}{10}$
1

35. $\dfrac{0.5}{x} = \dfrac{1.4}{0.7}$
$\dfrac{1}{4}$

▶ **36.** $\dfrac{0.3}{x} = \dfrac{2.4}{0.8}$
$\dfrac{1}{10}$

▶ **37.** $\dfrac{168}{324} = \dfrac{56}{x}$
108

38. $\dfrac{280}{530} = \dfrac{112}{x}$
212

▶ **39.** $\dfrac{429}{y} = \dfrac{858}{130}$
65

40. $\dfrac{573}{y} = \dfrac{2{,}292}{316}$
79

▶ **41.** $\dfrac{n}{39} = \dfrac{533}{507}$
41

42. $\dfrac{n}{47} = \dfrac{1{,}003}{799}$
59

43. $\dfrac{756}{903} = \dfrac{x}{129}$
108

▶ **44.** $\dfrac{321}{1{,}128} = \dfrac{x}{376}$
107

■ Getting Ready for the Next Section

Divide.

45. $360 \div 18$
20

46. $2{,}700 \div 6$
450

Multiply.

47. $3.5(85)$
297.5

48. $4.75(105)$
498.75

Solve each equation.

49. $\dfrac{x}{10} = \dfrac{270}{6}$
450

50. $\dfrac{x}{45} = \dfrac{8}{18}$
20

51. $\dfrac{x}{25} = \dfrac{4}{20}$
5

52. $\dfrac{x}{3.5} = \dfrac{85}{1}$
297.5

■ Maintaining Your Skills

Give the place value of the 5 in each number.

53. 250.14
Tens

54. 2.5014
Tenths

Add or subtract as indicated.

55. $2.3 + 0.18 + 24.036$
26.516

56. $5 + 0.03 + 1.9$
6.93

57. $3.18 - 2.79$
0.39

58. $3.4 - 1.975$
1.425

Proportions can be used to solve a variety of word problems. The examples that follow show some of these word problems. In each case we will translate the word problem into a proportion and then solve the proportion using the method developed in this chapter.

A Applications

EXAMPLE 1 A woman drives her car 270 miles in 6 hours. If she continues at the same rate, how far will she travel in 10 hours?

SOLUTION We let x represent the distance traveled in 10 hours. Using x, we translate the problem into the following proportion:

$$\text{Miles} \longrightarrow \frac{x}{10} = \frac{270}{6} \longleftarrow \text{Miles}$$
$$\text{Hours} \longrightarrow \qquad \qquad \longleftarrow \text{Hours}$$

Notice that the two ratios in the proportion compare the same quantities. That is, both ratios compare miles to hours. In words this proportion says:

$$x \text{ miles is to } 10 \text{ hours as } 270 \text{ miles is to } 6 \text{ hours}$$

$$\frac{x}{10} = \frac{270}{6}$$

Next, we solve the proportion.

$$x \cdot 6 = 10 \cdot 270$$
$$x \cdot 6 = 2{,}700$$
$$\frac{x \cdot 6}{6} = \frac{2{,}700}{6}$$
$$x = 450 \text{ miles}$$

If the woman continues at the same rate, she will travel 450 miles in 10 hours.

EXAMPLE 2 A baseball player gets 8 hits in the first 18 games of the season. If he continues at the same rate, how many hits will he get in 45 games?

SOLUTION We let x represent the number of hits he will get in 45 games. Then

$$x \text{ is to } 45 \text{ as } 8 \text{ is to } 18$$

$$\text{Hits} \longrightarrow \frac{x}{45} = \frac{8}{18} \longleftarrow \text{Hits}$$
$$\text{Games} \longrightarrow \qquad \qquad \longleftarrow \text{Games}$$

Notice again that the two ratios are comparing the same quantities, hits to games. We solve the proportion as follows:

$$18x = 360 \qquad 45 \cdot 8 = 360$$
$$\frac{18x}{18} = \frac{360}{18} \qquad \text{Divide both sides by 18}$$
$$x = 20 \qquad 360 \div 18 = 20$$

If he continues to hit at the rate of 8 hits in 18 games, he will get 20 hits in 45 games.

PRACTICE PROBLEMS

1. A man drives his car 288 miles in 6 hours. If he continues at the same rate, how far will he travel in:
   a. 10 hours
   b. 11 hours

2. A softball player gets 10 hits in the first 18 games of the season. If she continues at the same rate, how many hits will she get in:
   a. 54 games
   b. 27 games

Answers
1. **a.** 480 miles **b.** 528 miles
2. **a.** 30 hits **b.** 15 hits

3. A solution contains 8 milliliters of alcohol and 20 milliliters of water. If another solution is to have the same ratio of milliliters of alcohol to milliliters of water and must contain 35 milliliters of water, how much alcohol should it contain?

4. The scale on a map indicates that 1 inch on the map corresponds to an actual distance of 105 miles. Two cities are 4.75 inches apart on the map. What is the actual distance between the two cities?

EXAMPLE 3   A solution contains 4 milliliters of alcohol and 20 milliliters of water. If another solution is to have the same ratio of milliliters of alcohol to milliliters of water and must contain 25 milliliters of water, how much alcohol should it contain?

SOLUTION We let x represent the number of milliliters of alcohol in the second solution. The problem translates to

x milliliters is to 25 milliliters as 4 milliliters is to 20 milliliters

$$\text{Alcohol} \longrightarrow \frac{x}{25} = \frac{4}{20} \longleftarrow \text{Alcohol} \\ \text{Water} \longrightarrow \qquad\qquad \longleftarrow \text{Water}$$

$$20x = 100 \qquad 25 \cdot 4 = 100$$

$$\frac{20x}{20} = \frac{100}{20} \qquad \text{Divide both sides by 20}$$

$$x = 5 \text{ milliliters of alcohol} \qquad 100 \div 20 = 5$$

EXAMPLE 4   The scale on a map indicates that 1 inch on the map corresponds to an actual distance of 85 miles. Two cities are 3.5 inches apart on the map. What is the actual distance between the two cities?

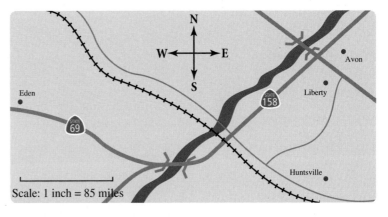

Scale: 1 inch = 85 miles

SOLUTION We let x represent the actual distance between the two cities. The proportion is

$$\text{Miles} \longrightarrow \frac{x}{3.5} = \frac{85}{1} \longleftarrow \text{Miles} \\ \text{Inches} \longrightarrow \qquad\qquad \longleftarrow \text{Inches}$$

$$x \cdot 1 = 3.5(85)$$

$$x = 297.5 \text{ miles}$$

Getting Ready for Class

After reading through the preceding section, respond in your own words and in complete sentences.

1. Give an example, not found in the book, of a proportion problem you may encounter.
2. Write a word problem for the proportion $\frac{2}{5} = \frac{4}{x}$.
3. What does it mean to translate a word problem into a proportion?
4. Name some jobs that may frequently require solving proportion problems.

Answers
3. 14 mL   **4.** 498.75 mi

Problem Set 4.5

A Solve each of the following word problems by translating the statement into a proportion. Be sure to show the proportion used in each case. [Examples 1–4]

▶ **1. Distance** A woman drives her car 235 miles in 5 hours. At this rate how far will she travel in 7 hours?

329 mi

▶ **2. Distance** An airplane flies 1,260 miles in 3 hours. How far will it fly in 5 hours?

2,100 mi

▶ **3. Basketball** A basketball player scores 162 points in 9 games. At this rate how many points will he score in 20 games?

360 points

▶ **4. Football** In the first 4 games of the season, a football team scores a total of 68 points. At this rate how many points will the team score in 11 games?

187 points

▶ **5. Mixture** A solution contains 8 pints of antifreeze and 5 pints of water. How many pints of water must be added to 24 pints of antifreeze to get a solution with the same concentration?

15 pt

▶ **6. Nutrition** If 10 ounces of a certain breakfast cereal contain 3 ounces of sugar, how many ounces of sugar do 25 ounces of the same cereal contain?

7.5 oz

▶ **7. Map Reading** The scale on a map indicates that 1 inch corresponds to an actual distance of 95 miles. Two cities are 4.5 inches apart on the map. What is the actual distance between the two cities?

427.5 mi

▶ **8. Map Reading** A map is drawn so that every 2.5 inches on the map corresponds to an actual distance of 100 miles. If the actual distance between two cities is 350 miles, how far apart are they on the map?

8.75 in.

▶ **9. Farming** A farmer knows that of every 50 eggs his chickens lay, only 45 will be marketable. If his chickens lay 1,000 eggs in a week, how many of them will be marketable?

900 eggs

▶ **10. Manufacturing** Of every 17 parts manufactured by a certain machine, only 1 will be defective. How many parts were manufactured by the machine if 8 defective parts were found?

136 parts

11. Nursing A patient is given a prescription of 10 pills. The total prescription contains 355 milligrams. How many milligrams is contained in each pill?

35.5 milligrams/pill

12. Nursing A child is given a prescription for 9 mg of a drug. If she has to take 3 chewable tablets, what is the strength of each tablet?

3 mg/tablet

13. Nursing An oral medication has a dosage strength of 275 mg/5 mL. If a patient takes a dosage of 300 mg, how many milliliters does he take? Round to the nearest tenth

5.5 mL

14. Nursing An atropine sulfate injection has a dosage strength of 0.1 mg/mL. If 4.5 mL was given to the patient, how many milligrams did she receive?

0.45 mg

▶ **15. Nursing** A tablet has a strength of 45 mg. If a patient is prescribed a dose of 112.5 mg, how many tablets does he take?

2.5 tablets

16. Nursing A tablet has a dosage strength of 35 mg. What was the prescribed dosage if the patient was told to take 1.5 tablets?

52.5 mg

Model Trains The size of a model train relative to an actual train is referred to as its scale. Each scale is associated with a ratio as shown in the table. For example, an HO model train has a ratio of 1 to 87, meaning it is $\frac{1}{87}$ as large as an actual train.

▶ **17. Length of a Boxcar** How long is an actual boxcar that has an HO scale model 5 inches long? Give your answer in inches, then divide by 12 to give the answer in feet.

435 in. = 36.25 ft

Scale	Ratio
LGB	1 to 22.5
#1	1 to 32
O	1 to 43.5
S	1 to 64
HO	1 to 87
TT	1 to 120

Spencer Grant/PhotoEdit

▶ **18. Length of a Flatcar** How long is an actual flatcar that has an LGB scale model 24 inches long? Give your answer in feet.

45 ft

19. Travel Expenses A traveling salesman figures it costs 55¢ for every mile he drives his car. How much does it cost him a week to drive his car if he travels 570 miles a week?

$313.50

▶ **20. Travel Expenses** A family plans to drive their car during their annual vacation. The car can go 350 miles on a tank of gas, which is 18 gallons of gas. The vacation they have planned will cover 1,785 miles. How many gallons of gas will that take?

91.8 gal

▶ **21. Nutrition** A 9-ounce serving of pasta contains 159 grams of carbohydrates. How many grams of carbohydrates do 15 ounces of this pasta contain?

265 g

▶ **22. Nutrition** If 100 grams of ice cream contains 13 grams of fat, how much fat is in 250 grams of ice cream?

32.5 g

▶ **23. Travel Expenses** If a car travels 378.9 miles on 50 liters of gas, how many liters of gas will it take to go 692 miles if the car travels at the same rate? (Round to the nearest tenth.)

91.3 liters

▶ **24. Nutrition** If 125 grams of peas contain 26 grams of carbohydrates, how many grams of carbohydrates do 375 grams of peas contain?

78 g

▶ **25. Elections** During a recent election, 47 of every 100 registered voters in a certain city voted. If there were 127,900 registered voters in that city, how many people voted?

60,113 people

▶ **26. Map Reading** The scale on a map is drawn so that 4.5 inches corresponds to an actual distance of 250 miles. If two cities are 7.25 inches apart on the map, how many miles apart are they? (Round to the nearest tenth.)

402.8 mi

27. Students to Teachers The chart shows the student to teacher ratio in the United States from 1975 to 2002. If a school had 1,400 students in 1985, how many teachers does the school have? Round to the nearest teacher.

78 teachers

Student Per Teacher Ratio In the U.S.

1975	20.4
1985	17.9
1995	17.8
2002	16.2

Source: nces.ed.gov

28. Skyscrapers The chart shows the heights of the three tallest buildings in the world. The ratio of feet to meters is given by 3.28/1. Using this information, convert the height of the Petronas Towers to meters. Round to the nearest hundredth.

452.13 meters

Such Great Heights

Petronas Tower 1 & 2
Kuala Lumpur, Malaysia
1,483 ft

Taipei 101
Taipei, Taiwan
1,670 ft

Sears Tower
Chicago, USA
1,450 ft

Source: www.tenmojo.com

29. Google Earth The Google Earth image shows the western side of The Mall in Washington, D.C. If the scale indicates that one inch is 800 meters and the distance between the Lincoln Memorial and the World War II memorial is $\frac{17}{16}$ inches, what is the actual distance between the two landmarks?

850 meters

Lincoln Memorial

WWII Memorial

Washington Monument

Google   Image © 2008 Sanborn

30. Google Earth The Google Earth image shows Disney World in Florida. A scale indicates that one inch is 200 meters. If the distance between Splash Mountain and the Jungle Cruise is 190 meters, what is the distance on the map in inches?

$\frac{19}{20}$ in

Splash Mountain

Jungle Cruise

Pirates of the Caribbean

Google   © 2008 Tele Atlas

Nursing Liquid medication is usually given in milligrams per milliliter. Use the information to find the amount a patient should take for a prescribed dosage.

31. A patient is prescribed a dosage of Ceclor® of 561 mg. The dosage strength is 187 mg per 5 mL. How many milliliters should he take?

15 mL

32. A brand of amoxicillin has a dosage strength of 125 mg/5 mL. If a patient is prescribed a dosage of 25 mg, how many milliliters should she take?

1 mL

Nursing For children, the amount of medicine prescribed is often determined by the child's mass. Usually it is calculated from the milligrams per kilogram per day listed on the medication's box.

33. How much should an 18 kg child be given a day if the dosage is 50 mg/kg/day?

900 mg/day

34. How much should a 13 kg child be given a day if the dosage is 24 mg/kg/day?

312 mg/day

■ Getting Ready for the Next Section

Simplify.

35. $\dfrac{320}{160}$

2

36. $21 \cdot 105$

2,205

37. $2{,}205 \div 15$

147

38. $\dfrac{48}{24}$

2

Solve each equation.

39. $\dfrac{x}{5} = \dfrac{28}{7}$

20

40. $\dfrac{x}{4} = \dfrac{6}{3}$

8

41. $\dfrac{x}{21} = \dfrac{105}{15}$

147

42. $\dfrac{b}{15} = 2$

30

■ Maintaining Your Skills

The problems below are a review of some of the concepts we covered previously.

Find the following products. (Multiply.)

43. 2.7×0.5

1.35

44. $(0.7)^2$

0.49

45. 3.18×1.2

3.816

46. $(0.3)^4$

0.0081

Find the following quotients. (Divide.)

47. $2.8 \div 0.7$

4

48. $0.042 \div 0.21$

0.2

49. $24 \div 0.15$

160

50. $6.99 \div 2.33$

3

Divide and round answers to the nearest hundredth.

51. $5{,}679 \div 30.9$

183.79

52. $4{,}070 \div 64.2$

63.40

Objectives

A Use proportions to find the lengths of sides of similar triangles.

B Use proportions to find the lengths of sides of other similar figures.

C Draw a figure similar to a given figure, given the length of one side.

D Use similar figures to solve application problems.

This 8-foot-high bronze sculpture "Cellarman" in Napa, California, is an exact replica of the smaller, 12-inch sculpture. Both pieces are the product of artist Tim Lloyd of Arroyo Grande, California.

Courtesy of Timothy Lloyd Sculpture

In mathematics, when two or more objects have the same shape, but are different sizes, we say they are similar. If two figures are similar, then their corresponding sides are proportional.

In order to give more details on what we mean by corresponding sides of similar figures, it will be helpful to introduce a simple way to label the parts of a triangle.

A Similar Triangles

Two triangles that have the same shape are similar when their corresponding sides are proportional, or have the same ratio. The triangles below are similar.

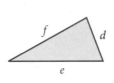

Corresponding Sides	Ratio
side a corresponds with side d	$\dfrac{a}{d}$
side b corresponds with side e	$\dfrac{b}{e}$
side c corresponds with side f	$\dfrac{c}{f}$

Because their corresponding sides are proportional, we write

$$\frac{a}{d} = \frac{b}{e} = \frac{c}{f}$$

LABELING TRIANGLES

One way to label the important parts of a triangle is to label the vertices with capital letters and the sides with lower-case letters.

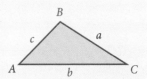

Notice that side a is opposite vertex A, side b is opposite vertex B, and side c is opposite vertex C. Also, because each vertex is the vertex of one of the angles of the triangle, we refer to the three interior angles as A, B, and C.

PRACTICE PROBLEMS

1. The two triangles below are similar. Find the missing side, x.

EXAMPLE 1   The two triangles below are similar. Find side x.

SOLUTION   To find the length x, we set up a proportion of equal ratios. The ratio of x to 5 is equal to the ratio of 24 to 6 and to the ratio of 28 to 7. Algebraically we have

$$\frac{x}{5} = \frac{24}{6} \quad \text{and} \quad \frac{x}{5} = \frac{28}{7}$$

We can solve either proportion to get our answer. The first gives us

$$\frac{x}{5} = 4 \qquad \tfrac{24}{6} = 4$$
$$x = 4 \cdot 5 \quad \text{Multiply both sides by 5}$$
$$x = 20 \quad \text{Simplify}$$

B Other Similar Figures

When one shape or figure is either a reduced or enlarged copy of the same shape or figure, we consider them similar. For example, video viewed over the Internet was once confined to a small "postage stamp" size. Now it is common to see larger video over the Internet. Although the width and height have increased, the shape of the video has not changed.

2. Find the height, h, in pixels of a video clip proportional to those in Example 2 with a width of 360 pixels.

> **Note**   A pixel is the smallest dot made on a computer monitor. Many computer monitors have a width of 800 pixels and a height of 600 pixels.

EXAMPLE 2   The width and height of the two video clips are proportional. Find the height, h, in pixels of the larger video window.

Image © Sint, 2010.
Used under license from Shutterstock.com

SOLUTION   We write our proportion as the ratio of the height of the new video to the height of the old video is equal to the ratio of the width of the new video to the width of the old video:

$$\frac{h}{120} = \frac{320}{160}$$
$$\frac{h}{120} = 2$$
$$h = 2 \cdot 120$$
$$h = 240$$

The height of the larger video is 240 pixels.

Answers
1. 35 **2.** 270 pixels

C Drawing Similar Figures

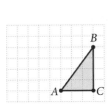 **EXAMPLE 3** Draw a triangle similar to triangle *ABC*, if *AC* is proportional to *DF*. Make *E* the third vertex of the new triangle.

3. Draw a triangle similar to triangle *ABC*, if *AC* is proportional to *GI*.

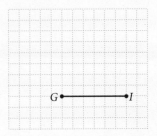

SOLUTION We see that *AC* is 3 units in length and *BC* has a length of 4 units. Since *AC* is proportional to *DF*, which has a length of 6 units, we set up a proportion to find the length *EF*.

$$\frac{EF}{BC} = \frac{DF}{AC}$$

$$\frac{EF}{4} = \frac{6}{3}$$

$$\frac{EF}{4} = 2$$

$$EF = 8$$

Now we can draw *EF* with a length of 8 units, then complete the triangle by drawing line *DE*.

 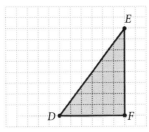

We have drawn triangle *DEF* similar to triangle *ABC*.

D Applications

EXAMPLE 4 A building casts a shadow of 105 feet while a 21-foot flagpole casts a shadow that is 15 feet. Find the height of the building.

4. A building casts a shadow of 42 feet, while an 18-foot flagpole casts a shadow that is 12 feet. Find the height of the building.

Answer
3. See solutions section.

SOLUTION The figure shows both the building and the flagpole, along with their respective shadows. From the figure it is apparent that we have two similar triangles. Letting x = the height of the building, we have

$$\frac{x}{21} = \frac{105}{15}$$

$$15x = 2205 \quad \text{Extremes/means property}$$

$$x = 147 \quad \text{Divide both sides by 15}$$

The height of the building is 147 feet.

THE VIOLIN FAMILY The instruments in the violin family include the bass, cello, viola, and violin. These instruments can be considered similar figures because the entire length of each instrument is proportional to its body length.

15 in.

24 in.

b

48 in.

> **Note** These numbers are whole number approximations used to simplify our calculations.

5. Find the body length of an instrument proportional to the violin family that has a total length of 32 inches.

EXAMPLE 5 The entire length of a violin is 24 inches, while the body length is 15 inches. Find the body length of a cello if the entire length is 48 inches.

SOLUTION Let b equal the body length of the cello, and set up the proportion.

$$\frac{b}{15} = \frac{48}{24}$$

$$\frac{b}{15} = 2$$

$$b = 2 \cdot 15$$

$$b = 30$$

The body length of a cello is 30 inches.

Getting Ready for Class

After reading through the preceding section, respond in your own words and in complete sentences.

1. What are similar figures?
2. How do we know if corresponding sides of two triangles are proportional?
3. When labeling a triangle *ABC*, how do we label the sides?
4. How are proportions used when working with similar figures?

Answers
4. 63 ft **5.** 20 in.

Problem Set 4.6

A In problems 1–4, for each pair of similar triangles, set up a proportion in order to find the unknown. [Example 1]

▶ **1.**

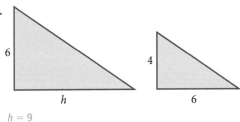

6

h

4

6

h = 9

▶ **2.**

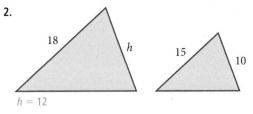

18   *h*   15   10

h = 12

▶ **3.**

8

y

12

21

y = 14

▶ **4.**

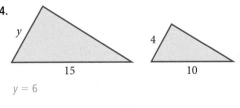

y   15   4   10

y = 6

B In problems 5–10, for each pair of similar figures, set up a proportion in order to find the unknown. [Example 2]

▶ **5.**

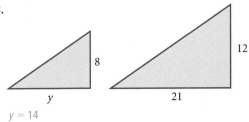

16

12

x

9

x = 12

▶ **6.**

x

9

40

24

x = 15

▶ **7.**

5

15

3

a

a = 25

▶ **8.**

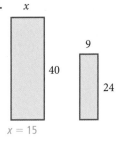

48

54   36

a

a = 32

▶ **9.**

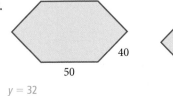

40

50

40

y

y = 32

▶ **10.**

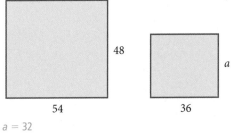

42   28

30   *y*

y = 20

▶ Selected exercises available online at www.webassign.net/brookscole

C For each problem, draw a figure on the grid on the right that is similar to the given figure. [Example 3]

11. *AC* is proportional to *DF*.

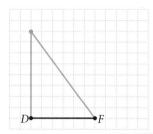

12. *AB* is proportional to *DE*.

▶ **13.** *BC* is proportional to *EF*.

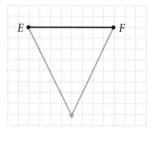

14. *AC* is proportional to *DF*.

15. *DC* is proportional to *HG*.

16. *AD* is proportional to *EH*.

17. *AB* is proportional to *FG*.

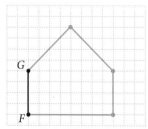

18. *BC* is proportional to *FG*.

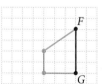

D Applying the Concepts [Examples 4, 5]

▶ **19. Length of a Bass** The entire length of a violin is 24 inches, while its body length is 15 inches. The bass is an instrument proportional to the violin. If the total length of a bass is 72 inches, find its body length.

45 in.

▶ **20. Length of an Instrument** The entire length of a violin is 24 inches, while the body length is 15 inches. Another instrument proportional to the violin has a body length of 25 inches. What is the total length of this instrument?

40 in.

▶ **21. Video Resolution** A new graphics card can increase the resolution of a computer's monitor. Suppose a monitor has a horizontal resolution of 800 pixels and a vertical resolution of 600 pixels. By adding a new graphics card, the resolutions remain in the same proportions, but the horizontal resolution increases to 1,280 pixels. What is the new vertical resolution?

960 pixels

▶ **22. Screen Resolution** The display of a 20" computer monitor is proportional to that of a 23" monitor. A 20" monitor has a horizontal resolution of 1,680 pixels and a vertical resolution of 1,050 pixels. If a 23" monitor has a horizontal resolution of 1,920 pixels, what is its vertical resolution?

1,200 pixels

▶ **23. Screen Resolution** The display of a 20" computer monitor is proportional to that of a 17" monitor. A 20" monitor has a horizontal resolution of 1,680 pixels and a vertical resolution of 1,050 pixels. If a 17" monitor has a vertical resolution of 900 pixels, what is its horizontal resolution?

1,440 pixels

▶ **24. Video Resolution** A new graphics card can increase the resolution of a computer's monitor. Suppose a monitor has a horizontal resolution of 640 pixels and a vertical resolution of 480 pixels. By adding a new graphics card, the resolutions remain in the same proportions, but the vertical resolution increases to 786 pixels. What is the new horizontal resolution?

1,048 pixels

▶ **25. Height of a Tree** A tree casts a shadow 38 feet long, while a 6-foot man casts a shadow 4 feet long. How tall is the tree?

57 ft

▶ **26. Height of a Building** A building casts a shadow 128 feet long, while a 24-foot flagpole casts a shadow 32 feet long. How tall is the building?

96 ft

▶ **27. Eiffel Tower** At the Paris Las Vegas Hotel is a replica of the Eiffel Tower in France. The heights of the tower in Las Vegas and the tower in France are 460 feet and 1,063 feet respectively. The base of the Eiffel Tower in France is 410 feet wide. What is the width of the base of the tower in Las Vegas? Round to the nearest foot.

177 feet

▶ **28. Pyramids** The Luxor Hotel in Las Vegas is almost an exact model of the pyramid of Khafre, the second largest Egyptian pyramid. The heights of the Luxor hotel and the pyramid of Khafre are 350 feet and 470 feet respectively. If the base of the pyramid in Khafre was 705 feet wide, what is the width of the base of the Luxor Hotel?

525 feet

◼ Maintaining Your Skills

The problems below are a review of the four basic operations with fractions and decimals.

Add.

29. $2.03 + 11.958 + 0.002$ 13.99

30. $\dfrac{3}{4} + \dfrac{1}{6} + \dfrac{5}{8}$ $1\dfrac{13}{24}$

Subtract.

31. $65.002 - 24.003$ 40.999

32. $5\dfrac{1}{8} - 2\dfrac{5}{8}$ $2\dfrac{1}{2}$

Multiply.

33. 42.18×0.0025 0.10545

34. $7\dfrac{1}{7} \times 2\dfrac{1}{3}$ $16\dfrac{2}{3}$

Divide.

35. $378.9 \div 21.05$ 18

36. $12.25 \div \dfrac{3}{4}$ $16\dfrac{1}{3}$

37. Find the sum of $2\dfrac{2}{3}$ and $1\dfrac{1}{2}$. $4\dfrac{1}{6}$

38. Find the difference of $2\dfrac{2}{3}$ and $1\dfrac{1}{2}$. $1\dfrac{1}{6}$

39. Find the product of $2\dfrac{2}{3}$ and $1\dfrac{1}{2}$.   4

40. Find the quotient of $2\dfrac{2}{3}$ and $1\dfrac{1}{2}$. $1\dfrac{7}{9}$

◼ Extending the Concepts

41. The rectangles shown here are similar, with similar rectangles within.

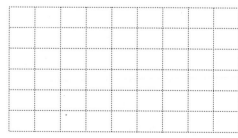

a. In the smaller figure, what is the ratio of the shaded to nonshaded rectangles?

$\dfrac{1}{2}$

b. Shade the larger rectangle such that the ratio of shaded to non-shaded rectangles is $\dfrac{1}{2}$.

Any 18 rectangles should be shaded.

c. For each of the figures, what is the ratio of the shaded rectangles to total rectangles? $\dfrac{1}{3}$

Chapter 4 Summary

Ratio [4.1]

The ratio of a to b is $\frac{a}{b}$. The ratio of two numbers is a way of comparing them using fraction notation.

EXAMPLES

1. The ratio of 6 to 8 is
$$\frac{6}{8}$$
which can be reduced to
$$\frac{3}{4}$$

Rates [4.2]

Whenever a ratio compares two quantities that have different units (and neither unit can be converted to the other), then the ratio is called a *rate*.

2. If a car travels 150 miles in 3 hours, then the ratio of miles to hours is considered a rate:
$$\frac{150 \text{ miles}}{3 \text{ hours}} = 50 \frac{\text{miles}}{\text{hour}}$$
$$= 50 \text{ miles per hour}$$

Unit Pricing [4.2]

The unit price of an item is the ratio of price to quantity when the quantity is one unit.

3. If a 10-ounce package of frozen peas costs 69¢, then the price per ounce, or unit price, is
$$\frac{69 \text{ cents}}{10 \text{ ounces}} = 6.9 \frac{\text{cents}}{\text{ounce}}$$
$$= 6.9 \text{ cents per ounce}$$

Solving Equations by Division [4.3]

Dividing both sides of an equation by the same number will not change the solution to the equation. For example, the equation $5 \cdot x = 40$ can be solved by dividing both sides by 5.

4. Solve: $5 \cdot x = 40$
$$5 \cdot x = 40$$
$$\frac{5 \cdot x}{5} = \frac{40}{5} \quad \text{Divide both sides by 5}$$
$$x = 8 \quad 40 \div 5 = 8$$

Proportion [4.4]

A proportion is an equation that indicates that two ratios are equal.

The numbers in a proportion are called *terms* and are numbered as follows:

First term $\longrightarrow$ $\dfrac{a}{b} = \dfrac{c}{d}$ $\longleftarrow$ Third term
Second term $\longrightarrow$ $\quad\quad$ $\longleftarrow$ Fourth term

The first and fourth terms are called the *extremes*. The second and third terms are called the *means*.

Means $\longrightarrow$ $\dfrac{a}{b} = \dfrac{c}{d}$ $\longleftarrow$ Extremes

5. The following is a proportion:
$$\frac{6}{8} = \frac{3}{4}$$

Fundamental Property of Proportions [4.4]

In any proportion the product of the extremes is equal to the product of the means. In symbols,

$$\text{If} \quad \frac{a}{b} = \frac{c}{d} \quad \text{then} \quad ad = bc$$

Finding an Unknown Term in a Proportion [4.4]

6. Find x: $\dfrac{2}{5} = \dfrac{8}{x}$

$2 \cdot x = 5 \cdot 8$

$2 \cdot x = 40$

$\dfrac{2 \cdot x}{2} = \dfrac{40}{2}$

$x = 20$

To find the unknown term in a proportion, we apply the fundamental property of proportions and solve the equation that results by dividing both sides by the number that is multiplied by the unknown. For instance, if we want to find the unknown in the proportion

$$\frac{2}{5} = \frac{8}{x}$$

we use the fundamental property of proportions to set the product of the extremes equal to the product of the means.

Using Proportions to Find Unknown Length with Similar Figures [4.6]

7. Find x.

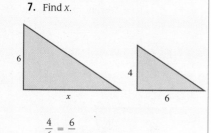

$\dfrac{4}{6} = \dfrac{6}{x}$

$36 = 4x$

$9 = x$

Two triangles that have the same shape are similar when their corresponding sides are proportional, or have the same ratio. The triangles below are similar.

Corresponding Sides	Ratio
side a corresponds with side d	$\dfrac{a}{d}$
side b corresponds with side e	$\dfrac{b}{e}$
side c corresponds with side f	$\dfrac{c}{f}$

Because their corresponding sides are proportional, we write

$$\frac{a}{d} = \frac{b}{e} = \frac{c}{f}$$

🚫 COMMON MISTAKES

A common mistake when working with ratios is to write the numbers in the wrong order when writing the ratio as a fraction. For example, the ratio 3 to 5 is equivalent to the fraction $\frac{3}{5}$. It cannot be written as $\frac{5}{3}$.

Write each of the following ratios as a fraction in lowest terms. [4.1]

1. 9 to 30

$\frac{3}{10}$

2. 30 to 9

$\frac{10}{3}$

3. $\frac{3}{7}$ to $\frac{4}{7}$

$\frac{3}{4}$

4. $\frac{8}{5}$ to $\frac{8}{9}$

$\frac{9}{5}$

5. $2\frac{1}{3}$ to $1\frac{2}{3}$

$\frac{7}{5}$

6. 3 to $2\frac{3}{4}$

$\frac{12}{11}$

7. 0.6 to 1.2

$\frac{1}{2}$

8. 0.03 to 0.24

$\frac{1}{8}$

9. $\frac{1}{5}$ to $\frac{3}{5}$

$\frac{1}{3}$

10. $\frac{2}{7}$ to $\frac{3}{7}$

$\frac{2}{3}$

The chart shows where each dollar spent on gasoline in the United States goes. Use the chart for problems 11–14. [4.1]

11. Ratio Find the ratio of money paid for taxes to money that goes to oil company profits.

$\frac{9}{2}$

Producing country 49¢
Oil company profits 4¢
Local station 13¢
Oil company costs 16¢
Taxes 18¢

12. Ratio What is the ratio of the number of cents spent on oil company costs to the number of cents that goes to local stations?

$\frac{16}{13}$

13. Ratio Give the ratio of oil company profits to oil company costs.

$\frac{1}{4}$

14. Ratio Give the ratio of taxes to oil company costs and profits.

$\frac{9}{10}$

15. Gas Mileage A car travels 285 miles on 15 gallons of gas. What is the rate of gas mileage in miles per gallon? [4.2]

19 mi/gal

16. Speed of Sound If it takes 2.5 seconds for sound to travel 2,750 feet, what is the speed of sound in feet per second? [4.2]

1,100 ft/sec

17. Unit Price A certain brand of ice cream comes in two different-sized cartons with prices marked as shown. Give the unit price for each carton, and indicate which is the better buy. [4.2]

9.05¢/ounce; 8.41¢/ounce; 32-ounce carton is the better buy

18. Unit Price A 6-pack of store-brand soda is $1.25, while a 24-pack of name-brand soda is $5.99. Find the price per soda for each, and determine which is less expensive. [4.2]

20.8¢/soda; 25.0¢/soda; the store brand is less expensive

64-ounce carton   32-ounce carton
$5.79   **$2.69**

Find the missing term in each of the following proportions. [4.4]

19. $\dfrac{5}{7} = \dfrac{35}{x}$

49

20. $\dfrac{n}{18} = \dfrac{18}{54}$

6

21. $\dfrac{\frac{1}{2}}{10} = \dfrac{y}{2}$

$\dfrac{1}{10}$

22. $\dfrac{x}{1.8} = \dfrac{5}{1.5}$

6

23. Chemistry Suppose every 2,000 milliliters of a solution contains 24 milliliters of a certain drug. How many milliliters of solution are required to obtain 18 milliliters of the drug? [4.5]

1,500 mL

24. Nutrition If $\frac{1}{2}$ cup of breakfast cereal contains 8 milligrams of calcium, how much calcium does $1\frac{1}{2}$ cups of the cereal contain? [4.5]

24 mg

25. Weight Loss A man loses 8 pounds during the first 2 weeks of a diet. If he continues losing weight at the same rate, how long will it take him to lose 20 pounds? [4.5]

5 weeks

26. Men and Women If the ratio of men to women in a math class is 2 to 3, and there are 12 men in the class, how many women are in the class? [4.5]

18 women

27. Nursing A patient received a dosage of 7.5 mg of a certain medication. How many tablets must he take if the tablet strength is 2.5 mg?

3 tablets

28. Nursing A patient is told to take 300 mg of a certain medication daily. If he takes it in two sittings, how many milligrams is he taking each time he takes the medication?

150 mg

29. Similar Triangles The triangles below are similar figures. Find x. [4.6]

$x = 9$

30. Find x if the two rectangles are similar.

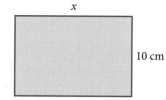

12 cm

8 cm

x

10 cm

$x = 15$ cm

31. Video Size The width and height of the two video clips are proportional. Find the height, h, in pixels of the larger video window.

120

180

Music Video

h

240

Music Video

$h = 160$

Simplify.

1. 8359
     401
   +1762
   ──────
   10,522

2. $3011 - 1032$
1979

3. $\dfrac{378}{21}$
18

4. $(3 \cdot 8) \cdot 2$
48

5. $31\overline{)15{,}689}$
$506\frac{3}{31}$

6. 5^3
125

7. $6 \cdot 2^3 - 1$
47

8. $135 \div 15$
9

9. $56 + 18$
74

10. $\dfrac{76}{4}$
19

11. $(11 - 2) + (403 - 102)$
310

12. $(3.6)(7.1)$
25.56

13. $83.6 - 12.12$
71.48

14. $6.4 + 3.12 + 5.07$
14.59

15. $30.6 \div 6.8$ 4.5

16. $\left(\dfrac{1}{3}\right)^2\left(\dfrac{1}{2}\right)^3$ $\frac{1}{72}$

17. $5 \div \left(\dfrac{1}{4}\right)^2$ 80

18. $\dfrac{1}{6} + \dfrac{2}{9}$ $\frac{7}{18}$

19. $5 \div \left(14 \div 1\dfrac{2}{3}\right)$ $\frac{25}{42}$

20. $12 - 5\dfrac{1}{4}$ $6\frac{3}{4}$

Solve.

21. $\dfrac{x}{20} = \dfrac{5}{4}$ 25

22. $\dfrac{9}{10} = \dfrac{18}{x}$ 20

23. Find the perimeter and area of the figure below.

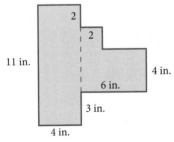

$P = 42$ in.; $A = 72$ in²

24. Find the perimeter and area of the figure below.

$P = 66$ cm; $A = 150$ cm²

25. Find x if the two rectangles are similar.

$x = 16$ cm

26. **Ratio** If the ratio of men to women in a self-defense class is 3 to 4, and there are 15 men in the class, how many women are in the class?
20 women

27. **Surfboard Length** A surfing company decides that a surfboard would be more efficient if its length were reduced by $3\frac{5}{8}$ inches. If the original length was 7 feet $\frac{3}{16}$ inches, what will be the new length of the board (in inches)?
$80\frac{9}{16}$ in.

28. **Average Distance** A bicyclist on a cross-country trip travels 72 miles the first day, 113 miles the second day, 108 miles the third day, and 95 miles the fourth day. What is her average distance traveled during the four days?
97 mi

29. **Teaching** A teacher lectures on five sections in two class periods. If she continues at the same rate, on how many sections can the teacher lecture in 60 class periods?
150 sections

Use the illustration to answer problems 30 and 31.

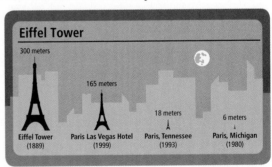

30. **Ratio** What is the ratio of the height of the Eiffel Tower in Las Vegas, Nevada to the height of the tower in Paris, France? $\frac{11}{20}$

31. **Ratio** What is the ratio of the height of the Eiffel tower in Paris, Michigan to the height of the Eiffel tower in Paris, Tennessee? $\frac{1}{3}$

Write each ratio as a fraction in lowest terms.

1. 24 to 18 $\frac{4}{3}$

2. $\frac{3}{4}$ to $\frac{5}{6}$ $\frac{9}{10}$

3. 5 to $3\frac{1}{3}$ $\frac{3}{2}$

4. 0.18 to 0.6 $\frac{3}{10}$

5. $\frac{3}{11}$ to $\frac{5}{11}$ $\frac{3}{5}$

A family of three budgeted the following amounts for some of their monthly bills:

Family Budget

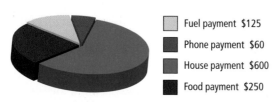

- Fuel payment **$125**
- Phone payment **$60**
- House payment **$600**
- Food payment **$250**

6. Ratio Find the ratio of house payment to fuel payment.

$\frac{24}{5}$

7. Ratio Find the ratio of phone payment to food payment.

$\frac{6}{25}$

8. Gas Mileage A car travels 414 miles on 18 gallons of gas. What is the rate of gas mileage in miles per gallon?

23 mpg

9. Unit Price A certain brand of frozen orange juice comes in two different-sized cans with prices marked as shown. Give the unit price for each can, and indicate which is the better buy.

16-ounce can
$2.59

12-ounce can
$1.89

16-ounce can: 16.2¢/ounce; 12-ounce can: 15.8¢/ounce; 12-ounce can is the better buy

Find the unknown term in each proportion.

10. $\frac{5}{6} = \frac{30}{x}$ 36

11. $\frac{1.8}{6} = \frac{2.4}{x}$ 8

12. Baseball A baseball player gets 9 hits in his first 21 games of the season. If he continues at the same rate, how many hits will he get in 56 games?

24 hits

13. Map Reading The scale on a map indicates that 1 inch on the map corresponds to an actual distance of 60 miles. Two cities are $2\frac{1}{4}$ inches apart on the map. What is the actual distance between the two cities?

135 miles

14. The triangles below are similar figures. Find h.

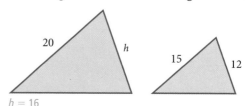

$h = 16$

Nursing Sometimes body surface area is used to calculate the necessary dosage for a patient.

15. The dosage for a drug is 15 mg/m². If an adult has a BSA of 1.8 m², what dosage should he take?

27 mg

16. Find the dosage an adult should take if her BSA is 1.3 m² and the dosage strength is 25.5 mg/m².

33.15 mg

Use the illustration to answer problem 17.

Student Per Teacher Ratio In the U.S.

Year	Ratio
1975	20.4
1985	17.9
1995	17.8
2002	16.2

Source: nces.ed.gov

17. If a school in 2002 had 65 teachers, how many students are enrolled   1,053 students

Chapter 4 Projects

RATIO AND PROPORTION

Soil Texture

Number of People	2–3
Time Needed	8–12 minutes
Equipment	Paper and pencil
Background	Soil texture is defined as the relative proportions of sand, silt, and clay. The figure shows the relative sizes of each of these soil particles. People who study soil science, or work with soil, become very familiar with ratios.

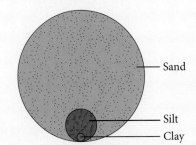

FIGURE 1 Relative sizes of sand, silt, and clay

Procedure A certain type of soil is one part silt, two parts clay, and three parts sand. Use your understanding of ratios and proportions to find the following ratios. Write these ratios as fractions.

1. Sand to total soil
2. Silt to total soil
3. Clay to total soil

4. What is the sum of the three fractions given in questions 1–3?

5. Let the 48 parts of the rectangle below each represent one cubic yard of the soil mixture above. Label each of the squares with either S (for sand), C (for clay), or T (for silt) based on the amount of each in 48 cubic yards of this soil.

The Golden Ratio

If you were going to design something with a rectangular shape—a television screen, a pool, or a house, for example—would one shape be more pleasing to the eye than another?

For many people, the most pleasing rectangles are rectangles in which the ratio of length to width is a number called the *golden ratio*, which we have written below.

$$\text{Golden Ratio} = \frac{\sqrt{5} + 1}{2} \approx 1.6180339\ldots$$

Kevin Schafer/Corbis

Research the golden ratio in mathematics and give examples of where it is used in architecture and art. Then measure the length and width of some rectangles around you (TV/computer monitor screen, picture frame, math book, calculator, a dollar, notebook paper, etc.). Calculate the ratio of length to width and indicate which are close to the golden ratio.

A Glimpse of Algebra

In "A Glimpse of Algebra" in Chapter 3, we spent some time adding polynomials. Now we can use the formula for the area of a rectangle developed in Chapter 1, $A = lw$, to multiply some polynomials.

   Suppose we have a rectangle with length $x + 3$ and width $x + 2$. Remember, the letter x is used to represent a number, so $x + 3$ and $x + 2$ are just numbers. Here is a diagram:

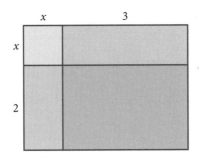

The area of the whole rectangle is the length times the width, or

$$\text{Total area} = (x + 3)(x + 2)$$

But we can also find the total area by first finding the area of each smaller rectangle, and then adding these smaller areas together. The area of each rectangle is its length times its width, as shown in the following diagram:

Because the total area $(x + 3)(x + 2)$ must be the same as the sum of the smaller areas, we have:

$$(x + 3)(x + 2) = x^2 + 2x + 3x + 6$$
$$= x^2 + 5x + 6 \qquad \text{Add } 2x \text{ and } 3x \text{ to get } 5x$$

The polynomial $x^2 + 5x + 6$ is the product of the two polynomials $x + 3$ and $x + 2$.
   Here are some more examples.

EXAMPLE 1   Find the product of $x + 5$ and $x + 2$ by using the following diagram:

1. Find the product of $x + 4$ and $x + 2$ by using the following diagram:

SOLUTION The total area is given by $(x + 5)(x + 2)$. We can fill in the smaller areas by multiplying length times width in each case:

The product of $(x + 5)$ and $(x + 2)$ is

$$(x + 5)(x + 2) = x^2 + 2x + 5x + 10$$
$$= x^2 + 7x + 10$$

EXAMPLE 2 Find the product of $2x + 5$ and $3x + 2$ by using the following diagram:

SOLUTION We fill in each of the smaller rectangles by multiplying length times width in each case:

Using the information from the diagram, we have:

$$(2x + 5)(3x + 2) = 6x^2 + 4x + 15x + 10$$
$$= 6x^2 + 19x + 10$$

---

2. Find the product of $3x + 7$ and $2x + 5$ by using the following diagram:

Answers

1. $x^2 + 6x + 8$

2. $6x^2 + 29x + 35$

A Glimpse of Algebra Problems

Use the diagram in each problem to help multiply the polynomials.

1. $(x + 4)(x + 2)$

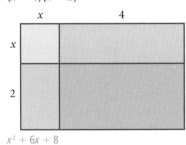

$x^2 + 6x + 8$

2. $(x + 1)(x + 3)$

$x^2 + 4x + 3$

3. $(2x + 3)(3x + 2)$

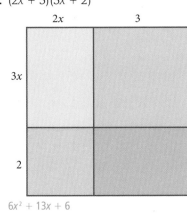

$6x^2 + 13x + 6$

4. $(5x + 4)(6x + 1)$

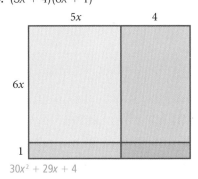

$30x^2 + 29x + 4$

5. $(7x + 2)(3x + 4)$

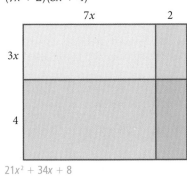

$21x^2 + 34x + 8$

6. $(3x + 5)(2x + 5)$

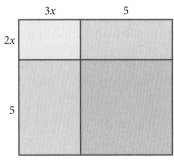

$6x^2 + 25x + 25$

Multiply each of the following pairs of polynomials. You may draw a rectangle to assist you, but you don't have to.

7. $(x + 2)(x + 5)$

$x^2 + 7x + 10$

8. $(x + 3)(x + 6)$

$x^2 + 9x + 18$

9. $(2x + 3)(x + 4)$

$2x^2 + 11x + 12$

10. $(2x + 4)(x + 3)$

$2x^2 + 10x + 12$

11. $(7x + 3)(2x + 5)$

$14x^2 + 41x + 15$

12. $(5x + 4)(3x + 3)$

$15x^2 + 27x + 12$

13. $(3x + 2)(3x + 2)$

$9x^2 + 12x + 4$

14. $(2x + 3)(2x + 3)$

$4x^2 + 12x + 9$

15. $(4a + 5)(a + 1)$

$4a^2 + 9a + 5$

16. $(5a + 7)(a + 2)$

$5a^2 + 17a + 14$

17. $(7y + 8)(6y + 9)$

$42y^2 + 111y + 72$

18. $(9y + 3)(2y + 8)$

$18y^2 + 78y + 24$

19. $(4 + 6x)(2 + 3x)$

$8 + 24x + 18x^2$

20. $(5 + 3x)(2 + 5x)$

$10 + 31x + 15x^2$

Percent

Chapter Outline

Introduction

The eruption of Mount St. Helens in 1980 was the most catastrophic volcanic eruption in American history. The volcano is located in the state of Washington about 100 miles south of Seattle. It's eruption caused dozens of deaths, and destroyed almost 230 acres of forest, along with more than 200 homes. The effects on the carrying capacity of nearby rivers were devastating as well. As the rivers filled with debris and sediment, surrounding lands flooded, more vegetation was lost, and the fish population was greatly reduced.

Effects of Lava Flows on Rivers

	Carrying Capacity of the Cowlitz River (cubic feet per second)	Channel Depth of Columbia River
Prior to 1980	76,000	40 feet
After 1980 Eruption	15,000	14 feet
Percent Decrease	80%	65%

Source: US Forest Service

In this chapter we will work with fractions, decimals, and percents. We will see how percents are used in everyday applications, including volcanoes.

The pretest below contains problems that are representative of the problems you will find in the chapter.
Change each percent to a decimal.

1. 68%
0.68

2. 2%
0.02

3. 21.5%
0.215

Change each decimal to a percent.

4. 0.39
39%

5. 0.386
38.6%

6. 3.98
398%

Change each percent to a fraction or mixed number in lowest terms.

7. 33%
$\frac{33}{100}$

8. 45%
$\frac{9}{20}$

9. 8.5%
$\frac{17}{200}$

Change each fraction or mixed number to a percent.

10. $\frac{67}{100}$
67%

11. $\frac{4}{5}$
80%

12. $2\frac{1}{4}$
225%

13. What number is 5% of 24?
1.2

14. What percent of 40 is 6?
15%

15. 12 is 24% of what number?
50

Getting Ready for Chapter 5

The problems below review material covered previously that you need to know in order to be successful in Chapter 5. If you have any difficulty with the problems here, you need to go back and review before going on to Chapter 5.

Perform the indicated operations.

1. $136 + 5.44$ 141.44

2. $300 - 75$ 225

3. $1,793,000 - 315,568$ 1,477,432

4. $\frac{65}{2} \times \frac{1}{100}$ $\frac{13}{40}$

5. 0.2×100 20

6. 4.89×100 489

7. $0.15 \cdot 63$ 9.45

8. $\frac{35.2}{100}$ 0.352

9. $3.62 \div 100$ 0.0362

10. $\frac{34}{0.29}$ (Round to the nearest tenth.)   117.2

11. $600 \times 0.04 \times \frac{60}{360}$ 4

Reduce.

12. $\frac{36}{100}$ $\frac{9}{25}$

13. $\frac{45}{1000}$ $\frac{9}{200}$

14. Change $32\frac{1}{2}$ to an improper fraction. $\frac{65}{2}$

Change each fraction or mixed number to a decimal.

15. $\frac{3}{8}$ 0.375

16. $\frac{5}{12}$ $0.41\overline{6}$

17. $2\frac{1}{2}$ 2.5

Solve

18. $25 = 0.40 \cdot n$ 62.5

19. $0.12n = 1,836$ 15,300

20. $1.075x = 3,200$ (Round to the nearest hundredth.)   2976.74

Objectives

A Change percents to fractions.

B Change percents to decimals.

C Change decimals to percents.

D Change percents to fractions in lowest terms.

E Change fractions to percents.

Introduction . . .

The sizes of categories in the pie chart below are given as percents. The whole pie chart is represented by 100%. In general, 100% of something is the whole thing.

In this section we will look at the meaning of percent. To begin, we learn to change decimals to percents and percents to decimals.

Factors Producing More Traffic Today

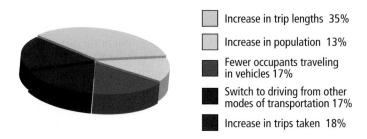

- Increase in trip lengths 35%
- Increase in population 13%
- Fewer occupants traveling in vehicles 17%
- Switch to driving from other modes of transportation 17%
- Increase in trips taken 18%

A The Meaning of Percent

Percent means "per hundred." Writing a number as a percent is a way of comparing the number with 100. For example, the number 42% (the % symbol is read "percent") is the same as 42 one-hundredths. That is:

$$42\% = \frac{42}{100}$$

Percents are really fractions (or ratios) with denominator 100.

Here are some examples that show the meaning of percent.

EXAMPLE 1 $50\% = \dfrac{50}{100}$

EXAMPLE 2 $75\% = \dfrac{75}{100}$

EXAMPLE 3 $25\% = \dfrac{25}{100}$

EXAMPLE 4 $33\% = \dfrac{33}{100}$

EXAMPLE 5 $6\% = \dfrac{6}{100}$

EXAMPLE 6 $160\% = \dfrac{160}{100}$

PRACTICE PROBLEMS

Write each number as an equivalent fraction without the % symbol.

1. 40%

2. 80%

3. 15%

4. 37%

5. 8%

6. 150%

Answers

1. $\frac{40}{100}$ 2. $\frac{80}{100}$ 3. $\frac{15}{100}$

4. $\frac{37}{100}$ 5. $\frac{8}{100}$ 6. $\frac{150}{100}$

7. Change to a decimal.
 a. 25.2%
 b. 2.52%

B Changing Percents to Decimals

To change a percent to a decimal number, we simply use the meaning of percent.

EXAMPLE 7 Change 35.2% to a decimal.

SOLUTION We drop the % symbol and write 35.2 over 100.

$$35.2\% = \frac{35.2}{100} \quad \text{Use the meaning of \% to convert to a fraction with denominator 100}$$

$$= 0.352 \quad \text{Divide 35.2 by 100}$$

We see from Example 7 that 35.2% is the same as the decimal 0.352. The result is that the % symbol has been dropped and the decimal point has been moved two places to the *left*. Because % always means "per hundred," we will always end up moving the decimal point two places to the left when we change percents to decimals. Because of this, we can write the following rule.

> **Rule**
> To change a percent to a decimal, drop the % symbol and move the decimal point two places to the *left*, inserting zeros as placeholders if needed.

Here are some examples to illustrate how to use this rule.

Change each percent to a decimal.
8. 40%

EXAMPLE 8 25% = 0.25

9. 80%

EXAMPLE 9 75% = 0.75   Notice that the results in Examples 8, 9, and 10 are consistent with the results in Examples 1, 2, and 3

10. 15%

EXAMPLE 10 50% = 0.50

11. 5.6%

EXAMPLE 11 6.8% = 0.068   Notice here that we put a 0 in front of the 6 so we can move the decimal point two places to the left

12. 4.86%

EXAMPLE 12 3.62% = 0.0362

13. 0.6%

EXAMPLE 13 0.4% = 0.004   This time we put two 0s in front of the 4 in order to be able to move the decimal point two places to the left

14. 0.58%

EXAMPLE 14 Cortisone cream is 0.5% hydrocortisone. Writing this number as a decimal, we have

$$0.5\% = 0.005$$

Answers
7. a. 0.252 **b.** 0.0252 **8.** 0.40
9. 0.80 **10.** 0.15 **11.** 0.056
12. 0.0486 **13.** 0.006 **14.** 0.0058

C Changing Decimals to Percents

Now we want to do the opposite of what we just did in Examples 7–14. We want to change decimals to percents. We know that 42% written as a decimal is 0.42, which means that in order to change 0.42 back to a percent, we must move the decimal point two places to the *right* and use the % symbol:

0.42 = 42%   Notice that we don't show the new decimal point if it is at the end of the number

> **Rule**
> To change a decimal to a percent, we move the decimal point two places to the *right* and use the % symbol.

Examples 15–20 show how we use this rule.

EXAMPLE 15   0.27 = 27%

EXAMPLE 16   4.89 = 489%

EXAMPLE 17   0.2 = 0.20 = 20%   Notice here that we put a 0 after the 2 so we can move the decimal point two places to the right

EXAMPLE 18   0.09 = 09% = 9%   Notice that we can drop the 0 at the left without changing the value of the number

EXAMPLE 19   25 = 25.00 = 2,500%   Here, we put two 0s after the 5 so that we can move the decimal point two places to the right

EXAMPLE 20   A softball player has a batting average of 0.650. As a percent, this number is 0.650 = 65.0%.

Eyewire/Getty Images

As you can see from the examples above, percent is just a way of comparing numbers to 100. To multiply decimals by 100, we move the decimal point two places to the right. To divide by 100, we move the decimal point two places to the left. Because of this, it is a fairly simple procedure to change percents to decimals and decimals to percents.

Write each decimal as a percent.
15. 0.35

16. 5.77

17. 0.4

18. 0.03

19. 45

20. 0.69

Answers
15. 35% **16.** 577% **17.** 40%
18. 3% **19.** 4,500% **20.** 69%

Who Pays Health Care Bills

☐ Patient 19%

■ Private insurance 36%

■ Government 45%

21. Change 82% to a fraction in lowest terms.

22. Change 6.5% to a fraction in lowest terms.

23. Change $42\frac{1}{2}$% to a fraction in lowest terms.

Instructor Note
Every time I have the chance to show division as multiplication by the reciprocal, I do so.

Answers

21. $\frac{41}{50}$ **22.** $\frac{13}{200}$ **23.** $\frac{17}{40}$

D Changing Percents to Fractions

To change a percent to a fraction, drop the % symbol and write the original number over 100.

EXAMPLE 21   The pie chart in the margin shows who pays health care bills. Change each percent to a fraction.

SOLUTION   In each case, we drop the percent symbol and write the number over 100. Then we reduce to lowest terms if possible.

$$19\% = \frac{19}{100} \qquad 45\% = \frac{45}{100} = \frac{9}{20} \qquad 36\% = \frac{36}{100} = \frac{9}{25}$$

$$\underset{\text{reduce}}{\uparrow} \qquad\qquad\qquad \underset{\text{reduce}}{\uparrow}$$

EXAMPLE 22   Change 4.5% to a fraction in lowest terms.

SOLUTION   We begin by writing 4.5 over 100:

$$4.5\% = \frac{4.5}{100}$$

We now multiply the numerator and the denominator by 10 so the numerator will be a whole number:

$$\frac{4.5}{100} = \frac{4.5 \times \mathbf{10}}{100 \times \mathbf{10}} \qquad \text{Multiply the numerator and the denominator by 10}$$

$$= \frac{45}{1,000}$$

$$= \frac{9}{200} \qquad \text{Reduce to lowest terms}$$

EXAMPLE 23   Change $32\frac{1}{2}$% to a fraction in lowest terms.

SOLUTION   Writing $32\frac{1}{2}$% over 100 produces a complex fraction. We change $32\frac{1}{2}$ to an improper fraction and simplify:

$$32\frac{1}{2}\% = \frac{32\frac{1}{2}}{100}$$

$$= \frac{\frac{65}{2}}{100} \qquad \text{Change } 32\frac{1}{2} \text{ to the improper fraction } \frac{65}{2}$$

$$= \frac{65}{2} \times \frac{1}{100} \qquad \text{Dividing by 100 is the same as multiplying by } \frac{1}{100}$$

$$= \frac{5 \cdot 13 \cdot 1}{2 \cdot 5 \cdot 20} \qquad \text{Multiplication}$$

$$= \frac{13}{40} \qquad \text{Reduce to lowest terms}$$

Note that we could have changed our original mixed number to a decimal first and then changed to a fraction:

$$32\frac{1}{2}\% = 32.5\% = \frac{32.5}{100} = \frac{32.5 \times 10}{100 \times 10} = \frac{325}{1000} = \frac{5 \cdot 5 \cdot 13}{5 \cdot 5 \cdot 40} = \frac{13}{40}$$

The result is the same in both cases.

E Changing Fractions to Percents

To change a fraction to a percent, we can change the fraction to a decimal and then change the decimal to a percent.

EXAMPLE 24   Suppose the price your bookstore pays for your textbook is $\frac{7}{10}$ of the price you pay for your textbook. Write $\frac{7}{10}$ as a percent.

SOLUTION   We can change $\frac{7}{10}$ to a decimal by dividing 7 by 10:

$$
\begin{array}{r}
0.7 \\
10\overline{)7.0} \\
\underline{7\ 0} \\
0
\end{array}
$$

We then change the decimal 0.7 to a percent by moving the decimal point two places to the *right* and using the % symbol:

$$0.7 = 70\%$$

You may have noticed that we could have saved some time in Example 24 by simply writing $\frac{7}{10}$ as an equivalent fraction with denominator 100. That is:

$$\frac{7}{10} = \frac{7 \cdot \mathbf{10}}{10 \cdot \mathbf{10}} = \frac{70}{100} = 70\%$$

This is a good way to convert fractions like $\frac{7}{10}$ to percents. It works well for fractions with denominators of 2, 4, 5, 10, 20, 25, and 50, because they are easy to change to fractions with denominators of 100.

EXAMPLE 25   Change $\frac{3}{8}$ to a percent.

SOLUTION   We write $\frac{3}{8}$ as a decimal by dividing 3 by 8. We then change the decimal to a percent by moving the decimal point two places to the right and using the % symbol.

$$\frac{3}{8} = 0.375 = 37.5\%$$

$$
\begin{array}{r}
.375 \\
8\overline{)3.000} \\
\underline{2\ 4} \\
60 \\
\underline{56} \\
40 \\
\underline{40} \\
0
\end{array}
$$

EXAMPLE 26   Change $\frac{5}{12}$ to a percent.

SOLUTION   We begin by dividing 5 by 12:

$$
\begin{array}{r}
.4166 \\
12\overline{)5.0000} \\
\underline{4\ 8} \\
20 \\
\underline{12} \\
80 \\
\underline{72} \\
80 \\
\underline{72}
\end{array}
$$

24. Change to a percent.
  a. $\frac{9}{10}$

  b. $\frac{9}{20}$

25. Change to a percent.
  a. $\frac{5}{8}$

  b. $\frac{9}{8}$

26. Change to a percent.
  a. $\frac{7}{12}$

  b. $\frac{13}{12}$

Answers
24. a. 90%   **b.** 45%
25. a. 62.5%   **b.** 112.5%

Note When rounding off, let's agree to round off to the nearest thousandth and then move the decimal point. Our answers in percent form will then be accurate to the nearest tenth of a percent, as in Example 26.

Because the 6s repeat indefinitely, we can use mixed number notation to write

$$\frac{5}{12} = 0.41\overline{6} = 41\frac{2}{3}\%$$

Or, rounding, we can write

$$\frac{5}{12} = 41.7\%$$ To the nearest tenth of a percent

27. Change to a percent.

a. $3\frac{3}{4}$

b. $3\frac{7}{8}$

EXAMPLE 27   Change $2\frac{1}{2}$ to a percent.

SOLUTION   We first change to a decimal and then to a percent:

$$2\frac{1}{2} = 2.5$$

$$= 250\%$$

Table 1 lists some of the most commonly used fractions and decimals and their equivalent percents.

TABLE 1		
Fraction	**Decimal**	**Percent**
$\frac{1}{2}$	0.5	50%
$\frac{1}{4}$	0.25	25%
$\frac{3}{4}$	0.75	75%
$\frac{1}{3}$	0.3	$33\frac{1}{3}\%$
$\frac{2}{3}$	0.6	$66\frac{2}{3}\%$
$\frac{1}{5}$	0.2	20%
$\frac{2}{5}$	0.4	40%
$\frac{3}{5}$	0.6	60%
$\frac{4}{5}$	0.8	80%

Getting Ready for Class

After reading through the preceding section, respond in your own words and in complete sentences.

1. What is the relationship between the word *percent* and the number *100*?

2. Explain in words how you would change 25% to a decimal.

3. Explain in words how you would change 25% to a fraction.

4. After reading this section you know that $\frac{1}{2}$, 0.5, and 50% are equivalent. Show mathematically why this is true.

Answers

26. a. $58\frac{1}{3}\% \approx 58.3\%$

   b. $108\frac{1}{3}\% \approx 108.3\%$

27. a. 375% **b.** 387.5%

Problem Set 5.1

A Write each percent as a fraction with denominator 100. [Examples 1–6]

▶ **1.** 20%

$\frac{20}{100}$

2. 40%

$\frac{40}{100}$

▶ **3.** 60%

$\frac{60}{100}$

4. 80%

$\frac{80}{100}$

5. 24%

$\frac{24}{100}$

▶ **6.** 48%

$\frac{48}{100}$

7. 65%

$\frac{65}{100}$

8. 35%

$\frac{35}{100}$

B Change each percent to a decimal. [Examples 7–14]

▶ **9.** 23%

0.23

10. 34%

0.34

▶ **11.** 92%

0.92

12. 87%

0.87

▶ **13.** 9%

0.09

14. 7%

0.07

▶ **15.** 3.4%

0.034

16. 5.8%

0.058

17. 6.34%

0.0634

▶ **18.** 7.25%

0.0725

19. 0.9%

0.009

20. 0.6%

0.006

C Change each decimal to a percent. [Examples 15–20]

▶ **21.** 0.23

23%

22. 0.34

34%

23. 0.92

92%

24. 0.87

87%

25. 0.45

45%

26. 0.54

54%

▶ **27.** 0.03

3%

28. 0.04

4%

29. 0.6

60%

▶ **30.** 0.9

90%

31. 0.8

80%

32. 0.5

50%

33. 0.27

27%

34. 0.62

62%

▶ **35.** 1.23

123%

36. 2.34

234%

D Change each percent to a fraction in lowest terms. [Examples 21–23]

▶ **37.** 60%   **38.** 40%   **39.** 75%   **40.** 25%   **41.** 4%   **42.** 2%

$\frac{3}{5}$ $\frac{2}{5}$ $\frac{3}{4}$ $\frac{1}{4}$ $\frac{1}{25}$ $\frac{1}{50}$

43. 26.5%   ▶ **44.** 34.2%   **45.** 71.87%   **46.** 63.6%   **47.** 0.75%   **48.** 0.45%

$\frac{53}{200}$ $\frac{171}{500}$ $\frac{7,187}{10,000}$ $\frac{159}{250}$ $\frac{3}{400}$ $\frac{9}{2,000}$

49. $6\frac{1}{4}$%   ▶ **50.** $5\frac{1}{4}$%   **51.** $33\frac{1}{3}$%   **52.** $66\frac{2}{3}$%

$\frac{1}{16}$ $\frac{21}{400}$ $\frac{1}{3}$ $\frac{2}{3}$

E Change each fraction or mixed number to a percent. [Examples 24–27]

53. $\frac{1}{2}$ **54.** $\frac{1}{4}$ **55.** $\frac{3}{4}$ **56.** $\frac{2}{3}$ **57.** $\frac{1}{3}$ ▶ **58.** $\frac{1}{5}$

50%   25%   75% $66\frac{2}{3}$% $33\frac{1}{3}$%   20%

59. $\frac{4}{5}$ **60.** $\frac{1}{6}$ ▶ **61.** $\frac{7}{8}$ **62.** $\frac{1}{8}$ ▶ **63.** $\frac{7}{50}$ **64.** $\frac{9}{25}$

80% $16\frac{2}{3}$%   87.5%   12.5%   14%   36%

65. $3\frac{1}{4}$ ▶ **66.** $2\frac{1}{8}$ **67.** $1\frac{1}{2}$ **68.** $1\frac{3}{4}$

325%   212.5%   150%   175%

▶ **69.** $\frac{21}{43}$ to the nearest tenth of a percent   **70.** $\frac{36}{49}$ to the nearest tenth of a percent

48.8%   73.5%

■ Applying the Concepts

71. Mothers The chart shows the percentage of women who continue working after having a baby.

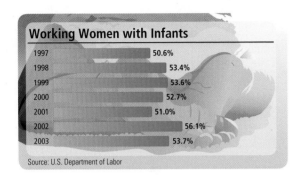

Working Women with Infants

1997	50.6%
1998	53.4%
1999	53.6%
2000	52.7%
2001	51.0%
2002	56.1%
2003	53.7%

Source: U.S. Department of Labor

Using the chart, convert the percentage for the following years to a decimal.

a. 1997   0.506

b. 2000   0.527

c. 2003   0.537

72. U.S. Energy The pie chart shows where Americans get their energy.

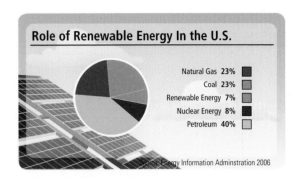

Role of Renewable Energy In the U.S.

Natural Gas **23%**
Coal **23%**
Renewable Energy **7%**
Nuclear Energy **8%**
Petroleum **40%**

Source: Energy Information Adminstration 2006

Using the chart, convert the percentage to a fraction for the following types of energy. Reduce to lowest terms.

a. Natural Gas $\frac{23}{100}$

b. Nuclear Energy $\frac{2}{25}$

c. Petroleum $\frac{2}{5}$

73. Paying Bills According to Pew Research, a non-political organization that provides information on the issues, attitudes and trends shaping America, most people still pay their monthly bills by check.

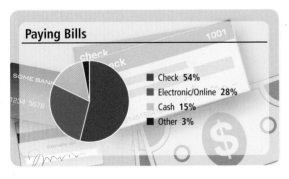

Paying Bills

■ Check **54%**
■ Electronic/Online **28%**
■ Cash **15%**
■ Other **3%**

a. Convert each percent to a fraction.
$\frac{27}{50}, \frac{7}{25}, \frac{3}{20}, \frac{3}{100}$

b. Convert each percent to a decimal.
0.54, 0.28, 0.15, 0.03

c. About how many times more likely are you to pay a bill with a check than by electronic or online methods?
About 2 times as likely.

74. Pizza Ingredients The pie chart below shows the decimal representation of each ingredient by weight that is used to make a sausage and mushroom pizza. We see that half of the pizza's weight comes from the crust. Change each decimal to a percent.

Mushroom and Sausage Pizza

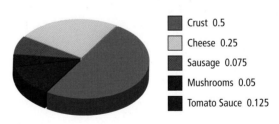

■ Crust 0.5
■ Cheese 0.25
■ Sausage 0.075
■ Mushrooms 0.05
■ Tomato Sauce 0.125

crust   50.0%
cheese   25.0%
sausage   7.5%
mushrooms   5.0%
tomato sauce   12.5%

■ Calculator Problems

Use a calculator to write each fraction as a decimal, and then change the decimal to a percent. Round all answers to the nearest tenth of a percent.

75. $\dfrac{29}{37}$ **76.** $\dfrac{18}{83}$ **77.** $\dfrac{6}{51}$ **78.** $\dfrac{8}{95}$ **79.** $\dfrac{236}{327}$ **80.** $\dfrac{568}{732}$

  78.4%   21.7%   11.8%   8.4%   72.2%   77.6%

■ Getting Ready for the Next Section

Multiply.

81. 0.25(74)   **82.** 0.15(63)   **83.** 0.435(25)   **84.** 0.635(45)
  18.5   9.45   10.875   28.575

Divide. Round the answers to the nearest thousandth, if necessary.

85. $\dfrac{21}{42}$ **86.** $\dfrac{21}{84}$ **87.** $\dfrac{25}{0.4}$ **88.** $\dfrac{31.9}{78}$

  0.5   0.25   62.5   0.409

Solve for n.

89. $42n = 21$ **90.** $25 = 0.40n$
  0.5   62.5

■ Maintaining Your Skills

Write as a decimal.

91. $\dfrac{1}{8}$ **92.** $\dfrac{3}{8}$ **93.** $\dfrac{5}{8}$ **94.** $\dfrac{7}{8}$
  0.125   0.375   0.625   0.875

95. $\dfrac{1}{16}$ **96.** $\dfrac{3}{16}$ **97.** $\dfrac{5}{16}$ **98.** $\dfrac{7}{16}$
  0.0625   0.1875   0.3125   0.4375

Divide.

99. $\dfrac{1}{8} \div \dfrac{1}{16}$ **100.** $\dfrac{3}{8} \div \dfrac{3}{16}$ **101.** $\dfrac{5}{8} \div \dfrac{5}{16}$ **102.** $\dfrac{7}{8} \div \dfrac{7}{16}$
  2   2   2   2

103. $0.125 \div 0.0625$ **104.** $0.375 \div 0.1875$ **105.** $0.625 \div 0.3125$ **106.** $0.875 \div 0.4375$
  2   2   2   2

5.2

Introduction . . .

The American Dietetic Association (ADA) recommends eating foods in which the number of calories from fat is less than 30% of the total number of calories. Foods that satisfy this requirement are considered healthy foods. Is the nutrition label shown below from a food that the ADA would consider healthy? This is the type of question we will be able to answer after we have worked through the examples in this section.

Nutrition Facts

Serving Size 1/2 cup (65g)
Servings Per Container: 8

Amount Per Serving	
Calories 150	Calories from fat 90

	% Daily Value*
Total Fat 10g	16%
Saturated Fat 6g	32%
Cholesterol 35mg	12%
Sodium 30mg	1%
Total Carbohydrate 14g	5%
Dietary Fiber 0g	0%
Sugars 11g	
Protein 2g	

Vitamin A 6%	●	Vitamin C 0%
Calcium 6%	●	Iron 0%

*Percent Daily Values are based on a 2,000 calorie diet.

FIGURE 1   Nutrition label from vanilla ice cream

This section is concerned with three kinds of word problems that are associated with percents. Here is an example of each type:

Type A: What number is 15% of 63?
Type B: What percent of 42 is 21?
Type C: 25 is 40% of what number?

A   Solving Percent Problems Using Equations

The first method we use to solve all three types of problems involves translating the sentences into equations and then solving the equations. The following translations are used to write the sentences as equations:

English	Mathematics
is	=
of	· (multiply)
a number	n
what number	n
what percent	n

The word *is* always translates to an = sign. The word *of* almost always means multiply. The number we are looking for can be represented with a letter, such as n or x.

Instructor Note
The problems in this section are the basis for all the application problems that follow in this chapter. I use this method of solving percent problems because it is more algebraic in nature than other methods.

PRACTICE PROBLEMS

1. a. What number is 25% of 74?
   b. What number is 50% of 74?

EXAMPLE 1 What number is 15% of 63?

SOLUTION We translate the sentence into an equation as follows:

What number is 15% of 63?

$$n = 0.15 \cdot 63$$

To do arithmetic with percents, we have to change to decimals. That is why 15% is rewritten as 0.15. Solving the equation, we have

$$n = 0.15 \cdot 63$$
$$n = 9.45$$

15% of 63 is 9.45

2. a. What percent of 84 is 21?
   b. What percent of 84 is 42?

EXAMPLE 2 What percent of 42 is 21?

SOLUTION We translate the sentence as follows:

What percent of 42 is 21?

$$n \cdot 42 = 21$$

We solve for *n* by dividing both sides by 42.

$$\frac{n \cdot 42}{42} = \frac{21}{42}$$

$$n = \frac{21}{42}$$

$$n = 0.50$$

Because the original problem asked for a percent, we change 0.50 to a percent:

$$n = 50\%$$

21 is 50% of 42

3. a. 35 is 40% of what number?
   b. 70 is 40% of what number?

EXAMPLE 3 25 is 40% of what number?

SOLUTION Following the procedure from the first two examples, we have

25 is 40% of what number?

$$25 = 0.40 \cdot n$$

Again, we changed 40% to 0.40 so we can do the arithmetic involved in the problem. Dividing both sides of the equation by 0.40, we have

$$\frac{25}{0.40} = \frac{0.40 \cdot n}{0.40}$$

$$\frac{25}{0.40} = n$$

$$62.5 = n$$

25 is 40% of 62.5

Answers
1. a. 18.5 **b.** 37
2. a. 25% **b.** 50%
3. a. 87.5 **b.** 175

As you can see, all three types of percent problems are solved in a similar manner. We write *is* as =, *of* as ·, and *what number* as *n*. The resulting equation is then solved to obtain the answer to the original question.

EXAMPLE 4 What number is 43.5% of 25?

$$n = 0.435 \cdot 25$$
$$n = 10.9 \qquad \text{Rounded to the nearest tenth}$$

10.9 is 43.5% of 25

4. What number is 63.5% of 45? (Round to the nearest tenth.)

EXAMPLE 5 What percent of 78 is 31.9?

$$n \cdot 78 = 31.9$$
$$\frac{n \cdot 78}{78} = \frac{31.9}{78}$$
$$n = \frac{31.9}{78}$$
$$n = 0.409 \qquad \text{Rounded to the nearest thousandth}$$
$$n = 40.9\%$$

40.9% of 78 is 31.9

5. What percent of 85 is 11.9?

EXAMPLE 6 34 is 29% of what number?

$$34 = 0.29 \cdot n$$
$$\frac{34}{0.29} = \frac{0.29 \cdot n}{0.29}$$
$$\frac{34}{0.29} = n$$
$$117.2 = n \qquad \text{Rounded to the nearest tenth}$$

34 is 29% of 117.2

6. 62 is 39% of what number? (Round to the nearest tenth.)

B Food Labels

EXAMPLE 7 As we mentioned in the introduction to this section, the American Dietetic Association recommends eating foods in which the number of calories from fat is less than 30% of the total number of calories. According to the nutrition label below, what percent of the total number of calories is fat calories?

7. The nutrition label below is from a package of vanilla frozen yogurt. What percent of the total number of calories is fat calories? Round your answer to the nearest tenth of a percent.

Nutrition Facts

Serving Size 1/2 cup (65g)
Servings Per Container: 8

Amount Per Serving

Calories 150	Calories from fat 90
	% Daily Value*
Total Fat 10g	**16%**
Saturated Fat 6g	**32%**
Cholesterol 35mg	**12%**
Sodium 30mg	**1%**
Total Carbohydrate 14g	**5%**
Dietary Fiber 0g	**0%**
Sugars 11g	
Protein 2g	
Vitamin A 6% • Vitamin C 0%	
Calcium 6% • Iron 0%	

*Percent Daily Values are based on a 2,000 calorie diet.

FIGURE 2 Nutrition label from vanilla ice cream

Nutrition Facts

Serving Size 1/2 cup (98g)
Servings Per Container: 4

Amount Per Serving

Calories 160	Calories from fat 25
	% Daily Value*
Total Fat 2.5g	**4%**
Saturated Fat 1.5g	**7%**
Cholesterol 45mg	**15%**
Sodium 55mg	**2%**
Total Carbohydrate 26g	**9%**
Dietary Fiber 0g	**0%**
Sugars 19g	
Protein 8g	
Vitamin A 0% • Vitamin C 0%	
Calcium 25% • Iron 0%	

*Percent Daily Values are based on a 2,000 calorie diet.

Answers
4. 28.6 **5.** 14% **6.** 159.0

316

Chapter 5 Percent

SOLUTION   To solve this problem, we must write the question in the form of one of the three basic percent problems shown in Examples 1–6. Because there are 90 calories from fat and a total of 150 calories, we can write the question this way: 90 is what percent of 150?

Now that we have written the question in the form of one of the basic percent problems, we simply translate it into an equation. Then we solve the equation.

$$90 \text{ is what percent of } 150?$$
$$90 = n \cdot 150$$
$$\frac{90}{150} = n$$
$$n = 0.60 = 60\%$$

The number of calories from fat in this package of ice cream is 60% of the total number of calories. Thus the ADA would not consider this to be a healthy food.

C Solving Percent Problems Using Proportions

We can look at percent problems in terms of proportions also. For example, we know that 24% is the same as $\frac{24}{100}$, which reduces to $\frac{6}{25}$. That is

$$\frac{24}{100} = \frac{6}{25}$$

24 is to 100   as   6 is to 25

We can illustrate this visually with boxes of proportional lengths:

In general, we say

$$\frac{\text{Percent}}{100} = \frac{\text{Amount}}{\text{Base}}$$

Percent is to 100   as   Amount is to Base

Answers

7. 15.6% of the calories are from fat. (So far as fat content is concerned, the frozen yogurt is a healthier choice than the ice cream.)

EXAMPLE 8   What number is 15% of 63?

SOLUTION   This is the same problem we worked in Example 1. We let n be the number in question. We reason that n will be smaller than 63 because it is only 15% of 63. The base is 63 and the amount is n. We compare n to 63 as we compare 15 to 100. Our proportion sets up as follows:

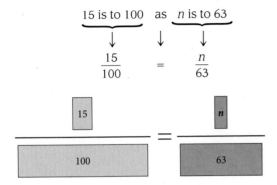

$$\frac{15}{100} = \frac{n}{63}$$

Solving the proportion, we have

$$15 \cdot 63 = 100n \qquad \text{Extremes/means property}$$
$$945 = 100n \qquad \text{Simplify the left side}$$
$$9.45 = n \qquad \text{Divide each side by 100}$$

This gives us the same result we obtained in Example 1.

EXAMPLE 9   What percent of 42 is 21?

SOLUTION   This is the same problem we worked in Example 2. We let n be the percent in question. The amount is 21 and the base is 42. We compare n to 100 as we compare 21 to 42. Here is our reasoning and proportion:

n is to 100   as   21 is to 42

$$\frac{n}{100} = \frac{21}{42}$$

Solving the proportion, we have

$$42n = 21 \cdot 100 \qquad \text{Extremes/means property}$$
$$42n = 2{,}100 \qquad \text{Simplify the right side}$$
$$n = 50 \qquad \text{Divide each side by 42}$$

Since n is a percent, our answer is 50%, giving us the same result we obtained in Example 2.

8. Rework Practice Problem 1 using proportions.

9. Rework Practice Problem 2 using proportions.

Answers
8. a. 18.5   **b.** 37
9. a. 25%   **b.** 50%

10. Rework Practice Problem 3 using proportions.

EXAMPLE 10 25 is 40% of what number?

SOLUTION This is the same problem we worked in Example 3. We let n be the number in question. The base is n and the amount is 25. We compare 25 to n as we compare 40 to 100. Our proportion sets up as follows:

40 is to 100   as   25 is to n

↓   ↓   ↓

$$\frac{40}{100} = \frac{25}{n}$$

$$\frac{40}{100} = \frac{25}{n}$$

Solving the proportion, we have

$$40 \cdot n = 25 \cdot 100 \qquad \text{Extremes/means property}$$
$$40 \cdot n = 2{,}500 \qquad \text{Simplify the right side}$$
$$n = 62.5 \qquad \text{Divide each side by 40}$$

So, 25 is 40% of 62.5, which is the same result we obtained in Example 3.

Note When you work the problems in the problem set, use whichever method you like, unless your instructor indicates that you are to use one method instead of the other.

Getting Ready for Class

After reading through the preceding section, respond in your own words and in complete sentences.

1. When we translate a sentence such as "What number is 15% of 63?" into symbols, what does each of the following translate to?

    a. *is*   b. *of*   c. *what number*

2. Look at Example 1 in your text and answer the question below.

    The number 9.45 is what percent of 63?

3. Show that the answer to the question below is the same as the answer to the question in Example 2 of your text.

    The number 21 is what percent of 42?

4. If 21 is 50% of 42, then 21 is what percent of 84?

Answer
10. a. 87.5   **b.** 175

Problem Set 5.2

A C Solve each of the following problems. [Examples 1–6]

▶ **1.** What number is 25% of 32?
8

2. What number is 10% of 80?
8

3. What number is 20% of 120?
24

▶ **4.** What number is 15% of 75?
11.25

5. What number is 54% of 38?
20.52

▶ **6.** What number is 72% of 200?
144

▶ **7.** What number is 11% of 67?
7.37

8. What number is 2% of 49?
0.98

9. What percent of 24 is 12?
50%

▶ **10.** What percent of 80 is 20?
25%

11. What percent of 50 is 5?
10%

▶ **12.** What percent of 20 is 4?
20%

13. What percent of 36 is 9?
25%

▶ **14.** What percent of 70 is 14?
20%

15. What percent of 8 is 6?
75%

▶ **16.** What percent of 16 is 9?
56.25%

17. 32 is 50% of what number?
64

18. 16 is 20% of what number?
80

19. 10 is 20% of what number?
50

▶ **20.** 11 is 25% of what number?
44

21. 37 is 4% of what number?
925

▶ **22.** 90 is 80% of what number?
112.5

23. 8 is 2% of what number?
400

▶ **24.** 6 is 3% of what number?
200

▶ Selected exercises available online at www.webassign.net/brookscole

A **C** The following problems can be solved by the same method you used in Problems 1–24. [Examples 1–6]

▶ **25.** What is 6.4% of 87?
5.568

26. What is 10% of 102?
10.2

27. 25% of what number is 30?
120

▶ **28.** 10% of what number is 22?
220

29. 28% of 49 is what number?
13.72

30. 97% of 28 is what number?
27.16

▶ **31.** 27 is 120% of what number?
22.5

32. 24 is 150% of what number?
16

▶ **33.** 65 is what percent of 130?
50%

34. 26 is what percent of 78?
$33\frac{1}{3}\%$

▶ **35.** What is 0.4% of 235,671?
942.684

▶ **36.** What is 0.8% of 721,423?
5,771.384

37. 4.89% of 2,000 is what number?
97.8

38. 3.75% of 4,000 is what number?
150

39. Write a basic percent problem, the solution to which can be found by solving the equation $n = 0.25(350)$.
What number is 25% of 350?

40. Write a basic percent problem, the solution to which can be found by solving the equation $n = 0.35(250)$.
What number is 35% of 250?

41. Write a basic percent problem, the solution to which can be found by solving the equation $n \cdot 24 = 16$.
What percent of 24 is 16?

42. Write a basic percent problem, the solution to which can be found by solving the equation $n \cdot 16 = 24$.
What percent of 16 is 24?

43. Write a basic percent problem, the solution to which can be found by solving the equation $46 = 0.75 \cdot n$.
46 is 75% of what number?

44. Write a basic percent problem, the solution to which can be found by solving the equation $75 = 0.46 \cdot n$.
75 is 46% of what number?

B **Applying the Concepts** [Example 7]

Nutrition For each nutrition label in Problems 45–48, find what percent of the total number of calories comes from fat calories. Then indicate whether the label is from a food considered healthy by the American Dietetic Association. Round to the nearest tenth of a percent if necessary.

▶ **45.** Spaghetti

Nutrition Facts

Serving Size 2 oz. (56g per 1/8 of pkg) dry
Servings Per Container: 8

Amount Per Serving

Calories 210	Calories from fat 10

	% Daily Value*
Total Fat 1g	2%
Saturated Fat 0g	0%
Polyunsaturated Fat 0.5g	
Monounsaturated Fat 0g	
Cholesterol 0mg	0%
Sodium 0mg	0%
Total Carbohydrate 42g	14%
Dietary Fiber 2g	7%
Sugars 3g	
Protein 7g	

Vitamin A 0%	●	Vitamin C 0%
Calcium 0%	●	Iron 10%
Thiamin 30%	●	Riboflavin 10%
Niacin 15%	●	

*Percent Daily Values are based on a 2,000 calorie diet

4.8% calories from fat; healthy

46. Canned Italian tomatoes

Nutrition Facts

Serving Size 1/2 cup (121g)
Servings Per Container: about 3 1/2

Amount Per Serving

Calories 25	Calories from fat 0

	% Daily Value*
Total Fat 0g	0%
Saturated Fat 0g	0%
Cholesterol 0mg	0%
Sodium 300mg	12%
Potassium 145mg	4%
Total Carbohydrate 4g	2%
Dietary Fiber 1g	4%
Sugars 4g	
Protein 1g	

Vitamin A 20%	●	Vitamin C 15%
Calcium 4%	●	Iron 15%

*Percent Daily Values are based on a 2,000 calorie diet.

0% calories from fat; healthy

▶ **47.** Shredded Romano cheese

Nutrition Facts

Serving Size 2 tsp (5g)
Servings Per Container: 34

Amount Per Serving

Calories 20	Calories from fat 10

	% Daily Value*
Total Fat 1.5g	2%
Saturated Fat 1g	5%
Cholesterol 5mg	2%
Sodium 70mg	3%
Total Carbohydrate 0g	0%
Fiber 0g	0%
Sugars 0g	
Protein 2g	

Vitamin A 0%	●	Vitamin C 0%
Calcium 4%	●	Iron 0%

*Percent Daily Values are based on a 2,000 calorie diet.

50% calories from fat; not healthy

▶ **48.** Tortilla chips

Nutrition Facts

Serving Size 1 oz (28g/About 12 chips)
Servings Per Container: about 2

Amount Per Serving

Calories 140	Calories from fat 60

	% Daily Value*
Total Fat 7g	1%
Saturated Fat 1g	6%
Cholesterol 0mg	0%
Sodium 170mg	7%
Total Carbohydrate 18g	6%
Dietary Fiber 1g	4%
Sugars less than 1g	
Protein 2g	

Vitamin A 0%	●	Vitamin C 0%
Calcium 4%	●	Iron 2%

*Percent Daily Values are based on a 2,000 calorie diet.

42.9% calories from fat; not healthy

■ Getting Ready for the Next Section

Solve each equation.

49. $96 = n \cdot 120$
0.80

50. $2{,}400 = 0.48 \cdot n$
5,000

51. $114 = 150n$
0.76

52. $3{,}360 = 0.42n$
8,000

53. What number is 80% of 60?
48

54. What number is 25% of 300?
75

■ Maintaining Your Skills

Multiply.

55. 2×0.125
0.25

56. 3×0.125
0.375

57. 4×0.125
0.5

58. 5×0.125
0.625

59. The sequence below is an arithmetic sequence in which each term is found by adding $\frac{1}{8}$ to the previous term. Find the next three numbers in the sequence.

$$\frac{1}{4}, \frac{3}{8}, \frac{1}{2}, \cdots \qquad \frac{5}{8} \ \frac{3}{4} \ \frac{7}{8}$$

60. The sequence below is an arithmetic sequence in which each term is found by adding $\frac{1}{16}$ to the previous term. Find the next three numbers in the sequence.

$$\frac{1}{8}, \frac{3}{16}, \frac{1}{4}, \cdots \qquad \frac{5}{16} \ \frac{3}{8} \ \frac{7}{16}$$

Simplify.

61. $\dfrac{1}{4} - \dfrac{1}{8} + \dfrac{1}{2} - \dfrac{3}{8}$
$\frac{1}{4}$

62. $\dfrac{7}{8} - \dfrac{3}{4} + \dfrac{5}{8} - \dfrac{1}{2}$
$\frac{1}{4}$

Write as a decimal.

63. $\dfrac{2}{8}$
0.25

64. $\dfrac{4}{8}$
0.5

65. $\dfrac{6}{8}$
0.75

66. $\dfrac{8}{8}$
1.0

67. $\dfrac{2}{16}$
0.125

68. $\dfrac{4}{16}$
0.25

69. $\dfrac{6}{16}$
0.375

70. $\dfrac{8}{16}$
0.5

Write in order from smallest to largest.

71. $\dfrac{3}{8}, \dfrac{1}{4}, \dfrac{5}{8}, \dfrac{1}{8}, \dfrac{1}{2}, \dfrac{3}{4}, \dfrac{7}{8}$ $\frac{1}{8}, \frac{1}{4}, \frac{3}{8}, \frac{1}{2}, \frac{5}{8}, \frac{3}{4}, \frac{7}{8}$

72. $\dfrac{3}{16}, \dfrac{1}{8}, \dfrac{1}{4}, \dfrac{3}{8}, \dfrac{7}{16}, \dfrac{1}{16}, \dfrac{1}{2}, \dfrac{5}{16}$ $\frac{1}{16}, \frac{1}{8}, \frac{3}{16}, \frac{1}{4}, \frac{5}{16}, \frac{3}{8}, \frac{7}{16}, \frac{1}{2}$

General Applications of Percent

Introduction . . .

As you know from watching television and reading the newspaper, we encounter percents in many situations in everyday life. A recent newspaper article discussing the effects of a cholesterol-lowering drug stated that the drug in question "lowered levels of LDL cholesterol by an average of 35%." As we progress through this chapter, we will become more and more familiar with percent. As a result, we will be better equipped to understand statements like the one above concerning cholesterol.

In this section we continue our study of percent by doing more of the translations that were introduced in Section 5.2. The better you are at working the problems in Section 5.2, the easier it will be for you to get started on the problems in this section.

A Applications Involving Percent

EXAMPLE 1 On a 120-question test, a student answered 96 correctly. What percent of the problems did the student work correctly?

SOLUTION We have 96 correct answers out of a possible 120. The problem can be restated as

$$96 \text{ is what percent of } 120?$$
$$96 = n \cdot 120$$

$$\frac{96}{120} = \frac{n \cdot 120}{120} \qquad \text{Divide both sides by 120}$$

$$n = \frac{96}{120} \qquad \begin{array}{l}\text{Switch the left and right} \\ \text{sides of the equation}\end{array}$$

$$n = 0.80 \qquad \text{Divide 96 by 120}$$

$$= 80\% \qquad \text{Rewrite as a percent}$$

When we write a test score as a percent, we are comparing the original score to an equivalent score on a 100-question test. That is, 96 correct out of 120 is the same as 80 correct out of 100.

EXAMPLE 2 How much HCl (hydrochloric acid) is in a 60-milliliter bottle that is marked 80% HCl?

SOLUTION If the bottle is marked 80% HCl, that means 80% of the solution is HCl and the rest is water. Because the bottle contains 60 milliliters, we can restate the question as:

$$\text{What is } 80\% \text{ of } 60?$$
$$n = 0.80 \cdot 60$$
$$n = 48$$

HCL 80%
60 ml

There are 48 milliliters of HCl in 60 milliliters of 80% HCl solution.

3. If 42% of the students in a certain college are female and there are 3,360 female students, what is the total number of students in the college?

EXAMPLE 3
If 48% of the students in a certain college are female and there are 2,400 female students, what is the total number of students in the college?

SOLUTION We restate the problem as:

2,400 *is* 48% *of what number*?

$$2{,}400 = 0.48 \cdot n$$

$$\frac{2{,}400}{0.48} = \frac{0.48 \cdot n}{0.48} \qquad \text{Divide both sides by 0.48}$$

$$n = \frac{2{,}400}{0.48} \qquad \text{Switch the left and right sides of the equation}$$

$$n = 5{,}000$$

There are 5,000 students.

4. Suppose in Example 4 that 35% of the students receive a grade of A. How many of the 300 students is that?

EXAMPLE 4
If 25% of the students in elementary algebra courses receive a grade of A, and there are 300 students enrolled in elementary algebra this year, how many students will receive A's?

SOLUTION After reading the question a few times, we find that it is the same as this question:

What number is 25% of 300?

$$n = 0.25 \cdot 300$$

$$n = 75$$

Thus, 75 students will receive A's in elementary algebra.

Almost all application problems involving percents can be restated as one of the three basic percent problems we listed in Section 5.2. It takes some practice before the restating of application problems becomes automatic. You may have to review Section 5.2 and Examples 1–4 above several times before you can translate word problems into mathematical expressions yourself.

Getting Ready for Class

After reading through the preceding section, respond in your own words and in complete sentences.

1. On the test mentioned in Example 1, how many questions would the student have answered correctly if she answered 40% of the questions correctly?
2. If the bottle in Example 2 contained 30 milliliters instead of 60, what would the answer be?
3. In Example 3, how many of the students were male?
4. How many of the students mentioned in Example 4 received a grade lower than A?

Answers
3. 8,000 students   4. 105 students

Problem Set 5.3

A Solve each of the following problems by first restating it as one of the three basic percent problems of Section 5.2. In each case, be sure to show the equation. [Examples 1–4]

▶ **1. Test Scores** On a 120-question test a student answered 84 correctly. What percent of the problems did the student work correctly?

70%

▶ **2. Test Scores** An engineering student answered 81 questions correctly on a 90-question trigonometry test. What percent of the questions did she answer correctly? What percent were answered incorrectly?

90% correct; 10% incorrect

▶ **3. Basketball** A basketball player made 63 out of 75 free throws. What percent is this?

84%

▶ **4. Family Budget** A family spends $450 every month on food. If the family's income each month is $1,800, what percent of the family's income is spent on food?

25%

5. Chemistry How much HCl (hydrochloric acid) is in a 60-milliliter bottle that is marked 75% HCl?

45mL

▶ **6. Chemistry** How much acetic acid is in a 5-liter container of acetic acid and water that is marked 80% acetic acid? How much is water?

4 liters acetic acid; 1 liter water

▶ **7. Farming** A farmer owns 28 acres of land. Of the 28 acres, only 65% can be farmed. How many acres are available for farming? How many are not available for farming?

18.2 acres for farming; 9.8 acres are not available for farming

▶ **8. Number of Students** Of the 420 students enrolled in a basic math class, only 30% are first-year students. How many are first-year students? How many are not?

126 are first-year students; 294 are not

9. Determining a Tip Servers and wait staff are often paid minimum wage and depend on tips for much of their income. It is common for tips to be 15% to 20% of the bill. After dinner at a local restaurant the total bill is $56.00. Since your service was above average you decide to give a 20% tip. Determine the amount of the tip you leave for your server.

$11.20

▶ **10. Determining a Tip** Suppose you decide to leave a 15% tip for services after your dinner out in the preceding problem. How much of a tip did you leave your server? How much smaller was the tip?

$8.40; $2.80 less

▶ **11. Voting** In the 2004 Presidential election, George Bush received 53.25% of the total electoral votes and John Kerry received 46.75% of the total electoral votes. If there were 537 total votes cast by the Electoral College how many electoral votes did each candidate receive? Round to the nearest vote.

Bush 286; Kerry 251

12. Census Data According to the U.S. Census Bureau, national population estimates grouped by age and gender for July, 2006, approximately 7.4% of the 147,512,152 males in our population are between the ages of 15 and 19 years old. How many males are in this age group? Round to the nearest person.

10,915,899

▶ **13. Bachelors** According to the U.S. Census Bureau data for the number of marriages in 2004 approximately 31.2% of the 109,830,000 males age 15 years or older have never been married. How many males age 15 years or older have never been married?

34,266,960

14. Bachelorettes According to the U.S. Census Bureau data for the number of marriages in 2004, approximately 25.8% of the 117,677,000 females age 15 years or older have never been married. How many females age 15 years or older have never been married?

30,360,666

▶ **15. Number of Students** If 48% of the students in a certain college are female and there are 1,440 female students, what is the total number of students in the college?

3,000 students

▶ **16. Mixture Problem** A solution of alcohol and water is 80% alcohol. The solution is found to contain 32 milliliters of alcohol. How many milliliters total (both alcohol and water) are in the solution?

40 mL

▶ **17. Number of Graduates** Suppose 60% of the graduating class in a certain high school goes on to college. If 240 students from this graduating class are going on to college, how many students are there in the graduating class?

400 students

▶ **18. Defective Parts** In a shipment of airplane parts, 3% are known to be defective. If 15 parts are found to be defective, how many parts are in the shipment?

500 parts

▶ **19. Number of Students** There are 3,200 students at our school. If 52% of them are female, how many female students are there at our school?

1,664 female students

▶ **20. Number of Students** In a certain school, 75% of the students in first-year chemistry have had algebra. If there are 300 students in first-year chemistry, how many of them have had algebra?

225 students

▶ **21. Population** In a city of 32,000 people, there are 10,000 people under 25 years of age. What percent of the population is under 25 years of age?

31.25%

▶ **22. Number of Students** If 45 people enrolled in a psychology course but only 35 completed it, what percent of the students completed the course? (Round to the nearest tenth of a percent.)

77.8%

■ Calculator Problems

The following problems are similar to Problems 1–22. They should be set up the same way. Then the actual calculations should be done on a calculator.

▶ **23. Number of People** Of 7,892 people attending an outdoor concert in Los Angeles, 3,972 are over 18 years of age. What percent is this? (Round to the nearest whole-number percent.)

50%

▶ **24. Manufacturing** A car manufacturer estimates that 25% of the new cars sold in one city have defective engine mounts. If 2,136 new cars are sold in that city, how many will have defective engine mounts?

534 cars

▶ **25. Population** The map shows the most populated cities in the United States. If the population of New York City is about 42% of the state's population, what is the approximate population of the state?

About 19.2 million

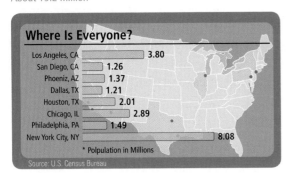

26. Prom The graph shows how much girls plan to spend on the prom. If 5,086 girls were surveyed, how many are planning on spending less than $200 on the prom? Round to the nearest whole number.

1,475 girls

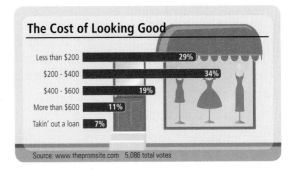

■ Getting Ready for the Next Section

Multiply.

27. 0.06(550)

33

28. 0.06(625)

37.5

29. 0.03(289,500)

8,685

30. 0.03(115,900)

3,477

Divide. Write your answers as decimals.

31. $5.44 \div 0.04$

136

32. $4.35 \div 0.03$

145

33. $19.80 \div 396$

0.05

34. $11.82 \div 197$

0.06

35. $\dfrac{1,836}{0.12}$

15,300

36. $\dfrac{115}{0.1}$

1,150

37. $\dfrac{90}{600}$

0.15

38. $\dfrac{105}{750}$

0.14

■ Maintaining Your Skills

The problems below review multiplication with fractions and mixed numbers.

Multiply.

39. $\dfrac{1}{2} \cdot \dfrac{2}{5}$

$\dfrac{1}{5}$

40. $\dfrac{3}{4} \cdot \dfrac{1}{3}$

$\dfrac{1}{4}$

41. $\dfrac{3}{4} \cdot \dfrac{5}{9}$

$\dfrac{5}{12}$

42. $\dfrac{5}{6} \cdot \dfrac{12}{13}$

$\dfrac{10}{13}$

43. $2 \cdot \dfrac{3}{8}$

$\dfrac{3}{4}$

44. $3 \cdot \dfrac{5}{12}$

$\dfrac{5}{4}$

45. $1\dfrac{1}{4} \cdot \dfrac{8}{15}$

$\dfrac{2}{3}$

46. $2\dfrac{1}{3} \cdot \dfrac{9}{10}$

$2\dfrac{1}{10}$

■ Extending the Concepts: Batting Averages

Batting averages in baseball are given as decimal numbers, rounded to the nearest thousandth. For example, at the end of June 2008, Milton Bradley had the highest batting average in the American League. At that time, he had 76 hits in 235 times at bat. His batting average was .323, which is found by dividing the number of hits by the number of times he was at bat and then rounding to the nearest thousandth.

$$\text{Batting average} = \frac{\text{number of hits}}{\text{number of times at bat}} = \frac{76}{235} = 0.323$$

Because we can write any decimal number as a percent, we can convert batting averages to percents and use our knowledge of percent to solve problems. Looking at Milton Bradley's batting average as a percent, we can say that he will get a hit 32.3% of the times he is at bat.

    Each of the following problems can be solved by converting batting averages to percents and translating the problem into one of our three basic percent problems. (All numbers are from the end of June 2008.)

47. Chipper Jones had the highest batting average in the National League with 100 hits in 254 times at bat. What percent of the time Chipper Jones is at bat can we expect him to get a hit?

39.4%, to the nearest tenth of a percent

48. Sammy Sosa had 104 hits in 412 times at bat. What percent of the time can we expect Sosa to get a hit?

25.2%, to the nearest tenth of a percent

49. Barry Bonds was batting .276. If he had been at bat 340 times, how many hits did he have? (Remember his batting average has been rounded to the nearest thousandth.)

94 hits

50. Joe Mauer was batting .321. If he had been at bat 265 times, how many hits did he have? (Remember, his batting average has been rounded to the nearest thousandth.)

85 hits

51. How many hits must Milton Bradley have in his next 50 times at bat to maintain a batting average of at least .323?

At least 16 hits

Problems 51 and 52 are easiest to solve if students think in terms of cumulative batting average instead of the batting average for the next 50 times at bat.

52. How many hits must Chipper Jones have in his next 50 times at bat to maintain a batting average of at least .394?

At least 20 hits

To solve the problems in this section, we will first restate them in terms of the problems we have already learned how to solve.

A Sales Tax

EXAMPLE 1 Suppose the sales tax rate in Mississippi is 6% of the purchase price. If the price of a refrigerator is $550, how much sales tax must be paid?

SOLUTION Because the sales tax is 6% of the purchase price, and the purchase price is $550, the problem can be restated as:

What is 6% of $550?

We solve this problem, as we did in Section 5.2, by translating it into an equation:

What is 6% of $550?
↓ ↓ ↓ ↓ ↓
$n = 0.06 \cdot 550$
$n = 33$

The sales tax is $33. The total price of the refrigerator would be

Purchase price		Sales tax		Total price
↓		↓		↓
$550	+	$33	=	$583

EXAMPLE 2 Suppose the sales tax rate is 4%. If the sales tax on a 10-speed bicycle is $5.44, what is the purchase price, and what is the total price of the bicycle?

SOLUTION We know that 4% of the purchase price is $5.44. We find the purchase price first by restating the problem as:

$5.44 is 4% of what number?
↓ ↓ ↓ ↓ ↓
$5.44 = 0.04 \cdot n$

We solve the equation by dividing both sides by 0.04:

$$\frac{5.44}{0.04} = \frac{0.04 \cdot n}{0.04}$$ Divide both sides by 0.04

$$n = \frac{5.44}{0.04}$$ Switch the left and right sides of the equation

$$n = 136$$ Divide

The purchase price is $136. The total price is the sum of the purchase price and the sales tax.

Purchase price = $136.00
Sales tax   = + 5.44
_____
Total price   = $141.44

PRACTICE PROBLEMS

1. What is the sales tax on a new washing machine if the machine is purchased for $625 and the sales tax rate is 6%?

Note In Example 1, the *sales tax* rate is 6%, and the *sales tax* is $33. In most everyday communications, people say "The sales tax is 6%," which is incorrect. The 6% is the tax *rate*, and the $33 is the actual tax.

2. Suppose the sales tax rate is 3%. If the sales tax on a 10-speed bicycle is $4.35, what is the purchase price, and what is the total price of the bicycle?

3. Suppose the purchase price of two speakers is $197 and the sales tax is $11.82. What is the sales tax rate?

EXAMPLE 3 Suppose the purchase price of a stereo system is $396 and the sales tax is $19.80. What is the sales tax rate?

SOLUTION We restate the problem as:

$19.80 *is what percent of* $396?

$$19.80 = n \cdot 396$$

To solve this equation, we divide both sides by 396:

$$\frac{19.80}{396} = \frac{n \cdot 396}{396} \quad \text{Divide both sides by 396}$$

$$n = \frac{19.80}{396} \quad \text{Switch the left and right sides of the equation}$$

$$n = 0.05 \quad \text{Divide}$$

$$n = 5\% \quad 0.05 = 5\%$$

The sales tax rate is 5%.

B Commission

Many salespeople work on a *commission* basis. That is, their earnings are a percentage of the amount they sell. The *commission rate* is a percent, and the actual commission they receive is a dollar amount.

Instructor Note
As was the case with sales tax and sales tax rate, students have a tendency to confuse commission and commission rate.

4. A real estate agent gets 3% of the price of each house she sells. If she sells a house for $115,000, how much money does she earn?

EXAMPLE 4 A real estate agent gets 3% of the price of each house she sells. If she sells a house for $289,500, how much money does she earn?

SOLUTION The commission is 3% of the price of the house, which is $289,500. We restate the problem as:

What is 3% of $289,500?

$$n = 0.03 \cdot 289,500$$

$$n = 8,685$$

The commission is $8,685.

5. An appliance salesperson's commission rate is 10%. If the commission on one of the ovens is $115, what is the purchase price of the oven?

EXAMPLE 5 Suppose a car salesperson's commission rate is 12%. If the commission on one of the cars is $1,836, what is the purchase price of the car?

SOLUTION 12% of the sales price is $1,836. The problem can be restated as:

12% *of what number is* $1,836?

$$0.12 \cdot n = 1,836$$

$$\frac{0.12 \cdot n}{0.12} = \frac{1,836}{0.12} \quad \text{Divide both sides by 0.12}$$

$$n = 15,300$$

The car sells for $15,300.

EXAMPLE 6 If the commission on a $600 dining room set is $90, what is the commission rate?

SOLUTION The commission rate is a percentage of the selling price. What we want to know is:

$90 *is what percent of* $600?

$$90 = n \cdot 600$$

$$\frac{90}{600} = \frac{n \cdot 600}{600} \qquad \text{Divide both sides by 600}$$

$$n = \frac{90}{600} \qquad \text{Switch the left and right sides of the equation}$$

$$n = 0.15 \qquad \text{Divide}$$
$$n = 15\% \qquad \text{Change to a percent}$$

The commission rate is 15%.

Getting Ready for Class

After reading through the preceding section, respond in your own words and in complete sentences.

1. Explain the difference between the sales tax and the sales tax rate.
2. Rework Example 1 using a sales tax rate of 7% instead of 6%.
3. Suppose the bicycle in Example 2 was purchased in California, where the sales tax rate in 2008 was 7.25%. How much more would the bicycle have cost?
4. Suppose the car salesperson in Example 5 receives a commission of $3,672. Assuming the same commission rate of 12%, how much does this car sell for?

6. If the commission on a $750 sofa is $105, what is the commission rate?

Answer
6. 14%

Problem Set 5.4

A These problems should be solved by the method shown in this section. In each case show the equation needed to solve the problem. Write neatly, and show your work. [Examples 1–3]

▶ **1. Sales Tax** Suppose the sales tax rate in Mississippi is 7% of the purchase price. If a new food processor sells for $750, how much is the sales tax?

$52.50

▶ **2. Sales Tax** If the sales tax rate is 5% of the purchase price, how much sales tax is paid on a television that sells for $980?

$49

▶ **3. Sales Tax and Purchase Price** Suppose the sales tax rate in Michigan is 6%. How much is the sales tax on a $45 concert ticket? What is the total price?

$2.70; $47.70

▶ **4. Sales Tax and Purchase Price** Suppose the sales tax rate in Hawaii is 4%. How much tax is charged on a new car if the purchase price is $16,400? What is the total price?

$656; $17,056

▶ **5. Total Price** The sales tax rate is 4%. If the sales tax on a 10-speed bicycle is $6, what is the purchase price? What is the total price?

$150; $156

▶ **6. Total Price** The sales tax on a new microwave oven is $30. If the sales tax rate is 5%, what is the purchase price? What is the total price?

$600; $630

▶ **7. Tax Rate** Suppose the purchase price of a dining room set is $450. If the sales tax is $22.50, what is the sales tax rate?

5%

▶ **8. Tax Rate** If the purchase price of a bottle of California wine is $24 and the sales tax is $1.50, what is the sales tax rate?

$6\frac{1}{4}$%, or 6.25%

9. Energy The chart shows the cost to install either solar panels or a wind turbine. A farmer is installing the equipment to generate energy from the wind. If he lives in a state that has a 6% sales tax rate, how much did the farmer pay in sales tax on the total equipment cost?

$420.90

10. Prom The graph shows how much guys plan to spend on prom. The sum of the tax on all the expenses a guy had for prom was $15.75. If he lived in a state that has a sales tax rate of 7.5%, what spending bracket would he have been in?

He spent $210, so he would be in the $200 to $300 bracket.

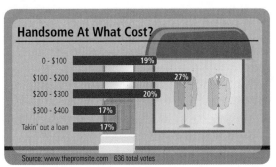

B [Examples 4–6]

▶ **11. Commission** A real estate agent has a commission rate of 3%. If a piece of property sells for $94,000, what is her commission?

$2,820

12. Commission A tire salesperson has a 12% commission rate. If he sells a set of radial tires for $400, what is his commission?

$48

▶ **13. Commission and Purchase Price** Suppose a salesperson gets a commission rate of 12% on the lawnmowers she sells. If the commission on one of the mowers is $24, what is the purchase price of the lawnmower?

$200

▶ **14. Commission and Purchase Price** If an appliance salesperson gets 9% commission on all the appliances she sells, what is the price of a refrigerator if her commission is $67.50?

$750

▶ **15. Commission Rate** If the commission on an $800 washer is $112, what is the commission rate?

14%

16. Commission Rate A realtor makes a commission of $11,400 on a $190,000 house he sells. What is his commission rate?

6%

17. Phone Bill You recently received your monthly phone bill for service in your local area. The total of the bill was $53.35. You pay $14.36 in surcharges and federal and local taxes. What percent of your phone bill is made up of surcharges and taxes? Round your answer to the nearest tenth of a percent.

26.9%

18. Wireless Phone Bill You recently received your Verizon wireless phone bill for the month. The total monthly bill is $70.52. Included in that total is $13.27 in surcharges and taxes. What percent of your wireless bill goes towards surcharges and taxes? Round your answer to the nearest tenth of a percent.

18.8%

19. Gasoline Tax New York state has one of the highest gasoline taxes in the country. If gas is currently selling at $4.27 for a gallon of regular gas and the tax rate is 14.7%, how much of the price of a gallon of gas goes towards taxes?

62.8 cents or $0.628

▶ **20. Cigarette Tax** In an effort to encourage people to quit smoking, many states place a high tax on a pack of cigarettes. Nine states place a tax of $2.00 or more on a pack of cigarettes, with New Jersey being the highest at $2.575 per pack. If this is 39% of the cost of a pack of cigarettes in New Jersey, how much does a single pack cost?

$6.60

21. Salary Plus Commission A computer salesperson earns a salary of $425 a week and a 6% commission on all sales over $4000 each week. Suppose she was able to sell $6,250 in computer parts and accessories one week. What was her salary for the week?

$560

22. Salary Plus Bonus The manager for a computer store is paid a weekly salary of $650 plus a bonus amounting to 1.5% of the net earnings of the store each week. Find her total salary for the week when earnings for the store are $26,875.56. Round your answer to the nearest cent.

$1053.13

■ Calculator Problems

The following problems are similar to Problems 1–22. Set them up in the same way, but use a calculator for the calculations.

▶ **23. Sales Tax** The sales tax rate on a certain item is 5.5%. If the purchase price is $216.95, how much is the sales tax? (Round to the nearest cent.)

$11.93

▶ **24. Purchase Price** If the sales tax rate is 4.75% and the sales tax is $18.95, what is the purchase price? What is the total price? (Both answers should be rounded to the nearest cent.)

$398.95; $417.90

▶ **25. Tax Rate** The purchase price for a new suit is $229.50. If the sales tax is $10.33, what is the sales tax rate? (Round to the nearest tenth of a percent.)

4.5%

▶ **26. Commission** If the commission rate for a mobile home salesperson is 11%, what is the commission on the sale of a $15,794 mobile home?

$1,737.34

▶ **27. Selling Price** Suppose the commission rate on the sale of used cars is 13%. If the commission on one of the cars is $519.35, what did the car sell for?

$3,995

▶ **28. Commission Rate** If the commission on the sale of $79.40 worth of clothes is $14.29, what is the commission rate? (Round to the nearest percent.)

18%

■ Getting Ready for the Next Section

Multiply.

29. 0.05(22,000)

1,100

30. 0.176(1,793,000)

315,568

31. 0.25(300)

75

32. 0.12(450)

54

Divide. Write your answers as decimals.

33. $4 \div 25$

0.16

34. $7 \div 35$

0.2

Subtract

35. $25 - 21$

4

36. $1,793,000 - 315,568$

1,477,432

37. $450 - 54$

396

38. $300 - 75$

225

Add.

39. $396 + 19.8$

415.8

40. $22,000 + 1,100$

23,100

■ Maintaining Your Skills

The problems below review some basic concepts of division with fractions and mixed numbers.

Divide.

41. $\dfrac{1}{3} \div \dfrac{2}{3}$

$\dfrac{1}{2}$

42. $\dfrac{2}{3} \div \dfrac{1}{3}$

2

43. $2 \div \dfrac{3}{4}$

$2\dfrac{2}{3}$

44. $3 \div \dfrac{1}{2}$

6

45. $\dfrac{3}{8} \div \dfrac{1}{4}$

$1\dfrac{1}{2}$

46. $\dfrac{5}{9} \div \dfrac{2}{3}$

$\dfrac{5}{6}$

47. $2\dfrac{1}{4} \div \dfrac{1}{2}$

$4\dfrac{1}{2}$

48. $1\dfrac{1}{4} \div 2\dfrac{1}{2}$

$\dfrac{1}{2}$

The table and bar chart below show some statistics compiled by insurance companies regarding stopping distances for automobiles traveling at 20 miles per hour on ice.

	Stopping Distance	Percent Decrease
Regular tires	150 ft	0
Snow tires	151 ft	−1%
Studded snow tires	120 ft	20%
Reinforced tire chains	75 ft	50%

Source: Copyrighted table courtesy of *The Casualty Adjuster's Guide*

Many times it is more effective to state increases or decreases as percents, rather than the actual number, because with percent we are comparing everything to 100.

A Percent Increase

EXAMPLE 1 If a person earns $22,000 a year and gets a 5% increase in salary, what is the new salary?

SOLUTION   We can find the dollar amount of the salary increase by finding 5% of $22,000:

$$0.05 \times 22,000 = 1,100$$

The increase in salary is $1,100. The new salary is the old salary plus the raise:

$22,000	Old salary
+ 1,100	Raise (5% of $22,000)
$23,100	New salary

1. A person earning $18,000 a year gets a 7% increase in salary. What is the new salary?

Answer
1. $19,260

2. In 1986, there were approximately 271,000 drunk drivers under correctional supervision (prison, jail, or probation). By 1997, that number had increased 89%. How many drunk drivers were under correctional supervision in 1997? Round to the nearest thousand.

B Percent Decrease

EXAMPLE 2   In 1986, there were approximately 1,793,000 arrests for driving under the influence of alcohol or drugs (DUI) in the United States. By 1997, the number of arrests for DUI had decreased 17.6% from the 1986 number. How many people were arrested for DUI in 1997? Round the answer to the nearest thousand.

SOLUTION   The decrease in the number of arrests is 17.6% of 1,793,000, or

$$0.176 \times 1,793,000 = 315,568$$

Subtracting this number from 1,793,000, we have the number of DUI arrests in 1997.

1,793,000	Number of arrests in 1986
− 315,568	Decrease of 17.6%
1,477,432	Number of arrests in 1997

To the nearest thousand, there were approximately 1,477,000 arrests for DUI in 1997.

3. Shoes that usually sell for $35 are on sale for $28. What is the percent decrease in price?

EXAMPLE 3   Shoes that usually sell for $25 are on sale for $21. What is the percent decrease in price?

SOLUTION   We must first find the decrease in price. Subtracting the sale price from the original price, we have

$$\$25 - \$21 = \$4$$

The decrease is $4. To find the percent decrease (from the original price), we have

$$\$4 \text{ is what percent of } \$25?$$
$$4 = n \cdot 25$$

$\dfrac{4}{25} = \dfrac{n \cdot 25}{25}$	Divide both sides by 25
$n = \dfrac{4}{25}$	Switch the left and right sides of the equation
$n = 0.16$	Divide
$n = 16\%$	Change to a percent

The shoes that sold for $25 have been reduced by 16% to $21. In a problem like this, $25 is the *original* (or *marked*) price, $21 is the *sale price*, $4 is the *discount*, and 16% is the *rate of discount*.

C Discount Rate

4. During a sale, a microwave oven that usually sells for $550 is marked "15% off." What is the discount? What is the sale price?

EXAMPLE 4   During a clearance sale, a suit that usually sells for $300 is marked "25% off." What is the discount? What is the sale price?

SOLUTION   To find the discount, we restate the problem as:

$$\text{What is 25\% of 300?}$$
$$n = 0.25 \cdot 300$$
$$n = 75$$

Answers
2. 512,000   **3.** 20%

The discount is $75. The sale price is the original price less the discount:

$300   Original price
−   75   Less the discount (25% of $300)
$225   Sale price

EXAMPLE 5   A man buys a washing machine on sale. The machine usually sells for $450, but it is on sale at 12% off. If the sales tax rate is 5%, how much is the total bill for the washer?

SOLUTION   First we have to find the sale price of the washing machine, and we begin by finding the discount:

What is 12% of $450?
$$n = 0.12 \cdot 450$$
$$n = 54$$

The washing machine is marked down $54. The sale price is

$450   Original price
−   54   Discount (12% of $450)
$396   Sale price

Because the sales tax rate is 5%, we find the sales tax as follows:

What is 5% of 396?
$$n = 0.05 \cdot 396$$
$$n = 19.80$$

The sales tax is $19.80. The total price the man pays for the washing machine is

$396.00   Sale price
+   19.80   Sales tax
$415.80   Total price

Getting Ready for Class

After reading through the preceding section, respond in your own words and in complete sentences.

1. Suppose the person mentioned in Example 1 was earning $32,000 per year and received the same percent increase in salary. How much more would the raise have been?

2. Suppose the shoes mentioned in Example 3 were on sale for $20, instead of $21. Calculate the new percent decrease in price.

3. Suppose a store owner pays $225 for a suit, and then marks it up $75, to $300. Find the percent increase in price.

4. Compare your answer to Problem 3 above with the problem given in Example 4 of your text. Do you think it is generally true that a 25% discount is equivalent to a $33\frac{1}{3}$% markup?

5. A woman buys a new coat on sale. The coat usually sells for $45, but it is on sale at 15% off. If the sales tax rate is 5%, how much is the total bill for the coat?

Problem Set 5.5

A B Solve each of these problems using the method developed in this section. [Examples 1–3]

▶ **1. Salary Increase** If a person earns $23,000 a year and gets a 7% increase in salary, what is the new salary?
$24,610

▶ **2. Salary Increase** A computer programmer's yearly income of $57,000 is increased by 8%. What is the dollar amount of the increase, and what is her new salary?
$4,560; $61,560

3. Tuition Increase The yearly tuition at a college is presently $6,000. Next year it is expected to increase by 17%. What will the tuition at this school be next year?
$7,020

4. Price Increase A market increased the price of cheese selling for $4.98 per pound by 3%. What is the new price for a pound of cheese? (Round to the nearest cent.)
$5.13 per pound

▶ **5. Car Value** In one year a new car decreased in value by 20%. If it sold for $16,500 when it was new, what was it worth after 1 year?
$13,200

▶ **6. Calorie Content** A certain light beer has 20% fewer calories than the regular beer. If the regular beer has 120 calories per bottle, how many calories are in the same-sized bottle of the light beer?
96 calories

▶ **7. Salary Increase** A person earning $3,500 a month gets a raise of $350 per month. What is the percent increase in salary?
10%

▶ **8. Rate Increase** A student reader is making $6.50 per hour and gets a $0.70 raise. What is the percent increase? (Round to the nearest tenth of a percent.)
10.8%

▶ **9. Shoe Sale** Shoes that usually sell for $25 are on sale for $20. What is the percent decrease in price?
20%

▶ **10. Enrollment Decrease** The enrollment in a certain elementary school was 410 in 2007. In 2008, the enrollment in the same school was 328. Find the percent decrease in enrollment from 2007 to 2008.
20%

▶ **11. Students to Teachers** The chart shows the student to teacher ratio in the United States from 1975 to 2002. What is the percent decrease in student to teacher ratio from 1975 to 2002? Round to the nearest percent.
21%

▶ **12. Health Care** The graph shows the rising cost of health care. What is the projected percent increase in health care costs from 2002 to 2014?
130%

C [Examples 4, 5]

▶ **13. Discount** During a clearance sale, a three-piece suit that usually sells for $300 is marked "15% off." What is the discount? What is the sale price?

$45; $255

▶ **14. Sale Price** On opening day, a new music store offers a 12% discount on all electric guitars. If the regular price on a guitar is $550, what is the sale price?

$484

▶ **15. Total Price** A man buys a washing machine that is on sale. The washing machine usually sells for $450 but is on sale at 20% off. If the sales tax rate in his state is 6%, how much is the total bill for the washer?

$381.60

▶ **16. Total Price** A bedroom set that normally sells for $1,450 is on sale for 10% off. If the sales tax rate is 5%, what is the total price of the bedroom set if it is bought while on sale?

$1,370.25

▶ **17. Real Estate Market** In 2006 the average price of a home began to fall in most real estate markets across the country. The median price of a single family home in the U.S. was $227,000 in 2006. The median price is now $195,500. By what percent did the median price of a single family home drop? Round your answer to the nearest tenth of a percent.

13.9%

▶ **18. Deep Discount** When buying some of today's newest electronic gadgets, good things come to those who wait. When Apple released its new iPhone in the summer of 2007, an 8GB model sold for $499. In July 2008, Apple released its new iPhone 3G. The 8GB model sells for $199. What is the percent decrease in price for this new model? Round your answer to the nearest tenth of a percent.

60.1%

19. Losing Weight According to the Centers for Disease Control and Prevention (CDC), more than 60% of U.S. adults are overweight, and about 15% of children and adolescents ages 6 to 19 are overweight. Your friend decides to go on a diet and goes from 155 pounds to 130 pounds over a 4 month period. What was her percentage weight loss? Round your answer to the nearest percent.

16%

▶ **20. Ordering Online** You are in the market for a new laptop. The model that you wish to purchase is $1,500 in a local store. However, you decide to buy the computer over the Internet for $1200, plus shipping charges. Taking into account shipping charges of $59, what percentage do you save by ordering it online? Round your answer to the nearest tenth of a percent.

16%

▶ **21. Product Error** When manufacturing a product, a certain amount of variation (or error) can occur in the process and still create a part or product that is useable. For one particular company, a 3% error is acceptable for their machine parts to be used safely. If the part they are manufacturing is 22.5 in. long, what is the range of measures that are acceptable for this part?

21.8 in. to 23.2 in.

22. Home Remodeling You have decided to update your house by laying a new wood floor in your living room. Your floor has an area of 440 sq ft. You decide to buy enough flooring to allow for a certain amount of waste so you purchase 470 sq ft of wood flooring materials. Express your waste allowance as a percent. Round your result to the nearest percent.

6.4%

■ Calculator Problems

Set up the following problems the same way you set up Problems 1–22. Then use a calculator to do the calculations.

▶ **23. Salary Increase** A teacher making $43,752 per year gets a 6.5% raise. What is the new salary?

$46,595.88

24. Utility Increase A homeowner had a $95.90 electric bill in December. In January the bill was $107.40. Find the percent increase in the electric bill from December to January. (Round to the nearest whole number.)

12%

▶ **25. Soccer** The rules for soccer state that the playing field must be from 100 to 120 yards long and 55 to 75 yards wide. The 1999 Women's World Cup was played at the Rose Bowl on a playing field 116 yards long and 72 yards wide. The diagram below shows the smallest possible soccer field, the largest possible soccer field, and the soccer field at the Rose Bowl.

Soccer Fields

100 yd · 55 yd · Smallest

116 yd · 72 yd · Rose Bowl

120 yd · 75 yd · Largest

a. Percent Increase A team plays on the smallest field, then plays in the Rose Bowl. What is the percent increase in the area of the playing field from the smallest field to the Rose Bowl? Round to the nearest tenth of a percent.

51.9%

b. Percent Increase A team plays a soccer game in the Rose Bowl. The next game is on a field with the largest dimensions. What is the percent increase in the area of the playing field from the Rose Bowl to the largest field? Round to the nearest tenth of a percent.

7.8%

▶ **26. Football** The diagrams below show the dimensions of playing fields for the National Football League (NFL), the Canadian Football League (CFL), and Arena Football.

Football Fields

100 yd · $53\frac{1}{3}$ yd · NFL

110 yd · 65 yd · Canadian

50yd · $28\frac{1}{3}$ yd · Arena

a. Percent Increase In 1999 Kurt Warner made a successful transition from Arena Football to the NFL, winning the Most Valuable Player award. What was the percent increase in the area of the fields he played on in moving from Arena Football to the NFL? Round to the nearest percent.

276%

b. Percent Decrease Doug Flutie played in the Canadian Football League before moving to the NFL. What was the percent decrease in the area of the fields he played on in moving from the CFL to the NFL? Round to the nearest tenth of a percent.

25.4%

■ Getting Ready for the Next Section

Multiply. Round to nearest hundredth if necessary.

27. 0.07(2,000)
140

28. 0.12(8,000)
960

29. $600(0.04)\left(\dfrac{1}{6}\right)$
4

30. $900(0.06)\left(\dfrac{1}{4}\right)$
13.5

31. $10,150(0.06)\left(\dfrac{1}{4}\right)$
152.25

32. $10,302.25(0.06)\left(\dfrac{1}{4}\right)$
154.53

Add.

33. 3,210 + 224.7
3,434.7

34. 900 + 13.50
913.50

35. 10,000 + 150
10,150

36. 10,150 + 152.25
10,302.25

37. 10,302.25 + 154.53
10,456.78

38. 10,456.78 + 156.85
10,613.63

Simplify.

39. 2,000 + 0.07(2,000)
2,140

40. 8,000 + 0.12(8,000)
8,960

41. 3,000 + 0.07(3,000)
3,210

42. 9,000 + 0.12(9,000)
10,080

■ Maintaining Your Skills

The problems below review some basic concepts of addition of fractions and mixed numbers.
Add each of the following and reduce all answers to lowest terms.

43. $\dfrac{1}{3} + \dfrac{2}{3}$
1

44. $\dfrac{3}{8} + \dfrac{1}{8}$
$\dfrac{1}{2}$

45. $\dfrac{1}{2} + \dfrac{1}{4}$
$\dfrac{3}{4}$

46. $\dfrac{1}{5} + \dfrac{3}{10}$
$\dfrac{1}{2}$

47. $\dfrac{3}{4} + \dfrac{2}{3}$
$1\dfrac{5}{12}$

48. $\dfrac{3}{8} + \dfrac{1}{6}$
$\dfrac{13}{24}$

49. $2\dfrac{1}{2} + 3\dfrac{1}{2}$
6

50. $3\dfrac{1}{4} + 2\dfrac{1}{8}$
$5\dfrac{3}{8}$

5.6

Anyone who has borrowed money from a bank or other lending institution, or who has invested money in a savings account, is aware of *interest.* Interest is the amount of money paid for the use of money. If we put $500 in a savings account that pays 6% annually, the interest will be 6% of $500, or 0.06(500) = $30. The amount we invest ($500) is called the *principal,* the percent (6%) is the *interest rate,* and the money earned ($30) is the *interest.*

EXAMPLE 1 A man invests $2,000 in a savings plan that pays 7% per year. How much money will be in the account at the end of 1 year?

SOLUTION We first find the interest by taking 7% of the principal, $2,000:

$$Interest = 0.07(\$2,000)$$
$$= \$140$$

The interest earned in 1 year is $140. The total amount of money in the account at the end of a year is the original amount plus the $140 interest:

$2,000	Original investment (principal)
+ 140	Interest (7% of $2,000)
$2,140	Amount after 1 year

The amount in the account after 1 year is $2,140.

EXAMPLE 2 A farmer borrows $8,000 from his local bank at 12%. How much does he pay back to the bank at the end of the year to pay off the loan?

SOLUTION The interest he pays on the $8,000 is

$$Interest = 0.12(\$8,000)$$
$$= \$960$$

At the end of the year, he must pay back the original amount he borrowed ($8,000) plus the interest at 12%:

$8,000	Amount borrowed (principal)
+ 960	Interest at 12%
$8,960	Total amount to pay back

The total amount that the farmer pays back is $8,960.

A Simple Interest

There are many situations in which interest on a loan is figured on other than a yearly basis. Many short-term loans are for only 30 or 60 days. In these cases we can use a formula to calculate the interest that has accumulated. This type of interest is called *simple interest.* The formula is

$$I = P \cdot R \cdot T$$

where

I = Interest
P = Principal
R = Interest rate (this is the percent)
T = Time (in years, 1 year = 360 days)

1. A man invests $3,000 in a savings plan that pays 8% per year. How much money will be in the account at the end of 1 year?

2. If a woman borrows $7,500 from her local bank at 12% interest, how much does she pay back to the bank if she pays off the loan in 1 year?

Answers
1. $3,240   2. $8,400

We could have used this formula to find the interest in Examples 1 and 2. In those two cases, T is 1. When the length of time is in days rather than years, it is common practice to use 360 days for 1 year, and we write T as a fraction. Examples 3 and 4 illustrate this procedure.

EXAMPLE 3   A student takes out an emergency loan for tuition, books, and supplies. The loan is for $600 at an interest rate of 4%. How much interest does the student pay if the loan is paid back in 60 days?

SOLUTION   The principal P is $600, the rate R is 4% = 0.04, and the time T is $\frac{60}{360}$. Notice that T must be given in years, and 60 days = $\frac{60}{360}$ year. Applying the formula, we have

$$I = P \cdot R \cdot T$$

$$I = 600 \times 0.04 \times \frac{60}{360}$$

$$I = 600 \times 0.04 \times \frac{1}{6} \qquad \tfrac{60}{360} = \tfrac{1}{6}$$

$$I = 4 \qquad \text{Multiplication}$$

The interest is $4.

EXAMPLE 4   A woman deposits $900 in an account that pays 6% annually. If she withdraws all the money in the account after 90 days, how much does she withdraw?

SOLUTION   We have $P = \$900$, $R = 0.06$, and $T = 90$ days = $\frac{90}{360}$ year. Using these numbers in the formula, we have

$$I = P \cdot R \cdot T$$

$$I = 900 \times 0.06 \times \frac{90}{360}$$

$$I = 900 \times 0.06 \times \frac{1}{4} \qquad \tfrac{90}{360} = \tfrac{1}{4}$$

$$I = 13.5 \qquad \text{Multiplication}$$

The interest earned in 90 days is $13.50. If the woman withdraws all the money in her account, she will withdraw

$900.00	Original amount (principal)
+ 13.50	Interest for 90 days
$913.50	Total amount withdrawn

The woman will withdraw $913.50.

B   Compound Interest

A second common kind of interest is *compound interest.* Compound interest includes interest paid on interest. We can use what we know about simple interest to help us solve problems involving compound interest.

EXAMPLE 5   A homemaker puts $3,000 into a savings account that pays 7% compounded annually. How much money is in the account at the end of 2 years?

SOLUTION   Because the account pays 7% annually, the simple interest at the end of 1 year is 7% of $3,000:

3. Another student takes out a loan like the one in Example 3. This loan is for $700 at 4%. How much interest does this student pay if the loan is paid back in 90 days?

4. Suppose $1,200 is deposited in an account that pays 9.5% interest per year. If all the money is withdrawn after 120 days, how much money is withdrawn?

5. If $5,000 is put into an account that pays 6% compounded annually, how much money is in the account at the end of 2 years?

Answers
3. $7   **4.** $1,238

Interest after 1 year = 0.07($3,000)

= $210

Because the interest is paid annually, at the end of 1 year the total amount of money in the account is

$3,000	Original amount
+ 210	Interest for 1 year
$3,210	Total in account after 1 year

The interest paid for the second year is 7% of this new total, or

Interest paid the second year = 0.07($3,210)

= $224.70

At the end of 2 years, the total in the account is

$3,210.00	Amount at the beginning of year 2
+ 224.70	Interest paid for year 2
$3,434.70	Account after 2 years

At the end of 2 years, the account totals $3,434.70. The total interest earned during this 2-year period is $210 (first year) + $224.70 (second year) = $434.70.

Note If the interest earned in Example 5 were calculated using the formula for simple interest, $I = P \cdot R \cdot T$, the amount of money in the account at the end of two years would be $3,420.00.

You may have heard of savings and loan companies that offer interest rates that are compounded quarterly. If the interest rate is, say, 6% and it is compounded quarterly, then after every 90 days ($\frac{1}{4}$ of a year) the interest is added to the account. If it is compounded semiannually, then the interest is added to the account every 6 months. Most accounts have interest rates that are compounded daily, which means the simple interest is computed daily and added to the account.

EXAMPLE 6 If $10,000 is invested in a savings account that pays 6% compounded quarterly, how much is in the account at the end of a year?

SOLUTION The interest for the first quarter ($\frac{1}{4}$ of a year) is calculated using the formula for simple interest:

$I = P \cdot R \cdot T$

$I = \$10,000 \times 0.06 \times \dfrac{1}{4}$ First quarter

$I = \$150$

At the end of the first quarter, this interest is added to the original principal. The new principal is $10,000 + $150 = $10,150. Again we apply the formula to calculate the interest for the second quarter:

$I = \$10,150 \times 0.06 \times \dfrac{1}{4}$ Second quarter

$I = \$152.25$

The principal at the end of the second quarter is $10,150 + $152.25 = $10,302.25. The interest earned during the third quarter is

$I = \$10,302.25 \times 0.06 \times \dfrac{1}{4}$ Third quarter

$I = \$154.53$ To the nearest cent

6. If $20,000 is invested in an account that pays 8% compounded quarterly, how much is in the account at the end of a year?

Answer
5. $5,618

The new principal is $10,302.25 + $154.53 = $10,456.78. Interest for the fourth quarter is

$$I = \$10,456.78 \times 0.06 \times \frac{1}{4} \qquad \text{Fourth quarter}$$

$$I = \$156.85 \qquad \text{To the nearest cent}$$

The total amount of money in this account at the end of 1 year is

$$\$10,456.78 + \$156.85 = \$10,613.63$$

USING TECHNOLOGY

Compound Interest from a Formula

We can summarize the work above with a formula that allows us to calculate compound interest for any interest rate and any number of compounding periods. If we invest P dollars at an annual interest rate r, compounded n times a year, then the amount of money in the account after t years is given by the formula

$$A = P\left(1 + \frac{r}{n}\right)^{nt}$$

Using numbers from Example 6 to illustrate, we have

$$P = \text{Principal} = \$10,000$$
$$r = \text{annual interest rate} = 0.06$$
$$n = \text{number of compounding periods} = 4 \text{ (interest is compounded quarterly)}$$
$$t = \text{number of years} = 1$$

Substituting these numbers into the formula above, we have

$$A = 10,000\left(1 + \frac{0.06}{4}\right)^{4 \times 1}$$
$$= 10,000(1 + 0.015)^4$$
$$= 10,000(1.015)^4$$

To simplify this last expression on a calculator, we have

Scientific calculator: 10,000 $\times$ 1.015 y^x 4 $=$

Graphing calculator: 10,000 $\times$ 1.015 $\wedge$ 4 ENTER

In either case, the answer is $10,613.63551, which rounds to $10,613.64.

Note The reason that this answer is different from the result we obtained in Example 6 is that, in Example 6, we rounded each calculation as we did it. The calculator will keep all the digits in all of the intermediate calculations.

Getting Ready for Class

After reading through the preceding section, respond in your own words and in complete sentences.

1. Suppose the man in Example 1 invested $3,000, instead of $2,000, in the savings plan. How much more interest would he have earned?

2. How much does the student in Example 3 pay back if the loan is paid off after a year, instead of after 60 days?

3. Suppose the homemaker mentioned in Example 5 invests $3,000 in an account that pays only $3\frac{1}{2}$% compounded annually. How much is in the account at the end of 2 years?

4. In Example 6, how much money would the account contain at the end of 1 year if it were compounded annually, instead of quarterly?

Answer
6. $21,648.64

Problem Set 5.6

A These problems are similar to the examples found in this section. They should be set up and solved in the same way. (Problems 1–12 involve simple interest.) [Examples 1–4]

▶ **1. Savings Account** A man invests $2,000 in a savings plan that pays 8% per year. How much money will be in the account at the end of 1 year?
$2,160

▶ **2. Savings Account** How much simple interest is earned on $5,000 if it is invested for 1 year at 5%?
$250

▶ **3. Savings Account** A savings account pays 7% per year. How much interest will $9,500 invested in such an account earn in a year?
$665

▶ **4. Savings Account** A local bank pays 5.5% annual interest on all savings accounts. If $600 is invested in this type of account, how much will be in the account at the end of a year?
$633

▶ **5. Bank Loan** A farmer borrows $8,000 from his local bank at 7%. How much does he pay back to the bank at the end of the year when he pays off the loan?
$8,560

▶ **6. Bank Loan** If $400 is borrowed at a rate of 12% for 1 year, how much is the interest?
$48

▶ **7. Bank Loan** A bank lends one of its customers $2,000 at 8% for 1 year. If the customer pays the loan back at the end of the year, how much does he pay the bank?
$2,160

▶ **8. Bank Loan** If a loan of $2,000 at 20% for 1 year is to be paid back in one payment at the end of the year, how much does the borrower pay the bank?
$2,400

▶ **9. Student Loan** A student takes out an emergency loan for tuition, books, and supplies. The loan is for $600 with an annual interest rate of 5%. How much interest does the student pay if the loan is paid back in 60 days?
$5

▶ **10. Short-Term Loan** If a loan of $1,200 at 9% is paid off in 90 days, what is the interest?
$27

▶ **11. Savings Account** A woman deposits $800 in a savings account that pays 5%. If she withdraws all the money in the account after 120 days, how much does she withdraw?
$813.33

▶ **12. Savings Account** $1,800 is deposited in a savings account that pays 6%. If the money is withdrawn at the end of 30 days, how much interest is earned?
$9

B The problems that follow involve compound interest. [Examples 5, 6]

Compound Interest The chart shows the interest rates for various CD accounts.

13. Last year Samuel invested $400 in a 6-month CD. If the interest is compounded quarterly, how much was in the account at the end of 6 months? Round to the nearest cent.

$406.34

14. If Alice deposited $200 in a $2\frac{1}{2}$ year CD account earlier this week, what will the account make at the end of its term if interest is compounded quarterly. Use the compound interest formula and round to the nearest cent.

$223.56

▶ 15. **Compound Interest** A woman puts $5,000 into a savings account that pays 6% compounded annually. How much money is in the account at the end of 2 years?

$5,618

▶ 16. **Compound Interest** A savings account pays 5% compounded annually. If $10,000 is deposited in the account, how much is in the account after 2 years?

$11,025

▶ 17. **Compound Interest** If $8,000 is invested in a savings account that pays 5% compounded quarterly, how much is in the account at the end of a year?

$8,407.56

Some answers may vary in the hundredths column depending on whether rounding is done in the intermediate steps.

▶ 18. **Compound Interest** Suppose $1,200 is invested in a savings account that pays 6% compounded semiannually. How much is in the account at the end of $1\frac{1}{2}$ years?

$1,311.27

▪ Calculator Problems

The following problems should be set up in the same way in which Problems 1–18 have been set up. Then the calculations should be done on a calculator.

▶ 19. **Savings Account** A woman invests $917.26 in a savings account that pays 6.25% annually. How much is in the account at the end of a year?

$974.59

▶ 20. **Business Loan** The owner of a clothing store borrows $6,210 for 1 year at 11.5% interest. If he pays the loan back at the end of the year, how much does he pay back?

$6,924.15

▶ 21. **Compound Interest** Suppose $10,000 is invested in each account below. In each case find the amount of money in the account at the end of 5 years.

a. Annual interest rate = 6%, compounded quarterly

$13,468.55

b. Annual interest rate = 6%, compounded monthly

$13,488.50

c. Annual interest rate = 5%, compounded quarterly

$12,820.37

d. Annual interest rate = 5%, compounded monthly

$12,833.59

▶ 22. **Compound Interest** Suppose $5,000 is invested in each account below. In each case find the amount of money in the account at the end of 10 years.

a. Annual interest rate = 5%, compounded quarterly

$8,218.10

b. Annual interest rate = 6%, compounded quarterly

$9,070.09

c. Annual interest rate = 7%, compounded quarterly

$10,007.99

d. Annual interest rate = 8%, compounded quarterly

$11,040.20

Getting Ready for the Next Section

Change to percent.

23. $\dfrac{75}{250}$

30%

24. $\dfrac{150}{250}$

60%

25. $\dfrac{400}{2,400}$

$16\frac{2}{3}\%$

26. $\dfrac{200}{2,400}$

$8\frac{1}{3}\%$

Multiply.

27. $0.3(360)$

108

28. $0.4(360)$

144

29. $0.45(360)$

162

30. $0.15(360)$

54

Divide.

31. $40 \div 5$

8

32. $45 \div 5$

9

33. $15 \div 5$

3

34. $5 \div 5$

1

Maintaining Your Skills

The problems below will allow you to review subtraction of fractions and mixed numbers.

35. $\dfrac{3}{4} - \dfrac{1}{4}$

$\frac{1}{2}$

36. $\dfrac{9}{10} - \dfrac{7}{10}$

$\frac{1}{5}$

37. $\dfrac{5}{8} - \dfrac{1}{4}$

$\frac{3}{8}$

38. $\dfrac{7}{10} - \dfrac{1}{5}$

$\frac{1}{2}$

39. $2 - \dfrac{4}{3}$

$\frac{2}{3}$

40. $2 + \dfrac{4}{3}$

$\frac{10}{3} = 3\frac{1}{3}$

41. $1 + \dfrac{1}{2}$

$\frac{3}{2} = 1\frac{1}{2}$

42. $1 - \dfrac{1}{2}$

$\frac{1}{2}$

43. $\dfrac{1}{3} - \dfrac{1}{4}$

$\frac{1}{12}$

44. $\dfrac{9}{12} - \dfrac{1}{5}$

$\frac{11}{20}$

45. $3\dfrac{1}{4} - 2$

$\frac{5}{4} = 1\frac{1}{4}$

46. $5\dfrac{1}{6} - 3\dfrac{1}{4}$

$\frac{23}{12} = 1\frac{11}{12}$

47. Find the sum of $\dfrac{8}{15}$ and $\dfrac{8}{35}$. $\frac{16}{21}$

48. Find the difference of $\dfrac{8}{15}$ and $\dfrac{8}{35}$. $\frac{32}{105}$

49. Find the product of $\dfrac{8}{15}$ and $\dfrac{8}{35}$. $\frac{64}{525}$

50. Find the quotient of $\dfrac{8}{15}$ and $\dfrac{8}{35}$. $\frac{7}{3} = 2\frac{1}{3}$

■ Extending the Concepts

The following problems are percent problems. Use any of the methods developed in this chapter to solve them.

51. Credit Card Debt Student credit-card debt is at an all-time high. Consolidated Credit Counseling Services Inc. reports that 20% of all college freshman got their first credit card in high school and nearly 40% sign up for one in their first year at college. Suppose your credit card company charges 1.3% in finance charges per month on the average daily balance in your credit card account. If your average daily balance for this month is $2,367.90 determine the finance charge for the month.

$30.78

52. Finding Your Interest Rate In early January, your bank sent out a form called a 1099-INT, which summarizes the amount of interest you have received on a savings account for the previous year. If you received $72 interest for the year on an account in which you started with $1,200, determine the annual interest rate paid by your bank.

6%

53. Movie Making The bar chart below shows the production costs for each of the first four *Star Wars* movies. Find the percent increase in production costs from each *Star Wars* movie to the next. Round your results to the nearest tenth.

Percent increase in production costs: *Star Wars* 1 to 2, 63.6%; *Star Wars* 2 to 3, 80.6%; *Star Wars* 3 to 4, 253.8%

54. Movie Making The table below shows how much money each of the first four *Star Wars* movies brought in during the first weekend they were shown. Find the percent increase in opening weekend income from each *Star Wars* movie to the next. Round to the nearest percent.

Opening Weekend Income	
Star Wars (1977)	$1,554,000
The Empire Strikes Back (1980)	$6,415,000
Return of the Jedi (1983)	$30,490,000
The Phantom Menace (1999)	$64,810,000

Percent increase in opening weekend income: *Star Wars* 1 to 2, 313%; *Star Wars* 2 to 3, 375%; *Star Wars* 3 to 4, 113%

Chapter 5 Summary

◼ The Meaning of Percent [5.1]

Percent means "per hundred." It is a way of comparing numbers to the number 100.

1. 42% means 42 per hundred or $\frac{42}{100}$.

◼ Changing Percents to Decimals [5.1]

To change a percent to a decimal, drop the percent symbol (%), and move the decimal point two places to the *left*.

2. 75% = 0.75

◼ Changing Decimals to Percents [5.1]

To change a decimal to a percent, move the decimal point two places to the *right*, and use the % symbol.

3. 0.25 = 25%

◼ Changing Percents to Fractions [5.1]

To change a percent to a fraction, drop the % symbol, and use a denominator of 100. Reduce the resulting fraction to lowest terms if necessary.

4. $6\% = \frac{6}{100} = \frac{3}{50}$

◼ Changing Fractions to Percents [5.1]

To change a fraction to a percent, either write the fraction as a decimal and then change the decimal to a percent, or write the fraction as an equivalent fraction with denominator 100, drop the 100, and use the % symbol.

5. $\frac{3}{4} = 0.75 = 75\%$

or

$\frac{9}{10} = \frac{90}{100} = 90\%$

◼ Basic Word Problems Involving Percents [5.2]

There are three basic types of word problems:

Type A: What number is 14% of 68?

Type B: What percent of 75 is 25?

Type C: 25 is 40% of what number?

To solve them, we write *is* as =, *of* as · (multiply), and *what number* or *what percent* as n. We then solve the resulting equation to find the answer to the original question.

6. Translating to equations, we have:

Type A: $n = 0.14(68)$

Type B: $75n = 25$

Type C: $25 = 0.40n$

Applications of Percent [5.3, 5.4, 5.5, 5.6]

There are many different kinds of application problems involving percent. They include problems on income tax, sales tax, commission, discount, percent increase and decrease, and interest. Generally, to solve these problems, we restate them as an equivalent problem of Type A, B, or C from the previous page. Problems involving simple interest can be solved using the formula

$$I = P \cdot R \cdot T$$

where I = interest, P = principal, R = interest rate, and T = time (in years). It is standard procedure with simple interest problems to use 360 days = 1 year.

⊘ COMMON MISTAKES

1. A common mistake is forgetting to change a percent to a decimal when working problems that involve percents in the calculations. We always change percents to decimals before doing any calculations.
2. Moving the decimal point in the wrong direction when converting percents to decimals or decimals to percents is another common mistake. Remember, *percent* means "per hundred." Rewriting a number expressed as a percent as a decimal will make the numerical part smaller.

   25% = 0.25

Write each percent as a decimal. [5.1]

1. 35%
0.35

2. 17.8%
0.178

3. 5%
0.05

4. 0.2%
0.002

Write each decimal as a percent. [5.1]

5. 0.95
95%

6. 0.8
80%

7. 0.495
49.5%

8. 1.65
165%

Write each percent as a fraction or mixed number in lowest terms. [5.1]

9. 75%

$\frac{3}{4}$

10. 4%

$\frac{1}{25}$

11. 145%

$1\frac{9}{20}$

12. 2.5%

$\frac{1}{40}$

Write each fraction or mixed number as a percent. [5.1]

13. $\frac{3}{10}$

30%

14. $\frac{5}{8}$

62.5%

15. $\frac{2}{3}$

$66\frac{2}{3}\%$

16. $4\frac{3}{4}$

475%

Solve the following problems. [5.2]

17. What number is 60% of 28?
16.8

18. What number is 122% of 55?
67.1

19. What percent of 38 is 19?
50%

20. What percent of 19 is 38?
200%

21. 24 is 30% of what number?
80

22. 16 is 8% of what number?
200

23. Survey Suppose 45 out of 60 people surveyed believe a college education will increase a person's earning potential. What percent believe this? [5.3]
75%

24. Discount A lawnmower that usually sells for $175 is marked down to $140. What is the discount? What is the discount rate? [5.5]

$35; 20%

25. **Total Price** A sewing machine that normally sells for $600 is on sale for 25% off. If the sales tax rate is 6%, what is the total price of the sewing machine if it is purchased during the sale? [5.4, 5.5]

$477

26. **Home Mortgage** If the interest rate on a home mortgage is 9%, then each month you pay 0.75% of the unpaid balance in interest. If the unpaid balance on one such loan is $60,000 at the beginning of a month, how much interest must be paid that month? [5.6]

$450

27. **Percent Increase** At the beginning of the summer, the price for a gallon of regular gasoline is $4.25. By the end of summer, the price has increased 16%. What is the new price of a gallon of regular gasoline? Round to the nearest cent. [5.5]

$4.93

28. **Percent Decrease** A gallon of regular gasoline is selling for $1.45 in September. If the price decreases 14% in October, what is the new price for a gallon of regular gasoline? Round to the nearest cent. [5.5]

$1.25

29. **Medical Costs** The table shows the average yearly cost of visits to the doctor, as reported in *USA Today*. What is the percent increase in cost from 1990 to 2000? Round to the nearest tenth of a percent. [5.5]

55.4% increase

30. **Commission** A real estate agent gets a commission of 6% on all houses he sells. If his total sales for December are $420,000, how much money does he make? [5.4]

$25,200

MEDICAL COSTS	
Year	Average Annual Cost
1990	$583
1995	$739
2000	$906
2005	$1,172

31. **Discount** A washing machine that usually sells for $300 is marked down to $240. What is the discount? What is the discount rate? [5.5]

$60; 20% off

32. **Total Price** A tennis racket that normally sells for $240 is on sale for 25% off. If the sales tax rate is 5%, what is the total price of the tennis racket if it is purchased during the sale? [5.4]

$189.00

Simplify.

1.
$$6,801$$
$$539$$
$$+\ 374$$
$$\overline{7,714}$$

2.
$$5,038$$
$$-\ 2,769$$
$$\overline{2,269}$$

3. 52(867)
45,084

4. 1,023 ÷ 15
68.2

5. 4.73)‾156.09‾
33

6. $\frac{7}{8} - \frac{5}{8}$ $\frac{1}{4}$

7. $\left(\frac{5}{6}\right)^3$ $\frac{125}{216}$

8. 4.551 + 3.08
7.631

9. 5 − 3.678
1.322

10. 1.2(0.21)
0.252

11. $\frac{7}{15} \cdot \frac{5}{14}$ $\frac{1}{6}$

12. $\frac{8}{27} \div \frac{20}{63}$ $\frac{14}{15}$

13. $\frac{3}{8} + \frac{7}{12}$ $\frac{23}{24}$

14. $8\frac{1}{5} - 5\frac{7}{10}$ $2\frac{1}{2}$

15. $9 \cdot 4\frac{2}{3}$ 42

16. Subtract $5\frac{3}{8}$ from 10.375.
5

17. Find the quotient of $1\frac{1}{2}$ and $\frac{1}{4}$.
6

18. Translate into symbols, and then simplify: Twice the sum of 2 and 9.   2(2 + 9) = 22

19. Write the ratio of 3 to 12 as a fraction in lowest terms.
$\frac{1}{4}$

20. If 1 mile is 5,280 feet, how many feet are there in 2.5 miles?   13,200 feet

21. If 1 square yard is 1,296 square inches, how many square inches are in $\frac{1}{2}$ square yard?   648 in²

22. Write $\frac{1}{8}$ as a percent.

12.5%

23. Convert 46% to a fraction.
$\frac{23}{50}$

24. Solve the equation $\frac{2}{x} = \frac{5}{8}$.

3.2

25. $3 \cdot 5^2 + 2 \cdot 4^2 - 5 \cdot 2^3$

67

26. What number is 5% of 32?

1.6

27. 55 is what percent of 275?

20%

28. 8.8 is 15% of what number?

$58\frac{2}{3}$

29. **Unit Pricing** If a six-pack of Coke costs $2.79, what is the price per can to the nearest cent?

47¢

30. **Unit Pricing** A quart of 2% reduced-fat milk contains four 1-cup servings. If the quart costs $1.61, find the price per serving to the nearest cent.

40¢

31. **Temperature** Use the formula $C = \frac{5(F - 32)}{9}$ to find the temperature in degrees Celsius when the Fahrenheit temperature is 212°F.

100°C

32. **Percent Increase** Kendra is earning $1,600 a month when she receives a raise to $1,800 a month. What is the percent increase in her monthly salary?

12.5%

33. **Driving Distance** If Ethan drives his car 230 miles in 4 hours, how far will he drive in 6 hours if he drives at the same rate?

345 miles

34. **Movie Tickets** A movie theater has a total of 250 seats. If they have a sellout crowd for a matinee and each ticket costs $7.25, how much money will ticket sales bring in that afternoon? $1,812.50

35. **Geometry** Find the perimeter and area of a square with side 8.5 inches.

P = 34 in., A = 72.25 in²

36. **Average** If a basketball team has scores of 64, 76, 98, 55, and 102 in their first five games, find the mean score.

79

37. **Hourly Pay** Jean tutors in the math lab and earns $56 in one week. If she works 8 hours that week, what is her hourly pay?

$7 per hour

Use the illustration to answer problem 38.

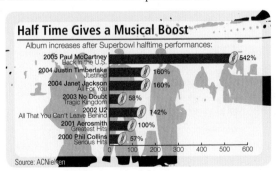

Half Time Gives a Musical Boost
Album increases after Superbowl halftime performances:

2005 Paul McCartney — Back in the U.S.   542%
2004 Justin Timberlake — Justified   160%
2004 Janet Jackson — All For You   160%
2003 No Doubt — Tragic Kingdom   58%
2002 U2 — All That You Can't Leave Behind   142%
2001 Aerosmith — Greatest Hits   100%
2000 Phil Collins — Serious Hits   57%

Source: ACNielsen

38. If Paul McCartney had sold 1.7 million albums before the Superbowl, what was the total numbers of albums sold before and after the Superbowl?   10.914 million albums

Write each percent as a decimal.

1. 18%
0.18

2. 4%
0.04

3. 0.5%
0.005

Write each decimal as a percent.

4. 0.45
45%

5. 0.7
70%

6. 1.35
135%

Write each percent as a fraction or a mixed number in lowest terms.

7. 65%
$\frac{13}{20}$

8. 146%
$1\frac{23}{50}$

9. 3.5%
$\frac{7}{200}$

Write each number as a percent.

10. $\frac{7}{20}$
35%

11. $\frac{3}{8}$
37.5%

12. $1\frac{3}{4}$
175%

13. What number is 75% of 60?
45

14. What percent of 40 is 18?
45%

15. 16 is 20% of what number?
80

16. Driver's Test On a 25-question driver's test, a student answered 23 questions correctly. What percent of the questions did the student answer correctly?
92%

17. Commission A salesperson gets an 8% commission rate on all computers she sells. If she sells $12,000 in computers in 1 day, what is her commission?
$960

18. Discount A washing machine that usually sells for $250 is marked down to $210. What is the discount? What is the discount rate?
$40; 16% off

19. Total Price A tennis racket that normally sells for $280 is on sale for 25% off. If the sales tax rate is 5%, what is the total price of the tennis racket if it is purchased during the sale?
$220.50

20. Simple Interest If $5,000 is invested at 8% simple interest for 3 months, how much interest is earned?
$100

21. Compound Interest How much interest will be earned on a savings account that pays 10% compounded annually, if $12,000 is invested for 2 years?
$2,520

22. Percent Increase A driver gets into a car accident and his insurance increases by 12%. If he paid $950 before the accident, how much is he paying now?
$1,064

Use the illustration to answer problem 23.

23. How many people said they like to play games if 6,000 people were surveyed.   2,940 people

Chapter 5 Projects

PERCENT

Group Project

Number of People   2

Time Needed   5 minutes

Equipment   Pencil, paper, and calculator.

Background   All of us spend time buying clothes and eating meals at restaurants. In all of these situations, it is good practice to check receipts. This project is intended to give you practice creating receipts of your own.

Procedure   Fill in the missing parts of each receipt.

SALES RECEIPT	
Jeans	29.99
Sales Tax (7.75%)	
Total	

SALES RECEIPT	
2 Buffet Dinners @ 9.99	19.98
Discount (10%)	
Total	

SALES RECEIPT	
Computer	400.00
Discount: 30% off	
Discounted Price	
Sales Tax (6%)	
Total	

SALES RECEIPT	
Couch	
Sales Tax (7%)	
Total	588.50

RESEARCH PROJECT

Credit-Card Debt

Credit-card companies are now offering credit-cards to college students who would not be able to get a card under normal credit-card criteria (due to lack of credit history and low income). The credit-card industry sees young people as a valuable market because research shows that they remain loyal to their first cards as they grow older. Nellie Mae, the student loan agency, found that 78% of college students had credit cards in 2000. For many of these students, lack of financial experience or education leads to serious debt. According to Nellie Mae, undergraduates with credit-cards carried an average balance of $2,748 in 2000. Half of credit-card-carrying college students don't pay their balances in full every month. Choose a credit-card and find out the minimum monthly payment and the APR (annual percentage rate). Compute the minimum monthly payment and interest charges for a balance of $2,748.

Stockbyte/SuperStock

A Glimpse of Algebra

There is really no direct extension of percent to algebra. Because that is the case, we will go back to some of the algebraic expressions we have encountered previously and evaluate them.

To evaluate an expression, such as $5x + 4$, when we know that x is 7, we simply substitute 7 for x in the expression $5x + 4$ and then simplify the result.

$$
\begin{aligned}
\text{When} \quad & x = 7 \\
\text{the expression} \quad & 5x + 4 \\
\text{becomes} \quad & 5(7) + 4 \\
\text{or} \quad & 35 + 4 \\
& = 39
\end{aligned}
$$

Here are some examples.

EXAMPLE 1 Find the value of the expression $4x + 3x - 8$ when x is 2.

SOLUTION Substituting 2 for x in the expression, we have:

$$
\begin{aligned}
4(2) + 3(2) - 8 &= 8 + 6 - 8 \\
&= 14 - 8 \\
&= 6
\end{aligned}
$$

We say that $4x + 3x - 8$ becomes 6 when x is 2.

EXAMPLE 2 Find the value of the following expression when a is 5:

$$\frac{4a + 8}{3a - 8}$$

SOLUTION Replacing a with 5 in the expression, we have:

$$
\begin{aligned}
\frac{4(5) + 8}{3(5) - 8} &= \frac{20 + 8}{15 - 8} \\
&= \frac{28}{7} \\
&= 4
\end{aligned}
$$

EXAMPLE 3 Find the value of $x^2 + 5x + 6$ when x is 4.

SOLUTION When x is 4, the expression $x^2 + 5x + 6$ becomes

$$
\begin{aligned}
(4)^2 + 5(4) + 6 &= 16 + 20 + 6 \\
&= 42
\end{aligned}
$$

PRACTICE PROBLEMS

1. Find the value of the expression $6x + 3x - 10$ when x is 3.

2. Find the value of the following expression when a is 10:

$$\frac{4a + 20}{5a - 20}$$

3. Find the value of $x^2 + 6x + 8$ when x is 3.

Answers
1. 17 **2.** 2 **3.** 35

4. Find the value of the following
   expression when x is 10 and
   y is 4:
   $$\frac{3x + y}{3x - y}$$

EXAMPLE 4 Find the value of $\frac{4x + y}{4x - y}$ when x is 5 and y is 2:

SOLUTION This time we have two different variables. We replace x with 5 and y with 2 to get

$$\frac{4(5) + 2}{4(5) - 2} = \frac{20 + 2}{20 - 2}$$
$$= \frac{22}{18}$$
$$= \frac{11}{9}$$

5. Find the value of
   $(4x + 1)(4x - 1)$ when x is 2.

EXAMPLE 5 Find the value of $(2x + 3)(2x - 3)$ when x is 4.

SOLUTION Replacing x with 4 in the expression, we have:

$$(2 \cdot 4 + 3)(2 \cdot 4 - 3) = (8 + 3)(8 - 3)$$
$$= (11)(5)$$
$$= 55$$

6. Find the value of the following
   expression when x is 5.
   $$\frac{x^3 + 8}{x + 2}$$

EXAMPLE 6 Find the value of $\frac{x^3 - 8}{x - 2}$ when x is 5:

SOLUTION We substitute 5 for x and then simplify:

$$\frac{5^3 - 8}{5 - 2} = \frac{125 - 8}{3}$$
$$= \frac{117}{3}$$
$$= 39$$

Answers

4. $\frac{17}{13}$ 5. 63   6. 19

A Glimpse of Algebra Problems

Find the value of each of the following expressions for the given values of the variables.

1. $6x + 2x - 7$ when x is 2
9

2. $8x + 10x - 5$ when x is 3
49

3. $4x + 6x + 8x$ when x is 10
180

4. $9x + 2x + 20x$ when x is 5
155

5. $\dfrac{4a + 20}{5a - 20}$ when a is 5
8

6. $\dfrac{4a + 8}{3a - 8}$ when a is 8
$2\frac{1}{2}$

7. $\dfrac{2a + 3a + 1}{4a + 5a + 3}$ when a is 3
$\dfrac{8}{15}$

8. $\dfrac{7a + a + 4}{6a + 2a + 3}$ when a is 10
$\dfrac{84}{83} = 1\frac{1}{83}$

9. $x^2 + 5x + 6$ when x is 2
20

10. $x^2 + 6x + 8$ when x is 6
80

11. $x^2 + 10x + 25$ when x is 1
36

12. $x^2 + 10x + 25$ when x is 0
25

13. $\dfrac{3x + y}{3x - y}$ when x is 5 and y is 2
$\dfrac{17}{13} = 1\frac{4}{13}$

14. $\dfrac{5x - y}{5x + y}$ when x is 10 and y is 5
$\dfrac{9}{11}$

15. $\dfrac{4x + 6y}{6x + 4y}$ when x is 5 and y is 4

$\dfrac{22}{23}$

16. $\dfrac{8x - 3y}{3x + 8y}$ when x is 5 and y is 10

$\dfrac{2}{19}$

17. $(3x + 2)(3x - 2)$ when x is 4

140

18. $(5x + 4)(5x - 4)$ when x is 2

84

19. $(2x + 3)^2$ when x is 1

25

20. $(2x + 3)^3$ when x is 2

343

21. $\dfrac{x^3 + 1}{x + 1}$ when x is 2

3

22. $\dfrac{x^3 - 1}{x - 1}$ when x is 4

21

23. $\dfrac{x^3 - 8}{x^2 + 2x + 4}$ when x is 3

1

24. $\dfrac{x^3 + 8}{x^2 - 2x + 4}$ when x is 3

5

25. $\dfrac{x^4 - 16}{x^2 + 4}$ when x is 5

21

26. $\dfrac{x^4 - 16}{x + 2}$ when x is 3

13

Descriptive Statistics

6

Image USDA Farm Service Agency
Image © 2009 TerraMetrics
Image © 2009 Digital Globe
Data SIO, NOAA, U.S. Navy, NGA, GEBCO
Google

Introduction

The United States is home to more than 300 million people of all ages, races, colors and creeds. You can group people by any number of factors: height, weight, education level, state of residence, race or, like we do below, by age. The *histogram* or *bar chart* pictured below shows the U.S. population grouped into five different age ranges. Histograms are an excellent way of presenting data in a way that is quick and easy to understand.

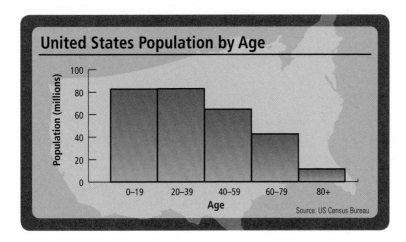

In this chapter we will continue the work you have done previously with averages, bar charts, line graphs and pie charts. You will also create some charts of your own. You will see how averages look when placed in a chart, and you will learn to make estimates and predictions from line charts you create.

Find the mean and median of each set.

1. 5, 6, 9, 4, 11
mean: 7, median: 6

2. 35, 27, 39, 31
mean: 33, median: 33

3. 14, 8, 17, 31
mean: 17.5, median: 15.5

Find the mode and range of each set.

4. 3, 6, 8, 6, 12
mode: 6, range: 9

5. 1, 9, 13, 1, 7
mode: 1, range: 12

6. 5, 6, 13, 7, 24
mode: none, range: 19

7. Create a stem-and-leaf diagram with the following data.
17, 31, 16, 28, 4, 27, 19, 23
see answers section

8. Create a histogram with 4 bins with the following data.
10, 14, 28, 21, 7, 16, 25, 34
see answers section

Getting Ready for Chapter 6

Simplify.

1. 9.3 − 7.2
2.1

2. 10.2 − 5.3
4.9

3. 12 − 4.1
7.9

4. 17 − 2.8
14.2

5. 5,478 − 309
5,169

6. 7,541 − 206
7,335

7. 270 + 63 + 4 + 9.3 + 0.9
347.2

8. 120 + 40 + 12.8 + 7.1 + 2.3
182.2

9. 18,464 + 1,733 + 2,929
23,126

10. 14,721 + 1,988 + 1,234
17,943

11. 0.6(360)
216

12. 0.25(360)
90

13. 347.2 ÷ 4
86.8

14. 182.2 ÷ 5
36.44

15. 23,126 ÷ 8
2,890.75

16. 17,943 ÷ 5
3,588.6

Change to a percent.

17. $\frac{150}{250}$
60%

18. $\frac{600}{2,400}$
25%

19. $\frac{5}{400}$
1.25%

20. $\frac{6}{400}$
1.5%

Objectives

A Find the mean given a set of numbers.

B Find the median given a set of numbers.

C Find the mode given a set of numbers.

D Find the range given a set of numbers.

Sets and Data

You will recall that previously we have worked with collections of data called sets. We defined a set as a collection of objects or things, with the objects in the set called elements or members of the set. More formally, we said:

$x \in A$ is read "x is an element (member) of set A"

If we let n represent the number of elements in a set, then we can use subscripts to write set A as follows:

$$A = \{x_1, x_2, x_3, ..., x_n\}$$

Many times we want to reduce the set to a single value called an *average*. Here is the definition from the Merriam-Webster online dictionary:

av · er · age *noun* 1 a : a single value (as a mean, mode, or median) that summarizes or represents the general significance of a set of unequal values . . .

In statistics we refer to the mean and median as *measures of central tendency*. In everyday language the word *average* can refer to the mean, the median, or the mode.

A Mean

The mean is probably the most common measure of central tendency and it refers to the arithmetic average for a set of numbers. It is typically used to describe data such as test scores, salary, and various averages having to do with sports.

> **Definition**
> The **mean** for a set of values is the sum of the values divided by the number of values.
>
> Algebraically: mean $\bar{x} = \dfrac{\{x_1 + x_2 + x_3 + ... + x_n\}}{n}$

EXAMPLE 1   An instructor at a community college earned the following salaries for the first five years of teaching. Find the mean of these salaries.

$35,344 $38,290 $39,199 $40,346 $42,866

PRACTICE PROBLEMS

1. A woman traveled the following distances on a 5-day business trip: 187 miles, 273 miles, 150 miles, 173 miles, and 227 miles. What was the mean distance the woman traveled each day?

SOLUTION   We add the five salaries and then divide by 5, the number of values in the set.

$$\text{Mean} = \frac{35{,}344 + 38{,}290 + 39{,}199 + 40{,}346 + 42{,}866}{5} = \frac{196{,}045}{5} = 39{,}209$$

The instructor's mean salary for the first five years of work is $39,209 per year.

B   Median

The median for a set of numbers is the number in the middle of the data, meaning half the numbers in the set have a value less than the median, and half the numbers in the set have a value greater than the median. Housing prices are frequently described by using a median.

> **Definition**
> The **median** of a set of numbers is the number in the middle when the set is written from least to greatest. If the set contains an even number of elements, the median is the mean of the two middle numbers.

2. Find the median for the distances in Practice Problem 1.

EXAMPLE 2   Find the median of the numbers given in Example 1.

SOLUTION   The numbers in Example 1 are already written from smallest to largest. Because there are an odd number of numbers in the set, the median is the middle number.

$$35{,}344 \quad 38{,}290 \quad \underset{\uparrow}{39{,}199} \quad 40{,}346 \quad 42{,}866$$
$$\text{median}$$

The instructor's median salary for the first five years of teaching is $39,199.

3. The selling prices of four homes are given below. Find the median.
$140,763 $242,635 $244,475
$146,320

EXAMPLE 3   The selling prices of four recently sold houses in a certain neighborhood are given below.

$$\$351{,}890 \quad \$253{,}745 \quad \$155{,}601 \quad \$157{,}412$$

Find the mean and the median for the four salaries.

SOLUTION   To find the mean, we add the four numbers and then divide by 4:

$$\frac{351{,}890 + 253{,}745 + 155{,}601 + 157{,}412}{4} = \frac{918{,}648}{4} = 229{,}662$$

To find the median, we write the numbers in order from smallest to largest. Then, because there is an even number of numbers, we average the middle two numbers to obtain the median.

$$155{,}601 \quad \underline{157{,}412 \quad 253{,}745} \quad 351{,}890$$
$$\text{median}$$
$$\downarrow$$
$$\frac{157{,}412 + 253{,}745}{2} = 205{,}578.5$$

The mean is $229,662, and the median is $205,578.50.

Answers
1. 202 miles   **2.** 187 miles
3. $194,477.50

C Mode

The mode is best used when we are looking for the most common eye color in a group of people, the most popular breed of dog in the United States, or the movie that was seen the most often. When we have a set of numbers in which one number occurs more often than the rest, that number is the mode. For example, consider this set of iPods:

Given the set of iPods, the most popular color is red. We call this the mode.

> **Definition**
> The **mode** for a set of numbers is the number that occurs most frequently. If all the numbers in the set occur the same number of times, there is no mode.

EXAMPLE 4 A math class with 18 students had the grades shown below on their first test. Find the mean, the median, and the mode.

77	87	100	65	79	87
79	85	87	95	56	87
56	75	79	93	97	92

SOLUTION To find the mean, we add all the numbers and divide by 18:

$$\text{mean} = \frac{77+87+100+65+79+87+79+85+87+95+56+87+56+75+79+93+97+92}{18}$$

$$= \frac{1,476}{18} = 82$$

To find the median, we must put the test scores in order from smallest to largest; then, because there are an even number of test scores, we must find the mean of the middle two scores.

56 56 65 75 77 79 79 79 85 87 87 87 87 92 93 95 97 100

$$\text{Median} = \frac{85 + 87}{2} = 86$$

The mode is the most frequently occurring score. Because 87 occurs 4 times, and no other scores occur that many times, 87 is the mode.

The mean is 82, the median is 86, and the mode is 87.

More Vocabulary

When we used the word *average* in the beginning of this section, we used it as a noun. It can also be used as an adjective and a verb. The following is the definition of the word *average* when it is used as a verb.

4. The students in a small math class have the following scores on their final exam. Find the mode.
56 89 74 68 97 74 68
74 88 45

av · er · age *verb* . . . 2 : to find the arithmetic mean of (a series of unequal quantities) . . .

If you are asked for the *average* of a set of numbers, the word *average* can represent the mean, the median, or the mode. When used in this way, the word *average* is a noun. However, if you are asked to *average* a set of numbers, then the word *average* is a verb, and you are being asked to find the mean of the numbers.

D Range

The range of a set of data is the difference between the least and greatest. While the range of scores on the latest math test may be high, the difference between the highest and lowest gas prices around town will be much smaller.

Average Price per Gallon of Gasoline, July 2008

MIDWEST	$4.44
ROCKY MOUNTAINS	$4.10
WEST COAST	$4.06
EAST COAST	$3.96
GULF COAST	$4.07

Source: http://www.fueleconomy.gov

From the information on average gas prices around the country, we see that the lowest average price was found in Gulf Coast states at $3.96 per gallon with the highest prices being paid on the West Coast at $4.44 per gallon. The range of this set of data is the difference between these two numbers:

$$\$4.44 - \$3.96 = \$0.48$$

We say the gas prices in July of 2008 had a range of $0.48.

> **Definition**
> The **range** for a set of numbers is the difference between the largest number and the smallest number in the sample.

EXAMPLE 5 Find the range of the test scores given in Example 4.

SOLUTION The highest score is 100, and the lowest score is 56. The range is $100 - 56 = 44$.

5. Find the range of the exam scores given in Practice Problem 4.

Getting Ready for Class

After reading through the preceding section, respond in your own words and in complete sentences.

1. The word *average* can refer to what three mathematical concepts?
2. What is the median for a set of numbers?
3. What is the mode for a set of numbers?
4. What number must we use for *x*, if the average of 6, 8, and *x* is to be 8?

Answer
5. 52

Problem Set 6.1

A   Find the mean for each set of numbers. [Examples 1, 3]

▶ **1.** 1, 2, 3, 4, 5
    3

▶ **2.** 2, 4, 6, 8, 10
    6

▶ **3.** 1, 3, 9, 11
    6

▶ **4.** 5, 7, 9, 12, 12
    9

5. 29,500, 10,650, 8,900, 15,120, 16,800
    16,194

6. 8,040, 5,505, 4,121, 9,910
    6,894

7. 12.5, 8.2, 1.8
    7.5

8. 4.1, 6.9, 2.2, 3.6
    4.2

B   Find the median for each set of numbers. [Examples 2, 3]

▶ **9.** 5, 9, 11, 13, 15
    11

▶ **10.** 42, 48, 50, 64
    49

▶ **11.** 10, 20, 50, 90, 100
    50

▶ **12.** 500, 800, 1200, 1300
    1,000

13. 900, 700, 1100
    900

14. 850, 100, 225, 480
    413.75

15. 1.0, 6.5, 3.2, 1.7, 2.1, 4.6, 3.9
    3.2

16. 2.7, 3.4, 1.8, 1.1, 2.3, 3.0
    2.5

C   Find the mode for each set of numbers. [Example 4]

▶ **17.** 14, 18, 27, 36, 18, 73
    18

▶ **18.** 11, 27, 18, 11, 72, 11
    11

▶ **19.** 98, 87, 65, 73, 82, 87, 65, 97, 87, 77
    87

▶ **20.** 3.0, 3.2, 2.5, 4.0, 3.1, 3.1, 2.6, 1.9, 1.8, 3.4, 3.1, 2.0
    3.1

21. 1, 1, 2, 3, 1, 3, 3, 2, 1, 2, 2, 3, 1
    1

22. 5, 8, 9, 9, 6, 6, 7, 7, 5, 8, 6, 8, 9, 5, 8, 8, 9
    8

▶ Selected exercises available online at www.webassign.net/brookscole

D Determine the range of the given data. [Example 5]

▶ **23.** 15, 34, 12, 25, 27
22

▶ **24.** 2.6, 4.1, 5.4, 3.9, 0.6
4.8

▶ **25.** 1.0, 3.9, 2.1, 3.6, 2.9, 3.8
2.9

▶ **26.** 12,000, 13,500, 10,120, 14,250, 11,490
4,130

27. 52, 69, 84, 81, 79, 46, 81, 73, 68
38

28. 4080, 2900, 1650, 1800, 1925, 690
3,390

▬ Applying the Concepts

▶ **29. Test Average** A student's scores for four exams in a basic math class were 79, 62, 87, and 90. What is the student's mean and median test score?
mean = 79.5; median = 83

▶ **30. Test Scores** A first-year math student had grades of 79, 64, 78, and 95 on the first four tests. What is the student's mean and median test grade?
mean = 79, median = 78.5

▶ **31. Average Salary** Over a 3-year period a woman's annual salaries were $28,000, $31,000, and $34,000. What was her mean annual salary and median annual salary for this 3-year period?
Both are $31,000.

▶ **32. Bowling** If a person has scores of 205, 222, 174, 236, 185, and 215 for six games of bowling, what is the median score for the six games?
210

Scores	
Game 1:	205
Game 2:	222
Game 3:	174
Game 4:	236
Game 5:	185
Game 6:	215

▶ **33. Average** If a basketball team has scores of 64, 76, 98, 55, 76, and 102 in their first six games, find:

a. the mean score

78.5

b. the median score

76

c. the mode of the scores

76

▶ **34. Home Sales** Below are listed the prices paid for 10 homes that sold during the month of February in a city in Texas.

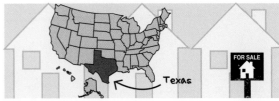

$210,000 $139,000 $122,000 $145,000 $120,000
$540,000 $167,000 $125,000 $125,000 $950,000

a. Find the mean housing price for the month.

$264,300

b. Find the median housing price for the month.

$142,000

c. Find the mode of the housing prices for the month.

$125,000

d. Which measure of "average" best describes the average housing price for the month? Explain your answer.

The median is probably the most representative measure of the "center" of these home prices. The mean is too heavily influenced by the two expensive homes.

▶ **35. Cost of College** The average cost of tuition for a 4-year public college varies by region. In 2008, the cost of tuition for different regions of the United States were the following:

$8,602, $7,785, $7,565, $6,421, $5,428, and $5,412

What was the mean and median national cost to attend college? Round to the nearest cent.

$6,868.83, $6,993

36. Cost of College The net cost of tuition is the cost that students actually pay when financial aid is taken into account. If the net cost for a 4-year public college for four different years was $2,260, $2,210, $2,130, and $2,850, what was the mean and median net cost? Round to the nearest cent.

$2,362.50, $2,235

▶ **37. Financial Aid** The following are the amounts of federal grants (in millions) that were given out from 2004 to 2008: $19,788, $20,304, $19,416, $19, 472, $20,946. What was the mean and median amount given out in federal grants? Round to the nearest dollar.

$19,985, $19,788

38. Financial Aid The following are the amounts of all financial aid distributed, this includes all grants, loans, and scholarships, from 2004 to 2008: $132,839, $143,694, $149,668, $154,044, $162,501. What was the mean and median amount of financial aid from 2004 to 2008. Round to the nearest cent.

$148,549.20, $149,668

39. Bowling Find the range of the bowling scores given in Problem 32.

62

40. Basketball Find the range of the basketball game scores given in Problem 33.

47

41. Cost of College Find the range of the average costs of tuition given in Problem 35.

$3,190

42. Cost of College Find the range of the net costs of tuition given in Problem 36.

$720

43. Financial Aid Find the range of the amounts of federal grants given in Problem 37.

$1,530

44. Financial Aid Find the range of the amounts of financial aid given in Problem 38.

$29,662

■ Extending the Concepts

45. An internet company wants to sell ad space on their web site to generate revenue, but they need to average 5,000 visitors each day for a week. Here is the data for the first six days of the week:

Day	Visitors
Monday	4,432
Tuesday	5,340
Wednesday	5,895
Thursday	6,003
Friday	5,486
Saturday	4,789

  a. How many visitors do they need on Sunday?

  3,055

  b. What type of average is this; a mean, a median, or a mode?

  Mean

46. Luke's test scores are 84, 65, 91, 75, and 92 points out of 100. He has one more test in the semester.
  a. What score does he need on the last test to average an 83 on all six tests?

  91

  b. If the teacher drops the lowest score, is it possible for Luke to average 90?

  No

47. The mean of a set of numbers is 234, and the sum of the numbers in the set is 1,638. How many numbers are in the set?

7

48. The mean of a set of numbers is 0.68, and the sum of the numbers in the set is 5.44. How many numbers are in the set?

8

6.2

Objectives

A Construct stem and leaf diagrams.

B Construct frequency tables.

C Construct histograms.

D Find the quartiles of a data set.

E Comstruct box-and-whisker plots.

The figure below shows the number of births to mothers of different ages in the United States in the year 2006.

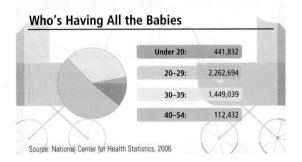

Who's Having All the Babies

Under 20:	441,832
20–29:	2,262,694
30–39:	1,449,039
40–54:	112,432

Source: National Center for Health Statistics, 2006

The data does not show the age of every mother, but rather a range of ages. By grouping the ages into different categories, the data becomes easier to analyze. For example, we can see right away that about half the babies born were born to mothers in their twenties.

In the previous section we worked with data in sets, but the sets were small enough that they didn't need to be organized before we used them. For larger sets of data, organization is very important. In this section we will study methods of organization for larger sets of data.

A Stem-and-Leaf Diagrams

Many times we will want to organize data as it is being collected. A stem-and-leaf diagram or plot is commonly used for this purpose. A stem-and-leaf diagram is a two-column display with the stems on the left and the leaves on the right. When the data is all two-digit numbers, the stems are the first digits and the leaves are the second digits. Here is an example.

EXAMPLE 1 A class of 35 students agreed to have a push-up contest. Use a stem-and-leaf diagram to display the results of the contest shown here.

25, 11, 15, 64, 33, 52, 40, 31, 23, 49, 16, 22, 20, 46, 14, 43, 51, 42, 37, 93, 61, 35, 27, 39, 48, 55, 47, 26, 58, 41, 67, 34, 30, 54, 43

SOLUTION By observing the data, we see that the values range from 11 to 93. Our stems will be the digits in the tens column, and our leaves will be the digits in the ones column.

Stem	Leaf
1	1, 5, 6, 4
2	5, 3, 2, 0, 7, 6
3	3, 1, 7, 5, 9, 4, 0
4	0, 9, 6, 3, 2, 8, 7, 1, 3
5	2, 1, 5, 8, 4
6	4, 1, 7
7	
8	
9	3

When the same data is organized and viewed in the stem-and-leaf diagram, it's clear that 11 is the least and that 93 is the greatest number of push-ups completed. The data also seems to have a shape to it, as it seems to peak in the 40's.

PRACTICE PROBLEMS

1. Use a stem-and-leaf diagram to display the data below.

14, 25, 7, 28, 36, 25, 17, 46, 9, 12, 16, 21, 26, 32, 38

Answer

1. See solutions section.

In the stem-and-leaf plot in the previous example, the 93 seems out of place, because there is no other data close to it. We call a data point that is not near other data points an *outlier*. Sometimes an outlier is significant, and sometimes it is caused by human error. Either way, an outlier is a piece of data that does not occur frequently.

B   Frequency Tables

Frequency tables allow us to record data by how often it occurs, but without keeping track of each individual piece of data. Instead, a frequency table groups the data in intervals. Data is grouped into intervals by first deciding the number of intervals, then dividing the range of data by the number of intervals to get the range for each interval.

EXAMPLE 2   The data below was collected from a survey asking 20 high school students to estimate the number of hours they spend on the internet each week. Construct a frequency table from the data.

$$11, 5, 8, 0, 12, 7, 9, 10, 22, 15, 13, 16, 5, 20, 8, 12, 16, 7, 25, 18$$

SOLUTION   The solution will consist of 6 steps. In step 1 we find the range. In step 2 we determine the length of the intervals. In step 3, we find the starting points of the intervals, and in step 4 we find the ending points of the intervals. In step 5 we tally the data and compute the frequencies. Finally, in step 6 we compute the relative frequencies.

Step 1: By examining the data, we see that the lowest value is 0 and the highest value is 25. Thus, the range is $25 - 0 = 25$.

Step 2: We decide to use 6 intervals. (In the Problem Set you will be told how many intervals to use.) We divide the range, 25, by 6 to get $4.1\overline{6}$. We round this up to the next whole number to get 5. Each interval will be 5 units.

Step 3: We start with the lowest value, 0, and add 5 each time to get the starting point of the next interval. The intervals will start at 0, $0 + 5 = 5$, $5 + 5 = 10$, $10 + 5 = 15$, $15 + 5 = 20$, and $20 + 5 = 25$. We also compute $25 + 5 = 30$ to use in the next step.

Step 4: We subtract 1 from the starting points to get the end points: $5 - 1 = 4$, $10 - 1 = 9$, $15 - 1 = 14$, $20 - 1 = 19$, $25 - 1 = 24$, and $30 - 1 = 29$. The intervals are 0 to 4, 5 to 9, 10 to 14, 15 to 19, 20 to 24, and 25 to 29. We place these in the first column of our frequency table.

Step 5: For the next column in our frequency table, we make a tally of the number of data points in each interval. Then, for the third column, we count the tallies to compute the frequencies.

Step 6: The relative frequencies, shown in the fourth column of our table, are found by dividing the frequencies by the total number of pieces of data collected, in this case 20, and expressing the result as a decimal.

Interval	Tally	Frequency	Relative Freq.
0–4	I	1	$\frac{1}{20} = 0.05$
5–9	ⅢⅡ II	7	$\frac{7}{20} = 0.35$
10–14	ⅢⅡ	5	$\frac{5}{20} = 0.25$
15–19	IIII	4	$\frac{4}{20} = 0.20$
20–24	II	2	$\frac{2}{20} = 0.10$
25–29	I	1	$\frac{1}{20} = 0.05$

2. Construct a frequency table from the data in Example 2, but using 5 intervals.

Answer

2. See solutions section.

C Histograms

Histograms offer a graphical view of data which, like with frequency tables, is grouped in intervals. Although a histogram looks like a bar chart, it is not the same. Histograms illustrate data that has been put into intervals or bins. These bins can be different widths, and therefore the areas of the rectangles in a histogram are used to measure the frequency of the data rather than the heights of the bars as in a bar chart.

 his · to · gram *noun* a representation of a frequency distribution by means of rectangles whose widths represent class intervals and whose areas are proportional to the corresponding frequencies

EXAMPLE 3 The data here show the grades for a class of 20 students on a recent algebra test. Construct a histogram from the data.

94, 65, 83, 82, 72, 98, 68, 79, 86, 62,
75, 83, 85, 92, 77, 61, 88, 79, 84, 92

SOLUTION Because these are test scores, it makes sense to have the bins cover the same intervals as a grading scale. Next, we make a frequency table without the last column to organize the data. Then, we draw the histogram with the bins along the horizontal axis and the frequencies along the vertical axis.

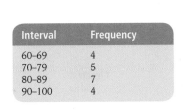

Interval	Frequency
60–69	4
70–79	5
80–89	7
90–100	4

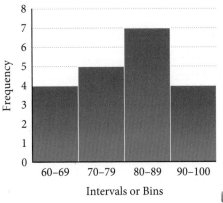

D Quartiles

Quartiles are the data points that are used to sort a set of data into fourths, or quarters, hence the name quartile. The second quartile, or Q_2, is the median of the data. The first quartile, or Q_1, is the median of the data below the second quartile, and the third quartile, or Q_3, is the midpoint of all the data above the median.

3. Use 4 intervals to create a histogram from the following data.

9, 16, 3, 27, 36, 21, 11, 10, 17, 8, 29, 30, 20, 28, 12, 23

Answer

3. See solutions section.

> **Rule How to find the quartiles of a data set**
>
> **Step 1:** Put the set in order from least to greatest.
>
> **Step 2:** Find the median of the data set. This is Q_2.
>
> **Step 3:** Find the median of the values less than (not including) the second quartile. This is Q_1.
>
> **Step 4:** Find the median of the values greater than (not including) the second quartile. This is Q_3.

4. Find the first, second, and third quartiles for the data in Practice Problem 3.

EXAMPLE 4   A math class with 18 students had the grades shown below on their first test. Find the first, second, and third quartiles.

$$77 \quad 87 \quad 100 \quad 65 \quad 79 \quad 87 \quad 79 \quad 85 \quad 87$$
$$95 \quad 56 \quad 87 \quad 56 \quad 75 \quad 79 \quad 93 \quad 97 \quad 92$$

SOLUTION   We find the quartiles by using steps 1 through 4.

Step 1: We rewrite the set in order from least to greatest;

$$56, 56, 65, 75, 77, 79, 79, 79, 85, 87, 87, 87, 87, 92, 93, 95, 97, 100$$

Step 2: Median $\dfrac{85 + 87}{2} = 86$ $Q_2 = 86$

Step 3: There are nine scores below the median score ranging from 56 to 85, with 77 as the median. $Q_1 = 77$.

Step 4: There are nine scores greater the median score ranging from 87 to 100, with 92 as the median. $Q_3 = 92$

E Box-and-Whisker Plots

Box-and-whisker plots are a visual representation of the three quartiles along with the two values, the least and the greatest, we used to find the range.

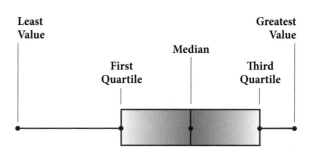

These five values are sometimes referred to as the *five-number summary*. In a box-and-whisker plot, the whiskers are the end points and the box is found from the quartiles.

EXAMPLE 5   Construct a box-and-whisker plot from the data in Example 4.

SOLUTION   To construct a box-and-whisker plot, we start with a number line which covers the range of the data.

From Example 4, our five-number summary is 56, 77, 86, 92, 100. We use these points on the number line as markers for our box-and-whisker plot.

We draw vertical lines at the first and third quartiles and use these to draw a box. We draw another vertical line for the median (second quartile).

The whiskers are made by drawing horizontal lines from the box to the smallest and largest values.

Getting Ready for Class

After reading through the preceding section, respond in your own words and in complete sentences.

1. When is a stem-and-leaf diagram a useful tool for displaying data?
2. What do we call a data point that is not close to other data points?
3. How are frequency tables and histograms related?
4. What is the relationship between quartiles and a box-and-whisker plot?

5. Construct a box-and-whisker plot from the data in Practice Problem 3.

Answer
5. See solutions section.

Problem Set 6.2

A Solve. [Example 1]

▶ **1. Test Scores** Create a stem-and-leaf diagram with the following scores students received on the ACT.

32 24 19 30 27 22 30
31 29 18 20 34 26

Stem	Leaf
1	9, 8
2	4, 7, 2, 9, 0, 6
3	2, 0, 0, 1, 4

▶ **2. Relay Race** At a 24-hour relay, these were the number of laps around a several-mile course each team completed. Create a stem-and-leaf diagram from the data.

29 34 74 55 36 51 62 98 56 67 69
73 57 78 62 82 63 84 76 88 61 99

Stem	Leaf
2	9
3	4, 6
4	
5	5, 1, 6, 7
6	2, 7, 9, 2, 3, 1
7	4, 3, 8, 6
8	2, 4, 8
9	8, 9

▶ **3. Art Show** The college art club hosted an art show for a fundraiser. The following are the prices different works of art sold for. Create a stem-and-leaf diagram from the data.

16 34 85 67 84 52 94 35 72 58 46
98 83 76 51 27 29 48 73 51 35 86

Stem	Leaf
1	6
2	7, 9
3	4, 5, 5
4	6, 8
5	2, 8, 1, 1
6	7
7	2, 6, 3
8	5, 4, 3, 6
9	4, 8

▶ **4. Auction** A local club held an auction. The final bids on several equally valued prizes were as follows. Create a stem-and-leaf diagram.

35 64 58 63 71 68 52
39 46 63 43 59 53 65

Stem	Leaf
3	5, 9
4	6, 3
5	8, 2, 9, 3
6	4, 3, 8, 3, 5
7	1

5. Temperature The following are the average daytime temperatures for the month of December for a coastal town. Use the data to create a stem-and-leaf diagram.

60 61 58 54 52 47 53 54 63 53 47
59 41 40 39 35 58 43 48 60 56 52
50 45 64 46 40 42 34 43 36

Stem	Leaf
3	9, 5, 4, 6
4	7, 7, 1, 0, 3, 8, 5, 6, 0, 2, 3
5	8, 4, 2, 3, 4, 3, 9, 8, 6, 2, 0
6	0, 1, 3, 0, 4

6. Art Classes A community center starts offering art classes. These are the ages of the students in the art class. Use this data to create a stem-and-leaf diagram.

16 34 14 32 57 65 53 61 52
58 64 38 46 35 66 73 58 64
56 53 51 43 62 43 36 24

Stem	Leaf
1	6, 4
2	4
3	4, 2, 8, 5, 6
4	6, 3, 3
5	7, 3, 2, 8, 8, 6, 3, 1
6	5, 1, 4, 6, 4, 2
7	3

▶ Selected exercises available online at www.webassign.net/brookscole

B [Example 2]

▶ **7. Basketball** The college basketball team just finished their season. These were their game scores. Use the data to make a frequency table with five intervals.

76 58 82 47 73 76 81 93 68 76
72 84 64 59 67 74 80 69 84 76

Interval	Tally	Frequency	Relative Freq.
47-56	I	1	$\frac{1}{20} = 0.05$
57-66	III	3	$\frac{3}{20} = 0.15$
67-76	IIII IIII	10	$\frac{10}{20} = 0.5$
77-86	IIII	5	$\frac{5}{20} = 0.25$
87-96	I	1	$\frac{1}{20} = 0.05$

▶ **8. Incomes** The data shows the annual incomes in thousands of a group of engineers. Use the data to create a frequency table. Use five intervals.

63 75 63 58 74 72 77 54
67 62 58 59 66 68 76

Interval	Tally	Frequency	Relative Freq.
54-58	III	3	$\frac{3}{15} = 0.2$
59-63	IIII	4	$\frac{4}{15} = 0.27$
64-68	III	3	$\frac{3}{15} = 0.2$
69-73	I	1	$\frac{1}{15} = 0.07$
74-78	IIII	4	$\frac{4}{15} = 0.27$

▶ **9. Golf Scores** The local golf course hosted a fundraiser tournament to raise money for a local school. The data set is the final scores of each of the participants. Use the data to create a histogram with five intervals.

69 72 76 85 67 73 78 86 81 96 103
87 96 84 100 79 84 72 79 97 84 86

▶ **10. Oil Prices** The data shows the price per barrel of oil rounded to the nearest dollar over the last 20 years. Use the data to construct a histogram with seven intervals.

18 23 20 19 17 16 17 20 19 12
17 27 23 22 28 38 50 58 64 98

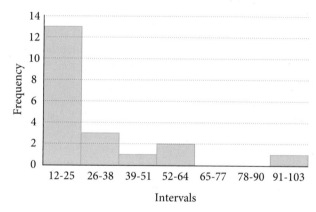

C [Example 3]

▶ **11. Candy** The frequency table shows the number of M&M's® in a bag of peanut M&M's®. Use the table to work the following problems.

Interval	Frequency
13-16	4
17-20	6
21-24	7
25-28	5

a. Create a histogram from the frequency table.

b. What is the relative frequency of bags containing 17 to 20 M&M's®?

$\frac{6}{22} = 0.27$

c. What is the relative frequency of bags containing 21 to 28 M&M's®?

$\frac{12}{22} = 0.55$

▶ **12. Test Scores** The following stem-and-leaf diagram shows test scores. Use the diagram to answer the questions.

Stem	Leaf
1	9
2	
3	
4	3, 8
5	
6	
7	8, 6, 4, 2
8	3, 4, 6, 6, 7, 8
9	1, 7, 6, 9, 3

a. What was the lowest test score?

19

b. What was the highest test score?

99

c. What was the median test score?

85

d. What is the range of the scores?

80

▶ **13. Watching TV** The frequency table shows the hours per week that each person in a class watches television. Use the table to work the following problems.

Interval	Frequency
0-2	2
3-5	10
6-9	7
10-12	2

a. Create a histogram from the frequency table.

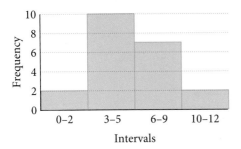

b. How many students are in the class?

21

c. What is the relative frequency of students that watch 3 to 5 hours of television?

$\frac{10}{21} = 0.48$

d. What is the relative frequency of students that watch 6 hours of television or more?

$\frac{9}{21} = 0.43$

▶ **14. Midterm Scores** The stem-and-leaf diagram shows the scores for a midterm. Use the diagram to answer the following questions.

Stem	Leaf
1	6
2	3
3	3, 7
4	
5	
6	
7	2, 6, 3, 6
8	5, 4, 3, 6, 9
9	4, 8, 9

a. What is the range of the test scores?

83

b. What is the mode?

76

c. What is the median of the test scores?

79.5

15. Graduate Students The stem-and-leaf diagram shows the age of students in a graduate class. Use the diagram to answer the following questions.

Stem	Leaf
2	2, 6, 7, 8
3	3, 4, 6, 7, 9
4	1, 3, 5
5	1

a. What is the range of their ages?

29

b. What is the median of their ages?

36

16. Football Scores The stem-and-leaf diagram shows the football scores for a school's football team. Use the stem-and-leaf diagram to create a six-interval histogram.

Stem	Leaf
0	7
1	0, 9
2	1, 8, 6
3	3, 1, 5, 4
4	2, 0

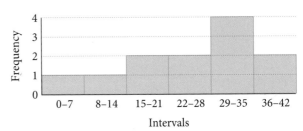

D Name the first, second, and third quartiles of each data set. [Example 4]

▶ **17.** 16, 24, 36, 20, 19, 32, 18, 23, 26

Q1: 18.5   Q2: 23   Q3: 29

18. 10, 16, 24, 23, 27, 30, 21

Q1: 16   Q2: 23   Q3: 27

▶ **19.** 1.3, 4.5, 0.9, 3.6, 2.8, 1.9

Q1: 1.3   Q2: 2.35   Q3: 3.6

20. 49, 39, 46, 52, 61, 39, 51, 42

Q1: 40.5   Q2: 47.5   Q3: 51.5

E   Use the data to create a box-and-whisker plot. [Example 5]

▶ **21.** 78, 64, 91, 83, 64, 85

22. 34, 25, 16, 41, 21, 36, 27, 39

Given the box-and-whisker plot, answer the following questions.

23. Write an inequality that shows where half the data numbers lie.

$x > 75$ or $x < 75$ or $70 < x < 85$

24. Write an inequality that shows where the top fourth of the data lies.

$x > 85$

▶ **25.** One quarter of the data numbers are less than what number?

70

26. Three quarters of the data numbers are less than what number?

85

▶ **27.** Half of the data numbers are greater than what number?

75

28. One quarter of the data numbers are greater than what number?

85

Given the box-and-whisker plot, answer the following questions.

29. Write an inequality that shows where half the data numbers lie.

$x > 85$ or $x < 85$ or $75 < x < 90$

▶ **30.** Write an inequality that shows where the top fourth of the data lies.

$x > 90$

31. One quarter of the data numbers are less than what number?

75

▶ **32.** Three quarters of the data numbers are less than what number?

90

33. Half of the data numbers are greater than what number?

85

▶ **34.** One quarter of the data numbers are greater than what number?

90

▶ **35. Quiz Scores** The following data are the class scores on a 5-point quiz. Use the data to build a box-and-whisker plot.

5, 4.5, 3.5, 3, 2, 5, 4.5, 4, 1.5, 1, 5, 4.5, 4.5, 3.5, 3, 3.5, 2.5, 1, 1.5, 2, 2, 5

36. Shoe Sizes The following data are the sizes of shoes that each person in class wears. Use the data to build a box-and-whisker plot.

5.5, 6, 12, 6.5, 10, 10.5, 7.5, 7.5, 13.5, 5, 10, 6, 8.5, 13, 6.5, 11.5, 9.5, 9, 8.5, 11, 7, 8, 5.5, 9, 7.5, 8.5, 10, 6.5, 7, 5.5, 5

6.3

Pie charts are another way in which to visualize numerical information. They lend themselves well to information that adds up to 100% and are very common in the world around us. In fact, it is hard to pick up a newspaper or magazine without seeing a pie chart. As the diagram below shows, even a computer will represent the amount of free space and used space on one of its disks by using a pie chart.

```
Local Disk (C:) Properties                           ? X

General | Tools | Hardware | Sharing | Quota |

  [disk icon]   [                              ]

Type:          Local Disk
File system:   NTFS

  ■ Used space:    11,549,433,856 bytes    10.7 GB
  ■ Free space:    28,441,874,432 bytes    26.4 GB

  Capacity:        39,991,308,288 bytes    37.2 GB

                    [ pie chart ]

                                       [ Disk Cleanup ]
              Drive C

  □ Compress drive to save disk space
  ☑ Allow Indexing Service to index this disk for fast file searching

              [  OK  ]   [ Cancel ]   [ Apply ]
```

A Reading a Pie Chart

Some of this introductory material will be review. We want to begin our study of pie charts by reading information from pie charts.

EXAMPLE 1 The pie chart shows the class rank of the members of a drama club. Use the pie chart to answer the following questions.

    a. Find the total membership of the club.

    b. Find the ratio of freshmen to total number of members.

    c. Find the ratio of seniors to juniors.

SOLUTION   **a.** To find the total membership in the club, we add the numbers in all sections of the pie chart.

$$9 + 11 + 15 + 10 = 45 \text{ members}$$

    b. The ratio of freshmen to total members is

$$\frac{\text{number of freshmen}}{\text{total number of members}} = \frac{11}{45}$$

    c. The ratio of seniors to juniors is

$$\frac{\text{number of seniors}}{\text{number of juniors}} = \frac{9}{15} = \frac{3}{5}$$

PRACTICE PROBLEMS

1. Work Example 1 again if one more junior joins the club.

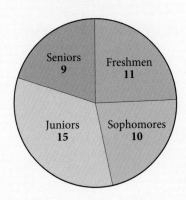

2. Work Example 2 again if 600 people responded to the survey.

Time Spent Checking E-mail

76% Daily
1% Less than once a week
23% Weekly

Source: UCLA Center for Communication Policy

3. Construct a pie chart that shows the used space and free space on a 256-MB flash memory stick that contains 102 MB of data.

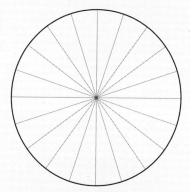

PIE CHART TEMPLATE   Each slice is 5% of the area of the circle.

Answer
2. a. 456 people   **b.** 144 people

 EXAMPLE 2   The pie chart shows the results of a survey on how often people check their e-mail. Use the pie chart to answer the following questions. Suppose 500 people participated in the survey.

a. How many people in the survey check their e-mail daily?

b. How many people check their e-mail once a week or less often?

SOLUTION **a.** To find out how many people in the survey check their e-mail daily, we need to find 76% of 500.

0.76(500) = 380 of the people surveyed check their e-mail daily.

b. The people checking their e-mail weekly or less often account for 23% + 1% = 24%. To find out how many of the 500 people are in this category, we must find 24% of 500.

0.24(500) = 120 of the people surveyed check their e-mail weekly or less often.

B   Constructing Pie Charts

EXAMPLE 3   Construct a pie chart that shows the free space and used space for a 256-MB flash memory stick that contains 77 MB of data.

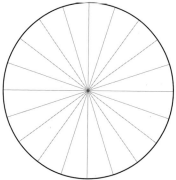

EDGE Tech Corp

SOLUTION 1   Using a Template   As mentioned previously, pie charts are constructed with percents. Therefore we must first convert data to percents. To find the percent of used space, we divide the amount of used space by the amount of total space. We have

$$\frac{77}{256} \approx 0.30078 \text{ which is 30\% to the nearest percent}$$

The area of each section of the template on the lower left is 5% of the area of the whole circle. If we shade 6 sections of the template, we will have shaded 30% of the area of the whole circle.

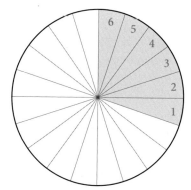

PIE CHART TEMPLATE   Each slice is 5% of the area of the circle.

CREATING A PIE CHART   To shade 30% of the circle, we shade 6 sections of the template.

The shaded area represents 30%, which is the amount of used disk space. The rest of the circle must represent the 70% free space on the disk. Shading each area with a different color and labeling each, we have our pie chart.

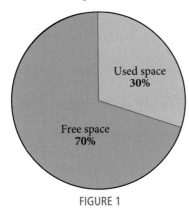

FIGURE 1

SOLUTION 2   Using a Protractor   Since a pie chart is a circle, and a circle contains 360°, we must now convert our data to degrees. We do this by multiplying our percents in decimal form by 360. We have

$$(0.30)360° = 108°$$

Now we place a protractor on top of a circle. First we draw a line from the center of the circle to 0° as shown in Figure 2. Now we measure and mark 108° from our starting point, as shown in Figure 3.

FIGURE 2   FIGURE 3

Finally we draw a line from the center of the circle to this mark, as shown in Figure 4. Then we shade and label the two regions as shown in Figure 5.

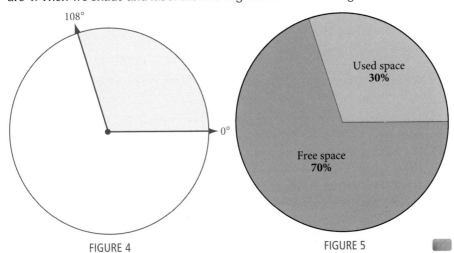

FIGURE 4   FIGURE 5

Answer
3. See solutions section.

4. The table below shows how the expenses for a paperback novel are divided. Use the information in the table to construct a pie chart.

Expense	Percent of Price
Bookstore	45%
Publisher	50%
Author	5%

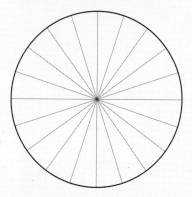

PIE CHART TEMPLATE Each slice is 5% of the area of the circle.

EXAMPLE 4 Construct a pie chart from the information in the following table.

WHERE DOES YOUR TEXTBOOK MONEY GO?	
Expense	**Percent of Price**
Bookstore	40%
Publisher	45%
Author	15%

SOLUTION Since our template uses sections that each represent 5% of the circle, we shade 8 sections, representing 40%, for the bookstore's share. Then we shade 9 sections, representing 45% for the publisher's share. We should have 3 sections remaining, which represent the 15% share going to the author.

  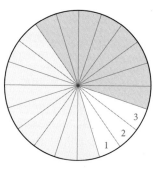

CREATING A PIE CHART

To shade 45% of the circle, we shade 9 sections of the template.

We are left with 3 sections. This represents the 15% share going to the author.

We label each section with the appropriate information, and our pie chart is complete.

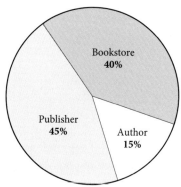

Getting Ready for Class

After reading through the preceding section, respond in your own words and in complete sentences.

1. If a circle is divided into 20 equal slices, then each of the slices is what percent of the total area enclosed by the circle?

2. If a 250 MB computer drive contains 75 MB of data, then how much of the drive is free space?

3. If a 250 MB computer drive contains 75 MB of data, then what percent of the drive contains data?

4. Explain how you would construct a pie chart of monthly expenses for a person who spends $700 on rent, $200 on food, and $100 on entertainment.

Answer
4. See solutions section.

Problem Set 6.3

A [Examples 1, 2]

▶ 1. **High School Seniors with Jobs** The pie chart shows the results of surveying 200 high school seniors to find out how many hours they worked per week at a job.

High School Seniors with Jobs

a. Find the ratio of students who work more than 15 hours a week to total students.

$\frac{41}{100}$

b. Find the ratio of students who don't have a job to students who work more than 15 hours a week.

$\frac{38}{41}$

c. Find the ratio of students with jobs to total students.

$\frac{31}{50}$

d. Find the ratio of students with jobs to students without jobs.

$\frac{31}{19}$

▶ 2. **Favorite Dip Flavor** The pie chart shows the results of a survey on favorite dip flavor.

a. What is the most preferred dip flavor?

Ranch

Favorite Dip Flavor

b. Which dip flavor is preferred second most?

Onion

c. Which dip flavor is least preferred?

Dill

d. What percentage of people preferred ranch?

56%

e. What percentage of people preferred onion or dill?

44%

f. If 50 people responded to the survey, how many people preferred ranch?

28 people

g. If 50 people responded to the survey, how many people preferred dill? (Round your answer to the nearest whole number.)

Approximately 4 people

▶ 3. **Food Dropped on the Floor** The pie chart shows the results of a survey about eating food that has been dropped on the floor. Participants were asked whether they eat food that has been on the floor for 3, 5, or 10 seconds.

a. What percentage of people say it is not safe to eat food dropped on the floor?

78%

Food Dropped On the Floor

b. What percentage of people believe the "three-second rule"?

10%

c. What percentage of people will eat food that stays on the floor for five seconds or less?

18%

d. What percentage of people will eat foot that stays on the floor for ten seconds or less?

22%

▶ Selected exercises available online at www.webassign.net/brookscole

▶ **4. Talking to Our Dogs** A survey showed that most dog owners talk to their dogs.

    a. What percentage of dog owners say they never talk to their dogs?

       1%

    b. What percentage of dog owners say they talk to their dogs all the time?

       71%

    c. What percentage of dog owners say they talk to their dogs sometimes or not often?

       28%

Talking To Our Dogs

- All the time
- Sometimes
- Not often
- Never

▶ **5. Monthly Car Payments** Suppose 3,000 people responded to a survey on car loan payments, the results of which are shown in the pie chart. Find the number of people whose monthly payments would be the following:

    a. $700 or more

       240 people

    b. Less than $300

       960 people

    c. $500 or more

       750 people

    d. $300 to $699

       1,800 people

Monthly Car Payments

- Less than $300
- $300-$499
- $500-$699
- $700 or more

▶ **6. Where Workers Say Germs Lurk** A survey asked workers where they thought the most germ-contaminated spot in the workplace was. Suppose the survey took place at a large company with 4,200 employees. Use the pie chart to determine the number of employees who would vote for each of the following as the most germ-contaminated areas.

    a. Keyboards

       420 employees

    b. Doorknobs

       1,218 employees

    c. Restrooms or other

       966 employees

    d. Telephones or doorknobs

       2,688 employees

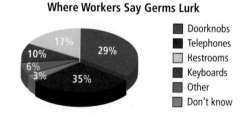

Where Workers Say Germs Lurk

- Doorknobs
- Telephones
- Restrooms
- Keyboards
- Other
- Don't know

B [Examples 3, 4]

▶ **7. Grade Distribution** Student scores, for a class of 20, on a recent math test are shown in the table below. Construct a pie chart that shows the number of A's, B's, and C's earned on the test. Use the template provided here or use a protractor.

GRADE DISTRIBUTION	
Grade	Number
A	5
B	8
C	7
Total	20

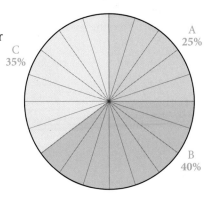

PIE CHART TEMPLATE   Each slice is 5% of the area of the circle.

▶ **8. Building Sizes** The Lean and Mean Gym Company recently ran a promotion for their four locations in the county. The table shows the locations along with the amount of square feet at each location. Use the information in the table to construct a pie chart, using the template provided here or using a protractor.

GYM LOCATION AND SIZE	
Location	Square Feet
Downtown	35,000
Uptown	85,000
Lakeside	25,000
Mall	75,000
Total	220,000

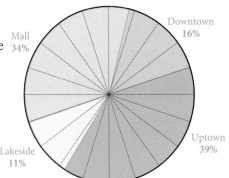

PIE CHART TEMPLATE   Each slice is 5% of the area of the circle.

▶ **9. Room Sizes** Scott and Amy are building their dream house. The size of the house will be 2,400 square feet. The table below shows the size of each room. Use the information in the table to construct a pie chart, using the template provided here or using a protractor.

ROOM SIZES	
Room	Square Feet
Kitchen	400
Dining room	310
Bedrooms	890
Living room	600
Bathrooms	200
Total	2,400

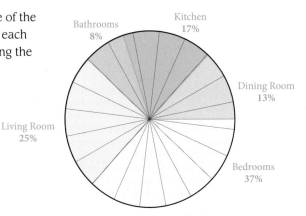

PIE CHART TEMPLATE   Each slice is 5% of the area of the circle.

▶ **10. Airline Seating** The table below gives the number of seats in each of the three classes of seating on an American Airlines Boeing 777 airliner. Create a pie chart from the information in the table.

AIRLINE SEATING	
Seating Class	Number Of Seats
First	18
Business	42
Coach	163

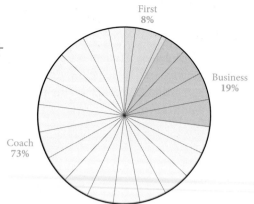

PIE CHART TEMPLATE   Each slice is 5% of the area of the circle.

▪ Maintaining Your Skills

Multiply.

11. $8 \cdot \dfrac{1}{3}$

$\dfrac{8}{3}$, or $2\dfrac{2}{3}$

12. $9 \cdot \dfrac{1}{3}$

3

13. $25 \cdot \dfrac{1}{1,000}$

$\dfrac{1}{40}$

14. $25 \cdot \dfrac{1}{100}$

$\dfrac{1}{4}$

15. $36.5 \cdot \dfrac{1}{100} \cdot 10$

$\dfrac{73}{20}$, or $3\dfrac{13}{20}$

16. $36.5 \cdot \dfrac{1}{1,000} \cdot 100$

$\dfrac{73}{20}$, or $3\dfrac{13}{20}$

17. $248 \cdot \dfrac{1}{10} \cdot \dfrac{1}{10}$

$\dfrac{62}{25}$, or $2\dfrac{12}{25}$

18. $969 \cdot \dfrac{1}{10} \cdot \dfrac{1}{10}$

$\dfrac{969}{100}$, or $9\dfrac{69}{100}$

19. $48 \cdot \dfrac{1}{12} \cdot \dfrac{1}{3}$

$\dfrac{4}{3}$, or $1\dfrac{1}{3}$

20. $56 \cdot \dfrac{1}{12} \cdot \dfrac{1}{2}$

$\dfrac{7}{3}$, or $2\dfrac{1}{3}$

6.4

Objectives

A Find the sample space for an experiment.

B Compute theoretical probabilities when the outcomes are equally likely.

C Compute observed probabilities

You know that your chances of winning the Lottery jackpot are slim. In fact, if you were to assign a probability to winning the lottery you would say it was close to 0. You have an intuitive sense of probabilities already. In this section we want to extend what you know about probabilities and lay the foundation for a systematic study of the topic.

A Sample Space for an Experiment

> **Definition**
> When working with probabilities, an **experiment** is an activity for which the outcome is unknown. The **sample space** for an experiment is the set of all possible outcomes. An **event** is a subset of the sample space.

EXAMPLE 1 You toss a coin in the air and observe the side facing up when it lands. Give the sample space.

SOLUTION The sample space is the set of all possible outcomes.

Experiment:
Toss a coin and observe the side facing up when it comes to rest.

Outcomes:
Heads (H) or tails (T)

Sample Space = {H, T}

B Equally Likely Outcomes

When each outcome of an experiment is just as likely to occur as any other outcome, then we say we are working with *equally likely outcomes*. In the coin-toss experiment above, each outcome, heads and tails, is just as likely to occur as the other, so they are equally likely outcomes. Likewise, if we roll a six-sided die and observe the number showing on the top side when it comes to rest, the possible outcomes (the numbers 1 through 6) are equally likely outcomes.

Answer
1. S = {R, G, B, Y}

2. What is the sample space of rolling a 12-sided die?

EXAMPLE 2 You roll a regular six-sided die and observe the number showing on the top side of the die when it comes to rest. Give the sample space.

SOLUTION The sample space is the set of all possible outcomes.

Experiment:
Roll a six-sided die and observe the number facing up when it comes to rest.

Outcomes:
Sample Space = $S = \{1, 2, 3, 4, 5, 6\}$.

Theoretical Probabilities

We can associate a number with the likelihood that an event will occur. Intuitively we know that heads is just as likely to occur as tails in the coin-toss experiment. That is, if we repeat this experiment many times, we will expect to see a head $\frac{1}{2}$ of the time and a tail $\frac{1}{2}$ of the time. We use an uppercase P to represent probability. Here are the probabilities associated with the coin-toss experiment:

$$P(\text{H}) = \frac{1}{2} \text{ and } P(\text{T}) = \frac{1}{2}$$

Definition

For an experiment with equally likely outcomes, the probability that event A occurs is the number of outcomes in A divided by the total number of outcomes. In symbols:

$$P(A) = \frac{\text{Number of outcomes in } A}{\text{Total number of outcomes}}$$

3. You roll a 12-sided die. What is the probability of observing

  a. a number greater than 7?

  b. an odd number?

  c. a multiple of 3?

EXAMPLE 3 You roll a die and observe the number showing on the top side when the die comes to rest. What is the probability of observing

  a. a 4?

  b. an even number?

  c. a number other than 4?

SOLUTION The sample space is $S = \{1, 2, 3, 4, 5, 6\}$.

  a. There is only one outcome that is a 4, so

$$P(4) = \frac{\text{Number of 4's}}{\text{Total number of outcomes}} = \frac{1}{6}$$

  b. Event A is rolling an even number, so $A = \{2, 4, 6\}$.

$$P(A) = \frac{\text{Number of even numbers}}{\text{Total number of outcomes}} = \frac{3}{6} = \frac{1}{2}$$

  c. Of the six outcomes in the sample space, five are not 4.

$$P(\text{not } 4) = \frac{\text{Number of non 4's}}{\text{Total number of outcomes}} = \frac{5}{6}$$

Answer

2. $S = \{1, 2, 3, 4, 5, 6, 7, 8, 9, 10, 11, 12\}$

> **Rule Probability Rule 1**
> If A is an event, then the probability that A will occur is denoted $P(A)$ and will always satisfy the condition
>
> $$0 \leq P(A) \leq 1$$

If $P(A) = 0$, then A will never occur. If $P(A) = 1$, then A is certain to occur. Events with probabilities closer to 1 are more likely to occur than events with probabilities closer to 0. The closer a probability is to 1, the more likely it is to occur. Likewise, the closer a probability is to 0, the less likely it is to occur.

EXAMPLE 4

A box contains five iPods, three of which are blue and two of which are red.

Without looking, you reach in the box and take out an iPod. What is the probability that

    a. it is blue?   **b.** it is red?   **c.** it is black?

SOLUTION

    a. $P(\text{blue}) = \dfrac{\text{Number of blue iPods}}{\text{Total number of iPods}} = \dfrac{3}{5}$

    b. $P(\text{red}) = \dfrac{\text{Number of red iPods}}{\text{Total number of iPods}} = \dfrac{2}{5}$

    c. $P(\text{black}) = \dfrac{\text{Number of black iPods}}{\text{Total number of iPods}} = \dfrac{0}{5} = 0$

EXAMPLE 5

Two dice are rolled at the same time and the numbers showing are observed. Find the following.

    a. The sample space
    b. $P(\text{sum} = 7)$
    c. $P(\text{sum} = 12)$
    d. $P(\text{the sum is an even number})$
    e. $P(\text{both dice show the same number})$

SOLUTION

    a. Assuming the first die is white and the second die is black, we can draw a diagram of the sample space. Notice how we can list the outcomes in the diagram by using ordered pairs, where the first number is the outcome of the white die, and the second number is the outcome of the black die.

---

4. If another blue iPod is added to the box in Example 4, what is the new probability that the iPod you choose is
    a. blue?
    b. red?
    c. blue or red?

5. Two dice are rolled as in Example 5. Find,
    a. $P(\text{sum} \geq 7)$.
    b. $P(\text{sum} = 9)$.
    c. $P(\text{both show an even number})$.

Answers

3. a. $\frac{5}{12}$ **b.** $\frac{1}{2}$ **c.** $\frac{1}{3}$

4. a. $\frac{2}{3}$ **b.** $\frac{1}{3}$ **c.** 1

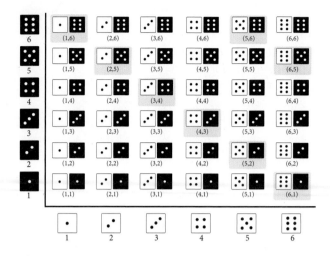

b. We can obtain a sum of 7 in six different ways: (1, 6), (6, 1), (2, 5), (5, 2), (3, 4), (4, 3).

$$P(A) = \frac{\text{Number of ways to get a sum of 7}}{\text{Total number of outcomes}} = \frac{6}{36} = \frac{1}{6}$$

c. We can obtain a sum of 12 in only one way: (6, 6).

$$P(A) = \frac{\text{Number of ways to get a sum of 12}}{\text{Total number of outcomes}} = \frac{1}{36}$$

d. We go to the table and count the numbers of ways an even sum can occur.

$$P(A) = \frac{\text{Number of ways to get an even sum}}{\text{Total number of outcomes}} = \frac{18}{36} = \frac{1}{2}$$

e. Both dice show the same number (i.e., doubles are rolled) for the outcomes (1, 1), (2, 2), (3, 3), (4, 4), (5, 5), and (6, 6).

$$P(A) = \frac{\text{Number of ways to roll doubles}}{\text{Total number of outcomes}} = \frac{6}{36} = \frac{1}{6}$$

Playing Cards

A regular deck of cards contains 52 cards in four suits: hearts (♥), clubs (♣), diamonds (♦), and spades (♠). The numbered cards are numbered 2 through 10. The face cards are jacks, queens, and kings. There are four aces.

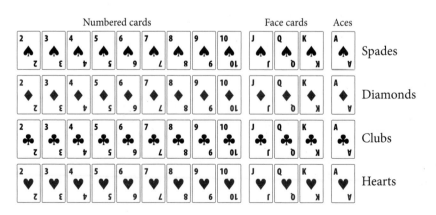

EXAMPLE 6 One card is drawn from a regular deck of 52 cards. Find the probabilities associated with the following events.

    a. The card is an ace.
    b. The card is a face card.
    c. The card is a heart.
    d. The card is not an ace.

SOLUTION

    a. Since there are four aces in the deck we have

$$P(\text{ace}) = \frac{\text{Number of aces}}{\text{Total number of cards}} = \frac{4}{52} = \frac{1}{13}$$

    b. Since there are 12 face cards in the deck we have

$$P(\text{face card}) = \frac{\text{Number of face cards}}{\text{Total number of cards}} = \frac{12}{52} = \frac{3}{13}$$

    c. Since there are 13 hearts in the deck we have

$$P(\text{heart}) = \frac{\text{Number of hearts}}{\text{Total number of cards}} = \frac{13}{52} = \frac{1}{4}$$

    d. Since there are four aces in the deck, there must be $52 - 4 = 48$ cards that are not aces.

$$P(\text{not ace}) = \frac{\text{Number of non-aces}}{\text{Total number of cards}} = \frac{48}{52} = \frac{12}{13}$$

C Observed Probabilities

The probabilities we have discussed above are all theoretical probabilities. *Observed probabilities* are taken from actual data. For example, if you toss a coin 100 times, would you expect to get 50 heads and 50 tails? Probably not. If you repeated the experiment over and over again, you would get an overall probability that was close to $\frac{1}{2}$ for either heads or tails. But for any experiment of tossing a coin 100 times, you wouldn't expect exactly 50 heads and 50 tails.

EXAMPLE 7 The pie chart shows the percent of college students who prefer Google, Yahoo!, or Bing, to search the Internet. According to these results, if a college student was chosen at random, answer the questions below.

    a. What is the probability of using Google for Internet searches?
    b. What is the probability of using Yahoo! or Google for Internet searches?
    c. What is the probability of not using Google for Internet searches?

---

6. If one card is drawn from a deck of 52 cards, find the probability that the card is

    a. black.

    b. an even number.

    c. a king or an ace.

7. Using the chart from Example 7, what is the probability of

    a. using Bing for Internet searches?

    b. using Bing or Yahoo! for Internet searches?

    c. not using Bing for Internet searches?

Answers

6. a. $\frac{1}{2}$ **b.** $\frac{5}{13}$ **c.** $\frac{2}{13}$

SOLUTION   Since percent means per hundred, we can write these percents as decimals or fractions for the probabilities.

a. $P(\text{Google}) = 0.65 = \dfrac{65}{100}$

b. $P(\text{Yahoo!} + \text{Google}) = 0.28 + 0.65 = 0.93 = \dfrac{93}{100}$

c. Since we know that Google has a 0.65 probability, we subtract 0.65 from 1, which is our sample space, to find $P(\text{not Google})$:

$$P(\text{not Google}) = 1.00 - 0.65 = 0.35 = \dfrac{35}{100}$$

8. Use the table from Example 8 to find the probability that a student

a. is undecided or has nothing planned.

b. plans to join the military.

c. isn't going to go to a 2-year college.

EXAMPLE 8   The following table shows the future plans for a graduating class of 300 high school seniors.

Plan	Number of Students
4-year College	259
2-year College	11
Technical/Vocational School	9
Military	13
Undecided	7
Nothing	1

If a senior from the high school is selected at random, find the probabilities of the following events. Give your answers as both reduced fractions and decimals.

a. The student plans to attend a 4-year college.

b. The student plans to attend a 2-year college or technical/vocational school.

SOLUTION

a. Of the 300 students, 259 plan to attend a 4-year college. The probability is

$$P(\text{4-year college}) = \frac{259}{300} \approx 0.86$$

b. Since 11 students plan to attend a 2-year college and 9 students plan to attend technical or vocational school, the probability is

$P(\text{2-year college or technical/vocational school})$

$$= \frac{11 + 9}{300} = \frac{20}{300} = \frac{1}{15} \approx 0.07$$

Getting Ready for Class

After reading through the preceding section, respond in your own words and in complete sentences.

1. How do we explain an event when working with probability?

2. Give an example, other than a coin toss, of an equally likely outcome.

3. How are theoretical probabilities different from observed probabilities?

4. When you roll a set of dice 50 times and then calculate the results, are you computing a theoretical or an observed probability?

Answers

7. a. $\dfrac{7}{100}$ **b.** $\dfrac{35}{100}$ **c.** $\dfrac{93}{100}$

8. a. 0.027 **b.** 0.04 **c.** 0.96

Problem Set 6.4

B [Examples 3–6]

▶ **1. Rolling Dice** You roll a six-sided die and observe the number showing on the top side when the die comes to rest. What is the probability of observing
   a. an odd number?
   $\frac{1}{2}$
   b. a number greater than 6?
   0
   c. a number less than 7?
   1
   d. a prime number?
   $\frac{2}{3}$

▶ **2. 12-Sided Die** The figure shows a die with 12 sides. Each side has one of the numbers from 1 to 12. If the die is as likely to land on one side as another, find the probabilities for the following events.

   a. Observing an even number
   $\frac{1}{2}$
   b. Observing a number less than 5
   $\frac{1}{3}$
   c. Observing a number greater than 5
   $\frac{7}{12}$
   d. Observing a 5
   $\frac{1}{12}$

▶ **3. Rolling Dice** Two dice are rolled at the same time and the numbers showing are observed. Find the following.
   a. $P(\text{sum} = 2)$
   $\frac{1}{36}$
   b. $P(\text{sum} = 11)$
   $\frac{1}{18}$
   c. $P(\text{sum is an odd number})$
   $\frac{1}{2}$
   d. $P(\text{the two dice show different numbers})$
   $\frac{5}{6}$

▶ **4. Rolling Dice** Two dice are rolled at the same time and the numbers showing are observed. Find the probabilities for the following events.
   a. The sum is 4.
   $\frac{1}{12}$
   b. The sum is 3 or 10.
   $\frac{5}{36}$
   c. The sum is less than 12.
   $\frac{35}{36}$
   d. One or both dice show a 5.
   $\frac{11}{36}$

▶ **5. Card Deck** One card is drawn from a regular deck of 52 cards. Find the probabilities associated with the following events.
   a. The card is a 10.
   $\frac{1}{13}$
   b. The card is a diamond.
   $\frac{1}{4}$
   c. The card is a not a queen.
   $\frac{12}{13}$
   d. The card is not a face card.
   $\frac{10}{13}$

▶ **6. Card Deck** One card is drawn from a regular deck of 52 cards. Find the following.
   a. $P(\text{a black card})$
   $\frac{1}{2}$
   b. $P(\text{a king or a 3})$
   $\frac{2}{13}$
   c. $P(\text{a red jack})$
   $\frac{1}{26}$
   d. $P(\text{a spade or a diamond})$
   $\frac{1}{2}$

▶ Selected exercises available online at www.webassign.net/brookscole

Board Game The spinner on the game board shown here spins, and when it comes to a stop, the color and number it is pointing to are noted.

▶ **7.** Find the following.

   a. $P(8)$

   $\frac{1}{8}$

   b. $P(\text{red})$

   $\frac{1}{4}$

   c. $P(\text{blue})$

   $\frac{1}{2}$

   d. $P(2)$

   $\frac{1}{8}$

▶ **8.** Find the probabilities of the following events.

   a. Spinning an odd number

   $\frac{1}{2}$

   b. Spinning a blue or an 8

   $\frac{5}{8}$

   c. Spinning a number less than 7

   $\frac{3}{4}$

   d. Spinning a number greater than or equal to 1

   1

C [Examples 7–8]

▶ **9. Ice Cream Flavors** A third-grade teacher surveyed her class to see which flavor of ice cream they wanted for their end-of-year party. The results of the survey are shown in the following table.

Flavor	Number of Votes
Vanilla	15
Chocolate	10
Strawberry	5

If a student from the class is selected at random, find the probability that the student voted for

   a. chocolate.

   $\frac{1}{3}$

   b. vanilla.

   $\frac{1}{2}$

   c. chocolate or strawberry.

   $\frac{1}{2}$

   d. vanilla or chocolate.

   $\frac{5}{6}$

▶ **10. Births** The chart shows the number of babies born to women in different age groups in 2004.

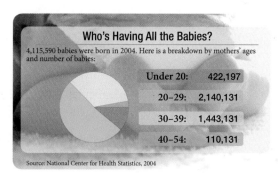

Who's Having All the Babies?

4,115,590 babies were born in 2004. Here is a breakdown by mothers' ages and number of babies:

Under 20:	422,197
20–29:	2,140,131
30–39:	1,443,131
40–54:	110,131

Source: National Center for Health Statistics, 2004

If a baby born in 2004 is selected at random, find the probabilities of the following events to the nearest hundredth.

   a. the mother is under 20 years of age

   0.10

   b. $20 \le \text{mother's age} \le 29$

   0.52

   c. mother's age ≤ 29

   0.62

   d. mother's age > 29

   0.38

▶ **11. iPods** A box contains 7 iPods, 4 of which are green and
3 of which are blue.

You select one iPod at random. Find the following
probabilities.

a. P(green)

$\frac{4}{7}$

b. P(blue)

$\frac{3}{7}$

c. P(green or blue)

1

d. P(orange)

0

▶ **12. Marbles** A jar contains 4 white marbles, 6 black marbles,
and 2 red marbles. If one marble is drawn at random,
find the probability that the marble is:

a. red.

$\frac{1}{6}$

b. not white.

$\frac{2}{3}$

c. black or white.

$\frac{5}{6}$

d. yellow.

0

▶ **13. YouTube** Approximately 80% of the videos on YouTube.
com consist of amateur content. If you randomly
select a YouTube video, what is the probability it is an
amateur video? Write your answer as a decimal and as
a reduced fraction.

$0.8 = \frac{4}{5}$

▶ **14. Voting** In the presidential election of November 2004, 64
percent of the voting-age citizens voted. If a citizen who
was of voting age during the election is chosen at random, find the probability that he or she voted. Give the
answer as a decimal and as a fraction.

$0.64 = \frac{16}{25}$

▶ **15. Student Ages** Recently, Mr. McKeague taught a college
algebra class that started the semester with 36 students having the following characteristics.

Age	Men	Women
18	3	5
19	2	3
20	6	2
21+	7	8

What is the probability that a student selected at random from this class is

a. male?

$\frac{1}{2}$

b. 19 years old?

$\frac{5}{36}$

c. 20 or older?

$\frac{23}{36}$

d. under 20 years of age?

$\frac{13}{36}$

▶ **16. Class Grades** Recently, Mr. McKeague taught a college
algebra class that started the semester with 36 students.
At the end of the semester the following grades were
given. (W is for withdrew and dropped the class.)

Grade	Men	Women
A	2	2
B	2	3
C	5	7
D	1	0
F	2	1
W	6	5

What is the probability that a student selected at random
from this class

a. is female?

$\frac{1}{2}$

b. received a grade of B?

$\frac{5}{36}$

c. received a grade above D?

$\frac{7}{12}$

d. withdrew from the class?

$\frac{11}{36}$

Chapter 6 Summary

Mean [6.1]

To find the *mean* for a set of numbers, we add all the numbers and then divide the sum by the number of numbers in the set. The mean is sometimes called the *arithmetic mean*.

Median [6.1]

To find the *median* for a set of numbers, we write the numbers in order from smallest to largest. If there is an odd number of numbers, the median is the middle number. If there is an even number of numbers, then the median is the mean of the two numbers in the middle.

Mode [6.1]

The *mode* for a set of numbers is the number that occurs most frequently. If all the numbers in the set occur the same number of times, there is no mode.

Range [6.1]

The *range* for a set of numbers is the difference between the largest number and the smallest number in the sample.

Stem-and-Leaf Diagrams [6.2]

A stem-and-leaf diagram is a way to organize data into two columns. For a collection of two-digit numbers, the first column, or stem, is the tens digit, while the second column, or leaf, is the ones digit.

EXAMPLES

1. Find the mean for test scores of 74, 63, 74, 80, 83, 88.
   We add the numbers and divide by 6:
   $$\frac{74 + 63 + 74 + 80 + 83 + 88}{6}$$
   $$= \frac{462}{6} = 77$$

2. The median for the test scores in Example 1 will be halfway between 74 and 80.
   $$\text{Median} = \frac{74 + 80}{2} = 77$$

3. The mode for the test scores in Example 1 will be the most frequently occurring score, which is 74.

4. The range for the test scores in Example 1 will be the difference between 88 and 63.
   Range = 88 − 63 = 25

5. A stem-and-leaf diagram for the data
   32, 15, 20, 26, 39, 11, 27
   is shown below

Stem	Leaf
1	1, 5
2	0, 6, 7
3	2, 9

Frequency Tables and Histograms [6.2]

A *frequency table* shows how often data within certain intervals occurs. A *histogram* is a graph of a frequency table.

Interval	Frequency
60–69	4
70–79	5
80–89	7
90–100	4

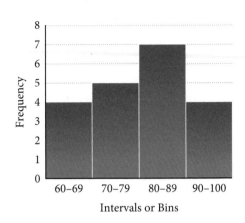

Quartiles [6.2]

6. For the data
3, 4, 6, 7, 8, 9, 11
$Q_2 = 7$, $Q_1 = 4$, $Q_3 = 9$

The quartiles of a data set are used to sort the data into fourths. The second quartile, Q_2, is the median of the data. The first quartile, Q_1, is the median of the values less than Q_2. The third quartile, Q_3, is the median of the data greater than Q_2.

Box-and-Whisker Plots [6.2]

A box-and-whisker plot creates a visual representation of our data by graphing the three quartiles and the least and the greatest value.

■ Pie Charts [6.3]

A pie chart is another way to give a visual representation of the information in a table.

Seating Class	Number Of Seats
First	18
Business	42
Coach	163

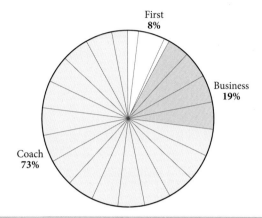

First
8%

Business
19%

Coach
73%

■ Equally Likely Outcomes [6.4]

In an experiment where all the outcomes are equally likely to happen, the probability that event A occurs is the number of outcomes in A divided by the total number of outcomes.

7. The probability of rolling a number less than 4 on a six-sided die is

$$P(< 4) = \frac{3}{6} = \frac{1}{2}$$

■ Probability Rule 1 [6.4]

If A is an event, then the probability that A will occur, denoted $P(A)$, will always satisfy the condition:

$$0 \leq P(A) \leq 1$$

■ Observed Probabilities [6.4]

Observed probabilities are taken from actual data.

8. In an algebra class, 86% of the students passed the first exam. If a student is selected at random from the class, the probability that he or she passed is $0.86 = \frac{86}{100} = \frac{43}{50}$.

1. **Coffee Prices** The table below shows the unit price of some popular coffees.
   a. To the nearest tenth, find the mean of the unit prices listed in the table. [6.1]
      12.6 cents/cup
   b. Find the median unit price of the items listed in the table. [6.1]
      10 cents/cup
   c. What is the range of unit prices for the items listed in the table? [6.1]
      27 cents/cup

Coffee	Price (cents/cup)
Green Mountain Kona Estate	32
Gevalia Kaffe Select	17
Dunkin' Donuts Original	11
Brothers Gourmet	10
Trader Joe's Colombian	7
Yuban Colombian	6
Folgers Classic	5

2. **Value of a Painting** A painting is purchased in 1990 for $125. The table below shows what the painting is worth at various times, if it doubles in value every 5 years.
   a. What is the range of values for the painting? [6.1]
      $1,875
   b. What is the mean value of the painting to the nearest dollar? [6.1]
      $775
   c. What is the median value of the painting? [6.1]
      $500

Year	Value
1990	$125
1995	$250
2000	$500
2005	$1,000
2010	$2,000

Find the mode for each set of numbers. [6.1]

3. 3, 2, 6, 2, 1, 2, 3, 1, 5   2

4. 16, 24, 31, 24, 19, 31, 32, 17, 24   24

Use the data to create a stem-and-leaf diagram. [6.2]

5. 16, 28, 32, 21, 19, 20

Stem	Leaf
1	6, 9
2	8, 1, 0
3	2

6. 89, 99, 100, 95, 72, 90, 93

Stem	Leaf
7	2
8	9
9	9, 5, 0, 3
10	0

Use the data to create a box-and-whisker plot. [6.2]

7. 19, 32, 53, 40, 56, 45, 68, 20, 70, 56, 64

8. 20, 21, 36, 41, 5, 17, 81, 45, 36, 41, 24

9. Create a frequency table with 5 intervals from the data below [6.2]

   21 36 27 42 19 57 23 32
   48 35 17 24 29 21 30

Interval	Tally	Frequency	Relative Freq.
17–25	⊥⊥⊥⊥ I	6	$\frac{6}{15} = 0.4$
26–34	IIII	4	$\frac{4}{15} = 0.267$
35–43	III	3	$\frac{3}{15} = 0.2$
44–52	I	1	$\frac{1}{15} = 0.067$
53–61	I	1	$\frac{1}{15} = 0.067$

10. Use the data to create a histogram with 5 bins. [6.2]

   6, 5, 11, 7, 12, 21, 15, 13, 25

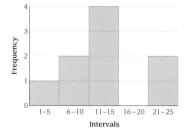

11. **Drinking Coffee** The pie chart shows the results of surveying 200 people to find out how much coffee they drink. [6.3]

Drinking Coffee

- 1 cup a day
- 2 cups a week
- 1 cup a week
- 2 or more cups a day

a. What percentage of people drink 1 or more cup a day?

72%

b. How many people said they drink 1 cup a day?

54

c. What percentage of people drink 1 or 2 cups a week?

28%

12. **Airline Seating** The table below gives the number of seats in each of the three classes of seating on a United Airlines Boeing 777 airliner. Create a pie chart from the information in the table. [6.3]

Seating Class	Ticket Price
First	12
Business	49
Coach	215

Airline Seating

- First Class
- Business Class
- Coach

Solve the following probability problems [6.4]

13. What is the probability of drawing a card less than 4 from a deck of 52 cards? (Ace is low.)

$\frac{3}{13}$

14. What is the probability of drawing a red king or a diamond from a deck of 52 cards?

$\frac{7}{26}$

15. What is the probability of rolling a 12-sided die and it landing on a number greater than 3 or an even number?

$\frac{5}{6}$

16. What is the probability of rolling a 12-sided die and it landing on a prime number or an odd number?

$\frac{7}{12}$

17. The chart shows how people surveyed feel about dogs and cats.

Opinion	Number of People
Like both	60
Like only dogs	29
Like only cats	4
Dislike both	2

If someone from the survey is selected, what is the probability they

a. like either only cats or only dogs?

$\frac{33}{95}$

b. dislike both?

$\frac{2}{95}$

c. like both or only cats?

$\frac{64}{95}$

18. A group of friends voted on what genre of movie they wanted to watch. The results are shown in the table below.

Genre	Number of Votes
Action	9
Comedy	6
Horror	3
Romance	2

If someone from the group is selected, what is the probability they wanted to watch

a. an action or horror movie?

$\frac{3}{5}$

b. a comedy or romance?

$\frac{2}{5}$

c. anything but romance?

$\frac{9}{10}$

Simplify.

1. $265.02 \div 6.31$

42

2. $\dfrac{5}{9} + \dfrac{1}{9}$

$\dfrac{2}{3}$

3. $\dfrac{2}{7} \cdot \dfrac{3}{8}$

$\dfrac{3}{28}$

4. $\left(\dfrac{2}{3}\right)^3$

$\dfrac{8}{27}$

5. $5 \cdot 3\dfrac{1}{2}$

$17\dfrac{1}{2}$

6. $6 - 2.15$

3.85

7. $4.8(2.01)$

9.648

8. $3\dfrac{1}{4} - 1\dfrac{1}{2}$

$1\dfrac{3}{4}$

9. $\dfrac{9}{28} \div \dfrac{3}{16}$

$1\dfrac{5}{7}$

10. $\dfrac{1}{4} - \dfrac{1}{5}$

$\dfrac{1}{20}$

11. $6.237 + 1.38$

7.617

12. Divide $3\dfrac{1}{4}$ by $\dfrac{1}{2}$

$6\dfrac{1}{2}$

13. Find the difference of 7 and 2.35.

4.65

14. Translate into symbols, and then simplify: Three more than the product of 6 and 4.

$6 \cdot 4 + 3 = 27$

15. Write the ratio 25 to 20 as a fraction in lowest terms.

$\dfrac{5}{4}$

16. Solve the equation $\dfrac{5}{x} = \dfrac{4}{7}$.

8.75

17. 3.2 is 20% of what number?

16

18. What number is 4% of 15?

0.6

19. **Percent Decrease** A $20 sweater is on sale for 15% off. Find the sale price of the sweater.

$17

20. **Sales Tax** The sales tax on a $25 purchase is $1.75. What is the sales tax rate?

7%

21. **Lemonade Stand** Some kids sell 32 cups of lemonade for 75¢ each. How much money do they take in?

$24

22. **Geometry** Find the perimeter and area of a 6.2 inch by 5 inch rectangle.

Perimeter = 22.4 in., area = 31 in²

23. **Number Problem** The quotient of 9 and 3 is how much smaller than the difference of 9 and 3?

3

24. **Miles/Hour** An athlete jogs 10 miles in 1.6 hours. What is the rate the athlete jogs in miles per hour?

6.25 mph

25. **Recipe** A recipe calls for 3 tablespoons of oil and 2 cups of flour. If the recipe is increased to 5 cups of flour, how many tablespoons of oil should be used?

7.5 tablespoons

26. **Unit Price** A 5-pound sack of store-brand flour is $0.99. A 2-pound sack of name-brand flour is $1.39. Give the unit price for each sack, and indicate which is the better buy.

5 LBS FOR $0.99   2 LBS FOR $1.39

5-pound sack: $0.198/lb, 2-pound sack: $0.695/lb; the store brand is the better buy

27. **Model Car** A toy company offers a $\dfrac{1}{24}$ scale model of a Checker Cab. If the length of the model is 8.5 inches, what is the length of the actual Checker Cab? Write your answer in inches, then divide by 12 to give the answer in feet.

204 in. = 17 ft

28. **Worrying** The snapshot shows how long it takes for people to start worrying about checking their phone, email, instant messaging, or public networking sites for messaging. If 2,914 people said they start worrying in one hour or less, how many people were surveyed?

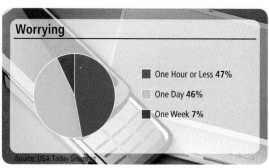

6,200 people

Suppose you draw a card from a deck of 52 cards. What is the probability of drawing

29. an ace?

$\dfrac{1}{13}$

30. a king or a spade?

$\dfrac{4}{13}$

1. **Car Speeds** The table below gives the number of seconds it takes various sport-utility vehicles to accelerate from 0 miles per hour to 60 miles per hour.

Car	Time (Seconds)
Chevrolet Blazer	9.1
Ford Explorer	10.7
Isuzu Trooper	10.9
Jeep Cherokee	9.7
Nissan Pathfinder	12.3
Toyota 4Runner	15.7

a. What is the range of acceleration times? 6.6 seconds

b. What is the mean acceleration time? 11.4 seconds

c. What is the median of the acceleration times? 10.8 sec

2. **Airline Ticket Prices** The table below shows a number of different ticket prices for a round trip ticket from Los Angeles to New York City in June 2002.

Seating Class	Ticket Price
Coach	261
Coach	335
Coach	1,525
Coach	2,443
Business	2,643
Business	3,637
First	1,211
First	2,443
First	3,825

a. Find the mean ticket price to the nearest dollar. $2,036

b. Find the median for the ticket prices. $2,443

c. What is the mode for the ticket prices? $2,443

d. What is the range of ticket prices? $3,564

Use the data to create a stem-and-leaf diagram.

3. 9, 4, 3, 6, 19, 20, 16, 24, 30, 12

Stem	Leaf
0	9, 4, 3, 6
1	9, 6, 2
2	0, 4
3	0

Use the data to make a histogram with 6 bins.

4. 9, 3, 25, 36, 17, 14, 27, 17, 21, 23

Use the data to create a box-and-whisker plot.

5. 36, 45, 12, 90, 62, 52, 34, 15, 17, 26, 38

6. **Barbecue** The chart shows what foods people like to barbecue. Use the illustration to create a pie chart.

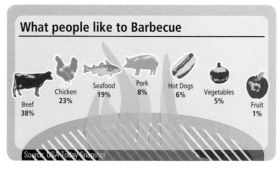

See answers section

7. What is the probability of drawing a diamond from a deck of 52 cards? $\frac{1}{4}$

8. What is the probability of drawing a two or an even card from a deck of 52 cards? $\frac{5}{13}$

Board Game Use the board game spinner to answer the following questions.

9. Find the probability of spinning a number greater than 3. $\frac{5}{8}$

10. Find the probability of spinning a 7 or a yellow. $\frac{3}{8}$

A survey was taken to determine the most popular color for club T-Shirts. Use the results to answer the questions.

Color	Number of Votes
blue	19
black	24
red	16
white	7
green	14

11. Find the probability someone chose a red or a black shirt. $\frac{1}{2}$

12. Find the probability someone chose a white shirt. $\frac{7}{80}$

Chapter 6 Projects

DESCRIPTIVE STATISTICS

Nutrition Labels

Number of People 2–3

Time Needed 15–20 minutes

Equipment Pencil, paper, and protractor

Background If you take a basic course in nutrition, you will find that all the calories we consume come from three different sources: fat, carbohydrates, and proteins. One gram of any carbohydrate or any protein contains 4 calories, whereas every gram of fat contains 9 calories. We can use this information, along with our ability to construct pie charts, to get a visual comparison of the carbohydrate, protein, and fat calories in different foods.

TORTILLA CHIPS

Nutrition Facts

Serving Size 1 oz. (28g/About 12 chips)
Serving Per Container About 2

Amount Per Serving	
Calories 140	Calories from fat 60

	% Daily Value*
Total Fat 7g	**11%**
Saturated Fat 1g	**6%**
Cholesterol 0mg	**0%**
Sodium 170mg	**7%**
Total Carbohydrate 18g	**6%**
Dietary Fiber 1g	**4%**
Sugars less than 1g	
Protein 2g	

Vitamin A 0%	•	Vitamin C 0%	
Calcium 4%	•	Iron 2%	

*Percent Daily Values are based on a 2,000 calorie diet

Procedure We want to calculate the percent of total calories in 1 serving of food that come from each of the three sources: protein, carbohydrate, and fat. We will begin by completing the table below for the nutrition label above. Notice that the number of grams of protein, carbohydrate, and fat from the nutrition label have already been placed in the table.

	Grams	Calories	Percent of Total Calories
Protein	2		
Carbohydrate	18		
Fat	7		
		Total Calories	100%

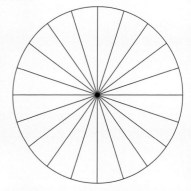

Pie Chart Template   Each slice is 5% of the area of the circle.

1. Multiply the number of grams of protein and the number of grams of carbohydrate by 4, and the number of grams of fat by 9, to fill in the calories column.

2. For protein, fill in the percent column by dividing the number of calories from protein by the total number of calories, and then changing the result to a percent. Do the same for carbohydrate and fat.

3. Use the template to construct a pie chart that shows the percent of the calories that come from the three sources: protein, carbohydrates, and fat.

4. Follow the same procedure to create a pie chart for the nutrition label that follows.

SPAGHETTI

Nutrition Facts

Serving Size 2 oz. (56g/l/8 of pkg) dry
Servings Per Container: 8

Amount Per Serving

Calories 210	Calories from fat 10

	% Daily Value*
Total Fat 1g	**2%**
Saturated Fat 0g	**0%**
Poly unsaturated Fat 0.5g	
Monounsaturated Fat 0g	
Cholesterol 0mg	**0%**
Sodium 0mg	**0%**
Total Carbohydrate 42g	**14%**
Dietary Fiber 2g	**7%**
Sugars 3g	
Protein 7g	

Vitamin A 0%	●	Vitamin C 0%
Calcium 0%	●	Iron 10%

*Percent Daily Values are based on a 2,000 calorie diet

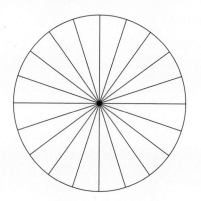

	Grams	Calories	Percent of Total Calories
Protein			
Carbohydrate			
Fat			
Total Calories			100%

Pie Chart Template

RESEARCH PROJECT

Displaying Information Visually

In this chapter we have worked with a number of diagrams and charts that help us visualize information. There are many other types of displays that we have not considered. The graphic below was created by the French engineer Charles Minard (1781–1870) in 1861. It shows the losses to Napolean's Army during the Russian campaign of 1812. The graphic is described by Edward Tufte in his book *The Visual Display of Quantitative Information* as possibly "the best statistical graphic ever drawn." Write an essay on the life of Charles Minard and include information as to why this particular graphic is held in such high regard.

Measurement

Image NASA
Image © 2008 TerraMetrics
Image © 2008 DigitalGlobe
© 2008 Cnes/Spot Image
Google

Introduction

The Google Earth image here shows the Nile River in Africa. The Nile is the longest river in the world, measuring 4,160 miles and stretching across ten different countries. Rivers across the world serve as important means of transportation, particularly in less developed countries, like those in Africa.

Nile River

	English Units	Metric Units
Length	4,160 mi	6,698 km
Nile Delta Area	1,004 mi²	2,601 ha
Flow Rate (monsoon season)	285,829 ft³/s	8,100 m³/s
Average Summer Temperature	86°F	30°C

Source: http://www.worldwildlife.org

In this chapter we look at the process we use to convert from one set of units, such as miles per hour, to another set of units, such as kilometers per hour. You will be interested to know that regardless of the units in question, the method we use is the same in all cases. The method is called *unit analysis* and it is the foundation of this chapter.

The pretest below contains problems that are representative of the problems you will find in the chapter.

Make the following conversions.

1. 8 ft to inches
96 in.

2. 90 in. to yards
$2\frac{1}{2}$ yd

3. 32 m to centimeters
3,200 cm

4. 61 mm to centimeters
6.1 cm

5. 30 yd² to square feet
270 ft²

6. 432 in² to square feet
3 ft²

7. 3,840 acres to square miles
6 mi²

8. 1.4 m² to square centimeters
14,000 cm²

9. 3 gallons to quarts
12 qt

10. 72 pints to gallons
9 gal

11. 251 mL to liters
0.251 L

12. 4 lb to ounces
64 oz

13. 2,142 mg to grams
2.142 g

14. 9 m to yards
9.84 yd

15. 3 gal to liters
11.37 L

16. 104°F to degrees Celsius
40°C

17. The speed limit on a certain road is 45 miles/hour. Convert this to feet/second.
66 ft/sec

18. If meat costs $3.05 per pound, how much will 2 lb 4 oz cost?
$6.86

Getting Ready for Chapter 7

The problems below review material covered previously that you need to know in order to be successful in Chapter 7. If you have any difficulty with the problems here, you need to go back and review before going on to Chapter 7.

Write each of the following ratios as a fraction in lowest terms.

1. 12 to 30 $\frac{2}{5}$

2. 5,280 to 1,320 $\frac{4}{1}$

Simplify.

3. 12×16 192

4. 50×250 12,500

5. $75 \times 43,560$ 3,267,000

6. $100 \times 3 \times 12$ 3,600

7. 2.49×3.75 9.3375

8. $5 \times 28 \times 1.36$ 190.4

9. $8 \times \frac{1}{3}$ $2\frac{2}{3}$

10. $25 \times \frac{1}{1000}$ 0.025

11. $\frac{1800}{4}$ 450

12. $256 \div 640$ 0.4

13. $\frac{80.5}{1.61}$ 50

14. $\frac{36.5 \times 10}{100}$ 3.65

15. $\frac{1100 \times 60 \times 60}{5280}$ 750

16. $10 \cdot \frac{12}{5}$ 24

17. $\frac{2 \times 1000}{16.39}$ (Round to the nearest whole number.)   122

18. $\frac{5(102 - 32)}{9}$ (Round to the nearest tenth.)   38.9

19. Convert $\frac{12}{16}$ to a decimal.   0.75

20. Find the perimeter and area of a 24 in. × 36 in. poster.
$P = 120$ in., $A = 864$ in²

Unit Analysis I: Length

Introduction . . .

In this section we will become more familiar with the units used to measure length. We will look at the U.S. system of measurement and the metric system of measurement.

A U.S. Units of Length

Measuring the length of an object is done by assigning a number to its length. To let other people know what that number represents, we include with it a unit of measure. The most common units used to represent length in the U.S. system are inches, feet, yards, and miles. The basic unit of length is the foot. The other units are defined in terms of feet, as Table 1 shows.

TABLE 1

12 inches (in.) =	1 foot (ft)
1 yard (yd) =	3 feet
1 mile (mi) =	5,280 feet

1 foot

As you can see from the table, the abbreviations for inches, feet, yards, and miles are in., ft, yd, and mi, respectively. What we haven't indicated, even though you may not have realized it, is what 1 foot represents. We have defined all our units associated with length in terms of feet, but we haven't said what a foot is.

There is a long history of the evolution of what is now called a foot. At different times in the past, a foot has represented different arbitrary lengths. Currently, a foot is defined to be exactly 0.3048 meter (the basic measure of length in the metric system), where a meter is 1,650,763.73 wavelengths of the orange-red line in the spectrum of krypton-86 in a vacuum (this doesn't mean much to me either). The reason a foot and a meter are defined this way is that we always want them to measure the same length. Because the wavelength of the orange-red line in the spectrum of krypton-86 will always remain the same, so will the length that a foot represents.

Now that we have said what we mean by 1 foot (even though we may not understand the technical definition), we can go on and look at some examples that involve converting from one kind of unit to another.

Instructor Note
I wrote the discussion you see here to point out that we need definitions for everything we use in mathematics. As a lead-in to this section, I have my students ask themselves what 1 foot represents.

> **EXAMPLE 1** Convert 5 feet to inches.

SOLUTION Because 1 foot = 12 inches, we can multiply 5 by 12 inches to get

$$5 \text{ feet} = 5 \times 12 \text{ inches}$$
$$= 60 \text{ inches}$$

This method of converting from feet to inches probably seems fairly simple. But as we go further in this chapter, the conversions from one kind of unit to another will become more complicated. For these more complicated problems, we need another way to show conversions so that we can be certain to end them with the correct unit of measure. For example, since 1 ft = 12 in., we can say that there are 12 in. per 1 ft or 1 ft per 12 in. That is:

$$\frac{12 \text{ in.}}{1 \text{ ft}} \longleftarrow \text{Per} \quad \text{or} \quad \frac{1 \text{ ft}}{12 \text{ in.}} \longleftarrow \text{Per}$$

PRACTICE PROBLEMS

1. Convert 8 feet to inches.

Answers
1. 96 in.

Instructor Note
The idea that conversion factors are
all just different representations for
the number 1 is central to what we
do in this chapter. When I do a problem in class that contains a conversion factor, I always say,
"...then we multiply by the number
1 in the form . . . ."

We call the expressions $\frac{12 \text{ in.}}{1 \text{ ft}}$ and $\frac{1 \text{ ft}}{12 \text{ in.}}$ *conversion factors*. The fraction bar is read as "per." Both these conversion factors are really just the number 1. That is:

$$\frac{12 \text{ in.}}{1 \text{ ft}} = \frac{12 \text{ in.}}{12 \text{ in.}} = 1$$

We already know that multiplying a number by 1 leaves the number unchanged. So, to convert from one unit to the other, we can multiply by one of the conversion factors without changing value. Both the conversion factors above say the same thing about the units feet and inches. They both indicate that there are 12 inches in every foot. The one we choose to multiply by depends on what units we are starting with and what units we want to end up with. If we start with feet and we want to end up with inches, we multiply by the conversion factor

$$\frac{12 \text{ in.}}{1 \text{ ft}}$$

The units of feet will divide out and leave us with inches.

$$5 \text{ feet} = 5 \text{ ft} \times \frac{12 \text{ in.}}{1 \text{ ft}}$$
$$= 5 \times 12 \text{ in.}$$
$$= 60 \text{ in.}$$

The key to this method of conversion lies in setting the problem up so that the correct units divide out to simplify the expression. We are treating units such as feet in the same way we treated factors when reducing fractions. If a factor is common to the numerator and the denominator, we can divide it out and simplify the fraction. The same idea holds for units such as feet.

We can rewrite Table 1 so that it shows the conversion factors associated with units of length, as shown in Table 2.

TABLE 2

UNITS OF LENGTH IN THE U.S. SYSTEM		
The Relationship Between	Is	To Convert From One To The Other, Multiply By
feet and inches	12 in. = 1 ft	$\frac{12 \text{ in.}}{1 \text{ ft}}$ or $\frac{1 \text{ ft}}{12 \text{ in.}}$
feet and yards	1 yd = 3 ft	$\frac{3 \text{ ft}}{1 \text{ yd}}$ or $\frac{1 \text{ yd}}{3 \text{ ft}}$
feet and miles	1 mi = 5,280 ft	$\frac{5,280 \text{ ft}}{1 \text{ mi}}$ or $\frac{1 \text{ mi}}{5,280 \text{ ft}}$

2. The roof of a two-story house is 26 feet above the ground. How many yards is this?

EXAMPLE 2 The most common ceiling height in houses is 8 feet. How many yards is this?

8 ft

SOLUTION   To convert 8 feet to yards, we multiply by the conversion factor $\frac{1 \text{ yd}}{3 \text{ ft}}$ so that feet will divide out and we will be left with yards.

$$8 \text{ ft} = 8 \text{ ft} \times \frac{1 \text{ yd}}{3 \text{ ft}} \qquad \text{Multiply by correct conversion factor}$$

$$= \frac{8}{3} \text{ yd} \qquad 8 \times \frac{1}{3} = \frac{8}{3}$$

$$= 2\frac{2}{3} \text{ yd} \qquad \text{Or 2.67 yd to the nearest hundredth}$$

EXAMPLE 3   A football field is 100 yards long. How many inches long is a football field?

100 yd

SOLUTION   In this example we must convert yards to feet and then feet to inches. (To make this example more interesting, we are pretending we don't know that there are 36 inches in a yard.) We choose the conversion factors that will allow all the units except inches to divide out.

$$100 \text{ yd} = 100 \text{ yd} \times \frac{3 \text{ ft}}{1 \text{ yd}} \times \frac{12 \text{ in.}}{1 \text{ ft}}$$

$$= 100 \times 3 \times 12 \text{ in.}$$

$$= 3{,}600 \text{ in.}$$

B Metric Units of Length

In the metric system the standard unit of length is a meter. A meter is a little longer than a yard (about 3.4 inches longer). The other units of length in the metric system are written in terms of a meter. The metric system uses prefixes to indicate what part of the basic unit of measure is being used. For example, in *millimeter* the prefix *milli* means "one thousandth" of a meter. Table 3 gives the meanings of the most common metric prefixes.

TABLE 3	
THE MEANING OF METRIC PREFIXES	
Prefix	**Meaning**
milli	0.001
centi	0.01
deci	0.1
deka	10
hecto	100
kilo	1,000

We can use these prefixes to write the other units of length and conversion factors for the metric system, as given in Table 4.

3. How many inches are in 220 yards?

TABLE 4		
METRIC UNITS OF LENGTH		
The Relationship Between	**Is**	**To Convert From One To The Other, Multiply By**
millimeters (mm) and meters (m)	1,000 mm = 1 m	$\dfrac{1,000 \text{ mm}}{1 \text{ m}}$ or $\dfrac{1 \text{ m}}{1,000 \text{ mm}}$
centimeters (cm) and meters	100 cm = 1 m	$\dfrac{100 \text{ cm}}{1 \text{ m}}$ or $\dfrac{1 \text{ m}}{100 \text{ cm}}$
decimeters (dm) and meters	10 dm = 1 m	$\dfrac{10 \text{ dm}}{1 \text{ m}}$ or $\dfrac{1 \text{ m}}{10 \text{ dm}}$
dekameters (dam) and meters	1 dam = 10 m	$\dfrac{10 \text{ m}}{1 \text{ dam}}$ or $\dfrac{1 \text{ dam}}{10 \text{ m}}$
hectometers (hm) and meters	1 hm = 100 m	$\dfrac{100 \text{ m}}{1 \text{ hm}}$ or $\dfrac{1 \text{ hm}}{100 \text{ m}}$
kilometers (km) and meters	1 km = 1,000 m	$\dfrac{1,000 \text{ m}}{1 \text{ km}}$ or $\dfrac{1 \text{ km}}{1,000 \text{ m}}$

Instructor Note
Again, I don't use the word *cancel* when I do these problems. I say the units "divide out," because I think that phrase gives a better indication of the operation, division, being used.

We use the same method to convert between units in the metric system as we did with the U.S. system. We choose the conversion factor that will allow the units we start with to divide out, leaving the units we want to end up with.

4. Convert 67 centimeters to meters.

EXAMPLE 4   Convert 25 millimeters to meters.

SOLUTION   To convert from millimeters to meters, we multiply by the conversion factor $\dfrac{1 \text{ m}}{1,000 \text{ mm}}$:

$$25 \text{ mm} = 25 \text{ mm} \times \frac{1 \text{ m}}{1,000 \text{ mm}}$$

$$= \frac{25 \text{ m}}{1,000}$$

$$= 0.025 \text{ m}$$

5. Convert 78.4 mm to decimeters.

EXAMPLE 5   Convert 36.5 centimeters to decimeters.

SOLUTION   We convert centimeters to meters and then meters to decimeters:

$$36.5 \text{ cm} = 36.5 \text{ cm} \times \frac{1 \text{ m}}{100 \text{ cm}} \times \frac{10 \text{ dm}}{1 \text{ m}}$$

$$= \frac{36.5 \times 10}{100} \text{ dm}$$

$$= 3.65 \text{ dm}$$

The most common units of length in the metric system are millimeters, centimeters, meters, and kilometers. The other units of length we have listed in our table of metric lengths are not as widely used. The method we have used to convert from one unit of length to another in Examples 2–5 is called *unit analysis*. If you take a chemistry class, you will see it used many times. The same is true of many other science classes as well.

Answers
4. 0.67 m   **5.** 0.784 dm

We can summarize the procedure used in unit analysis with the following steps:

> **Strategy   Unit Analysis**
> **Step 1:** Identify the units you are starting with.
> **Step 2:** Identify the units you want to end with.
> **Step 3:** Find conversion factors that will bridge the starting units and the ending units.
> **Step 4:** Set up the multiplication problem so that all units except the units you want to end with will divide out.

C   Applications

EXAMPLE 6   A sheep rancher is making new lambing pens for the upcoming lambing season. Each pen is a rectangle 6 feet wide and 8 feet long. The fencing material he wants to use sells for $1.36 per foot. If he is planning to build five separate lambing pens (they are separate because he wants a walkway between them), how much will he have to spend for fencing material?

6. The rancher in Example 6 decides to build six pens instead of five and upgrades his fencing material so that it costs $1.72 per foot. How much does it cost him to build the six pens?

SOLUTION   To find the amount of fencing material he needs for one pen, we find the perimeter of a pen.

$$\text{Perimeter} = 6 + 6 + 8 + 8 = 28 \text{ feet}$$

We set up the solution to the problem using unit analysis. Our starting unit is *pens* and our ending unit is *dollars*. Here are the conversion factors that will form a bridge between pens and dollars:

1 pen = 28 feet of fencing
1 foot of fencing = 1.36 dollars

Next we write the multiplication problem, using the conversion factors, that will allow all the units except dollars to divide out:

$$5 \text{ pens} = 5 \text{ pens} \times \frac{28 \text{ feet of fencing}}{1 \text{ pen}} \times \frac{1.36 \text{ dollars}}{1 \text{ foot of fencing}}$$

$$= 5 \times 28 \times 1.36 \text{ dollars}$$
$$= \$190.40$$

Instructor Note
At this point in my classes, I allow calculators on all the remaining problems. However, I also require that each problem be "set up" with all conversion factors, including units, showing.

Answer
6. $288.96

7. Assume that the mistake in the advertisement is that feet per second should read feet per minute. Is 1,100 feet per minute a reasonable speed for a chair lift?

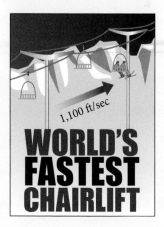

EXAMPLE 7 A number of years ago, a ski resort in Vermont advertised their new high-speed chair lift as "the world's fastest chair lift, with a speed of 1,100 feet per second." Show why the speed cannot be correct.

SOLUTION To solve this problem, we can convert feet per second into miles per hour, a unit of measure we are more familiar with on an intuitive level. Here are the conversion factors we will use:

$$1 \text{ mile} = 5{,}280 \text{ feet}$$

$$1 \text{ hour} = 60 \text{ minutes}$$

$$1 \text{ minute} = 60 \text{ seconds}$$

$$1{,}100 \text{ ft/second} = \frac{1{,}100 \text{ feet}}{1 \text{ second}} \times \frac{1 \text{ mile}}{5{,}280 \text{ feet}} \times \frac{60 \text{ seconds}}{1 \text{ minute}} \times \frac{60 \text{ minutes}}{1 \text{ hour}}$$

$$= \frac{1{,}100 \times 60 \times 60 \text{ miles}}{5{,}280 \text{ hours}}$$

$$= 750 \text{ miles/hour}$$

Getting Ready for Class

After reading through the preceding section, respond in your own words and in complete sentences.

1. Write the relationship between feet and miles. That is, write an equality that shows how many feet are in every mile.
2. Give the metric prefix that means "one hundredth."
3. Give the metric prefix that is equivalent to 1,000.
4. As you know from reading the section in the text, conversion factors are ratios. Write the conversion factor that will allow you to convert from inches to feet. That is, if we wanted to convert 27 inches to feet, what conversion factor would we use?

Answer

7. 12.5 mi/hr is a reasonable speed for a chair lift.

Problem Set 7.1

A Make the following conversions in the U.S. system by multiplying by the appropriate conversion factor. Write your answers as whole numbers or mixed numbers. [Examples 1–3]

▶ **1.** 5 ft to inches
60 in.

2. 9 ft to inches
108 in.

3. 10 ft to inches
120 in.

▶ **4.** 20 ft to inches
240 in.

5. 2 yd to feet
6 ft

▶ **6.** 8 yd to feet
24 ft

▶ **7.** 4.5 yd to inches
162 in.

8. 9.5 yd to inches
342 in.

▶ **9.** 27 in. to feet
$2\frac{1}{4}$ ft

▶ **10.** 36 in. to feet
3 ft

11. 2.5 mi to feet
13,200 ft

12. 6.75 mi to feet
35,640 ft

▶ **13.** 48 in. to yards
$1\frac{1}{3}$ yd

14. 56 in. to yards
$1\frac{5}{9}$ yd

B Make the following conversions in the metric system by multiplying by the appropriate conversion factor. Write your answers as whole numbers or decimals. [Examples 4, 5]

▶ **15.** 18 m to centimeters
1,800 cm

▶ **16.** 18 m to millimeters
18,000 mm

17. 4.8 km to meters
4,800 m

18. 8.9 km to meters
8,900 m

▶ **19.** 5 dm to centimeters
50 cm

▶ **20.** 12 dm to millimeters
1,200 mm

21. 248 m to kilometers
0.248 km

▶ **22.** 969 m to kilometers
0.969 km

23. 67 cm to millimeters
670 mm

24. 67 mm to centimeters
6.7 cm

▶ **25.** 3,498 cm to meters
34.98 m

26. 4,388 dm to meters
438.8 m

▶ **27.** 63.4 cm to decimeters
6.34 dm

28. 89.5 cm to decimeters
8.95 dm

C Applying the Concepts [Examples 6, 7]

29. Mountains The map shows the heights of the tallest mountains in the world. According to the map, K2 is 28,238 ft. Convert this to miles. Round to the nearest tenth of a mile.

5.3 miles

The Greatest Heights

K2 **28,238 ft**
Mount Everest **29,035 ft**
Kangchenjunga **28,208 ft**

PAKISTAN
NEPAL
CHINA
INDIA

Source: Forrester Research, 2005

30. Classroom Energy The chart shows how much energy is wasted in the classroom by leaving appliances on.

Energy Estimates
All units given as watts per hour.

Ceiling fan	125
Stereo	400
Television	130
VCR/DVD player	20
Printer	400
Photocopier	400
Coffee maker	1000

Source: dosomething.org 2008

Convert the the wattage of the following appliances to kilowatts.
a. Ceiling fan   0.125 kilowatts
b. VCR/DVD player   0.02 kilowatts
c. Coffee maker   1 kilowatt

31. Softball If the distance between first and second base in softball is 60 feet, how many yards is it from first to second base?

20 yd

60 ft

32. Notebook Width Standard-sized notebook paper is 21.6 centimeters wide. Express this width in millimeters.

216 mm

21.6 cm

▶ **33. High Jump** If a person high jumps 6 feet 8 inches, how many inches is the jump?

80 in.

34. Desk Width A desk is 48 inches wide. What is the width in yards?

$1\frac{1}{3}$ yd

▶ **35. Ceiling Height** Suppose the ceiling of a home is 2.44 meters above the floor. Express the height of the ceiling in centimeters.

244 cm

36. Tower Height A transmitting tower is 100 feet tall. How many inches is that?

1,200 in.

Problems 37–42 involve unfamiliar units. I like these problems, because students can't solve them intuitively. They have to use the method we present in class.

37. Surveying A unit of measure sometimes used in surveying is the *chain*. There are 80 chains in 1 mile. How many chains are in 37 miles?

2,960 chains

▶ **38. Surveying** Another unit of measure used in surveying is a *link;* 1 link is about 8 inches. About how many links are there in 5 feet?

7.5 links

▶ **39. Metric System** A very small unit of measure in the metric system is the *micron* (abbreviated μm). There are 1,000 μm in 1 millimeter. How many microns are in 12 centimeters?

120,000 μm

40. Metric System Another very small unit of measure in the metric system is the *angstrom* (abbreviated Å). There are 10,000,000 Å in 1 millimeter. How many angstroms are in 15 decimeters?

15,000,000,000 Å

41. Horse Racing In horse racing, 1 *furlong* is 220 yards. How many feet are in 12 furlongs?

7,920 ft

43. Speed Limit The maximum speed limit on part of Highway 101 in California is 55 miles/hour. Convert 55 miles/hour to feet/second. (Round to the nearest tenth.)

80.7 ft/sec

45. Track and Field A person who runs the 100-yard dash in 10.5 seconds has an average speed of 9.52 yards/second. Convert 9.52 yards/second to miles/hour. (Round to the nearest tenth.)

19.5 mi/hr

47. Speed of a Bullet The bullet from a rifle leaves the barrel traveling 1,500 feet/second. Convert 1,500 feet/second to miles/hour. (Round to the nearest whole number.)

1,023 mi/hr

42. Speed of a Bullet A bullet from a machine gun on a B-17 Flying Fortress in World War II had a muzzle speed of 1,750 feet/second. Convert 1,750 feet/second to miles/hour. (Round to the nearest whole number.)

1,193 mi/hr

Courtesy of the U.S. Air Force Museum

44. Speed Limit The maximum speed limit on part of Highway 5 in California is 65 miles/hour. Convert 65 miles/hour to feet/second. (Round to the nearest tenth.)

95.3 ft/sec

46. Track and Field A person who runs a mile in 8 minutes has an average speed of 0.125 miles/minute. Convert 0.125 miles/minute to miles/hour.

7.5 mi/hr

48. Sailing A *fathom* is 6 feet. How many yards are in 19 fathoms?

38 yd

■ Calculator Problems

Set up the following conversions as you have been doing. Then perform the calculations on a calculator.

49. Change 751 miles to feet.

3,965,280 ft

51. Change 4,982 yards to inches.

179,352 in.

53. Mount Whitney is the highest point in California. It is 14,494 feet above sea level. Give its height in miles to the nearest tenth.

2.7 mi

55. California has 3,427 miles of shoreline. How many feet is this?

18,094,560 ft

50. Change 639.87 centimeters to meters.

6.3987 m

52. Change 379 millimeters to kilometers.

0.000379 km

54. The tallest mountain in the United States is Mount McKinley in Alaska. It is 20,320 feet tall. Give its height in miles to the nearest tenth.

3.8 mi

56. The tip of the TV tower at the top of the Empire State Building in New York City is 1,472 feet above the ground. Express this height in miles to the nearest hundredth.

0.28 mi

Getting Ready for the Next Section

Perform the indicated operations.

57. 12×12
144

58. 36×24
864

59. $1 \times 4 \times 2$
8

60. $5 \times 4 \times 2$
40

61. $10 \times 10 \times 10$
1,000

62. $100 \times 100 \times 100$
1,000,000

63. $75 \times 43,560$
3,267,000

64. $55 \times 43,560$
2,395,800

65. $864 \div 144$
6

66. $1,728 \div 144$
12

67. $256 \div 640$
0.4

68. $960 \div 240$
4

69. $45 \times \dfrac{9}{1}$
405

70. $36 \times \dfrac{9}{1}$
324

71. $1,800 \times \dfrac{1}{4}$
450

72. $2,000 \times \dfrac{1}{4} \times \dfrac{1}{10}$
50

73. 1.5×30
45

74. 1.5×45
67.5

75. $2.2 \times 1,000$
2,200

76. $3.5 \times 1,000$
3,500

77. 67.5×9
607.5

78. 43.5×9
391.5

Maintaining Your Skills

Write your answers as whole numbers, proper fractions, or mixed numbers.

Find each product. (Multiply.)

79. $\dfrac{2}{3} \cdot \dfrac{1}{2}$
$\dfrac{1}{3}$

80. $\dfrac{7}{9} \cdot \dfrac{3}{14}$
$\dfrac{1}{6}$

81. $8 \cdot \dfrac{3}{4}$
6

82. $12 \cdot \dfrac{1}{3}$
4

83. $1\dfrac{1}{2} \cdot 2\dfrac{1}{3}$
$3\dfrac{1}{2}$

84. $\dfrac{1}{6} \cdot 4\dfrac{2}{3}$
$\dfrac{7}{9}$

Find each quotient. (Divide.)

85. $\dfrac{3}{4} \div \dfrac{1}{8}$
6

86. $\dfrac{3}{5} \div \dfrac{6}{25}$
$\dfrac{5}{2} = 2\dfrac{1}{2}$

87. $4 \div \dfrac{2}{3}$
6

88. $1 \div \dfrac{1}{3}$
3

89. $1\dfrac{3}{4} \div 2\dfrac{1}{2}$
$\dfrac{7}{10}$

90. $\dfrac{9}{8} \div 1\dfrac{7}{8}$
$\dfrac{3}{5}$

Extending the Concepts

91. Fitness Walking The guidelines for fitness now indicate that a person who walks 10,000 steps daily is physically fit. According to *The Walking Site* on the Internet, "The average person's stride length is approximately 2.5 feet long. That means it takes just over 2,000 steps to walk one mile, and 10,000 steps is close to 5 miles." Use your knowledge of unit analysis to determine if these facts are correct.

$$10,000 \text{ steps} \cdot \frac{2.5 \text{ ft}}{1 \text{ step}} \cdot \frac{1 \text{ mi}}{5,280 \text{ ft}} = 4.7 \text{ mi}$$

Objectives

A Convert between areas using the U.S. system.

B Convert between areas using the metric system.

C Convert between volumes using the U.S. system.

D Convert between volumes using the metric system.

Figure 1 below gives a summary of the geometric objects we have worked with in previous chapters, along with the formulas for finding the area of each object.

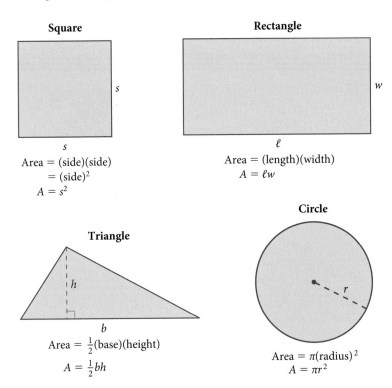

Square

Area = (side)(side)
= (side)^2
$A = s^2$

Rectangle

Area = (length)(width)
$A = \ell w$

Triangle

Area = $\frac{1}{2}$(base)(height)
$A = \frac{1}{2}bh$

Circle

Area = π(radius)^2
$A = \pi r^2$

FIGURE 1   AREAS OF COMMON GEOMETRIC SHAPES

A   Conversion Factors in the U.S. System

EXAMPLE 1   Find the number of square inches in 1 square foot.

SOLUTION   We can think of 1 square foot as 1 ft^2 = 1 ft × 1 ft. To convert from feet to inches, we use the conversion factor 1 foot = 12 inches. Because the unit foot appears twice in 1 ft^2, we multiply by our conversion factor twice.

$$1 \text{ ft}^2 = 1 \text{ ft} \times 1 \text{ ft} \times \frac{12 \text{ in.}}{1 \text{ ft}} \times \frac{12 \text{ in.}}{1 \text{ ft}} = 12 \text{ in.} \times 12 \text{ in.} = 144 \text{ in}^2$$

Now that we know that 1 ft^2 is the same as 144 in^2, we can use this fact as a conversion factor to convert between square feet and square inches. Depending on which units we are converting from, we would use either

$$\frac{144 \text{ in}^2}{1 \text{ ft}^2} \quad \text{or} \quad \frac{1 \text{ ft}^2}{144 \text{ in}^2}$$

PRACTICE PROBLEMS

1. Find the number of square feet in 1 square yard.

Answer
1. 1 yd^2 = 9 ft^2

2. If the poster in Example 2 is surrounded by a frame 6 inches wide, find the number of square feet of wall space covered by the framed poster.

EXAMPLE 2 A rectangular poster measures 36 inches by 24 inches. How many square feet of wall space will the poster cover?

SOLUTION One way to work this problem is to find the number of square inches the poster covers, and then convert square inches to square feet.

$$\text{Area of poster} = \text{length} \times \text{width} = 36 \text{ in.} \times 24 \text{ in.} = 864 \text{ in}^2$$

To finish the problem, we convert square inches to square feet:

$$864 \text{ in}^2 = 864 \text{ in}^2 \times \frac{1 \text{ ft}^2}{144 \text{ in}^2}$$

$$= \frac{864}{144} \text{ ft}^2$$

$$= 6 \text{ ft}^2$$

Image © Sint, 2010.
Used under license from Shutterstock.com

36"

24"

Table 1 gives the most common units of area in the U.S. system of measurement, along with the corresponding conversion factors.

TABLE 1		
U.S. UNITS OF AREA		
The Relationship Between	**Is**	**To Convert From One To The Other, Multiply By**
square inches and square feet	$144 \text{ in}^2 = 1 \text{ ft}^2$	$\frac{144 \text{ in}^2}{1 \text{ ft}^2}$ or $\frac{1 \text{ ft}^2}{144 \text{ in}^2}$
square yards and square feet	$9 \text{ ft}^2 = 1 \text{ yd}^2$	$\frac{9 \text{ ft}^2}{1 \text{ yd}^2}$ or $\frac{1 \text{ yd}^2}{9 \text{ ft}^2}$
acres and square feet	$1 \text{ acre} = 43{,}560 \text{ ft}^2$	$\frac{43{,}560 \text{ ft}^2}{1 \text{ acre}}$ or $\frac{1 \text{ acre}}{43{,}560 \text{ ft}^2}$
acres and square miles	$640 \text{ acres} = 1 \text{ mi}^2$	$\frac{640 \text{ acres}}{1 \text{ mi}^2}$ or $\frac{1 \text{ mi}^2}{640 \text{ acres}}$

3. The same dressmaker orders a bolt of material that is 1.5 yards wide and 45 yards long. How many square feet of material were ordered?

EXAMPLE 3 A dressmaker orders a bolt of material that is 1.5 yards wide and 30 yards long. How many square feet of material were ordered?

SOLUTION The area of the material in square yards is

$$A = 1.5 \text{ yd} \times 30 \text{ yd}$$
$$= 45 \text{ yd}^2$$

Converting this to square feet, we have

$$45 \text{ yd}^2 = 45 \text{ yd}^2 \times \frac{9 \text{ ft}^2}{1 \text{ yd}^2}$$

$$= 405 \text{ ft}^2$$

Answers
2. 12 ft² **3.** 607.5 ft²

EXAMPLE 4   A farmer has 75 acres of land. How many square feet of land does the farmer have?

SOLUTION   Changing acres to square feet, we have

$$75 \text{ acres} = 75 \text{ acres} \times \frac{43,560 \text{ ft}^2}{1 \text{ acre}}$$

$$= 75 \times 43,560 \text{ ft}^2$$

$$= 3,267,000 \text{ ft}^2$$

EXAMPLE 5   A new shopping center is to be constructed on 256 acres of land. How many square miles is this?

SOLUTION   Multiplying by the conversion factor that will allow acres to divide out, we have

$$256 \text{ acres} = 256 \text{ acres} \times \frac{1 \text{ mi}^2}{640 \text{ acres}}$$

$$= \frac{256}{640} \text{mi}^2$$

$$= 0.4 \text{ mi}^2$$

B   Area: The Metric System

Units of area in the metric system are considerably simpler than those in the U.S. system because metric units are given in terms of powers of 10. Table 2 lists the conversion factors that are most commonly used.

TABLE 2		
METRIC UNITS OF AREA		
The Relationship Between	**Is**	**To Convert From One To The Other, Multiply By**
square millimeters and square centimeters	$1 \text{ cm}^2 = 100 \text{ mm}^2$	$\dfrac{100 \text{ mm}^2}{1 \text{ cm}^2}$ or $\dfrac{1 \text{ cm}^2}{100 \text{ mm}^2}$
square centimeters and square decimeters	$1 \text{ dm}^2 = 100 \text{ cm}^2$	$\dfrac{100 \text{ cm}^2}{1 \text{ dm}^2}$ or $\dfrac{1 \text{ dm}^2}{100 \text{ cm}^2}$
square decimeters and square meters	$1 \text{ m}^2 = 100 \text{ dm}^2$	$\dfrac{100 \text{ dm}^2}{1 \text{ m}^2}$ or $\dfrac{1 \text{ m}^2}{100 \text{ dm}^2}$
square meters and ares (a)	$1 \text{ a} = 100 \text{ m}^2$	$\dfrac{100 \text{ m}^2}{1 \text{ a}}$ or $\dfrac{1 \text{ a}}{100 \text{ m}^2}$
ares and hectares (ha)	$1 \text{ ha} = 100 \text{ a}$	$\dfrac{100 \text{ a}}{1 \text{ ha}}$ or $\dfrac{1 \text{ ha}}{100 \text{ a}}$

4. A farmer has 55 acres of land. How many square feet of land does the farmer have?

5. A school is to be constructed on 960 acres of land. How many square miles is this?

Answers
4. 2,395,800 ft²
5. 1.5 mi²

6. How many square centimeters are in 1 square meter?

EXAMPLE 6   How many square millimeters are in 1 square meter?

SOLUTION   We start with 1 m² and end up with square millimeters:

$$1 \text{ m}^2 = 1 \text{ m}^2 \times \frac{100 \text{ dm}^2}{1 \text{ m}^2} \times \frac{100 \text{ cm}^2}{1 \text{ dm}^2} \times \frac{100 \text{ mm}^2}{1 \text{ cm}^2}$$

$$= 100 \times 100 \times 100 \text{ mm}^2$$
$$= 1{,}000{,}000 \text{ mm}^2$$

C   Volume: The U.S. System

Table 3 lists the units of volume in the U.S. system and their conversion factors.

TABLE 3		
UNITS OF VOLUME IN THE U.S. SYSTEM		
The Relationship Between	**Is**	**To Convert From One To The Other, Multiply By**
cubic inches (in³) and cubic feet (ft³)	$1 \text{ ft}^3 = 1{,}728 \text{ in}^3$	$\dfrac{1{,}728 \text{ in}^3}{1 \text{ ft}^3}$ or $\dfrac{1 \text{ ft}^3}{1{,}728 \text{ in}^3}$
cubic feet and cubic yards (yd³)	$1 \text{ yd}^3 = 27 \text{ ft}^3$	$\dfrac{27 \text{ ft}^3}{1 \text{ yd}^3}$ or $\dfrac{1 \text{ yd}^3}{27 \text{ ft}^3}$
fluid ounces (fl oz) and pints (pt)	$1 \text{ pt} = 16 \text{ fl oz}$	$\dfrac{16 \text{ fl oz}}{1 \text{ pt}}$ or $\dfrac{1 \text{ pt}}{16 \text{ fl oz}}$
pints and quarts (qt)	$1 \text{ qt} = 2 \text{ pt}$	$\dfrac{2 \text{ pt}}{1 \text{ qt}}$ or $\dfrac{1 \text{ qt}}{2 \text{ pt}}$
quarts and gallons (gal)	$1 \text{ gal} = 4 \text{ qt}$	$\dfrac{4 \text{ qt}}{1 \text{ gal}}$ or $\dfrac{1 \text{ gal}}{4 \text{ qt}}$

7. How many pints are in a 5-gallon pail?

EXAMPLE 7   What is the capacity (volume) in pints of a 1-gallon container of milk?

SOLUTION   We change from gallons to quarts and then quarts to pints by multiplying by the appropriate conversion factors as given in Table 3.

$$1 \text{ gal} = 1 \text{ gal} \times \frac{4 \text{ qt}}{1 \text{ gal}} \times \frac{2 \text{ pt}}{1 \text{ qt}}$$

$$= 1 \times 4 \times 2 \text{ pt}$$

$$= 8 \text{ pt}$$

A 1-gallon container has the same capacity as 8 one-pint containers.

EXAMPLE 8 A dairy herd produces 1,800 quarts of milk each day. How many gallons is this equivalent to?

SOLUTION   Converting 1,800 quarts to gallons, we have

$$1,800 \text{ qt} = 1,800 \text{ qt} \times \frac{1 \text{ gal}}{4 \text{ qt}}$$

$$= \frac{1,800}{4} \text{ gal}$$

$$= 450 \text{ gal}$$

We see that 1,800 quarts is equivalent to 450 gallons.

D   Volume: The Metric System

In the metric system the basic unit of measure for volume is the liter. A liter is the volume enclosed by a cube that is 10 cm on each edge, as shown in Figure 2. We can see that a liter is equivalent to 1,000 cm³.

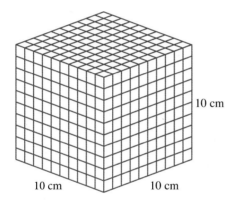

$$1 \text{ liter} = 10 \text{ cm} \times 10 \text{ cm} \times 10 \text{ cm}$$
$$= 1,000 \text{ cm}^3$$

FIGURE 2

The other units of volume in the metric system use the same prefixes we encountered previously. The units with prefixes centi, deci, and deka are not as common as the others, so in Table 4 we include only liters, milliliters, hectoliters, and kiloliters.

TABLE 4		
METRIC UNITS OF VOLUME		
The Relationship Between	**Is**	**To Convert From One To The Other, Multiply By**
milliliters (mL) and liters	1 liter (L) = 1,000 mL	$\frac{1,000 \text{ mL}}{1 \text{ liter}}$ or $\frac{1 \text{ liter}}{1,000 \text{ mL}}$
hectoliters (hL) and liters	100 liters = 1 hL	$\frac{100 \text{ liters}}{1 \text{ hL}}$ or $\frac{1 \text{ hL}}{100 \text{ liters}}$
kiloliters (kL) and liters	1,000 liters (L) = 1 kL	$\frac{1,000 \text{ liters}}{1 \text{ kL}}$ or $\frac{1 \text{ kL}}{1,000 \text{ liters}}$

8. A dairy herd produces 2,000 quarts of milk each day. How many 10-gallon containers will this milk fill?

Note As you can see from the table and the discussion above, a cubic centimeter (cm³) and a milliliter (mL) are equal. Both are one thousandth of a liter. It is also common in some fields (like medicine) to abbreviate the term cubic centimeter as cc. Although we will use the notation mL when discussing volume in the metric system, you should be aware that
$1 \text{ mL} = 1 \text{ cm}^3 = 1 \text{ cc}$.

Answer
8. 50 containers

Here is an example of conversion from one unit of volume to another in the metric system.

9. A 3.5-liter engine will have a volume of how many milliliters?

EXAMPLE 9 A sports car has a 2.2-liter engine. What is the displacement (volume) of the engine in milliliters?

SOLUTION Using the appropriate conversion factor from Table 4, we have

$$2.2 \text{ liters} = 2.2 \text{ liters} \times \frac{1{,}000 \text{ mL}}{1 \text{ liter}}$$

$$= 2.2 \times 1{,}000 \text{ mL}$$
$$= 2{,}200 \text{ mL}$$

Getting Ready for Class

After reading through the preceding section, respond in your own words and in complete sentences.

1. Write the formula for the area of each of the following:
   a. a square of side *s*.
   b. a rectangle with length *l* and width *w*.
2. What is the relationship between square feet and square inches?
3. Fill in the numerators below so that each conversion factor is equal to 1.

   a. $\dfrac{\text{qt}}{1 \text{ gal}}$ b. $\dfrac{\text{mL}}{1 \text{ liter}}$ c. $\dfrac{\text{acres}}{1 \text{ mi}^2}$

4. Write the conversion factor that will allow us to convert from square yards to square feet.

Problem Set 7.2

A Use the tables given in this section to make the following conversions. Be sure to show the conversion factor used in each case. [Examples 1–5]

1. 3 ft² to square inches
432 in²

▶ **2.** 5 ft² to square inches
720 in²

3. 288 in² to square feet
2 ft²

4. 720 in² to square feet
5 ft²

▶ **5.** 30 acres to square feet
1,306,800 ft²

6. 92 acres to square feet
4,007,520 ft²

7. 2 mi² to acres
1,280 acres

▶ **8.** 7 mi² to acres
4,480 acres

9. 1,920 acres to square miles
3 mi²

▶ **10.** 3,200 acres to square miles
5 mi²

▶ **11.** 12 yd² to square feet
108 ft²

▶ **12.** 20 yd² to square feet
180 ft²

B [Example 6]

13. 17 cm² to square millimeters
1,700 mm²

14. 150 mm² to square centimeters
1.5 cm²

15. 2.8 m² to square centimeters
28,000 cm²

▶ **16.** 10 dm² to square millimeters
100,000 mm²

17. 1,200 mm² to square meters
0.0012 m²

▶ **18.** 19.79 cm² to square meters
0.001979 m²

▶ **19.** 5 a to square meters
500 m²

20. 12 a to square centimeters
12,000,000 cm²

▶ **21.** 7 ha to ares
700 a

22. 3.6 ha to ares
360 a

▶ **23.** 342 a to hectares
3.42 ha

24. 986 a to hectares
9.86 ha

Make the following conversions using the conversion factors given in Tables 3 and 4.

C [Examples 7, 8]

25. 5 yd³ to cubic feet
135 ft³

▶ **26.** 3.8 yd³ to cubic feet
102.6 ft³

▶ **27.** 3 pt to fluid ounces
48 fl oz

28. 8 pt to fluid ounces
128 fl oz

29. 2 gal to quarts
8 qt

▶ **30.** 12 gal to quarts
48 qt

▶ **31.** 2.5 gal to pints
20 pt

32. 7 gal to pints
56 pt

33. 15 qt to fluid ounces
480 fl oz

▶ **34.** 5.9 qt to fluid ounces
188.8 fl oz

35. 64 pt to gallons
8 gal

▶ **36.** 256 pt to gallons
32 gal

37. 12 pt to quarts
6 qt

▶ **38.** 18 pt to quarts
9 qt

39. 243 ft³ to cubic yards
9 yd³

40. 864 ft³ to cubic yards
32 yd³

D [Example 9]

▶ **41.** 5 L to milliliters
5,000 mL

42. 9.6 L to milliliters
9,600 mL

43. 127 mL to liters
0.127 L

44. 93.8 mL to liters
0.0938 L

45. 4 kL to milliliters
4,000,000 mL

46. 3 kL to milliliters
3,000,000 mL

▶ **47.** 14.92 kL to liters
14,920 L

48. 4.71 kL to liters
4,710 L

■ Applying the Concepts

49. Google Earth The Google Earth map shows Yellowstone National Park. If the area of the park is roughly 3,402 square miles, how many acres does the park cover?

2,177,280 acres

50. Google Earth The Google Earth image shows an aerial view of a crop circle found near Wroughton, England. If the crop circle has a radius of about 59 meters, how many ares does it cover? Round to the nearest are.

109 ares

51. Swimming Pool A public swimming pool measures 100 meters by 30 meters and is rectangular. What is the area of the pool in ares?

30 a

52. Construction A family decides to put tiles in the entryway of their home. The entryway has an area of 6 square meters. If each tile is 5 centimeters by 5 centimeters, how many tiles will it take to cover the entryway?

2,400 tiles

53. Landscaping A landscaper is putting in a brick patio. The area of the patio is 110 square meters. If the bricks measure 10 centimeters by 20 centimeters, how many bricks will it take to make the patio? Assume no space between bricks.

5,500 bricks

54. Sewing A dressmaker is using a pattern that requires 2 square yards of material. If the material is on a bolt that is 54 inches wide, how long a piece of material must be cut from the bolt to be sure there is enough material for the pattern?

48 in.

55. Filling Coffee Cups If a regular-size coffee cup holds about $\frac{1}{2}$ pint, about how many cups can be filled from a 1-gallon coffee maker?

16 cups

56. Filling Glasses If a regular-size drinking glass holds about 0.25 liter of liquid, how many glasses can be filled from a 750-milliliter container?

3 glasses

57. Capacity of a Refrigerator A refrigerator has a capacity of 20 cubic feet. What is the capacity of the refrigerator in cubic inches?

34,560 in³

58. Volume of a Tank The gasoline tank on a car holds 18 gallons of gas. What is the volume of the tank in quarts?

72 qt

59. Filling Glasses How many 8-fluid-ounce glasses of water will it take to fill a 3-gallon aquarium?

48 glasses

60. Filling a Container How many 5-milliliter test tubes filled with water will it take to fill a 1-liter container?

200 test tubes

■ Calculator Problems

Set up the following problems as you have been doing. Then use a calculator to perform the actual calculations. Round answers to two decimal places where appropriate.

61. Geography Lake Superior is the largest of the Great Lakes. It covers 31,700 square miles of area. What is the area of Lake Superior in acres?

20,288,000 acres

62. Geography The state of California consists of 156,360 square miles of land and 2,330 square miles of water. Write the total area (both land and water) in acres.

101,561,600 acres   Some calculators will give the results of Problems 61 and 62 in scientific notation.

63. Geography Death Valley National Monument contains 2,067,795 acres of land. How many square miles is this?

3,230.93 mi²

64. Geography The Badlands National Monument in South Dakota was established in 1929. It covers 243,302 acres of land. What is the area in square miles?

380.16 mi²

▶ **65.** Convert 93.4 qt to gallons.

23.35 gal

▶ **66.** Convert 7,362 fl oz to gallons.

57.52 gal

▶ **67.** How many cubic feet are contained in 796 cubic yards?

21,492 ft³

▶ **68.** The engine of a car has a displacement of 440 cubic inches. What is the displacement in cubic feet?

0.25 ft³

■ Getting Ready for the Next Section

Perform the indicated operations.

69. 12×16
192

70. 15×16
240

71. $3 \times 2,000$
6,000

72. $5 \times 2,000$
10,000

73. $3 \times 1,000 \times 100$
300,000

74. $5 \times 1,000 \times 100$
500,000

75. $12,500 \times \dfrac{1}{1,000}$
12.5

76. $15,000 \times \dfrac{1}{1,000}$
15

■ Maintaining Your Skills

The following problems review addition and subtraction with fractions and mixed numbers.

77. $\dfrac{3}{8} + \dfrac{1}{4}$
$\dfrac{5}{8}$

78. $\dfrac{1}{2} + \dfrac{1}{4}$
$\dfrac{3}{4}$

79. $3\dfrac{1}{2} + 5\dfrac{1}{2}$
9

80. $6\dfrac{7}{8} + 1\dfrac{5}{8}$
$8\dfrac{1}{2}$

81. $\dfrac{7}{15} - \dfrac{2}{15}$
$\dfrac{1}{3}$

82. $\dfrac{5}{8} - \dfrac{1}{4}$
$\dfrac{3}{8}$

83. $\dfrac{5}{36} - \dfrac{1}{48}$
$\dfrac{17}{144}$

84. $\dfrac{7}{39} - \dfrac{2}{65}$
$\dfrac{29}{195}$

7.3

A Weights: The U.S. System

The most common units of weight in the U.S. system are ounces, pounds, and tons. The relationships among these units are given in Table 1.

TABLE 1		
UNITS OF WEIGHT IN THE U.S. SYSTEM		
The Relationship Between	**Is**	**To Convert From One To The Other, Multiply By**
ounces (oz) and pounds (lb)	1 lb = 16 oz	$\dfrac{16\ oz}{1\ lb}$ or $\dfrac{1\ lb}{16\ oz}$
pounds and tons (T)	1 T = 2,000 lb	$\dfrac{2,000\ lb}{1\ T}$ or $\dfrac{1\ T}{2,000\ lb}$

EXAMPLE 1 Convert 12 pounds to ounces.

SOLUTION Using the conversion factor from the table, and applying the method we have been using, we have

$$12\ lb = 12\ \cancel{lb} \times \frac{16\ oz}{1\ \cancel{lb}}$$
$$= 12 \times 16\ oz$$
$$= 192\ oz$$

12 pounds is equivalent to 192 ounces.

EXAMPLE 2 Convert 3 tons to pounds.

SOLUTION We use the conversion factor from the table. We have

$$3\ T = 3\ \cancel{T} \times \frac{2,000\ lb}{1\ \cancel{T}}$$
$$= 6,000\ lb$$

6,000 pounds is the equivalent of 3 tons.

B Weights: The Metric System

In the metric system the basic unit of weight is a gram. We use the same prefixes we have already used to write the other units of weight in terms of grams. Table 2 lists the most common metric units of weight and their conversion factors.

TABLE 2		
METRIC UNITS OF WEIGHT		
The Relationship Between	**Is**	**To Convert From One To The Other, Multiply By**
milligrams (mg) and grams (g)	1 g = 1,000 mg	$\dfrac{1,000\ mg}{1\ g}$ or $\dfrac{1g}{1,000\ mg}$
centigrams (cg) and grams	1 g = 100 cg	$\dfrac{100\ cg}{1\ g}$ or $\dfrac{1\ g}{100\ cg}$
kilograms (kg) and grams	1,000 g = 1 kg	$\dfrac{1,000\ g}{1\ kg}$ or $\dfrac{1\ kg}{1,000\ g}$
metric tons (t) and kilograms	1,000 kg = 1 t	$\dfrac{1,000\ kg}{1\ t}$ or $\dfrac{1\ t}{1,000\ kg}$

1. Convert 15 pounds to ounces.

2. Convert 5 tons to pounds.

Answers
1. 240 oz **2.** 10,000 lb

3. Convert 5 kilograms to milligrams.

EXAMPLE 3 Convert 3 kilograms to centigrams.

SOLUTION We convert kilograms to grams and then grams to centigrams:

$$3 \text{ kg} = 3 \text{ kg} \times \frac{1,000 \text{ g}}{1 \text{ kg}} \times \frac{100 \text{ cg}}{1 \text{ g}}$$

$$= 3 \times 1,000 \times 100 \text{ cg}$$
$$= 300,000 \text{ cg}$$

4. A bottle of vitamin C contains 75 tablets. If each tablet contains 200 milligrams of vitamin C, what is the total number of grams of vitamin C in the bottle?

EXAMPLE 4 A bottle of vitamin C contains 50 tablets. Each tablet contains 250 milligrams of vitamin C. What is the total number of grams of vitamin C in the bottle?

SOLUTION We begin by finding the total number of milligrams of vitamin C in the bottle. Since there are 50 tablets, and each contains 250 mg of vitamin C, we can multiply 50 by 250 to get the total number of milligrams of vitamin C:

$$\text{Milligrams of vitamin C} = 50 \times 250 \text{ mg}$$
$$= 12,500 \text{ mg}$$

Next we convert 12,500 mg to grams:

$$12,500 \text{ mg} = 12,500 \text{ mg} \times \frac{1 \text{ g}}{1,000 \text{ mg}}$$

$$= \frac{12,500}{1,000} \text{ g}$$

$$= 12.5 \text{ g}$$

The bottle contains 12.5 g of vitamin C.

Getting Ready for Class

After reading through the preceding section, respond in your own words and in complete sentences.

1. What is the relationship between pounds and ounces?

2. Write the conversion factor used to convert from pounds to ounces.

3. Write the conversion factor used to convert from milligrams to grams.

4. What is the relationship between grams and kilograms?

Answers
3. 5,000,000 mg   **4.** 15 g

Problem Set 7.3

Use the conversion factors in Tables 1 and 2 to make the following conversions.

A [Examples 1, 2]

▶ 1. 8 lb to ounces
128 oz

▶ 2. 5 lb to ounces
80 oz

▶ 3. 2 T to pounds
4,000 lb

4. 5 T to pounds
10,000 lb

▶ 5. 192 oz to pounds
12 lb

6. 176 oz to pounds
11 lb

▶ 7. 1,800 lb to tons
0.9 T

8. 10,200 lb to tons
5.1 T

▶ 9. 1 T to ounces
32,000 oz

▶ 10. 3 T to ounces
96,000 oz

▶ 11. $3\frac{1}{2}$ lb to ounces
56 oz

12. $5\frac{1}{4}$ lb to ounces
84 oz

▶ 13. $6\frac{1}{2}$ T to pounds
13,000 lb

▶ 14. $4\frac{1}{5}$ T to pounds
8,400 lb

B [Examples 3, 4]

▶ 15. 2 kg to grams
2,000 g

16. 5 kg to grams
5,000 g

▶ 17. 4 cg to milligrams
40 mg

▶ 18. 3 cg to milligrams
30 mg

▶ 19. 2 kg to centigrams
200,000 cg

20. 5 kg to centigrams
500,000 cg

▶ 21. 5.08 g to centigrams
508 cg

▶ 22. 7.14 g to centigrams
714 cg

▶ 23. 450 cg to grams
4.5 g

24. 979 cg to grams
9.79 g

▶ 25. 478.95 mg to centigrams
47.895 cg

▶ 26. 659.43 mg to centigrams
65.943 cg

▶ 27. 1,578 mg to grams
1.578 g

28. 1,979 mg to grams
1.979 g

▶ 29. 42,000 cg to kilograms
0.42 kg

▶ 30. 97,000 cg to kilograms
0.97 kg

■ Applying the Concepts

31. Fish Oil A bottle of fish oil contains 60 soft gels, each containing 800 mg of the omega-3 fatty acid. How many total grams of the omega-3 fatty acid are in this bottle?
48 g

32. Fish Oil A bottle of fish oil contains 50 soft gels, each containing 300 mg of the omega-6 fatty acid. How many total grams of the omega-6 fatty acid are in this bottle?
15 g

▶ **33. B-Complex** A certain B-complex vitamin supplement contains 50 mg of riboflavin, or vitamin B_2. A bottle contains 80 vitamins. How many total grams of riboflavin are in this bottle?
4 g

34. B-Complex A certain B-complex vitamin supplement contains 30 mg of thiamine, or vitamin B_1. A bottle contains 80 vitamins. How many total grams of thiamine are in this bottle?
2.4 g

35. Aspirin A bottle of low-strength aspirin contains 120 tablets. Each tablet contains 81 mg of aspirin. How many total grams of aspirin are in this bottle?
9.72 g

36. Aspirin A bottle of maximum-strength aspirin contains 90 tablets. Each tablet contains 500 mg of aspirin. How many total grams of aspirin are in this bottle?
45 g

▶ **37. Vitamin C** A certain brand of vitamin C contains 500 mg per tablet. A bottle contains 240 tablets. How many total grams of vitamin C are in this bottle?
120 g

38. Vitamin C A certain brand of vitamin C contains 600 mg per tablet. A bottle contains 150 vitamins. How many total grams of vitamin C are in this bottle?
90 g

Coca-Cola Bottles The soft drink Coke is sold throughout the world. Although the size of the bottle varies between different countries, a "six-pack" is sold everywhere. For each of the problems below, find the number of liters in a "6-pack" from the given bottle size.

Country	Bottle size	Liters in a 6-pack
39. Estonia	500 mL	3 L
40. Israel	350 mL	2.1 L
41. Jordan	250 mL	1.5 L
42. Kenya	300 mL	1.8 L

Paul A. Souders/Corbis

43. Nursing A patient is prescribed a dosage of Ceclor® of 561 mg. How many grams is the dosage?
0.561 grams

44. Nursing A patient is prescribed a dosage of 425 mg. How many grams is the dosage?
0.425 grams

45. Nursing Dilatrate®-SR comes in 40 milligram capsules. Use this information to determine how many capsules should be given for the prescribed dosages.

    a. 120 mg   3 capsules

    b. 40 mg   1 capsule

    c. 80 mg   2 capsules

46. Nursing A brand of methyldopa comes in 250 milligram tablets. Use this information to determine how many capsules should be given for the prescribed dosages.

    a. 0.125 gram $\frac{1}{2}$ tablet

    b. 750 milligrams   3 tablets

    c. 0.5 gram   2 tablets

■ Getting Ready for the Next Section

Perform the indicated operations.

47. 8×2.54
20.32

48. 9×3.28
29.52

49. $3 \times 1.06 \times 2$
6.36

50. $3 \times 5 \times 3.79$
56.85

51. $80.5 \div 1.61$
50

52. $96.6 \div 1.61$
60

53. $125 \div 2.50$
50

54. $165 \div 2.20$
75

55. $2,000 \div 16.39$
(Round your answer to the nearest whole number.)
122

56. $2,200 \div 16.39$
(Round your answer to the nearest whole number.)
134

57. $\frac{9}{5}(120) + 32$
248

58. $\frac{9}{5}(40) + 32$
104

59. $\frac{5(102 - 30)}{9}$
40

60. $\frac{5(105 - 42)}{9}$
35

■ Maintaining Your Skills

Write each decimal as an equivalent proper fraction or mixed number.

61. 0.18

$\frac{9}{50}$

62. 0.04

$\frac{1}{25}$

63. 0.09

$\frac{9}{100}$

64. 0.045

$\frac{9}{200}$

65. 0.8

$\frac{4}{5}$

66. 0.08

$\frac{2}{25}$

67. 1.75

$1\frac{3}{4}$

68. 3.125

$3\frac{1}{8}$

Write each fraction or mixed number as a decimal.

69. $\frac{3}{4}$

0.75

70. $\frac{9}{10}$

0.9

71. $\frac{17}{20}$

0.85

72. $\frac{1}{8}$

0.125

73. $\frac{3}{5}$

0.6

74. $\frac{7}{8}$

0.875

75. $3\frac{5}{8}$

3.625

76. $1\frac{1}{16}$

1.0625

Use the definition of exponents to simplify each expression.

77. $\left(\frac{1}{2}\right)^3$

$\frac{1}{8}$

78. $\left(\frac{5}{9}\right)^2$

$\frac{25}{81}$

79. $\left(2\frac{1}{2}\right)^2$

$6\frac{1}{4}$

80. $\left(\frac{1}{3}\right)^4$

$\frac{1}{81}$

81. $(0.5)^3$

0.125

82. $(0.05)^3$

0.000125

83. $(2.5)^2$

6.25

84. $(0.5)^4$

0.0625

Converting Between the U.S. and Metric Systems and Temperature

A Converting Between the U.S. and Metric Systems

Because most of us have always used the U.S. system of measurement in our everyday lives, we are much more familiar with it on an intuitive level than we are with the metric system. We have an intuitive idea of how long feet and inches are, how much a pound weighs, and what a square yard of material looks like. The metric system is actually much easier to use than the U.S. system. The reason some of us have such a hard time with the metric system is that we don't have the feel for it that we do for the U.S. system. We have trouble visualizing how long a meter is or how much a gram weighs. The following list is intended to give you something to associate with each basic unit of measurement in the metric system:

1. A meter is just a little longer than a yard.

2. The length of the edge of a sugar cube is about 1 centimeter.

3. A liter is just a little larger than a quart.

4. A sugar cube has a volume of approximately 1 milliliter.

5. A paper clip weighs about 1 gram.

6. A 2-pound can of coffee weighs about 1 kilogram.

TABLE 1

ACTUAL CONVERSION FACTORS BETWEEN THE METRIC AND U.S. SYSTEMS OF MEASUREMENT

The Relationship Between	Is	To Convert From One To The Other, Multiply By
Length		
inches and centimeters	2.54 cm = 1 in.	$\dfrac{2.54 \text{ cm}}{1 \text{ in.}}$ or $\dfrac{1 \text{ in.}}{2.54 \text{ cm}}$
feet and meters	1 m = 3.28 ft	$\dfrac{3.28 \text{ ft}}{1 \text{ m}}$ or $\dfrac{1 \text{ m}}{3.28 \text{ ft}}$
miles and kilometers	1.61 km = 1 mi	$\dfrac{1.61 \text{ km}}{1 \text{ mi}}$ or $\dfrac{1 \text{ mi}}{1.61 \text{ km}}$
Area		
square inches and square centimeters	6.45 cm² = 1 in²	$\dfrac{6.45 \text{ cm}^2}{1 \text{ in}^2}$ or $\dfrac{1 \text{ in}^2}{6.45 \text{ cm}^2}$
square meters and square yards	1.196 yd² = 1 m²	$\dfrac{1.196 \text{ yd}^2}{1 \text{ m}^2}$ or $\dfrac{1 \text{ m}^2}{1.196 \text{ yd}^2}$
acres and hectares	1 ha = 2.47 acres	$\dfrac{2.47 \text{ acres}}{1 \text{ ha}}$ or $\dfrac{1 \text{ ha}}{2.47 \text{ acres}}$
Volume		
cubic inches and milliliters	16.39 mL = 1 in³	$\dfrac{16.39 \text{ mL}}{1 \text{ in}^3}$ or $\dfrac{1 \text{ in}^3}{16.39 \text{ mL}}$
liters and quarts	1.06 qt = 1 liter	$\dfrac{1.06 \text{ qt}}{1 \text{ liter}}$ or $\dfrac{1 \text{ liter}}{1.06 \text{ qt}}$
gallons and liters	3.79 liters = 1 gal	$\dfrac{3.79 \text{ liters}}{1 \text{ gal}}$ or $\dfrac{1 \text{ gal}}{3.79 \text{ liters}}$
Weight		
ounces and grams	28.3 g = 1 oz	$\dfrac{28.3 \text{ g}}{1 \text{ oz}}$ or $\dfrac{1 \text{ oz}}{28.3 \text{ g}}$
kilograms and pounds	2.20 lb = 1 kg	$\dfrac{2.20 \text{ lb}}{1 \text{ kg}}$ or $\dfrac{1 \text{ kg}}{2.20 \text{ lb}}$

There are many other conversion factors that we could have included in Table 1. We have listed only the most common ones. Almost all of them are approximations. That is, most of the conversion factors are decimals that have been rounded to the nearest hundredth. If we want more accuracy, we obtain a table that has more digits in the conversion factors.

PRACTICE PROBLEMS

1. Convert 10 inches to centimeters.

EXAMPLE 1 Convert 8 inches to centimeters.

SOLUTION Choosing the appropriate conversion factor from Table 1, we have

$$8 \text{ in.} = 8 \text{ in.} \times \frac{2.54 \text{ cm}}{1 \text{ in.}}$$
$$= 8 \times 2.54 \text{ cm}$$
$$= 20.32 \text{ cm}$$

2. Convert 16.4 feet to meters.

EXAMPLE 2 Convert 80.5 kilometers to miles.

SOLUTION Using the conversion factor that takes us from kilometers to miles, we have

$$80.5 \text{ km} = 80.5 \text{ km} \times \frac{1 \text{ mi}}{1.61 \text{ km}}$$
$$= \frac{80.5}{1.61} \text{ mi}$$
$$= 50 \text{ mi}$$

So 50 miles is equivalent to 80.5 kilometers. If we travel at 50 miles per hour in a car, we are moving at the rate of 80.5 kilometers per hour.

3. Convert 10 liters to gallons. Round to the nearest hundredth.

EXAMPLE 3 Convert 3 liters to pints.

SOLUTION Because Table 1 doesn't list a conversion factor that will take us directly from liters to pints, we first convert liters to quarts, and then convert quarts to pints.

$$3 \text{ liters} = 3 \text{ liters} \times \frac{1.06 \text{ qt}}{1 \text{ liter}} \times \frac{2 \text{ pt}}{1 \text{ qt}}$$
$$= 3 \times 1.06 \times 2 \text{ pt}$$
$$= 6.36 \text{ pt}$$

4. The engine in a car has a 2.2-liter displacement. What is the displacement in cubic inches (to the nearest cubic inch)?

EXAMPLE 4 The engine in a car has a 2-liter displacement. What is the displacement in cubic inches?

SOLUTION We convert liters to milliliters and then milliliters to cubic inches:

$$2 \text{ liters} = 2 \text{ liters} \times \frac{1,000 \text{ mL}}{1 \text{ liter}} \times \frac{1 \text{ in}^3}{16.39 \text{ mL}}$$
$$= \frac{2 \times 1,000}{16.39} \text{ in}^3 \quad \text{This calculation should be done on a calculator}$$
$$= 122 \text{ in}^3 \quad \text{To the nearest cubic inch}$$

Answers
1. 25.4 cm **2.** 5 m
3. 2.64 gal **4.** 134 in³

EXAMPLE 5 If a person weighs 125 pounds, what is her weight in kilograms?

SOLUTION Converting from pounds to kilograms, we have

$$125 \text{ lb} = 125 \text{ lb} \times \frac{1 \text{ kg}}{2.20 \text{ lb}}$$

$$= \frac{125}{2.20} \text{ kg}$$

$$= 56.8 \text{ kg} \quad \text{To the nearest tenth}$$

5. A person who weighs 165 pounds weighs how many kilograms?

B Temperature

We end this section with a discussion of temperature in both systems of measurement.

In the U.S. system we measure temperature on the Fahrenheit scale. On this scale, water boils at 212 degrees and freezes at 32 degrees. When we write 32 degrees measured on the Fahrenheit scale, we use the notation

$32°F$ (read, "32 degrees Fahrenheit.")

In the metric system the scale we use to measure temperature is the Celsius scale (formerly called the centigrade scale). On this scale, water boils at 100 degrees and freezes at 0 degrees. When we write 100 degrees measured on the Celsius scale, we use the notation

$100°C$ (read, "100 degrees Celsius.")

Table 2 is intended to give you a feel for the relationship between the two temperature scales. Table 3 gives the formulas, in both symbols and words, that are used to convert between the two scales.

TABLE 2		
Situation	**Temperature Fahrenheit**	**Temperature Celsius**
Water freezes	32°F	0°C
Room temperature	68°F	20°C
Normal body temperature	98.6°F	37°C
Water boils	212°F	100°C
Bake cookies	350°F	176.7°C
Broil meat	554°F	290°C

Answer
5. 75 kg

TABLE 3

To Convert From	Formula In Symbols	Formula In Words
Fahrenheit to Celsius	$C = \dfrac{5(F - 32)}{9}$	Subtract 32, multiply by 5, and then divide by 9.
Celsius to Fahrenheit	$F = \dfrac{9}{5}C + 32$	Multiply by $\dfrac{9}{5}$, and then add 32.

The following examples show how we use the formulas given in Table 3.

EXAMPLE 6 Convert 120°C to degrees Fahrenheit.

SOLUTION We use the formula

$$F = \frac{9}{5}C + 32$$

and replace C with 120:

When $C = 120$

the formula $F = \dfrac{9}{5}C + 32$

becomes $F = \dfrac{9}{5}(120) + 32$

$F = 216 + 32$

$F = 248$

We see that 120°C is equivalent to 248°F; they both mean the same temperature.

EXAMPLE 7 A man with the flu has a temperature of 102°F. What is his temperature on the Celsius scale?

SOLUTION When $F = 102$

the formula $C = \dfrac{5(F - 32)}{9}$

becomes $C = \dfrac{5(102 - 32)}{9}$

$C = \dfrac{5(70)}{9}$

$C = 38.9$ Rounded to the nearest tenth

The man's temperature, rounded to the nearest tenth, is 38.9°C on the Celsius scale.

Getting Ready for Class

After reading through the preceding section, respond in your own words and in complete sentences.

1. Write the equality that gives the relationship between centimeters and inches.

2. Write the equality that gives the relationship between grams and ounces.

3. Fill in the numerators below so that each conversion factor is equal to 1.

   a. $\dfrac{\text{ft}}{1 \text{ meter}}$ b. $\dfrac{\text{qt}}{1 \text{ liter}}$ c. $\dfrac{\text{lb}}{1 \text{ kg}}$

4. Is it a hot day if the temperature outside is 37°C?

---

6. Convert 40°C to degrees Fahrenheit.

7. A child is running a temperature of 101.6°F. What is her temperature, to the nearest tenth of a degree, on the Celsius scale?

Answers
6. 104°F 7. 38.7°C

Problem Set 7.4

A B Use Tables 1 and 3 to make the following conversions. [Examples 1–7]

▶ **1.** 6 in. to centimeters
   15.24 cm

2. 1 ft to centimeters
   30.48 cm

▶ **3.** 4 m to feet
   13.12 ft

▶ **4.** 2 km to feet
   6,560 ft

▶ **5.** 6 m to yards
   6.56 yd

▶ **6.** 15 mi to kilometers
   24.15 km

7. 20 mi to meters (round to the nearest hundred meters) ▶
   32,200 m

8. 600 m to yards
   656 yd

▶ **9.** 5 m² to square yards (round to the nearest hundredth)
   5.98 yd²

10. 2 in² to square centimeters (round to the nearest tenth)
   12.9 cm²

▶ **11.** 10 ha to acres
   24.7 acres

12. 50 a to acres
   1.235 acres

13. 500 in³ to milliliters
   8,195 mL

▶ **14.** 400 in³ to liters
   6.556 L

▶ **15.** 2 L to quarts
   2.12 qt

16. 15 L to quarts
   15.9 qt

▶ **17.** 20 gal to liters
   75.8 L

18. 15 gal to liters
   56.85 L

▶ **19.** 12 oz to grams
   339.6 g

20. 1 lb to grams (round to the nearest 10 grams)
   450 g

21. 15 kg to pounds
   33 lb

▶ **22.** 10 kg to ounces
   352 oz

▶ **23.** 185°C to degrees Fahrenheit
   365°F

24. 20°C to degrees Fahrenheit
   68°F

▶ **25.** 86°F to degrees Celsius
   30°C

▶ **26.** 122°F to degrees Celsius
   50°C

▶ Selected exercises available online at www.webassign.net/brookscole

■ Applying the Concepts

27. Temperature The chart shows the temperatures for some of the world's hottest places. Convert the temperature in Al'Aziziyah to Celsius.

58°C

Heating Up

136.4°F	Al'Aziziyah, Libya
134.0°F	Greenland Ranch, Death Valley, United States
131.0°F	Ghudamis, Libya
131.0°F	Kebili, Tunisia
130.1°F	Tombouctou, Mali

Source: Aneki.com

28. Google Earth The Google Earth image is of Lake Clark National Park in Alaska. Lake Clark has an average temperature of 40 degrees Fahrenheit. What is its average temperature in Celsius to the nearest degree?

4°C

Image © 2008 TerraMetrics
Image NASA
Image © 2008 DigitalGlobe

Nursing Liquid medication is usually given in milligrams per milliliter. Use the information to find the amount a patient should take for a prescribed dosage.

29. Vantin© has a dosage strength of 100 mg/5 mL. If a patient is prescribed a dosage of 150 mg, how many milliliters should she take?

7.5 mL

30. A brand of amoxicillin has a dosage strength of 125 mg/5 mL. If a patient is prescribed a dosage of 25 mg, how many milliliters should she take?

1 mL

■ Calculator Problems

Set up the following problems as we have set up the examples in this section. Then use a calculator for the calculations and round your answers to the nearest hundredth.

▶ **31.** 10 cm to inches
3.94 in.

32. 100 mi to kilometers
161 km

33. 25 ft to meters
7.62 m

▶ **34.** 400 mL to cubic inches
24.41 in³

▶ **35.** 49 qt to liters
46.23 L

▶ **36.** 65 L to gallons
17.15 gal

37. 500 g to ounces
17.67 oz

▶ **38.** 100 lb to kilograms
45.45 kg

39. Weight Give your weight in kilograms.
Answers will vary.

40. Height Give your height in meters and centimeters.
Answers will vary.

▶ **41. Sports** The 100-yard dash is a popular race in track. How far is 100 yards in meters?
91.46 m

▶ **42. Engine Displacement** A 351-cubic-inch engine has a displacement of how many liters?
5.75 L

▶ **43. Sewing** 25 square yards of material is how many square meters?
20.90 m²

44. Weight How many grams does a 5 lb 4 oz roast weigh?
2,377.2 g

45. Speed 55 miles per hour is equivalent to how many kilometers per hour?
88.55 km/hr

▶ **46. Capacity** A 1-quart container holds how many liters?
0.94 liter

▶ **47. Sports** A high jumper jumps 6 ft 8 in. How many meters is this?
2.03 m

48. Farming A farmer owns 57 acres of land. How many hectares is that?
23.08 ha

▶ **49. Body Temperature** A person has a temperature of 101°F. What is the person's temperature, to the nearest tenth, on the Celsius scale?
38.3°C

50. Air Temperature If the temperature outside is 30°C, is it a better day for water skiing or for snow skiing?
Water skiing

■ Getting Ready for the Next Section

Perform the indicated operations.

51. $15 + 60$
75

52. $25 + 60$
85

53.
$$\begin{array}{r} 37 \\ + 45 \\ \hline 82 \end{array}$$

54.
$$\begin{array}{r} 27 \\ + 46 \\ \hline 73 \end{array}$$

55. $3 + 0.25$
3.25

56. $2 + 0.75$
2.75

57. $82 - 60$
22

58. $73 - 60$
13

59.
$$\begin{array}{r} 75 \\ - 34 \\ \hline 41 \end{array}$$

60.
$$\begin{array}{r} 85 \\ - 42 \\ \hline 43 \end{array}$$

61. 12×4
48

62. 8×4
32

63. $3 \times 60 + 15$
195

64. $2 \times 65 + 45$
175

65. $3 + 17 \times \dfrac{1}{65}$
3.26

66. $2 + 45 \times \dfrac{1}{60}$
2.75

67. If fish costs $6.00 per pound, find the cost of 15 pounds.
$90.00

68. If fish costs $5.00 per pound, find the cost of 14 pounds.
$70.00

◼ Maintaining Your Skills

Find the mean and the range for each set of numbers.

69. 5, 7, 9, 11
mean = 8, range = 6

70. 6, 8, 10, 12
mean = 9, range = 6

71. 1, 4, 5, 10, 10
mean = 6, range = 9

72. 2, 4, 4, 6, 9
mean = 5, range = 7

Find the median and the range for each set of numbers.

73. 15, 18, 21, 24, 29
median = 21, range = 14

74. 20, 30, 35, 45, 50
median = 35, range = 30

75. 32, 38, 42, 48
median = 40, range = 16

76. 53, 61, 67, 75
median = 64, range = 22

Find the mode and the range for each set of numbers.

77. 20, 15, 14, 13, 14, 18
mode = 14, range = 7

78. 17, 31, 31, 26, 31, 29
mode = 31, range = 14

79. A student has quiz scores of 65, 72, 70, 88, 70, and 73. Find each of the following:
a. mean score
73
b. median score
71
c. mode of the scores
70
d. range of scores
23

80. A person has bowling scores of 207, 224, 195, 207, 185, and 182. Find each of the following:
a. mean score
200
b. median score
201
c. mode of the scores
207
d. range of scores
42

◼ Extending the Concepts

Nursing For children, the amount of medicine prescribed is often determined by the child's weight. Usually, it is calculated from the milligrams per kilogram per day listed on the medication's box.

81. Ceclor® has a dosage strength of 250 mg/mL. How much should a 42 lb child be given a day if the dosage is 20 mg/kg/day? How many milliliters is that?
381.8 mg/day; 1.53 mL/day

Operations with Time and Mixed Units

Many occupations require the use of a time card. A time card records the number of hours and minutes at work. At the end of a work week the hours and minutes are totaled separately, and then the minutes are converted to hours.

In this section we will perform operations with mixed units of measure. Mixed units are used when we use 2 hours 30 minutes, rather than two and a half hours, or 5 feet 9 inches, rather than five and three-quarter feet. As you will see, many of these types of problems arise in everyday life.

A Converting Time to Single Units

The Relationship Between	is	To Convert from One to the Other, Multiply by
minutes and seconds	1 min = 60 sec	$\dfrac{1 \text{ min}}{60 \text{ sec}}$ or $\dfrac{60 \text{ sec}}{1 \text{ min}}$
hours and minutes	1 hr = 60 min	$\dfrac{1 \text{ hr}}{60 \text{ min}}$ or $\dfrac{60 \text{ min}}{1 \text{ hr}}$

EXAMPLE 1 Convert 3 hours 15 minutes to
a. Minutes **b.** Hours

SOLUTION **a.** To convert to minutes, we multiply the hours by the conversion factor and then add minutes:

$$3 \text{ hr } 15 \text{ min} = 3 \text{ hr} \times \frac{60 \text{ min}}{1 \text{ hr}} + 15 \text{ min}$$
$$= 180 \text{ min} + 15 \text{ min}$$
$$= 195 \text{ min}$$

b. To convert to hours, we multiply the minutes by the conversion factor and then add hours:

$$3 \text{ hr } 15 \text{ min} = 3 \text{ hr} + 15 \text{ min} \times \frac{1 \text{ hr}}{60 \text{ min}}$$
$$= 3 \text{ hr} + 0.25 \text{ hr}$$
$$= 3.25 \text{ hr}$$

B Addition and Subtraction with Mixed Units

EXAMPLE 2 Add 5 minutes 37 seconds and 7 minutes 45 seconds.

SOLUTION First, we align the units properly

$$\begin{array}{rr} 5 \text{ min} & 37 \text{ sec} \\ + 7 \text{ min} & 45 \text{ sec} \\ \hline 12 \text{ min} & 82 \text{ sec} \end{array}$$

Since there are 60 seconds in every minute, we write 82 seconds as 1 minute 22 seconds. We have

$$12 \text{ min } 82 \text{ sec} = 12 \text{ min} + 1 \text{ min } 22 \text{ sec}$$
$$= 13 \text{ min } 22 \text{ sec}$$

PRACTICE PROBLEMS

1. Convert 2 hours 45 minutes to
   a. Minutes **b.** Hours

2. Add 4 min. 27 sec. and 8 min. 46 sec.

Answers
1. **a** 165 minutes **b.** 2.75 hours
2. 13 min 13 sec

The idea of adding the units separately is similar to adding mixed fractions. That is, we align the whole numbers with the whole numbers and the fractions with the fractions.

Similarly, when we subtract units of time, we "borrow" 60 seconds from the minutes column, or 60 minutes from the hours column.

3. Subtract 42 min from 6 hr 25 min.

EXAMPLE 3 Subtract 34 minutes from 8 hours 15 minutes.

SOLUTION Again, we first line up the numbers in the hours column, and then the numbers in the minutes column:

$$
\begin{array}{rr}
8\ \text{hr} & 15\ \text{min} \\
- & 34\ \text{min} \\
\hline
\end{array}
\qquad
\begin{array}{rr}
7\ \text{hr} & 75\ \text{min} \\
- & 34\ \text{min} \\
\hline
7\ \text{hr} & 41\ \text{min}
\end{array}
$$

C Multiplication with Mixed Units

Next we see how to multiply and divide using units of measure.

4. Rob is purchasing 4 halibut. The fish cost $5.00 per pound, and each weighs 3 lb 8 oz. What is the cost of the fish?

EXAMPLE 4 Jake purchases 4 halibut. The fish cost $6.00 per pound, and each weighs 3 lb 12 oz. What is the cost of the fish?

SOLUTION First, we multiply each unit by 4, the number of halibut purchased:

$$
\begin{array}{rr}
3\ \text{lb} & 12\ \text{oz} \\
\times & 4 \\
\hline
12\ \text{lb} & 48\ \text{oz}
\end{array}
$$

To convert the 48 ounces to pounds, we multiply the ounces by the conversion factor.

$$
\begin{aligned}
12\ \text{lb}\ 48\ \text{oz} &= 12\ \text{lb} + 48\ \text{oz} \times \frac{1\ \text{lb}}{16\ \text{oz}} \\
&= 12\ \text{lb} + 3\ \text{lb} \\
&= 15\ \text{lb}
\end{aligned}
$$

Finally, we multiply the 15 lb and $6.00/lb for a total price of $90.00

Getting Ready for Class

After reading through the preceding section, respond in your own words and in complete sentences.

1. Explain the difference between saying *two and a half hours* and saying *2 hours and 30 minutes.*
2. How are operations with mixed units of measure similar to operations with mixed numbers?
3. Why do we borrow a 60 from the minutes column for the seconds column when subtracting in Example 3?
4. Give an example of when you may have to use multiplication with mixed units of measure.

Answers
3. 5 hr 43 min   **4.** $70

Problem Set 7.5

A Use the tables of conversion factors given in this section and other sections in this chapter to make the following conversions. (Round your answers to the nearest hundredth.) [Example 1]

▶ **1.** 4 hours 30 minutes to
   a. Minutes
   270 min
   b. Hours
   4.5 hr

2. 2 hours 45 minutes to
   a. Minutes
   165 min
   b. Hours
   2.75 hr

3. 5 hours 20 minutes to
   a. Minutes
   320 min
   b. Hours
   5.33 hr

▶ **4.** 4 hours 40 minutes to
   a. Minutes
   280 min
   b. Hours
   4.67 hr

▶ **5.** 6 minutes 30 seconds to
   a. Seconds
   390 sec
   b. Minutes
   6.5 min

6. 8 minutes 45 seconds to
   a. Seconds
   525 sec
   b. Minutes
   8.75 min

▶ **7.** 5 minutes 20 seconds to
   a. Seconds
   320 sec
   b. Minutes
   5.33 min

8. 4 minutes 40 seconds to
   a. Seconds
   280 sec
   b. Minutes
   4.67 min

▶ **9.** 2 pounds 8 ounces to
   a. Ounces
   40 oz
   b. Pounds
   2.5 lb

10. 3 pounds 4 ounces to
   a. Ounces
   52 oz
   b. Pounds
   3.25 lb

▶ **11.** 4 pounds 12 ounces to
   a. Ounces
   76 oz
   b. Pounds
   4.75 lb

▶ **12.** 5 pounds 16 ounces to
   a. Ounces
   96 oz
   b. Pounds
   6 lb

▶ **13.** 4 feet 6 inches to
   a. Inches
   54 in.
   b. Feet
   4.5 ft

14. 3 feet 3 inches to
   a. Inches
   39 in.
   b. Feet
   3.25 ft

▶ **15.** 5 feet 9 inches to
   a. Inches
   69 in.
   b. Feet
   5.75 ft

16. 3 feet 4 inches to
   a. Inches
   40 in.
   b. Feet
   3.33 ft

▶ **17.** 2 gallons 1 quart
   a. Quarts
   9 qt
   b. Gallons
   2.25 gal

▶ **18.** 3 gallons 2 quarts
   a. Quarts
   14 qt
   b. Gallons
   3.5 gal

B Perform the indicated operation. Again, remember to use the appropriate conversion factor. [Examples 2, 3]

▶ **19.** Add 4 hours 47 minutes and 6 hours 13 minutes.
11 hr

20. Add 5 hours 39 minutes and 2 hours 21 minutes.
8 hr

▶ **21.** Add 8 feet 10 inches and 13 feet 6 inches
22 ft 4 in.

22. Add 16 feet 7 inches and 7 feet 9 inches.
24 ft 4 in.

▶ **23.** Add 4 pounds 12 ounces and 6 pounds 4 ounces.
11 lb

24. Add 11 pounds 9 ounces and 3 pounds 7 ounces.
15 lb

25. Subtract 2 hours 35 minutes from 8 hours 15 minutes.
5 hr 40 min

▶ **26.** Subtract 3 hours 47 minutes from 5 hours 33 minutes.
1 hr 46 min

27. Subtract 3 hours 43 minutes from 7 hours 30 minutes.
3 hr 47 min

▶ **28.** Subtract 1 hour 44 minutes from 6 hours 22 minutes.
4 hr 38 min

▶ **29.** Subtract 4 hours 17 minutes from 5 hours 9 minutes.
52 min

30. Subtract 2 hours 54 minutes from 3 hours 7 minutes.
13 min

■ Applying the Concepts

31. Fifth Avenue Mile The chart shows the times of the five fastest runners for 2005's Continental Airlines Fifth Avenue Mile. How much faster was Craig Mottram than Rui Silva?
7.5 seconds

32. Cars The chart shows the fastest cars in America. Convert the speed of the Ford GT to feet per second. Round to the nearest tenth.
300.7 ft/s

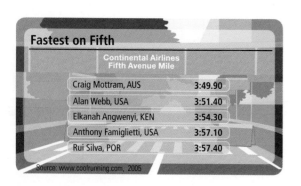

Fastest on Fifth

Continental Airlines Fifth Avenue Mile	
Craig Mottram, AUS	3:49.90
Alan Webb, USA	3:51.40
Elkanah Angwenyi, KEN	3:54.30
Anthony Famiglietti, USA	3:57.10
Rui Silva, POR	3:57.40

Source: www.coolrunning.com, 2005

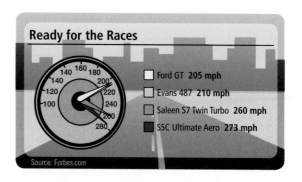

Ready for the Races

☐ Ford GT	205 mph
☐ Evans 487	210 mph
☐ Saleen S7 Twin Turbo	260 mph
■ SSC Ultimate Aero	273 mph

Source: Forbes.com

Triathlon The Ironman Triathlon World Championship, held each October in Kona on the island of Hawaii, consists of three parts: a 2.4-mile ocean swim, a 112-mile bike race, and a 26.2-mile marathon. The table shows the results from the 2003 event.

Triathlete	Swim Time (Hr:Min:Sec)	Bike Time (Hr:Min:Sec)	Run Time (Hr:Min:Sec)	Total Time (Hr:Min:Sec)
Peter Reid	0:50:36	4:40:04	2:47:38	8:18:18
Lori Bowden	0:56:51	5:09:00	3:02:10	9:08:01

33. Fill in the total time column.

34. How much faster was Peter's total time than Lori's?
00:49:43

35. How much faster was Peter than Lori in the swim?
00:06:15

36. How much faster was Peter than Lori in the run?
00:14:32

C [Example 4]

▶ **37. Cost of Fish** Fredrick is purchasing four whole salmon. The fish cost $4.00 per pound, and each weighs 6 lb 8 oz. What is the cost of the fish?
$104

38. Cost of Steak Mike is purchasing eight top sirloin steaks. The meat costs $4.00 per pound, and each steak weighs 1 lb 4 oz. What is the total cost of the steaks?
$40

39. Stationary Bike Maggie rides a stationary bike for 1 hour and 15 minutes, 4 days a week. After 2 weeks, how many hours has she spent riding the stationary bike?
10 hr

▶ **40. Gardening** Scott works in his garden for 1 hour and 5 minutes, 3 days a week. After 4 weeks, how many hours has Scott spent gardening?
13 hr

41. Cost of Fabric Allison is making a quilt. She buys 3 yards and 1 foot each of six different fabrics. The fabrics cost $7.50 a yard. How much will Allison spend?
$150

42. Cost of Lumber Trish is building a fence. She buys six fence posts at the lumberyard, each measuring 5 ft 4 in. The lumber costs $3 per foot. How much will Trish spend?
$96

▶ **43. Cost of Avocados** Jacqueline is buying six avocados. Each avocado weighs 8 oz. How much will they cost her if avocados cost $2.00 a pound?
$6

44. Cost of Apples Mary is purchasing 12 apples. Each apple weighs 4 oz. If the cost of the apples is $1.50 a pound, how much will Mary pay?
$4.50

■ Maintaining Your Skills

▶ **45. Caffeine Content** The following bar chart shows the amount of caffeine in five different soft drinks. Use the information in the bar chart to fill in the table.

CAFFEINE CONTENT IN SOFT DRINKS	
Drink	Caffeine (In Milligrams)
Jolt	100
Mountain Dew	55
Coca-Cola	45
Diet Pepsi	36
7 Up	0

▶ **46. Exercise** The following bar chart shows the number of calories burned in 1 hour of exercise by a person who weighs 150 pounds. Use the information in the bar chart to fill in the table.

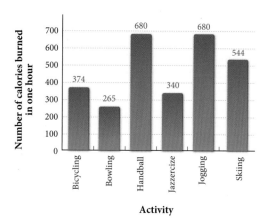

Activity

CALORIES BURNED BY A 150-POUND PERSON IN ONE HOUR	
Activity	Calories
Bicycling	374
Bowling	265
Handball	680
Jazzercise	340
Jogging	680
Skiing	544

■ Extending the Concepts

47. In 2003, the horse Funny Cide won the Kentucky Derby with a time of 2:01.19, or two minutes and 1.19 seconds. The record time for the Kentucky Derby is still held by Secretariat, who won the race with a time of 1:59.40 in 1973. How much faster did Secretariat run than Funny Cide 30 years later?

1.79 sec

48. In 2003, the horse Empire Maker won the Belmont Stakes with a time of 2:28.20, or two minutes and 28.2 seconds. The record time for the Belmont Stakes is still held by Secretariat, who won the race with a time of 2:24.00 in 1973. How much faster did Secretariat run in 1973 than Empire Maker 30 years later?

4.2 sec

Chapter 7 Summary

Conversion Factors [7.1, 7.2, 7.3, 7.4, 7.5]

To convert from one kind of unit to another, we choose an appropriate conversion factor from one of the tables given in this chapter. For example, if we want to convert 5 feet to inches, we look for conversion factors that give the relationship between feet and inches. There are two conversion factors for feet and inches:

$$\frac{12 \text{ in}}{1 \text{ ft}} \quad \text{and} \quad \frac{1 \text{ ft}}{12 \text{ in}}$$

Length [7.1]

U.S. SYSTEM

The Relationship Between	Is	To Convert From One To The Other, Multiply By
feet and inches	12 in. = 1 ft	$\frac{12 \text{ in.}}{1 \text{ ft}}$ or $\frac{1 \text{ ft}}{12 \text{ in.}}$
feet and yards	1 yd = 3 ft	$\frac{3 \text{ ft}}{1 \text{ yd}}$ or $\frac{1 \text{ yd}}{3 \text{ ft}}$
feet and miles	1 mi = 5,280 ft	$\frac{5,280 \text{ ft}}{1 \text{ mi}}$ or $\frac{1 \text{ mi}}{5,280 \text{ ft}}$

METRIC SYSTEM

The Relationship Between	Is	To Convert From One To The Other, Multiply By
millimeters (mm) and meters (m)	1,000 mm = 1 m	$\frac{1,000 \text{ mm}}{1 \text{ m}}$ or $\frac{1 \text{ m}}{1,000 \text{ mm}}$
centimeters (cm) and meters	100 cm = 1 m	$\frac{100 \text{ cm}}{1 \text{ m}}$ or $\frac{1 \text{ m}}{100 \text{ cm}}$
decimeters (dm) and meters	10 dm = 1 m	$\frac{10 \text{ dm}}{1 \text{ m}}$ or $\frac{1 \text{ m}}{10 \text{ dm}}$
dekameters (dam) and meters	1 dam = 10 m	$\frac{10 \text{ m}}{1 \text{ dam}}$ or $\frac{1 \text{ dam}}{10 \text{ m}}$
hectometers (hm) and meters	1 hm = 100 m	$\frac{100 \text{ m}}{1 \text{ hm}}$ or $\frac{1 \text{ hm}}{100 \text{ m}}$
kilometers (km) and meters	1 km = 1,000 m	$\frac{1,000 \text{ m}}{1 \text{ km}}$ or $\frac{1 \text{ km}}{1,000 \text{ m}}$

EXAMPLES

1. Convert 5 feet to inches.
$$5 \text{ ft} = 5 \text{ ft} \times \frac{12 \text{ in.}}{1 \text{ ft}}$$
$$= 5 \times 12 \text{ in.}$$
$$= 60 \text{ in.}$$

2. Convert 8 feet to yards.
$$8 \text{ ft} = 8 \text{ ft} \times \frac{1 \text{ yd}}{3 \text{ ft}}$$
$$= \frac{8}{3} \text{ yd}$$
$$= 2\frac{2}{3} \text{ yd}$$

3. Convert 25 millimeters to meters.
$$25 \text{ mm} = 25 \text{ mm} \times \frac{1 \text{ m}}{1,000 \text{ mm}}$$
$$= \frac{25 \text{ m}}{1,000}$$
$$= 0.025 \text{ m}$$

4. Convert 256 acres to square miles.

$$256 \text{ acres} = 256 \text{ acres} \times \frac{1 \text{ mi}^2}{640 \text{ acres}}$$
$$= \frac{256}{640} \text{ mi}^2$$
$$= 0.4 \text{ mi}^2$$

Area [7.2]

U.S. SYSTEM		
The Relationship Between	Is	To Convert From One To The Other, Multiply By
square inches and square feet	$144 \text{ in}^2 = 1 \text{ ft}^2$	$\frac{144 \text{ in}^2}{1 \text{ ft}^2}$ or $\frac{1 \text{ ft}^2}{144 \text{ in}^2}$
square yards and square feet	$9 \text{ ft}^2 = 1 \text{ yd}^2$	$\frac{9 \text{ ft}^2}{1 \text{ yd}^2}$ or $\frac{1 \text{ yd}^2}{9 \text{ ft}^2}$
acres and square feet	$1 \text{ acre} = 43{,}560 \text{ ft}^2$	$\frac{43{,}560 \text{ ft}^2}{1 \text{ acre}}$ or $\frac{1 \text{ acre}}{43{,}560 \text{ ft}^2}$
acres and square miles	$640 \text{ acres} = 1 \text{ mi}^2$	$\frac{640 \text{ acres}}{1 \text{ mi}^2}$ or $\frac{1 \text{ mi}^2}{640 \text{ acres}}$

METRIC SYSTEM		
The Relationship Between	Is	To Convert From One To The Other, Multiply By
square millimeters and square centimeters	$1 \text{ cm}^2 = 100 \text{ mm}^2$	$\frac{100 \text{ mm}^2}{1 \text{ cm}^2}$ or $\frac{1 \text{ cm}^2}{100 \text{ mm}^2}$
square centimeters and square decimeters	$1 \text{ dm}^2 = 100 \text{ cm}^2$	$\frac{100 \text{ cm}^2}{1 \text{ dm}^2}$ or $\frac{1 \text{ dm}^2}{100 \text{ cm}^2}$
square decimeters and square meters	$1 \text{ m}^2 = 100 \text{ dm}^2$	$\frac{100 \text{ dm}^2}{1 \text{ m}^2}$ or $\frac{1 \text{ m}^2}{100 \text{ dm}^2}$
square meters and ares (a)	$1 \text{ a} = 100 \text{ m}^2$	$\frac{100 \text{ m}^2}{1 \text{ a}}$ or $\frac{1 \text{ a}}{100 \text{ m}^2}$
ares and hectares (ha)	$1 \text{ ha} = 100 \text{ a}$	$\frac{100 \text{ a}}{1 \text{ ha}}$ or $\frac{1 \text{ ha}}{100 \text{ a}}$

Volume [7.2]

U.S. SYSTEM		
The Relationship Between	Is	To Convert From One To The Other, Multiply By
cubic inches (in³) and cubic feet (ft³)	$1 \text{ ft}^3 = 1{,}728 \text{ in}^3$	$\frac{1{,}728 \text{ in}^3}{1 \text{ ft}^3}$ or $\frac{1 \text{ ft}^3}{1{,}728 \text{ in}^3}$
cubic feet and cubic yards (yd³)	$1 \text{ yd}^3 = 27 \text{ ft}^3$	$\frac{27 \text{ ft}^3}{1 \text{ yd}^3}$ or $\frac{1 \text{ yd}^3}{27 \text{ ft}^3}$
fluid ounces (fl oz) and pints (pt)	$1 \text{ pt} = 16 \text{ fl oz}$	$\frac{16 \text{ fl oz}}{1 \text{ pt}}$ or $\frac{1 \text{ pt}}{16 \text{ fl oz}}$
pints and quarts (qt)	$1 \text{ qt} = 2 \text{ pt}$	$\frac{2 \text{ pt}}{1 \text{ qt}}$ or $\frac{1 \text{ qt}}{2 \text{ pt}}$
quarts and gallons (gal)	$1 \text{ gal} = 4 \text{ qt}$	$\frac{4 \text{ qt}}{1 \text{ gal}}$ or $\frac{1 \text{ gal}}{4 \text{ qt}}$

METRIC SYSTEM		
The Relationship Between	Is	To Convert From One To The Other, Multiply By
milliliters (mL) and liters	1 liter (L) = 1,000 mL	$\dfrac{1,000 \text{ mL}}{1 \text{ liter}}$ or $\dfrac{1 \text{ liter}}{1,000 \text{ mL}}$
hectoliters (hL) and liters	100 liters = 1 hL	$\dfrac{100 \text{ liters}}{1 \text{ hL}}$ or $\dfrac{1 \text{ hL}}{100 \text{ liters}}$
kiloliters (kL) and liters	1,000 liters (L) = 1 kL	$\dfrac{1,000 \text{ liters}}{1 \text{ kL}}$ or $\dfrac{1 \text{ kL}}{1,000 \text{ liters}}$

5. Convert 2.2 liters to milliliters.

$$2.2 \text{ liters} = 2.2 \text{ liters} \times \frac{1,000 \text{ mL}}{1 \text{ liters}}$$
$$= 2.2 \times 1,000 \text{ mL}$$
$$= 2,200 \text{ mL}$$

■ Weight [7.3]

U.S. SYSTEM		
The Relationship Between	Is	To Convert From One To The Other, Multiply By
ounces (oz) and pounds (lb)	1 lb = 16 oz	$\dfrac{16 \text{ oz}}{1 \text{ lb}}$ or $\dfrac{1 \text{ lb}}{16 \text{ oz}}$
pounds and tons (T)	1 T = 2,000 lb	$\dfrac{2,000 \text{ lb}}{1 \text{ T}}$ or $\dfrac{1 \text{ T}}{2,000 \text{ lb}}$

6. Convert 12 pounds to ounces.

$$12 \text{ lb} = 12 \text{ lb} \times \frac{16 \text{ oz}}{1 \text{ lb}}$$
$$= 12 \times 16 \text{ oz}$$
$$= 192 \text{ oz}$$

METRIC SYSTEM		
The Relationship Between	Is	To Convert From One To The Other, Multiply By
milligrams (mg) and grams (g)	1 g = 1,000 mg	$\dfrac{1,000 \text{ mg}}{1 \text{ g}}$ or $\dfrac{1 \text{ g}}{1,000 \text{ mg}}$
centigrams (cg) and grams	1 g = 100 cg	$\dfrac{100 \text{ cg}}{1 \text{ g}}$ or $\dfrac{1 \text{ g}}{100 \text{ cg}}$
kilograms (kg) and grams	1,000 g = 1 kg	$\dfrac{1,000 \text{ g}}{1 \text{ kg}}$ or $\dfrac{1 \text{ kg}}{1,000 \text{ g}}$
metric tons (t) and kilograms	1,000 kg = 1 t	$\dfrac{1,000 \text{ kg}}{1 \text{ t}}$ or $\dfrac{1 \text{ t}}{1,000 \text{ kg}}$

7. Convert 3 kilograms to centigrams.

$$3 \text{ kg} = 3 \text{ kg} \times \frac{1,000 \text{ g}}{1 \text{ kg}} \times \frac{100 \text{ cg}}{1 \text{ g}}$$
$$= 3 \times 1,000 \times 100 \text{ cg}$$
$$= 300,000 \text{ cg}$$

Converting Between the U.S. and Metric Systems [7.4]

8. Convert 8 inches to centimeters.

$8 \text{ in.} = 8 \text{ in.} \times \dfrac{2.54 \text{ cm}}{1 \text{ in.}}$

$= 8 \times 2.54 \text{ cm}$

$= 20.32 \text{ cm}$

CONVERSION FACTORS		
The Relationship Between	Is	To Convert From One To The Other, Multiply By
Length		
inches and centimeters	2.54 cm = 1 in.	$\dfrac{2.54 \text{ cm}}{1 \text{ in.}}$ or $\dfrac{1 \text{ in.}}{2.54 \text{ cm}}$
feet and meters	1 m = 3.28 ft	$\dfrac{3.28 \text{ ft}}{1 \text{ m}}$ or $\dfrac{1 \text{ m}}{3.28 \text{ ft}}$
miles and kilometers	1.61 km = 1 mi	$\dfrac{1.61 \text{ km}}{1 \text{ mi}}$ or $\dfrac{1 \text{ mi}}{1.61 \text{ km}}$
Area		
square inches and square centimeters	6.45 cm² = 1 in²	$\dfrac{6.45 \text{ cm}^2}{1 \text{ in}^2}$ or $\dfrac{1 \text{ in}^2}{6.45 \text{ cm}^2}$
square meters and square yards	1.196 yd² = 1 m²	$\dfrac{1.196 \text{ yd}^2}{1 \text{ m}^2}$ or $\dfrac{1 \text{ m}^2}{1.196 \text{ yd}^2}$
acres and hectares	1 ha = 2.47 acres	$\dfrac{2.47 \text{ acres}}{1 \text{ ha}}$ or $\dfrac{1 \text{ ha}}{2.47 \text{ acres}}$
Volume		
cubic inches and milliliters	16.39 mL = 1 in³	$\dfrac{16.39 \text{ mL}}{1 \text{ in}^3}$ or $\dfrac{1 \text{ in}^3}{16.39 \text{ mL}}$
liters and quarts	1.06 qt = 1 liter	$\dfrac{1.06 \text{ qt}}{1 \text{ liter}}$ or $\dfrac{1 \text{ liter}}{1.06 \text{ qt}}$
gallons and liters	3.79 liters = 1 gal	$\dfrac{3.79 \text{ liters}}{1 \text{ gal}}$ or $\dfrac{1 \text{ gal}}{3.79 \text{ liters}}$
Weight		
ounces and grams	28.3 g = 1 oz	$\dfrac{28.3 \text{ g}}{1 \text{ oz}}$ or $\dfrac{1 \text{ oz}}{28.3 \text{ g}}$
kilograms and pounds	2.20 lb = 1 kg	$\dfrac{2.20 \text{ lb}}{1 \text{ kg}}$ or $\dfrac{1 \text{ kg}}{2.20 \text{ lb}}$

Temperature [7.4]

9. Convert 120°C to degrees Fahrenheit.

$F = \dfrac{9}{5}C + 32$

$F = \dfrac{9}{5}(120) + 32$

$F = 216 + 32$

$F = 248 \text{ °F}$

To Convert From	Formula In Symbols	Formula In Words
Fahrenheit to Celsius	$C = \dfrac{5(F - 32)}{9}$	Subtract 32, multiply by 5, and then divide by 9.
Celsius to Fahrenheit	$F = \dfrac{9}{5}C + 32$	Multiply by $\dfrac{9}{5}$, and then add 32.

Time [7.5]

10. Convert 3 hours 45 minutes to minutes.

$= 3 \text{ hr} \times \dfrac{60 \text{ min}}{1 \text{ hr}} + 45 \text{ min}$

$= 180 \text{ min} + 45 \text{ min}$

$= 225 \text{ min}$

The Relationship Between	Is	To Convert From One To The Other, Multiply By
minutes and seconds	1 min = 60 sec	$\dfrac{1 \text{ min}}{60 \text{ sec}}$ or $\dfrac{60 \text{ sec}}{1 \text{ min}}$
hours and minutes	1 hr = 60 min	$\dfrac{1 \text{ hr}}{60 \text{ min}}$ or $\dfrac{60 \text{ min}}{1 \text{ hr}}$

Use the tables given in this chapter to make the following conversions. [7.1-7.4]

1. 12 ft to inches
144 in.

2. 18 ft to yards
6 yd

3. 49 cm to meters
0.49 m

4. 2 km to decimeters
20,000 dm

5. 10 acres to square feet
435,600 ft²

6. 7,800 m² to ares
78 ares

7. 4 ft² to square inches
576 in²

8. 7 qt to pints
14 pt

9. 24 qt to gallons
6 gal

10. 5 L to milliliters
5,000 mL

11. 8 lb to ounces
128 oz

12. 2 lb 4 oz to ounces
36 oz

13. 5 kg to grams
5,000 g

14. 5 t to kilograms
5,000 kg

15. 4 in. to centimeters
10.16 cm

16. 7 mi to kilometers
11.27 km

17. 7 L to quarts
7.42 qt

18. 5 gal to liters
18.95 L

19. 5 oz to grams
141.5 g

20. 9 kg to pounds
19.8 lb

21. 120°C to degrees Fahrenheit
248°F

22. 122°F to degrees Celsius
50°C

Work the following problems. Round answers to the nearest hundredth where necessary.

23. A case of soft drinks holds 24 cans. If each can holds 355 ml, how many liters are there in the whole case? [7.2]

8.52 L

24. Change 862 mi to feet. [7.1]

4,551,360 ft

25. Glacier Bay National Monument covers 2,805,269 acres. What is the area in square miles? [7.2]

4,383.23 mi²

26. How many ounces does a 134-lb person weigh? [7.3]

2,144 oz

27. Change 250 mi to kilometers. [7.1]

402.5 km

28. How many grams is 7 lb 8 oz? [7.4]

3,396 g

29. **Construction** A 12-square-meter patio is to be built using bricks that measure 10 centimeters by 20 centimeters. How many bricks will be needed to cover the patio? [7.2]

600 bricks

30. **Capacity** If a regular drinking glass holds 0.25 liter of liquid, how many glasses can be filled from a 6.5-liter container? [7.2]

26 glasses

31. **Filling an Aquarium** How many 8-fluid-ounce glasses of water will it take to fill a 5-gallon aquarium? [7.2]

80 glasses

32. **Comparing Area** On April 3, 2000, *USA Today* changed the size of its paper. Previous to this date, each page of the paper was $13\frac{1}{2}$ inches wide and $22\frac{1}{4}$ inches long, giving each page an area of $300\frac{3}{8}$ in². Convert this area to square feet. [7.2]

$2\frac{11}{128}$ ft²

33. **Speed** The instrument display below shows a speed of 188 kilometers per hour. What is the speed in miles per hour? Round to the nearest whole number. [7.4]

117 miles per hour

34. **Volcanoes** Pyroclastic flows are high speed avalanches of volcanic gases and ash that accompany some volcano eruptions. Pyroclastic flows have been known to travel at more than 80 kilometers per hour.

USGS

   a. Convert 80 km/hr to miles per hour. Round to the nearest whole number.

   50 mi/hr

   b. Could you outrun a pyroclastic flow on foot, on a bicycle, or in a car?

   In a car

35. **Speed** A race car is traveling at 200 miles per hour. What is the speed in kilometers per hour? [7.4]

322 kilometers per hour

36. 4 hours 45 minutes to [7.5]

   a. Minutes

   285 min

   b. Hours

   4.75 hr

37. Add 4 pounds 4 ounces and 8 pounds 12 ounces. [7.5]

13 lb

38. **Cost of Fish.** Mark is purchasing two whole salmon. The fish cost $5.00 per pound, and each weighs 12 lb 8 oz. What is the cost of the fish? [7.5]

$125

Simplify:

1. 7,520
    599
+8,640
─────
16,759

2. 6,000
−3,999
─────
2,001

3. 156 ÷ 13
12

4. 9(7 · 2)
126

5. 64)‾31,362‾ $490\frac{1}{32}$

6. 2^8
256

7. 12 + 81 ÷ 3²
21

8. $\dfrac{329}{47}$
7

9. 25 + 13
38

10. (10 + 4) + (212 − 100)
126

11. $\dfrac{39}{3}$
13

12. 10.5(2.7)
28.35

13. 5.4 + 2.58 + 3.09
11.07

14. 45.7 − 2.86
42.84

15. 2.5)‾40.5‾
16.2

16. $\left(\dfrac{1}{4}\right)^3\left(\dfrac{1}{2}\right)^2$ $\dfrac{1}{256}$

17. $17 \div \left(\dfrac{1}{3}\right)^2$
153

18. $\dfrac{8}{25} + \dfrac{7}{50}$ $\dfrac{23}{50}$

19. $\left(16 \div 1\dfrac{1}{4}\right) \div 2$ $6\dfrac{2}{5}$

20. $15 - 3\dfrac{1}{2}$ $11\dfrac{1}{2}$

21. $\dfrac{3}{8}(2.4) - \dfrac{3}{5}(0.25)$
0.75

22. $\dfrac{5}{6}(3.6) - \dfrac{3}{4}(3.2)$
0.6

23. $13 + \dfrac{3}{14} \div \dfrac{5}{42}$ $14\dfrac{4}{5}$

Solve.

24. 2 · x = 15
7.5

25. 46 = 4 · y
11.5

26. $\dfrac{2}{3} = \dfrac{12}{x}$
18

Solve.

27. Find the perimeter and area of the figure below.

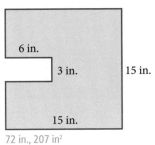

72 in., 207 in²

28. Find the perimeter of the figure below.

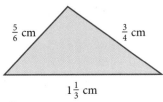

$\frac{5}{6}$ cm $\frac{3}{4}$ cm

$1\frac{1}{3}$ cm

$2\frac{11}{12}$ cm

29. Find the difference between 62 and 15.
47

30. If a car travels 142 miles in $2\frac{1}{2}$ hours, what is its rate in miles per hour?   56.8 mi/hr

31. What number is 24% of 7,450?
1,788

32. Factor 126 into a product of prime factors.
2 · 3 · 3 · 7

33. Find $\frac{2}{3}$ of the product of 7 and 9.
42

34. If 5,280 feet = 1 mile, convert 3,432 feet to miles.
0.65 mi

Use the illustration to answer problem 35.

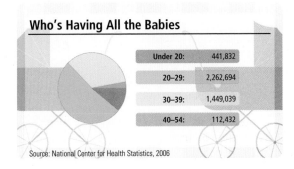

Who's Having All the Babies

Under 20:	441,832
20–29:	2,262,694
30–39:	1,449,039
40–54:	112,432

Source: National Center for Health Statistics, 2006

35. What percentage of babies were born to mothers who were between the ages of 20 and 39. Round to the nearest percentage.   87%

Use the tables in the chapter to make the following conversions.

1. 7 yd to feet
21 ft

2. 750 m to kilometers
0.75 km

3. 3 acres to square feet
130,680 ft²

4. 432 in² to square feet
3 ft²

5. 10 L to milliliters
10,000 mL

6. 5 mi to kilometers
8.05 km

7. 10 L to quarts
10.6 qt

8. 80°F to degrees Celsius (round to the nearest tenth)
26.7°C

9. 1.2 T to pounds
2,400 lb

10. 144 oz to pounds
9 lb

11. 504 in² to square feet
3.5 ft²

12. 4.5 a to square meters
450 m²

13. 175.5 ft³ to cubic yards
6.5 yd³

14. 40°C to degrees Farenheit
104°F

Work the following problems. Round answers to the nearest hundredth.

15. How many gallons are there in a 1-liter bottle of cola?
0.26 gal

16. Change 579 yd to inches.
20,844 in.

17. A car engine has a displacement of 409 in³. What is the displacement in cubic feet?   0.24 ft³

18. Change 75 qt to liters.
70.75 L

19. Change 245 ft to meters.
74.70 m

20. How many liters are contained in an 8-quart container?   7.55 L

21. 16 cm to inches
6.30 in.

22. 5 mi to kilometers
8.05 km

23. 17 in² to square centimeters
109.65 cm²

24. 7 ha to acres
17.29 acres

25. 5 qt to liters
4.72 L

26. 17 lb to kilograms
7.73 kg

27. Construction A 40-square-foot pantry floor is to be tiled using tiles that measure 8 inches by 8 inches. How many tiles will be needed to cover the pantry floor?
90 tiles

28. Filling an Aquarium How many 12-fluid-ounce glasses of water will it take to fill a 6-gallon aquarium?
64 glasses

29. 5 hours 30 minutes to
   a. Minutes   330 min
   b. Hours   5.5 hr

30. Add 3 pounds 4 ounces and 7 pounds 12 ounces.
11 lb

Use the illustration to answer problem 31.

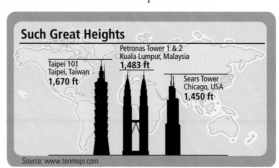

31. Convert the height of the Taipei 101 tower to kilometers. Round to the nearest hundredth.   0.51 km

Chapter 7 Projects

MEASUREMENT

GROUP PROJECT

Body Mass Index

Number of People 2

Time Needed 25 minutes

Equipment Pencil, paper, and calculator

Background Body mass index (BMI) is computed by using a mathematical formula in which one's weight in kilograms is divided by the square of one's height in meters. According to the Centers for Disease Control and Prevention, a healthy BMI for adults is between 18.5 and 24.9. Children aged 2–20 have a healthy BMI if they are in the 5th to 84th percentile for their age and sex. A high BMI is predictive of cardiovascular disease.

Height	4'10"	5'2"	5'9"	6'1"
Weight (lbs)				
100				
120				
140				
200				

Procedure Complete the given BMI chart using the following conversion factors.

1 inch = 2.54 cm, 1 meter = 100 cm, 1 kg = 2.2 lb

Example 5'4", 120 lbs

1. Convert height to inches.

$$5 \text{ feet} \times \frac{12 \text{ in.}}{1 \text{ ft}} = 60 \text{ in.}$$

$$5'4" = 64 \text{ in.}$$

Then, convert height to meters.

$$64 \text{ in.} \times \frac{2.54 \text{ cm}}{1 \text{ in.}} = 162.56 \text{ cm}$$

$$162.56 \text{ cm} \times \frac{1 \text{ m}}{100 \text{ cm}} = 1.6256 \text{ m}$$

2. Convert weight to kilograms.

$$120 \text{ lbs} \times \frac{1 \text{ kg}}{2.2 \text{ lbs}} \approx 54.5 \text{ kg}$$

3. Compute $\dfrac{\text{weight in kg}}{(\text{height in m})^2}$.

$$\frac{54.5}{(1.6256)^2} \approx 21$$

RESEARCH PROJECT

Richard Alfred Tapia

Richard A. Tapia is a mathematician and professor at Rice University in Houston, Texas, where he is Noah Harding Professor of Computational and Applied Mathematics. His parents immigrated from Mexico, separately, as teenagers to provide better educational opportunities for themselves and future generations. Born in Los Angeles, Tapia was the first in his family to attend college. In addition to being internationally known for his research, Tapia has helped his department at Rice become a national leader in awarding Ph.D. degrees to women and minority recipients. Research the life and work of Dr. Tapia. Summarize your results in an essay.

Courtesy of Rice University

Geometry

Introduction

The Colosseum at Rome is one of the iconic structures of the ancient world. Construction began around 70 A.D. under the Emperor Vespasian and was completed 10 years later by his son, Emperor Titus. Vespasian's younger son, Emperor Domitian, added the tunnels beneath the structure to hold animals and slaves, and added a gallery to the top of the structure to increase the seating capacity.

The Colosseum

Circumference
$C = 2\pi r$

Volume
$V = \pi r^2 h$

In this chapter you will see a variety of simple geometric shapes and the common characteristics we use to describe them. You will learn about perimeter, circumference, area and volume of a variety of shapes in both two and three dimensions.

Find the area and the perimeter or circumferene of each figure.

1.
P = 16 in.
A = 16 in²

4 in.

2.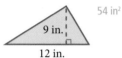
3 cm   P = 18 cm
A = 18 cm²

6 cm

3.
5 in.
C = 31.4 in.
A = 78.5 in²

Find the area of each figure.

4.
9 in.
54 in²

12 in.

5.
25 m
212.5 m²

17 m

6.
12 ft
180 ft²

30 ft

Find the volume and surface area of each figure.

7.
258 m²

5 m
6 m
9 m

8.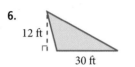
8 ft
527.52 ft²

6 ft

9.
3 mm
113.04 mm²

Simplify each expression.

10. $\sqrt{81}$ 9

11. $\sqrt{\dfrac{16}{49}}$ $\dfrac{4}{7}$

12. $\sqrt{49} - \sqrt{169}$ -6

Find *h*.

13.
h
5 m

12 m
h = 13 m

Getting Ready for Chapter 8

Simplify each of the following.

1. 4(35)
140

2. 3.14(4)
12.56

3. 3.14(23.25)
73.005

4. 2(3.14)(0.52)
3.2656

5. 2(8) + 2(5)
26

6. 2(3)(4) + 2(3)(5)
54

7. $\dfrac{1}{2}$(6)(3)
9

8. $\dfrac{1}{2}\left(2\dfrac{5}{8}\right)\left(1\dfrac{1}{4}\right)$
$1\dfrac{41}{64} \approx 1.64$

9. $2\dfrac{3}{8} + 1\dfrac{5}{8} + 4$
8

10. $2\dfrac{5}{8} + 1\dfrac{7}{8} + 1\dfrac{7}{8}$
$6\dfrac{3}{8} = 6.375$

11. $\dfrac{22}{7}(2)^2$
$\dfrac{88}{7} \approx 12.57$

12. $\dfrac{22}{7}(7)^2$
154

13. $\left(\dfrac{1}{2} \cdot 27\right)^2$
$\dfrac{729}{4} = 182.25$

14. 144 − 36(3.14)
30.96

15. 2(1.56) + 2(0.99)
5.1

16. 2(21.4) + 2(35.8)
114.4

17. 4(3.14)6²
452.16

18. $\dfrac{4}{3}$(3.14)2³
≈ 33.49

19. $4\left(\dfrac{22}{7}\right)6^2$
$\dfrac{3,168}{7} \approx 452.57$

20. $\dfrac{4}{3}\left(\dfrac{22}{7}\right)2^3$
$\dfrac{704}{21} \approx 33.52$

Divide and round to the nearest whole number.

21. 24,900 ÷ 3.14
7,930

22. $\dfrac{6,790}{3.14}$
2,162

Objectives
A Find the perimeter of a polygon.
B Find the circumference of a circle.

Introduction . . .

The world around us is filled with things that can be described in mathematical terms using perimeter and circumference. Here are a few of the items we will use to explore perimeter and circumference.

A Perimeter

We begin this section by reviewing the definition of a polygon and the definition of perimeter.

> **Definition**
> A **polygon** is a closed geometric figure, with at least three sides, in which each side is a straight line segment.

The most common polygons are squares, rectangles, and triangles.

> **Definition**
> The **perimeter** of any polygon is the sum of the lengths of the sides, and it is denoted with the letter P.

To find the perimeter of a polygon we add all the lengths of the sides together. Here are the most common polygons, along with the formula for the perimeter of each.

  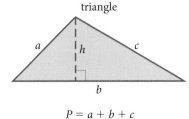

square	rectangle	triangle
$P = 4s$	$P = 2l + 2w$	$P = a + b + c$

We can justify our formulas as follows. If each side of a square is s units long, then the perimeter is found by adding all four sides together:

$$\text{Perimeter} = P = s + s + s + s = 4s$$

Likewise, if a rectangle has a length of l and a width of w, then to find the perimeter we add all four sides together:

$$\text{Perimeter} = P = l + l + w + w = 2l + 2w$$

PRACTICE PROBLEMS

1. Find the perimeter of the rectangle in Example 1 if the length and width are each increased by 1 yard.

   Find the perimeter of the given rectangle.

5 yd

8 yd

SOLUTION   The given rectangle has a width of 5 yards and a length of 8 yards. We can use the formula for $P = 2l + 2w$ to find the perimeter.

We have: $P = 2(8) + 2(5)$
$= 16 + 10$
$= 26$ yards

   Find the perimeter of each of the following stamps. Write your answer as a decimal, rounded to the nearest tenth if necessary.

2. Find the perimeter of each stamp in Example 2 from the dimensions given below.
   a. Each side is 1.38 inches

   a. Each side is 35.0 millimeters

   b. Base = 6.6 centimeters, other two sides = 4.7 centimeters

   b. Base = $2\frac{5}{8}$ inches
   Other two sides = $1\frac{7}{8}$ inches

   c. Length = 39.6 millimeters, width = 25.1 millimeters

   c. Length = 1.56 inches
   Width = 0.99 inches

Peanuts: © United Feature Syndicate, Inc.

SOLUTION   We can add all the sides together, or we can apply our formulas. Let's apply the formulas.

a. $P = 4s = 4 \cdot 35 = 140$ mm

b. $P = a + b + c = 2\frac{5}{8} + 1\frac{7}{8} + 1\frac{7}{8} = 6\frac{3}{8} \approx 6.4$ in.

c. $P = 2l + 2w = 2(1.56) + 2(0.99) = 5.1$ in.

B   Circumference

The *circumference* of a circle is the distance around the outside, just as the perimeter of a polygon is the distance around the outside. The circumference of a circle can be found by measuring its radius or diameter and then using the appropriate

Answers
1. 30 yards
2. **a.** 5.52 in.   **b.** 16 cm
   c. 129.4 mm

formula. The *radius* of a circle is the distance from the center of the circle to the circle itself. The radius is denoted by the letter r. The *diameter* of a circle is the distance from one side to the other, through the center. The diameter is denoted by the letter d. In the figure below we can see that the diameter is twice the radius, or

$$d = 2r$$

The relationship between the circumference and the diameter or radius is not as obvious. As a matter of fact, it takes some fairly complicated mathematics to show just what the relationship between the circumference and the diameter is.

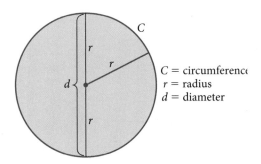

C = circumference
r = radius
d = diameter

If you took a string and actually measured the circumference of a circle by wrapping the string around the circle and then measured the diameter of the same circle, you would find that the ratio of the circumference to the diameter, C/d, would be approximately equal to 3.14. The actual ratio of C to d in any circle is an irrational number. It can't be written in decimal form. We use the symbol π (Greek *pi*) to represent this ratio. In symbols, the relationship between the circumference and the diameter in any circle is

$$\frac{C}{d} = \pi$$

Knowing what we do about the relationship between division and multiplication, we can rewrite this formula as

$$C = \pi d$$

This is the formula for the circumference of a circle. When we do the actual calculations, we will use the approximation 3.14 for π.

Because $d = 2r$, the same formula written in terms of the radius is

$$C = 2\pi r$$

EXAMPLE 3   Find the circumference of each coin.

a. 1 Euro coin (Round to the nearest whole number.)

Diameter = 23.25 millimeters

b. Susan B. Anthony dollar (Round to the nearest hundredth.)

Radius = 0.52 inch

3. Find the circumference for each coin in Example 3 from the dimensions given below. Round answers to the nearest hundredth.
a. Diameter = 0.92 inches
b. Radius = 13.20 millimeters

SOLUTION Applying our formulas for circumference we have:

a. $C = \pi d \approx (3.14)(23.25) \approx 73$ mm

b. $C = 2\pi r \approx 2(3.14)(0.52) \approx 3.27$ in.

Circles and the Earth

There are many circles found on the surface of the earth. The most familiar are the latitude and longitude lines. Of these circles, the ones with the largest circumference are called *great circles.* All of the longitude lines are great circles. Of the lattitude lines, only the equator is a great circle.

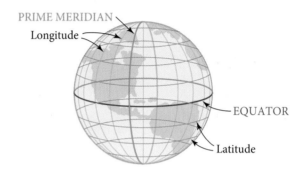

4. The circumference of the moon at the equator is 6,790 miles. To the nearest 10 miles, find the diameter of the moon

EXAMPLE 4 If the circumference of the earth is approximately 24,900 miles at the equator, what is the diameter of the earth to the nearest 10 miles?

SOLUTION We substitute 24,900 for C in the formula $C = \pi d$, and then we solve for d.

$$24,900 = \pi d$$

$$24,900 \approx 3.14d \qquad \text{Substitute 3.14 for } \pi$$

$$d \approx \frac{24,900}{3.14} \qquad \text{Divide each side by 3.14}$$

$$d \approx 7,930 \text{ miles}$$

Getting Ready for Class

After reading through the preceding section, respond in your own words and in complete sentences.

1. What is the perimeter of a polygon?

2. How are perimeter and circumference related?

3. How do you find the perimeter of a square if each side is 15 inches long?

4. A rectangle has a width of 24 feet and a length of 37 feet. How do you find the perimeter?

Answers
3. **a.** 2.89 in. **b.** 82.90 mm
4. Approximately 2,160 miles

Problem Set 8.1

A Find the perimeter of each figure. [Examples 1, 2]

1.

4 yds

16 yds

▶ **2.**

6.5 cm

26 cm

3.

3.2 ft

12.8 ft

▶ **4.**

6 in.

12 in.

36 in.

5.

7.5 ft

3.5 ft

22 ft

6.

.7 ft

1.2 ft

3.8 ft

7.

3.6 yds

1.4 yds

10 yds

8.

1.8 in.

4.2 in.

12 in.

9.

7 ft

13.2 ft

40.4 ft

10.

7.2 cm   6.3 cm

12.5 cm

26 cm

11.

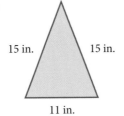

15 in.   15 in.

11 in.

41 in.

▶ **12.**

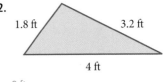

1.8 ft   3.2 ft

4 ft

9 ft

▶ **13.**

11 in.

8 in.   7 in.

24 in.

50 in.

▶ **14.**

8 yd

2 yd

6 yd

4 yd

28 yds

15.

11 yd

4 yd

3 yd

2 yd

40 yds

▶ **16.**

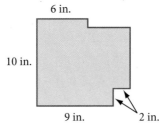

6 in.

10 in.

9 in.   2 in.

42 in.

▶ **17.**

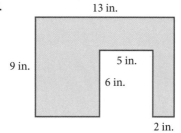

13 in.

9 in.

5 in.

6 in.

2 in.

56 in.

18.

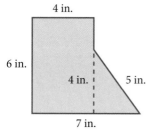

4 in.

6 in.

4 in.   5 in.

7 in.

24 in.

B Find the circumference of each circle. [Example 3]

▶ **19.**

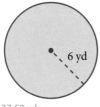

6 yd

37.68 yds

▶ **20.**

3.5 in.

21.98 in.

21.

11 ft

69.08 ft

22.

0.2 ft

1.256 ft

23.

6 ft

18.84 ft

24.

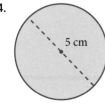

5 cm

15.7 cm

■ Applying the Concepts

▶ **25. Perimeter of an MP3 Player** The MP3 player below is the smallest of all MP3 player.

0.24 in.   ⊢1.5 in.⟶

3.6 in.

a. Find the perimeter of the face of the MP3 player.
    10.2 in.
b. Find the perimeter of the side of the MP3 player.
    7.68 in.

26. Perimeter of an MP3 Player The MP3 player below can hold up to 30,000 songs.

0.41 in.   ⊢ 2.4 in.⟶

4.1 in.

a. Find the perimeter of the face of the MP3 player.
    13 in.
b. Find the perimeter of the side of the MP3 player.
    9.02 in.

27. Circumference of a Logo The diameter of the corporate logo here is 12.4 millimeters, find the circumference.
38.94 mm

▶ **28. Circumference of a Logo** The diameter of the corporate logo here is 9.2 millimeters, find the circumference.
28.9 mm

▶ **29. Perimeter of a TV** A normal TV has a 4:3 ratio between its length and width. If the diameter (measured from one corner to the opposite corner) is 35 inches, what is the perimeter of the TV?
98 in.

30. Perimeter of a TV A normal TV has a 4:3 ratio between its length and width. If the diameter (measured from one corner to the opposite corner) is 30 inches, what is the perimeter of the TV?
84 in.

31. Perimeter of a Football Field A standard football field has a length of 100 yards, plus two 10 yard end zones, and have a width of 160 feet. What is the perimeter of the football field in feet?
1040 ft

▶ **32. Perimeter of a Track** Some football fields, like the one seen in this Google Earth image, have a track surrounding them. Assuming both ends are perfect semicircles that start at the end of each end zone, and the track is 10 yards away from the sidelines on each side, what is the perimeter of the inside part of the track in feet?
1410.8 ft

▶ **33. Geometry** If a rectangle has a perimeter of 20 feet, is it possible for the rectangle to be a square? Explain your answer.

Yes, when $w = l = 5$ ft.

34. Geometry If a rectangle has a perimeter of 10 feet, is it possible for the rectangle to be a square? Explain your answer.

Yes, but the length of the sides will not be a whole number.

35. Geometry A rectangle has a perimeter of 9.5 inches. If the length is 2.75 inches, find the width.

2 in.

▶ **36. Geometry** A rectangle has a perimeter of 11 inches. If the width is 2.5 inches, find the length.

3 in.

■ Getting Ready for the Next Section

Simplify each expression. Round your answers to the nearest hundredth.

37. $\frac{1}{2} \cdot 6 \cdot 3$

9

38. $\frac{1}{2} \cdot 4 \cdot 2$

4

39. $\frac{1}{2}\left(2\frac{5}{8}\right)\left(1\frac{1}{4}\right)$

1.64

40. $\frac{1}{2}(6.6)(3.3)$

10.89

41. $3.14(14.5)^2$

660.19

42. $3.14(5)^2$

78.5

43. $144 - 36(3.14)$

30.96

44. $100 - 25(3.14)$

21.5

■ Maintaining Your Skills

45. Convert 100 yards to meters. Round to the nearest tenth.

91.5 m

46. Convert 5,280 feet to kilometers.

1.61 km

47. Convert to inches. Round to the nearest hundredth
   a. 16 centimeters

   6.30 in.

   b. 129.4 millimeters

   5.09 in.

48. Convert to millimeters. Round to the nearest whole number.
   a. 5.52 inches

   140 mm

   b. 2.89 inches

   73 mm

■ Extending the Concepts

Find the perimeter of each figure. Use 3.14 for π.

49.

Half circle

4 in.

4 in.

18.28 in.

50.

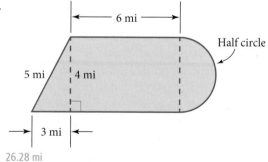

6 mi

5 mi   4 mi   Half circle

3 mi

26.28 mi

Objectives

A Find the area of a polygon.
B Find the area of a circle.

Introduction . . .

Recall that the area of a flat object is a measure of the amount of surface the object has. The area of the rectangle below is 8 square centimeters, because it takes 8 square centimeters to cover it.

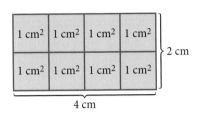

As we have noted previously, the area of this rectangle can also be found by multiplying the length and the width.

$$\text{Area} = (\text{length}) \cdot (\text{width})$$
$$= (4 \text{ centimeters}) \cdot (2 \text{ centimeters})$$
$$= (4 \cdot 2) \cdot (\text{centimeters} \cdot \text{centimeters})$$
$$= 8 \text{ square centimeters}$$

From this example, and others, we conclude that the area of any rectangle is the product of the length and width.

Here are the most common geometric figures along with the formula for the area of each one. The only formulas that are new to us are the ones that accompany the parallelogram and the circle.

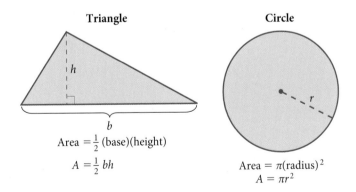

Square
Area = (side)(side)
= (side)^2
= s^2

Rectangle
Area = (length)(width)
= lw

Parallelogram
Area = (base)(height)
= bh

Triangle
Area = $\frac{1}{2}$(base)(height)
$A = \frac{1}{2}bh$

Circle
Area = π(radius)^2
$A = \pi r^2$

PRACTICE PROBLEMS

1. Find the area.

A Area of a Polygon

EXAMPLE 1   The parallelogram below has a base of 5 centimeters and a height of 2 centimeters. Find the area.

SOLUTION   If we apply our formula we have

$$\text{Area} = (\text{base})(\text{height})$$
$$A = bh$$
$$= 5 \cdot 2$$
$$= 10 \text{ cm}^2$$

Or, we could simply count the number of square centimeters it takes to cover the object. There are 8 complete squares and 4 half-squares, giving a total of 10 squares for an area of 10 square centimeters. Counting the squares in this manner helps us see why the formula for the area of a parallelogram is the product of the base and the height.

To justify our formula in general, we simply rearrange the parts to form a rectangle.

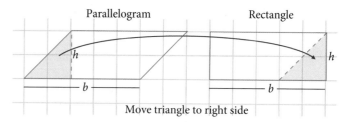

Move triangle to right side

2. Find the area.

EXAMPLE 2   The triangle below has a base of 6 centimeters and a height of 3 centimeters. Find the area.

SOLUTION   If we apply our formula we have

$$\text{Area} = \frac{1}{2}(\text{base})(\text{height})$$

$$A = \frac{1}{2}bh$$

$$= \frac{1}{2} \cdot 6 \cdot 3$$

$$= 9 \text{ cm}^2$$

Answers
1. 6 cm² **2.** 4 cm²

As was the case in Example 1, we can also count the number of square centimeters it takes to cover the triangle. There are 6 complete squares and 6 half-
squares, giving a total of 9 squares for an area of 9 square centimeters.

EXAMPLE 3 Find the area of each of the following stamps.

a. Each side is 35.0 millimeters.

b. Write your answer as a decimal, rounded to the nearest
hundredth.

$$\text{Base} = 2\frac{5}{8} \text{ inches}$$
$$\text{Height} = 1\frac{1}{4} \text{ inches}$$

c. Round to the nearest hundred

Length = 1.56 inches
Width = 0.99 inches

Peanuts: © United Feature Syndicate, Inc.

SOLUTION Applying our formulas for area we have

a. $A = s^2 = (35 \text{ mm})^2 = 1{,}225 \text{ mm}^2$

b. $A = \frac{1}{2}bh = \frac{1}{2}\left(2\frac{5}{8} \text{ in.}\right)\left(1\frac{1}{4} \text{ in.}\right) = \frac{1}{2} \cdot \frac{21}{8} \cdot \frac{5}{4} \text{ in}^2 \approx 1.64 \text{ in}^2$

c. $A = lw = (1.56 \text{ in.})(0.99 \text{ in.}) \approx 1.54 \text{ in}^2$

B Area of a Circle

EXAMPLE 4 The circle shown in the stamp in Example 3a has a radius
of 14.5 millimeters. Find the area of the circle to the nearest whole number.

SOLUTION Using our formula for the area of a circle, and using 3.14 for π, we
have

$A = \pi r^2$	Formula for area
$\approx 3.14(14.5)^2$	Substitute in values
$= 3.14(210.25)$	Square 14.5
$= 660.185 \text{ mm}^2$	Multiply
$\approx 660 \text{ mm}^2$	Round to the nearest whole number

---

3. Find the area of each stamp in
Example 3 from the dimensions
given below. Round answers to
the nearest hundredth.
a. Each side is 1.38 inches

b. Base = 6.6 centimeters,
height = 3.3 centimeters

c. Length = 39.6 millimeters,
width = 25.1 millimeters

4. A circle has a radius of 5 feet.
Find the area.

Answers
3. a. 1.90 in² b. 10.89 cm²
c. 993.96 mm²
4. 78.5 ft²

5. Find the area of the shaded portion of this figure.

EXAMPLE 5   Find the area of the shaded portion of this figure.

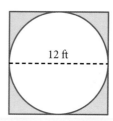

SOLUTION   We have a circle inscribed in a square. We notice the diameter of the circle is the same length as one side of the square. To find the area of the shaded region, we subtract the area of the circle from the area of the square as follows:

$$A = 12^2 - 6^2\pi$$
$$= 144 - 36\pi$$
$$\approx 30.96 \text{ ft}^2$$

Getting Ready for Class

After reading through the preceding section, respond in your own words and in complete sentences.

1. Suppose a rectangle is 8 inches long and 3 inches wide. How many square inches will it take to cover the rectangle?

2. A rectangle measures 4 feet by 6 feet. What units will you assign to the perimeter and to the area?

3. What does π represent?

4. How do you find the area of a circle?

Answers

5. 21.5 cm² to the nearest tenth

Problem Set 8.2

A **B** Find the area enclosed by each figure. [Examples 1–4]

1.

3 in.

3 in.

9 in²

2.

5.5 cm

5.5 cm

30.25 cm²

3.
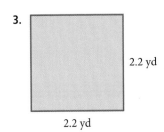
2.2 yd

2.2 yd

4.84 yd²

4.

3.6 in.

8 in.

28.8 in²

5.

15 yd

9 yd

135 yd²

6.

3 m

7 m

21 m²

7.
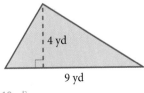
4 yd

9 yd

18 yd²

8.

2 cm

12.5 cm

12.5 cm²

9.

1.73 ft

2 ft

1.73 ft²

10.

3.2 in.

7 in

11.2 in²

11.
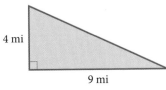
4 mi

9 mi

18 mi²

12.
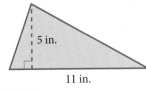
5 in.

11 in.

27.5 in²

13.
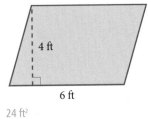
4 ft

6 ft

24 ft²

14.

3.2 m

7 m

22.4 m²

15.

5.3 cm

11 cm

58.3 cm²

▶ **16.**

9 ft

254.34 ft²

17.

12 in

113.04 in²

18.

1 km

.785 km²

▶ **19.**

2 cm
4 cm
5 cm
4 cm
5 cm
4 cm
6 cm
16 cm
4 cm
18 cm

156 cm²

▶ **20.**

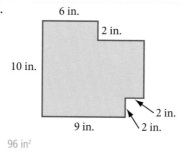

6 in.
2 in.
10 in.
9 in.
2 in.
2 in.

96 in²

21.

5 ft
4 ft
3 ft
15 ft

59.13 ft²

22.

4 in.
6 in.
4 in.
5 in.
7 in.

30 in²

23.

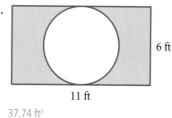

6 ft
11 ft

37.74 ft²

24.

4 m
4 m
2 m
3 m
6 m
1.5 m

52.935 m²

■ Applying the Concepts

▶ **25. Area of an MP3 Player** The MP3 player below is the smallest of all MP3 players.

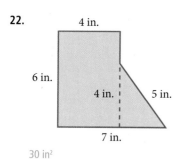

0.24 in.
1.5 in.

Music
Video
Photos
Radio
Settings

3.6 in.

a. Find the area of the face of the MP3 player.
5.4 in²

b. Find the area of the side of the MP3 player.
.864 in²

▶ **26. Area of an MP3 Player** The MP3 player below can hold up to 30,000 songs.

0.41 in.
2.4 in.

Video
Music
Photos
Radio

4.1 in.

a. Find the area of the face of the MP3 player.
9.84 in²

b. Find the area of the side of the MP3 player.
1.681 in²

▶ **27. Area of a Logo** The diameter of
the corporate logo here is 12.4
millimeters, find the area.
120.70 mm²

28. Area of a Logo The diameter of the
corporate logo here is 9.2 millimeters, find the area.
66.44 mm²

▶ **29. Area of a TV** A normal TV has a 4:3 ratio between its
length and width. If the diameter (measured from one
corner to the opposite corner) is 35 inches, what is the
area of the TV?
588 in²

30. Area of a TV A normal TV has a 4:3 ratio between its
length and width. If the diameter (measured from one
corner to the opposite corner) is 30 inches, what is the
area of the TV?
504 in²

31. Area to Perimeter Ratio The perimeter of each of the following shapes is 28. Find the area of each.
  a. Rectangle with length 12, width 2.
     24
  b. Rectangle with length 10, width 4.
     40
  c. Rectangle with length 8, width 6.
     48
  d. Square with side length 7.
     49
  e. Circle with radius $\dfrac{14}{\pi}$.
     62.42
  f. Which shape has the greatest area to perimeter
     ratio?
     Circle

32. Area to Perimeter Ratio The perimeter of each of the following shapes is 14. Find the area of each.
  a. Rectangle with length 20, width 8.
     160
  b. Rectangle with length 18, width 10.
     180
  c. Rectangle with length 16, width 12.
     192
  d. Square with side length 14.
     196
  e. Circle with radius $\dfrac{28}{\pi}$.
     249.68
  f. Which shape has the greatest area to perimeter ratio?
     Circle

33. The circle here is said to be *inscribed* in the square. If
the area of the circle is 64π square centimeters, find
the length of one of the sides of the square.

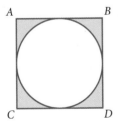

16 cm

34. The painting below is from the Getty Museum. Find the
diameter, circumference, and area of the circle that is
inside of the square.

$17\frac{7}{8}$ in.

© The J. Paul Getty Museum

$d = 17\frac{7}{8}$ in.
$C = 56.13$ in.
$A = 250.82$ in²

■ Getting Ready for the Next Section

Simplify.

35. $2 \cdot 3 \cdot 4$
24

36. $2(12)(15)$
360

37. $12 + 20 + 40$
72

38. $54 + 40 + 46$
140

39. $2(3.14)(0.125)(6)$
4.71

40. $314 \div 2$
157

41. $78.5 + 311.5 + 157$
547

42. $\frac{1}{2}[4(3.14)(100)]$
628

■ Maintaining Your Skills

43. A home has 1,800 square feet of living space. How many square yards is this?
200 yd²

44. A city covers 10 square miles of land. How many acres is this?
6,400 acres

45. A fire burns 3,200 acres. How many square miles are burned?
5 mi²

46. A square is 1 meter on each side. What is the area in square centimeters?
10,000 cm²

Find the area enclosed by each figure.

▶ **47.**

Half circle

4 in.

4 in.

22.28 in²

▶ **48.**

6 mi

Half circle

4 mi

2 mi

34.28 in²

Introduction . . .

You have probably heard that 70% of the Earth's surface is water and only 30% is land. In this section we will learn how to compute the surface area of any sphere, such as a planet, given its radius. We will also find the surface area of three dimensional shapes, such as cubes and cylinders.

NASA

A Surface Area of a Rectangular Solid

The figure below shows a closed box with length l, width w, and height h. The surfaces of the box are labeled as sides, top, bottom, front, and back. A box like this is called a *rectangular solid*. In general, a rectangular solid is a closed figure in which all sides are rectangles that meet at right angles.

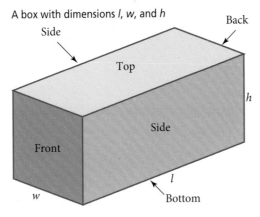

A box with dimensions l, w, and h

$$S = 2lh + 2hw + 2lw$$

To find the *surface area* of the box, we add the areas of each of the six surfaces that are labeled in the figure.

$$\text{Surface area} = \text{side} + \text{side} + \text{front} + \text{back} + \text{top} + \text{bottom}$$
$$S = l \cdot h + l \cdot h + h \cdot w + h \cdot w + l \cdot w + l \cdot w$$
$$= 2lh + 2hw + 2lw$$

PRACTICE PROBLEMS

1. A family is painting a dining room that is 12 feet wide and 15 feet long.
   a. If the ceiling is 8 feet high, find the surface area of the walls and the ceiling, but not the floor.
   b. If a gallon of paint will cover 400 square feet, how many gallons should they buy to paint the walls and the ceiling?

EXAMPLE 1 Find the surface area of the box shown here.

5 in.

3 in.   4 in.

SOLUTION To find the surface area we find the area of each surface individually, and then we add them together:

$$\text{Surface area} = 2(3 \text{ in.})(4 \text{ in.}) + 2(3 \text{ in.})(5 \text{ in.}) + 2(4 \text{ in.})(5 \text{ in.})$$
$$= 24 \text{ in}^2 + 30 \text{ in}^2 + 40 \text{ in}^2$$
$$= 94 \text{ in}^2$$

The total surface area is 94 square inches.

B Surface Area of a Cylinder

Here are the formulas for the surface area of some right circular cylinders. A *right circular cylinder* is a cylinder whose base is a circle and whose sides are perpendicular to the base.

Open at both ends

h

r

$S = 2\pi rh$

Closed at one end

h

r

$S = \pi r^2 + 2\pi rh$

Closed at both ends

h

r

$S = 2\pi r^2 + 2\pi rh$

2. Find the surface area of the straw pictured in Example 2 if the radius is doubled.

EXAMPLE 2 The drinking straw shown below has a radius of 0.125 inch and a length of 6 inches. How much material was used to make the straw?

SOLUTION A straw is a cylinder that is open at both ends. We find the amount of material needed to make the straw by calculating the surface area.

0.125 in.

6 in.

$$S = 2\pi rh$$
$$\approx 2(3.14)(0.125)(6)$$
$$= 4.71 \text{ in}^2$$

It takes 4.71 square inches of material to make the straw.

Answers

1. **a.** 612 ft²
   b. 2 gallons will cover everything with some paint left over.
2. 9.42 in²

C Surface Area of a Sphere

The figure below shows a sphere and the formula for its surface area.

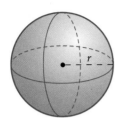

Surface Area = $4\pi(\text{radius})^2$

$S = 4\pi r^2$

EXAMPLE 3 Find the surface area of the given sphere.

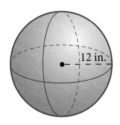

12 in.

3. Find the surface area of the sphere in Example 3 if the radius is halved.

SOLUTION The surface area is

$S = 4\pi r^2$

$\approx 4(3.14)(12)^2$

$= 1{,}808.64 \text{ in}^2$

The surface area is ,1808.64 square inches.

EXAMPLE 4 The figure below is composed of a right circular cylinder with half a sphere on top. (A half-sphere is called a hemisphere.) Find the surface area of the figure assuming it is closed on the bottom.

4. If the radius is doubled so that it becomes 10 inches instead of 5 inches, what is the new surface area of the figure?

10 in.

5 in.

SOLUTION The total surface area is found by adding the surface area of the cylinder to the surface area of the hemisphere.

S = surface area of bottom of cylinder + surface area of side of cylinder + surface area of hemisphere

$= \pi r^2 + 2\pi rh + \dfrac{1}{2}(4\pi r^2)$

$\approx (3.14)(5)^2 + 2(3.14)(5)(10) + \dfrac{1}{2}[4(3.14)(5^2)]$

$= 78.5 + 314 + 157$

$= 549.5 \text{ in}^2$

The total surface area is 549.5 square inches.

Answers

3. 452.16 in²

4. 1,570 in²

Getting Ready for Class

After reading through the preceding section, respond in your own words and in complete sentences.

1. What is a rectangular solid?

2. How do the formulas for a cylinder open at both ends and a cylinder closed at both ends differ?

3. What is a hemisphere?

4. How are a circle and a sphere related?

Problem Set 8.3

A Find the surface area of each rectangular solid. [Example 1]

1.

3 m
3 m
3 m

54 m²

2.

3 cm
6 cm
5 cm

126 cm²

3.

2 in.
4 in.
6 in.

88 in²

4.

5 ft
9 ft
5 ft

230 ft²

5.

3 yd
6 yd
4 yd

108 yd²

6.

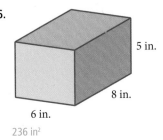

5 in.
8 in.
6 in.

236 in²

B Find the surface area of each cylinder (assume each cylinder is closed at both ends). [Example 2]

7.

4 in.
1 in.

31.4 in²

8.

8 ft
2 ft

125.6 in²

9.

7 cm
5 cm

149.15 cm²

10.

7 in.
.5 in.

23.55 in²

11.

25 ft
20 ft

2,198 ft²

12.

3.2 in.
1.2 in.

33.16 in²

▶ Selected exercises available online at www.webassign.net/brookscole

C Find the surface area of each sphere. [Example 3]

▶ **13.**

2.5 m

78.5 m²

▶ **14.**

4.5 yd

254.34 yd²

▶ **15.**

7 ft

153.86 ft²

▶ **16.**

4 ft

200.96 ft²

17.

3.6 in.

162.78 in²

18.

10 cm

1,256 cm²

Find the surface area of each figure. [Example 4]

▶ **19.**

4 in.

2 in.

87.92 in²

▶ **20.**

7 ft

5 ft

455.3 ft²

21.

10 cm

7 cm

901.18 cm²

▶ **22.** 2 in.

2 in.

3 in.

4 in.

4 in.

72 in²

23. 1 m

2 m

2 m

2 m

6 m

100 m²

24.

1 m

3 m

3 m

4 m

3 m

206 m²

5 m

■ Applying the Concepts

▶ **25. Surface Area of a Cake** The cake shown here is a wonder cake and has a radius of 7 inches. If the thickness of the cake is 3 inches, what is the surface area of the whole cake (including the bottom)?

439.6 in²

26. Surface Area of a Cake If they stacked another cake of the same size on top of the cake, what would the new surface area be?

571.48 in²

Making a Cylinder. Make an $8\frac{1}{2}$ by 11 inch piece of notebook paper into a cylinder as shown. Use the diagrams to help with Problems 27 and 28.

11 in.

$8\frac{1}{2}$ in.

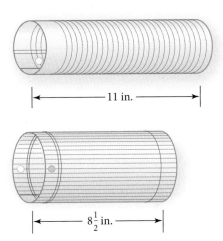

27. a. If the length of the cylinder is 11 inches, what is the largest possible radius? Round to the nearest thousandth.

1.354 in.

b. Using the radius from Part a, and the formula for the surface area of a cylinder, find the surface area of the rolled piece of notebook paper. Round to the nearest tenth.

93.5 in²

c. Find the area of the original piece of notebook paper by multiplying length by width. Does this area match the area you found in Part b?

Yes

28. a. If the length of the cylinder is $8\frac{1}{2}$ inches, what is the largest possible radius? Round to the nearest thousandth.

1.752 in.

b. Using the radius from Part a, and the formula for the surface area of a cylinder, find the surface area of the rolled piece of notebook paper. Round to the nearest tenth.

93.5 in²

c. Find the area of the original piece of notebook paper by multiplying length by width. Does this area match the area you found in Part b?

Yes

▶ **29.** A living room is 10 feet long and 8 feet wide. If the ceiling is 8 feet high, what is the total surface area of the four walls?

288 ft²

▶ **30.** A family room is 12 feet wide and 14 feet long. If the ceiling is 8 feet high, what is the total surface area of the four walls?

416 ft²

■ Extending the Concepts

31. The surface of the earth is 70% water. If the diameter of the earth is 8,000 miles, how many square miles of the earth are covered by land?

60,288,000 mi²

32. The surface of the earth is 70% water. How many square kilometers of the earth are covered by land if the diameter is 12,874 kilometers?

156,126,963 km²

Surface Area of a Cone. The surface area of a cone is given by the formula $S = \pi r^2 + \pi r l$ where l is called the slant height. We can use the Pythagorean Theorem to find the slant height (see left figure). Using the formula, find the surface area of the following cones.

33.

13 cm

12 cm

5 cm

282.6 cm²

34.

4 in.

5 in.

6 in.

75.36 in²

■ Getting Ready for the Next Section

Simplify each expression.

35. 3^3

27

36. $15 \cdot 3 \cdot 5$

225

37. $\dfrac{1}{2} \cdot \dfrac{4}{3}$

$\dfrac{2}{3}$

38. 0.125^2

0.015625

Simplify each expression. Round to the nearest thousandth.

39. $3.14(0.125)^2(6)$

0.294

40. $\dfrac{2}{3}(392.6)$

261.733

41. $3.14(25)(10)$

785

42. $785 \div 3$

261.667

■ Maintaining Your Skills

43. How many cubic inches are in 1 cubic foot?

1,728 in³

44. Convert 12 pints to quarts.

6 qt

45. Convert 12 pints to gallons.

1.5 gal

46. A bottle holds 12 fluid ounces. Is this more or less than a pint?

Less than a pint

Introduction . . .

Next, we move up one dimension and consider what is called volume. Volume is the measure of the space enclosed by a solid. For instance, if each edge of a cube is 3 feet long, then we can think of the cube as being made up of a number of smaller cubes, each of which is 1 foot long, 1 foot wide, and 1 foot high. Each of these smaller cubes is called a cubic foot. To count the number of them in the larger cube, think of the large cube as having three layers. You can see that the top layer contains 9 cubic feet. Because there are three layers, the total number of cubic feet in the large cube is $9 \cdot 3 = 27$.

On the other hand, if we multiply the length, the width, and the height of the cube, we have the same result:

$$Volume = (3 \text{ feet})(3 \text{ feet})(3 \text{ feet})$$
$$= (3 \cdot 3 \cdot 3)(\text{feet} \cdot \text{feet} \cdot \text{feet})$$
$$= 27 \text{ cubic feet}$$

A Volume of a Rectangular Solid

For the present we will confine our discussion of volume to volumes of *rectangular solids.* Rectangular solids are the three-dimensional equivalents of rectangles: Opposite sides are parallel, and any two sides that meet, meet at right angles. A rectangular solid is shown below, along with the formula used to calculate its volume.

Volume = (length)(width)(height)
$$V = lwh$$

EXAMPLE 1 Find the volume of a rectangular solid with length 15 inches, width 3 inches, and height 5 inches.

SOLUTION To find the volume we apply the formula shown above:

$$V = l \cdot w \cdot h$$
$$= (15 \text{ in.})(3 \text{ in.})(5 \text{ in.})$$
$$= 225 \text{ in}^3$$

PRACTICE PROBLEMS

1. A home has a dining room that is 12 feet wide and 15 feet long. If the ceiling is 8 feet high, find the volume of the dining room.

Answer
1. 1,440 cubic feet

B Volume of a Cylinder

Here is the formula for the volume of a right circular cylinder, a cylinder whose base is a circle and whose sides are perpendicular to the base.

Volume = π(radius)²(height)

$$V = \pi r^2 h$$

EXAMPLE 2 The drinking straw shown below has a radius of 0.125 inch and a length of 6 inches. To the nearest thousandth, find the volume of liquid that it will hold.

2. Find the volume of the straw in Example 2 if the radius is doubled. Round your answer to the nearest thousandth.

0.125 in.

6 in.

SOLUTION The total volume is found from the formula for the volume of a right circular cylinder. In this case, the radius is $r = 0.125$, and the height is $h = 6$. We approximate π with 3.14.

$$V = \pi r^2 h$$
$$\approx (3.14)(0.125)^2(6)$$
$$= (3.14)(0.015625)(6)$$
$$\approx 0.294 \text{ in}^3 \text{ to the nearest thousandth}$$

C Volume of a Cone

Next, we have the formula for the volume of a cone. As you can see, the relevant dimensions of a cone are the radius of its circular base and its height. You will also notice that this formula involves both a fraction, the number $\frac{1}{3}$, and a decimal, the number π, for which we have been using 3.14.

Volume = $\frac{1}{3}$ π(radius)²(height)

$$V = \frac{1}{3}\pi r^2 h$$

EXAMPLE 3   Find the volume of the given cone.

SOLUTION   The volume is found by using the formula for the volume of a cone. In this case, the radius = 3 cm, and the height = 5 cm. Again, we use 3.14 for π.

$$V = \frac{1}{3}\pi r^2 h$$

$$\approx \frac{1}{3}(3.14)(3^2)(5)$$

$$= \frac{1}{3}(3.14)(9)(5)$$

$$= (3.14)(3)(5)$$

$$= (3.14)(15)$$

$$= 47.1 \text{ cm}^3$$

D Volume of a Sphere

Next we have a sphere and the formula for its volume. Once again, the formula contains both the fraction $\frac{4}{3}$ and the number π.

$$\text{Volume} = \tfrac{4}{3}\pi(\text{radius})^3$$
$$= \tfrac{4}{3}\pi r^3$$

EXAMPLE 4   Find the volume of the given sphere. Round your answer to the nearest hundredth.

SOLUTION   The volume is

$$V = \frac{4}{3}\pi r^3$$

$$\approx \frac{4}{3}(3.14)(8)^3$$

$$\approx 2,143.57 \text{ cm}^3$$

---

3. Find the volume of the given cone. Round your answer to the nearest thousandth.

4. Find the volume of the sphere in Example 4 if the radius is halved. Round to the nearest hundredth.

Answers
3. 16.747 ft³
4. 267.95 cm³

5. If the radius in the figure in example 4 is doubled so that it becomes 10 inches instead of 5 inches, what is the new volume of the figure? Round your answer to the nearest tenth.

EXAMPLE 5 The figure here is composed of a right circular cylinder with half a sphere on top. (A half-sphere is called a hemisphere.) To the nearest tenth, find the total volume enclosed by the figure.

10 in.

5 in.

SOLUTION The total volume is found by adding the volume of the cylinder to the volume of the hemisphere.

$$V = \text{volume of cylinder} + \text{volume of hemisphere}$$

$$= \pi r^2 h + \frac{1}{2} \cdot \frac{4}{3}\pi r^3$$

$$\approx (3.14)(5)^2(10) + \frac{1}{2} \cdot \frac{4}{3}(3.14)(5)^3$$

$$= (3.14)(25)(10) + \frac{1}{2} \cdot \frac{4}{3}(3.14)(125)$$

$$= 785 + \frac{2}{3}(392.5) \qquad \text{Multiply: } \frac{1}{2} \cdot \frac{4}{3} = \frac{4}{6} = \frac{2}{3}$$

$$= 785 + \frac{785}{3} \qquad \text{Multiply: } 2(392.5) = 785$$

$$= 785 + 261.7 \qquad \text{Divide 785 by 3, and round to the nearest tenth}$$

$$= 1,046.7 \text{ in}^3$$

Getting Ready for Class

After reading through the preceding section, respond in your own words and in complete sentences.

1. If the dimensions of a rectangular solid are given in inches, what units will be associated with the volume?
2. What is the relationship between area and volume?
3. What formulas from this section involve both a fraction and a decimal?
4. State the volume formula for a cube, a cylinder, a cone, and a sphere.

Answer

5. 5,233.3 in³

Problem Set 8.4

A Find the volume of each rectangular solid. Round to the nearest hundredth, if necessary. [Example 1]

▶ **1.**

3 m
3 m
3 m
27 m³

▶ **2.**

2 yd
3 yd
3 yd
18 yd³

▶ **3.**

1.2 in.
3.4 in.
5 in.
20.4 in³

4.

11 ft
15 ft
12 ft
1,980 ft³

▶ **5.**

3.2 m
4 m
1.6 m
20.48 m³

6.

3 in.
4.5 in.
1.5 in.
20.25 in³

B Find the volume of each cylinder. Round to the nearest hundredth, if necessary. [Example 2]

▶ **7.**

10 yd
1.5 yd
70.65 yd³

▶ **8.**

4 m
3.5 m
153.86 m³

▶ **9.**

3.2 in.
1.2 in.
14.47 in³

10.

2.6 ft
2.6 ft
55.19 ft³

11.

4.3 m
3 m
121.52 m³

▶ **12.**

7 cm
5 cm
137.38 cm³

C Find the volume of each cone. Round to the nearest hundredth, if necessary. [Example 3]

13.

3 m

1.5 m

7.07 m³

▶ **14.**

4 ft

2 ft

16.75 ft³

15.

4 cm

4 cm

66.99 cm³

16.

3.5 cm

2.5 cm

22.90 cm³

▶ **17.**

4.5 cm

1.5 cm

10.60 cm³

18.

6.5 m

2.5 m

42.52 m³

D Find the volume of each sphere. Round to the nearest hundredth, if necessary. [Example 4]

▶ **19.**

4 ft

267.95 ft³

▶ **20.**

3.6 in.

195.33 in³

▶ **21.**

10 cm

4,186.67 cm³

22.

2.4 ft

57.88 ft³

▶ **23.**

7.6 m

1,837.85 m³

24.

5.1 m

555.37 m³

Find the volume of each figure. Round to the nearest hundredth, if necessary. [Example 5]

▶ 25.

4 in.

3 in.

169.56 in³

▶ 26.

5 ft

1.5 ft

42.39 ft³

27.

1.5 ft

0.2 ft

0.21 ft³

▶ 28.

2 m

2 m

3 m

4 m   4 m

32 m³

29.

1 ft

2 ft   2 ft

2 ft

6 ft   4 ft

80 ft³

30.

1 cm

3 cm

4 cm   3 cm   3 cm

5 cm

165 cm³

Triangular Pyramid. The formula for finding the volume of a triangular pyramid is one-third the area of the base times the height, or $V = \frac{1}{3} Bh$, where B = the area of the base.

Find the volume of each pyramid. Round to the nearest hundredth.

31.

5.3 cm

5.3 cm   5.3 cm

49.63 cm³

32.

11.5 ft

7.3 ft   5.1 ft

142.72 ft³

33.

2.5 m

4.5 m   6.0 m

22.5 m³

34.

3.2 cm

7.1 cm   3.2 cm

24.23 cm³

● Getting Ready for the Next Section

The problems below review the material on exponents we have covered previously.

Expand and simplify.

35. $\left(\dfrac{1}{3}\right)^4$

$\dfrac{1}{81}$

36. $\left(\dfrac{3}{4}\right)^3$

$\dfrac{27}{64}$

37. $\left(\dfrac{5}{6}\right)^2$

$\dfrac{25}{36}$

38. $\left(\dfrac{3}{5}\right)^3$

$\dfrac{27}{125}$

39. $(0.5)^2$

0.25

40. $(0.1)^3$

0.001

41. $(1.2)^2$

1.44

42. $(2.1)^2$

4.41

43. $3^2 + 4^2$

25

44. $5^2 + 12^2$

169

45. $6^2 + 8^2$

100

46. $2^2 + 3^2$

13

● Maintaining Your Skills

Divide each of the following and write your answers in lowest terms.

47. $\dfrac{2}{3} \div \dfrac{4}{9}$

$\dfrac{3}{2}$

48. $\dfrac{1}{6} \div \dfrac{2}{3}$

$\dfrac{1}{4}$

49. $\dfrac{4}{7} \div \dfrac{3}{14}$

$\dfrac{8}{3}$

50. $\dfrac{3}{4} \div \dfrac{9}{16}$

$\dfrac{4}{3}$

51. $\dfrac{7}{15} \div \dfrac{21}{30}$

$\dfrac{2}{3}$

52. $\dfrac{4}{9} \div \dfrac{12}{27}$

1

53. $\dfrac{4}{7} \div \dfrac{2}{3}$

$\dfrac{6}{7}$

54. $\dfrac{5}{12} \div \dfrac{7}{15}$

$\dfrac{25}{28}$

55. $\dfrac{36}{15} \div \dfrac{24}{10}$

1

56. $\dfrac{23}{56} \div \dfrac{2}{4}$

$\dfrac{23}{28}$

57. $\dfrac{48}{40} \div \dfrac{6}{8}$

$\dfrac{8}{5}$

58. $\dfrac{27}{20} \div \dfrac{9}{50}$

$\dfrac{15}{2}$

59. $\dfrac{2}{5} \div 2$

$\dfrac{1}{5}$

60. $\dfrac{3}{4} \div 21$

$\dfrac{1}{28}$

61. $\dfrac{5}{8} \div 10$

$\dfrac{1}{16}$

62. $\dfrac{4}{7} \div 2$

$\dfrac{2}{7}$

● Extending the Concepts

63. Containment System. Holding tanks for hazardous liquids are often surrounded by containment tanks that will hold the hazardous liquid if the
main tank begins to leak. In the graphic to the right, the center tank has a
height of 16 feet and a radius of 6 feet. The outside containment tank has
a height of 4 feet and a radius of 8 feet. If the center tank is full of heating
fuel and develops a leak at the bottom, will the containment tank be able
to hold all the heating fuel that leaks out?

No

Square Roots and the Pythagorean Theorem

Introduction . . .

Figure 1 shows the front view of the roof of a tool shed. How do we find the length d of the diagonal part of the roof? (Imagine that you are drawing the plans for the shed. Since the shed hasn't been built yet, you can't just measure the diagonal, but you need to know how long it will be so you can buy the correct amount of material to build the shed.)

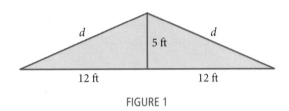

FIGURE 1

There is a formula from geometry that gives the length d:

$$d = \sqrt{12^2 + 5^2}$$

where $\sqrt{}$ is called the *square root symbol.* If we simplify what is under the square root symbol, we have this:

$$d = \sqrt{144 + 25}$$
$$= \sqrt{169}$$

The expression $\sqrt{169}$ stands for the number we *square* to get 169. Because $13 \cdot 13 = 169$, that number is 13. Therefore the length d in our original diagram is 13 feet.

A Square Roots

Here is a more detailed discussion of square roots. In Chapter 1, we did some work with exponents. In particular, we spent some time finding squares of numbers. For example, we considered expressions like this:

$$5^2 = 5 \cdot 5 = 25$$
$$7^2 = 7 \cdot 7 = 49$$
$$x^2 = x \cdot x$$

We say that "the square of 5 is 25" and "the square of 7 is 49." To square a number, we multiply it by itself. When we ask for the *square root* of a given number, we want to know what number we *square* in order to obtain the given number. We say that the square root of 49 is 7, because 7 is the number we square to get 49. Likewise, the square root of 25 is 5, because $5^2 = 25$. The symbol we use to denote square root is $\sqrt{}$, which is also called a *radical sign.* Here is the precise definition of square root.

> ### Definition
>
> The **square root** of a positive number a, written $\sqrt{a}$, is the number we square to get a. In symbols:
>
> If $\sqrt{a} = b$ then $b^2 = a$.

We list some common square roots in Table 1.

Instructor Note
This section gives a simple introduction to square roots. I have purposely left out some of the details, especially negative roots. My goal is to give students experience with roots, so the concept will seem familiar to them when they take an algebra class.

 The square root we are describing here is actually the principal square root. There is another square root that is a negative number. We won't see it in this book, but, if you go on to take an algebra course, you will see it there.

TABLE 1

Statement	In Words	Reason
$\sqrt{0} = 0$	The square root of 0 is 0	Because $0^2 = 0$
$\sqrt{1} = 1$	The square root of 1 is 1	Because $1^2 = 1$
$\sqrt{4} = 2$	The square root of 4 is 2	Because $2^2 = 4$
$\sqrt{9} = 3$	The square root of 9 is 3	Because $3^2 = 9$
$\sqrt{16} = 4$	The square root of 16 is 4	Because $4^2 = 16$
$\sqrt{25} = 5$	The square root of 25 is 5	Because $5^2 = 25$

Numbers like 1, 9, and 25, whose square roots are whole numbers, are called *perfect squares.* To find the square root of a perfect square, we look for the whole number that is squared to get the perfect square. The following examples involve square roots of perfect squares.

PRACTICE PROBLEMS

1. Simplify: $4\sqrt{25}$

EXAMPLE 1 Simplify: $7\sqrt{64}$

SOLUTION The expression $7\sqrt{64}$ means 7 times $\sqrt{64}$. To simplify this expression, we write $\sqrt{64}$ as 8 and multiply:

$$7\sqrt{64} = 7 \cdot 8 = 56$$

We know $\sqrt{64} = 8$, because $8^2 = 64$.

2. Simplify: $\sqrt{36} + \sqrt{4}$

EXAMPLE 2 Simplify: $\sqrt{9} + \sqrt{16}$

SOLUTION We write $\sqrt{9}$ as 3 and $\sqrt{16}$ as 4. Then we add:

$$\sqrt{9} + \sqrt{16} = 3 + 4 = 7$$

3. Simplify: $\sqrt{\dfrac{36}{100}}$

EXAMPLE 3 Simplify: $\sqrt{\dfrac{25}{81}}$

SOLUTION We are looking for the number we square (multiply times itself) to get $\frac{25}{81}$. We know that when we multiply two fractions, we multiply the numerators and multiply the denominators. Because $5 \cdot 5 = 25$ and $9 \cdot 9 = 81$, the square root of $\frac{25}{81}$ must be $\frac{5}{9}$.

$$\sqrt{\frac{25}{81}} = \frac{5}{9} \quad \text{because} \quad \left(\frac{5}{9}\right)^2 = \frac{5}{9} \cdot \frac{5}{9} = \frac{25}{81}$$

In Examples 4–6, we simplify each expression as much as possible.

Simplify each expression as much as possible.

4. $14\sqrt{36}$

EXAMPLE 4 Simplify: $12\sqrt{25} = 12 \cdot 5 = 60$

EXAMPLE 5 Simplify: $\sqrt{100} - \sqrt{36} = 10 - 6 = 4$

5. $\sqrt{81} - \sqrt{25}$

6. $\sqrt{\dfrac{64}{121}}$

EXAMPLE 6 Simplify: $\sqrt{\dfrac{49}{121}} = \dfrac{7}{11}$ because $\left(\dfrac{7}{11}\right)^2 = \dfrac{7}{11} \cdot \dfrac{7}{11} = \dfrac{49}{121}$

B Approximating Square Roots

Answers

1. 20 **2.** 8 **3.** $\frac{3}{5}$ **4.** 84

5. 4 **6.** $\frac{8}{11}$

So far in this section we have been concerned only with square roots of perfect squares. The next question is, "What about square roots of numbers that are not perfect squares, like $\sqrt{7}$, for example?" We know that

$$\sqrt{4} = 2 \quad \text{and} \quad \sqrt{9} = 3$$

And because 7 is between 4 and 9, $\sqrt{7}$ should be between $\sqrt{4}$ and $\sqrt{9}$. That is, $\sqrt{7}$ should be between 2 and 3. But what is it exactly? The answer is, we cannot write it exactly in decimal or fraction form. Because of this, it is called an *irrational number.* We can approximate it with a decimal, but we can never write it exactly with a decimal. Table 2 gives some decimal approximations for $\sqrt{7}$. The decimal approximations were obtained by using a calculator. We could continue the list to any accuracy we desired. However, we would never reach a number in decimal form whose square was exactly 7.

TABLE 2

APPROXIMATIONS FOR THE SQUARE ROOT OF 7		
Accurate to the Nearest	The Square Root of 7 is	Check by Squaring
Tenth	$\sqrt{7} = 2.6$	$(2.6)^2 = 6.76$
Hundredth	$\sqrt{7} = 2.65$	$(2.65)^2 = 7.0225$
Thousandth	$\sqrt{7} = 2.646$	$(2.646)^2 = 7.001316$
Ten thousandth	$\sqrt{7} = 2.6458$	$(2.6458)^2 = 7.00025764$

EXAMPLE 7 Give a decimal approximation for the expression $5\sqrt{12}$ that is accurate to the nearest ten thousandth.

SOLUTION Let's agree not to round to the nearest ten thousandth until we have first done all the calculations. Using a calculator, we find $\sqrt{12} \approx 3.4641016$. Therefore,

$$5\sqrt{12} \approx 5(3.4641016) \quad \text{\footnotesize $\sqrt{12}$ on calculator}$$
$$= 17.320508 \quad \text{\footnotesize Multiplication}$$
$$\approx 17.3205 \quad \text{\footnotesize To the nearest ten thousandth}$$

EXAMPLE 8 Approximate $\sqrt{301} + \sqrt{137}$ to the nearest hundredth.

SOLUTION Using a calculator to approximate the square roots, we have

$$\sqrt{301} + \sqrt{137} \approx 17.349352 + 11.704700 = 29.054052$$

To the nearest hundredth, the answer is 29.05.

EXAMPLE 9 Approximate $\sqrt{\dfrac{7}{11}}$ to the nearest thousandth.

SOLUTION Because we are using calculators, we first change $\dfrac{7}{11}$ to a decimal and then find the square root:

$$\sqrt{\dfrac{7}{11}} \approx \sqrt{0.6363636} \approx 0.7977240$$

To the nearest thousandth, the answer is 0.798.

C The Pythagorean Theorem

FACTS FROM GEOMETRY Perimeter

A *right triangle* is a triangle that contains a 90° (or right) angle. The longest side in a right triangle is called the *hypotenuse*, and we use the letter c to denote it. The two shorter sides are denoted by the letters a and b. The Pythagorean theorem states that the hypotenuse is the square root of the sum of the squares of the two shorter sides. In symbols:

$$c = \sqrt{a^2 + b^2}$$

7. Give a decimal approximation for the expression $5\sqrt{14}$ that is accurate to the nearest ten thousandth.

8. Approximate $\sqrt{405} + \sqrt{147}$ to the nearest hundredth.

9. Approximate $\sqrt{\dfrac{7}{12}}$ to the nearest thousandth.

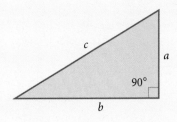

Answers
7. 18.7083 **8.** 32.25 **9.** 0.764

10. Find the length of the hypotenuse in each right triangle.

a.

5 ft

c

5 ft

b.

c

12 cm

16 cm

11. A wire from the top of a 12-foot pole is fastened to the ground by a stake that is 5 feet from the bottom of the pole. What is the length of the wire?

EXAMPLE 10 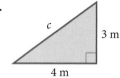 Find the length of the hypotenuse in each right triangle.

a.

c

3 m

4 m

b.

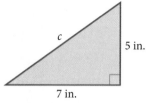

c

5 in.

7 in.

SOLUTION We apply the formula given above.

a. When $a = 3$ and $b = 4$:

$c = \sqrt{3^2 + 4^2}$
$= \sqrt{9 + 16}$
$= \sqrt{25}$
$c = 5$ meters

b. When $a = 5$ and $b = 7$:

$c = \sqrt{5^2 + 7^2}$
$= \sqrt{25 + 49}$
$= \sqrt{74}$
$c \approx 8.60$ inches

In part a, the solution is a whole number, whereas in part b, we must use a calculator to get 8.60 as an approximation to $\sqrt{74}$.

EXAMPLE 11 A ladder is leaning against the top of a 6-foot wall. If the bottom of the ladder is 8 feet from the wall, how long is the ladder?

SOLUTION A picture of the situation is shown in Figure 2. We let c denote the length of the ladder. Applying the Pythagorean theorem, we have

6 ft
c
90°
8 ft

FIGURE 2

$c = \sqrt{6^2 + 8^2}$
$= \sqrt{36 + 64}$
$= \sqrt{100}$
$= 10$ feet

The ladder is 10 feet long.

Getting Ready for Class

After reading through the preceding section, respond in your own words and in complete sentences.

1. Which number is larger, the square of 10 or the square root of 10?
2. Give a definition for the square root of a number.
3. What two numbers will the square root of 20 fall between?
4. What is the Pythagorean theorem?

Answers
10. a. approx. 7.07 ft **b.** 20 cm
11. 13 ft

Problem Set 8.5

A Find each of the following square roots without using a calculator. [Example 1]

1. $\sqrt{64}$
8

▶ **2.** $\sqrt{100}$
10

3. $\sqrt{81}$
9

4. $\sqrt{49}$
7

5. $\sqrt{36}$
6

6. $\sqrt{144}$
12

▶ **7.** $\sqrt{25}$
5

8. $\sqrt{169}$
13

A Simplify each of the following expressions without using a calculator. [Examples 1–6]

9. $3\sqrt{25}$
15

▶ **10.** $9\sqrt{49}$
63

11. $6\sqrt{64}$
48

▶ **12.** $11\sqrt{100}$
110

▶ **13.** $15\sqrt{9}$
45

14. $8\sqrt{36}$
48

▶ **15.** $16\sqrt{9}$
48

16. $9\sqrt{16}$
36

▶ **17.** $\sqrt{49} + \sqrt{64}$
15

▶ **18.** $\sqrt{1} + \sqrt{0}$
1

▶ **19.** $\sqrt{16} - \sqrt{9}$
1

20. $\sqrt{25} - \sqrt{4}$
3

▶ **21.** $3\sqrt{25} + 9\sqrt{49}$
78

22. $6\sqrt{64} + 11\sqrt{100}$
158

▶ **23.** $15\sqrt{9} - 9\sqrt{16}$
9

24. $7\sqrt{49} - 2\sqrt{4}$
45

▶ **25.** $\sqrt{\dfrac{16}{49}}$
$\dfrac{4}{7}$

26. $\sqrt{\dfrac{100}{121}}$
$\dfrac{10}{11}$

27. $\sqrt{\dfrac{36}{64}}$
$\dfrac{3}{4}$

▶ **28.** $\sqrt{\dfrac{81}{144}}$
$\dfrac{3}{4}$

Indicate whether each of the statements in Problems 29–32 is *True* or *False*.

29. $\sqrt{4} + \sqrt{9} = \sqrt{4 + 9}$
False

30. $\sqrt{\dfrac{16}{25}} = \dfrac{\sqrt{16}}{\sqrt{25}}$
True

▶ **31.** $\sqrt{25 \cdot 9} = \sqrt{25} \cdot \sqrt{9}$
True

▶ **32.** $\sqrt{100} - \sqrt{36} = \sqrt{100 - 36}$
False

▶ Selected exercises available online at www.webassign.net/brookscole

C Find the length of the hypotenuse in each right triangle. Round to the nearest hundredth, if necessary. [Examples 10, 11]

33.

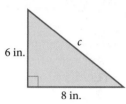

6 in.

c

8 in.

10 in.

34.

7.07 yd

5 yd

c

5 yd

35. ▶

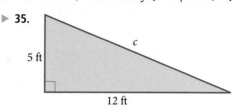

5 ft

c

12 ft

13 ft

36. ▶

25 cm

24 cm

c

7 cm

37.

c

4 in.

5 in.

6.40 in.

38. ▶

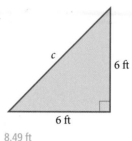

c

6 ft

6 ft

8.49 ft

39. ▶

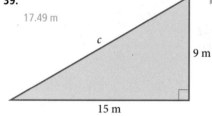

17.49 m

c

9 m

15 m

40. ▶

c

1 km

8 km

8.06 km

B **Calculator Problems** [Examples 7–9]

Use a calculator to work problems 41 through 60.

Approximate each of the following square roots to the nearest ten thousandth.

41. $\sqrt{1.25}$
1.1180

42. $\sqrt{12.5}$
3.5355

43. $\sqrt{125}$
11.1803

44. $\sqrt{1250}$
35.3553

Approximate each of the following expressions to the nearest hundredth.

45. $2\sqrt{3}$
3.46

46. ▶ $3\sqrt{2}$
4.24

47. $5\sqrt{5}$
11.18

48. $5\sqrt{3}$
8.66

49. $\dfrac{\sqrt{3}}{3}$
0.58

50. $\dfrac{\sqrt{2}}{2}$
0.71

51. ▶ $\sqrt{\dfrac{1}{3}}$
0.58

52. $\sqrt{\dfrac{1}{2}}$
0.71

Approximate each of the following expressions to the nearest thousandth.

53. ▶ $\sqrt{12} + \sqrt{75}$
12.124

54. $\sqrt{18} + \sqrt{50}$
11.314

55. ▶ $\sqrt{87}$
9.327

56. $\sqrt{68}$
8.246

57. ▶ $2\sqrt{3} + 5\sqrt{3}$
12.124

58. $3\sqrt{2} + 5\sqrt{2}$
11.314

59. $7\sqrt{3}$
12.124

60. $8\sqrt{2}$
11.314

■ Applying the Concepts

61. Google Earth The Google Earth image shows a right triangle between three cities in the Los Angeles area. If the distance between Pomona and Ontario is 5.7 miles, and the distance between Ontario and Upland is 3.6 miles, what is the distance between Pomona and Upland? Round to the nearest tenth of a mile.

6.7 miles

62. Google Earth The Google Earth image shows three cities in Colorado. If the distance between Denver and North Washington is 2.5 miles, and the distance between Edgewater and Denver is 4 miles, what is the distance between North Washington and Edgewater? Round to the nearest tenth.

4.7 miles

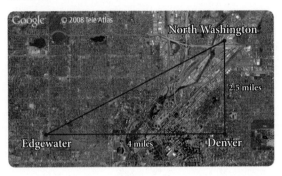

▶ **63. Geometry** One end of a wire is attached to the top of a 24-foot pole; the other end of the wire is anchored to the ground 18 feet from the bottom of the pole. If the pole makes an angle of 90° with the ground, find the length of the wire.

30 ft

▶ **64. Geometry** Two children are trying to cross a stream. They want to use a log that goes from one bank to the other. If the left bank is 5 feet higher than the right bank and the stream is 12 feet wide, how long must a log be to just barely reach?

13 ft

65. Geometry A ladder is leaning against the top of a 15-foot wall. If the bottom of the ladder is 20 feet from the wall, how long is the ladder?

25 ft

66. Geometry A wire from the top of a 24-foot pole is fastened to the ground by a stake that is 10 feet from the bottom of the pole. How long is the wire?

26 ft

67. Surveying A surveying team wants to calculate the length of a straight tunnel through a mountain. They form a right angle by connecting lines from each end of the proposed tunnel. One of the connecting lines is 3 miles, and the other is 4 miles. What is the length of the proposed tunnel?

5 miles

68. Surveying A surveying team wants to calculate the length of a straight tunnel through a mountain. They form a right angle by connecting lines from each end of the proposed tunnel. One of the connecting lines is 6 miles, and the other is 8 miles. What is the length of the proposed tunnel?

10 miles

Factor each of the following numbers into the product of two numbers, one of which is a perfect square. (Remember from Chapter 1, a perfect square is 1, 4, 9, 16, 25, 36, . . ., etc.)

69. 32
$16 \cdot 2$

70. 200
$100 \cdot 2$

71. 75
$25 \cdot 3$

72. 12
$4 \cdot 3$

73. 50
$25 \cdot 2$

74. 20
$4 \cdot 5$

75. 40
$4 \cdot 10$

76. 18
$9 \cdot 2$

77. 32
$16 \cdot 2$

78. 27
$9 \cdot 3$

79. 98
$49 \cdot 2$

80. 72
$36 \cdot 2$

81. 48
$16 \cdot 3$

82. 121
$121 \cdot 1$

■ Maintaining Your Skills

The problems below review material involving fractions and mixed numbers. Perform the indicated operations. Write your answers as whole numbers, proper fractions, or mixed numbers.

83. $\dfrac{5}{7} \cdot \dfrac{14}{25}$
$\dfrac{2}{5}$

84. $1\dfrac{1}{4} \div 2\dfrac{1}{8}$
$\dfrac{10}{17}$

85. $4\dfrac{3}{10} + 5\dfrac{2}{100}$
$9\dfrac{8}{25}$

86. $8\dfrac{1}{5} + 1\dfrac{1}{10}$
$9\dfrac{3}{10}$

87. $3\dfrac{2}{10} \cdot 2\dfrac{5}{10}$
8

88. $6\dfrac{9}{10} \div 2\dfrac{3}{10}$
3

89. $7\dfrac{1}{10} - 4\dfrac{3}{10}$
$2\dfrac{4}{5}$

90. $3\dfrac{7}{10} - 1\dfrac{97}{100}$
$1\dfrac{73}{100}$

91. $\dfrac{\dfrac{3}{8}}{\dfrac{6}{7}}$
$\dfrac{7}{16}$

92. $\dfrac{\dfrac{3}{4}}{\dfrac{1}{2} + \dfrac{1}{4}}$
1

93. $\dfrac{\dfrac{2}{3} + \dfrac{3}{5}}{\dfrac{2}{3} - \dfrac{3}{5}}$
19

94. $\dfrac{\dfrac{4}{5} - \dfrac{1}{3}}{\dfrac{4}{5} + \dfrac{1}{3}}$
$\dfrac{7}{17}$

Chapter 8 Summary

■ **Formulas for Perimeter and Area of Polygons [8.1, 8.2]**

EXAMPLES

Square

$$P = 4s$$
$$A = s^2$$

Rectangle

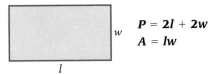

$$P = 2l + 2w$$
$$A = lw$$

1. **a.** Find the perimeter and the area.

2 in.

5 in.

$P = 2 \cdot 5 + 2 \cdot 2$
  $= 14$ in.
$A = 5 \cdot 2$
  $= 10$ in^2

Triangle

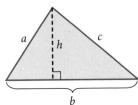

$$P = a + b + c$$
$$A = \frac{1}{2} bh$$

Parallelogram

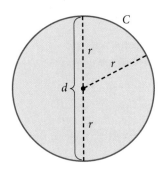

$$A = bh$$

b. Find the area.

3 cm

10 cm

$A = \dfrac{1}{2}(10)(3)$

  $= 15$ cm^2

■ **Formulas for Diameter and Radius of a Circle [8.1, 8.2]**

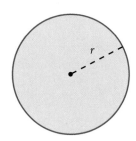

C = circumference
r = radius
d = diameter
$d = 2r$
$r = \dfrac{d}{2}$

2. If the radius of a circle is 5.7 feet, find the diameter.
   $d = 2(5.7)$
     $= 11.4$ ft

■ **Formulas for Circumference and Area of a Circle [8.1, 8.2]**

$$C = 2\pi r$$
$$A = \pi r^2$$

3. Find the circumference and the area.

3 cm

$C = 2(3.14)(3)$
  $= 18.84$ cm
$A = 3.14(3)^2$
  $= 28.26$ cm^2

Formulas for Surface Area and Volume [8.3, 8.4]

4. Find the volume and the surface area.

a.

$V = 7 \cdot 3 \cdot 2$
$\quad = 42 \text{ in}^3$
$S = 2(3)(2) + 2(3)(7) + 2(2)(7)$
$\quad = 12 + 42 + 28$
$\quad = 82 \text{ in}^2$

b.

$V = (3.14)(2)^2 \cdot 4$
$\quad = 50.24 \text{ mm}^3$
$S = 2(3.14)(2)^2 + 2(3.14)(2)(4)$
$\quad = 75.36 \text{ mm}^2$

c.

$V = \frac{4}{3}(3.14)5^3$

$\quad = 523 \text{ in}^3$, to the nearest whole number
$S = 4(3.14)5^2$
$\quad = 314 \text{ in}^2$

d. (Volume only.)

$V = \frac{1}{3}(3.14) \cdot 4^2(6)$

$\quad = 100.48 \text{ cm}^2$

Rectangular Solid

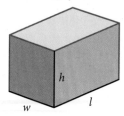

Volume = *lwh*
Surface Area = *2lh* + *2hw* + *2lw*

Cylinder

Volume = $\pi r^2 h$
Surface Area = $2\pi r^2 + 2\pi rh$
(closed at both ends)

Sphere

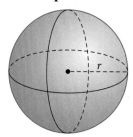

Volume = $\frac{4}{3}\pi r^3$
Surface Area = $4\pi r^2$

Cone

Volume = $\frac{1}{3}\pi r^2 h$

■ Square Roots [8.5]

The square root of a positive number a, written $\sqrt{a}$, is the number we square to get a.

5. $\sqrt{49} = 7$ because
$7^2 = 7 \cdot 7 = 49$

■ Pythagorean Theorem [8.5]

In any right triangle, the length of the longest side (the hypotenuse) is equal to the square root of the sum of the squares of the two shorter sides.

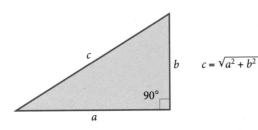

$c = \sqrt{a^2 + b^2}$

6. Find the length of the hypotenuse to the nearest tenth.

$c = \sqrt{3.1^2 + 4.2^2}$
$= \sqrt{27.25}$
≈ 5.2 cm

Find the perimeter of each figure.

1.

$\frac{1}{8}$ mm

$\frac{1}{8}$ mm

$\frac{1}{2}$ mm

2.

5 ft

8 ft

26 ft

3.

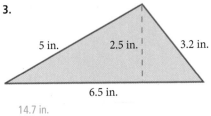

5 in.   2.5 in.   3.2 in.

6.5 in.

14.7 in.

4.

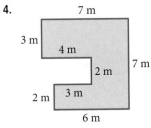

7 m

3 m

4 m

2 m   7 m

2 m   3 m

6 m

34 m

5.

$3\frac{9}{16}$ cm

$3\frac{9}{16}$ cm   3 cm   5 cm

$2\frac{7}{16}$ cm   10 cm

$24\frac{9}{16}$ cm

6.

5 km

31.4 km

Find the area enclosed by each figure.

7.

3 in.

9 in.

27 in²

8.

12 mm

12 mm

144 mm²

9.

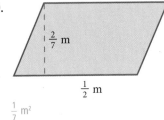

$\frac{2}{7}$ m

$\frac{1}{2}$ m

$\frac{1}{7}$ m²

10.

25 cm

30 cm

375 cm²

11.

2.5 in.

19.625 in²

12.

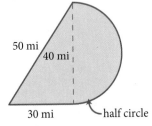

50 mi   40 mi

30 mi   half circle

1228 mi²

13.

7 cm
2 cm
3 cm
2 cm
3 cm
6 cm

32 cm²

14. The base of a triangle is $\frac{5}{8}$ feet and the height is $\frac{3}{2}$ feet. Find the area.

$\frac{15}{32}$ ft²

15. Find the perimeter and the area of the parallelogram below.

7 ft   8 ft

12 ft

Perimeter = 40 ft; area = 84 ft²

Find the volume and surface area of each figure. Round to the nearest hundredth, if necessary.

16.

7 in.

5 in.   2 in.

V = 70 in³; S = 118 in²

17.

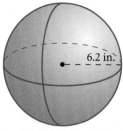

6.2 in.

V = 997.80 km³; S = 482.81 km²

18.

←8.4 m→

3.6 m

V = 537.17 m³; S = 352.68 m²

Find the volume of each figure. Round to the nearest hundredth, if necessary.

19.

8 in.

5 in.

628 in³

20.

2 ft   13 ft

6 ft   5 ft

3 ft

4 ft   4 ft

126 ft³

21.

7 ft

5 ft

183.17 ft³

22. Area of a Garden A gardener with a yard that is 22 feet by 30 feet wants to plant a garden that is 15 feet by 15 feet. How much larger is the square footage of the yard than that of the garden?

435 ft²

15 ft   22 ft

15 ft

30 ft

23. Spaceship Earth Spaceship Earth is a geodesic sphere at Walt Disney World's Epcot Center in Florida. The inner sphere has a diameter of 165 feet, while the outer sphere is 180 feet in diameter. Find the difference in volume between the outer sphere and the inner sphere.

701,201.25 ft³

Douglas Peebles/Corbis

Simplify.

1.
$$\begin{array}{r} 8,340 \\ -\ 2,785 \\ \hline 5,555 \end{array}$$

2. 55(101)
5,555

3. 1845 ÷ 25
73.8

4. $0.25\overline{)1.845}$
7.38

5. $\dfrac{15}{16} - \dfrac{7}{16}$ $\dfrac{1}{2}$

6. $\left(\dfrac{4}{5}\right)^3$ $\dfrac{64}{125}$

7. 3.846 + 5.09
8.936

8. 9 − 5.678
3.322

9. 3.4(0.34)
1.156

10. $\dfrac{8}{15} \cdot \dfrac{5}{16}$ $\dfrac{1}{6}$

11. $\dfrac{7}{12} \div \dfrac{21}{4}$ $\dfrac{1}{9}$

12. $\dfrac{5}{9} + \dfrac{2}{27}$ $\dfrac{17}{27}$

13. $3\dfrac{1}{5} - 1\dfrac{1}{10}$ $2\dfrac{1}{10}$

14. Add $2\dfrac{1}{4}$ to 3.75.
6

15. Find the product of $\dfrac{3}{4}$ and $1\dfrac{1}{2}$. $1\dfrac{1}{8}$

16. Translate and simplify: The sum of twice 9 and 2.
2(9) + 2; 20

17. Write the ratio of 2 feet to 36 inches as a fraction in lowest terms. $\dfrac{2}{3}$

18. Convert 20 feet per second to miles per hour. Round to the nearest tenth.   13.6 mi/hr

19. Convert 2.5 square miles to acres.
1,600 acres

20. Write $\dfrac{5}{8}$ as a percent.
62.5%

21. Convert 55% to a fraction. $\dfrac{11}{20}$

22. Solve the equation $\dfrac{3}{x} = \dfrac{6}{7}$. $\dfrac{7}{2} = 3.5$

23. Write 30,405 in expanded form.
$3 \cdot 10^4 + 4 \cdot 10^2 + 5$

24. What number is 30% of 700?
210

25. 26 is what percent of 39? $66\dfrac{2}{3}\%$

26. $\dfrac{3}{4}$ is 75% of what number?   1

27. If 1 mile is 1.61 kilometers, convert 50 miles per hour to kilometers per hour.   80.5 km/hr

28. Textbook Prices A used copy of a textbook sells for $56.25, which is 75% of the price of a new book. What is the price of a new book?
$75

29. Ratio and Areas The figure here shows a circular image within a square postage stamp. If each side of the square is 35.0 millimeters and the radius of the circle is 14.5 millimeters, find the ratio of the area of the circle to the area of the square. Round to the nearest hundredth.
0.54

30. Pythagorean Theorem Use the Pythagorean theorem and the diagram of the square softball diamond to find the distance from third base to first base. Round to the nearest tenth.   84.9 ft

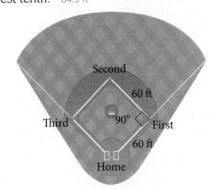

Use the illustration to answer problem 31.

31. Gas Prices If you buy 16 gallons of gasoline at $3.02 per gallon, how much did you pay for the crude oil and refining? Round to the nearest cent.
$41.07

Find the perimeter of each figure.

1.

12 ft

5 ft

34 ft

2.

3.6 cm

6 cm

4.8 cm

14.4 cm

3. 38 in.

5 in.

3 in.

5 in.

4 in.

6 in.

7 in.

2 in.   3 in.

10 in.

4. Find the circumference of the circle. Use 3.14 for π.

10 yd

62.8 yd

5. Find the perimeter of a square with side 6 meters.

24 m

Find the area enclosed by each figure.

6.

7 cm

7 cm

49 cm²

7.

4 in.

13 in.

52 in²

8.

$\frac{4}{3}$ ft

$\frac{5}{2}$ ft

$\frac{5}{3}$ ft²

9. 77.13 mm²

5 mm

Half Circle

3 mm

9 mm

6 mm

8 mm

10. A circle has radius of 3 inches. Find its area. Round to the nearest whole number.

28 in²

Find the volume of each figure

11.

4 ft

2 ft   6 ft

2 ft

10 ft

3 ft

84 ft³

12.

4.5 m

2.2 m

68.39 m³

13.

3 cm

113.04 cm³

14.

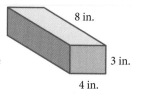

Hemisphere

3 in.

4 in.

284.69 in³

15. Find the volume and the surface area of the rectangular solid shown below.

Volume = 96 in³; surface area = 136 in²

8 in.

3 in.

4 in.

16. Perimeter of a Garden A rectangular garden is $20\frac{1}{2}$ feet long and 10 feet wide. What length of fence is needed to enclose the garden?

61 ft

17. Volume of a Coin The 1 euro coin below has a diameter of 23.25 millimeters and a thickness of 2.33 millimeters. Find the volume of the coin, to the nearest whole number.

989 mm²

Each pair of figures are similar. In each case find x.

18.

10 cm

8 cm

x

3 cm

3.75 cm

19. 0.2 ft

x

0.5 ft

0.4 ft

1 ft

Use the illustration to answer problem 20.

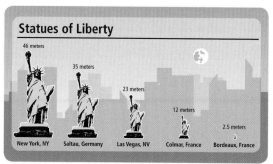

Statues of Liberty

46 meters

35 meters

23 meters

12 meters

2.5 meters

New York, NY   Saltau, Germany   Las Vegas, NV   Colmar, France   Bordeaux, France

20. If the length of the tablet of the Statue of Liberty in New York is about 7.2 meters, how long is the tablet of the Statue of liberty in Colmar, France? Figures are similar.

1.88 meters

Chapter 8 Projects

GEOMETRY

Perimeter and Area

Number of People 3

Time Needed 10 minutes

Equipment Pencil and paper

Background This group project is intended to give you a more thorough understanding of the relationship between the perimeter and the area of a rectangle. It will answer this question: "If you have 32 feet of fencing that you are going to use to form a rectangle, will it always enclose the same amount of area?"

Width (ft)	Length (ft)	Area (ft)
1		
2		
3		
4		
5		
6		
7		
8		

Procedure

1. The perimeter of each rectangle below is 32 feet. As you can see, the width of each rectangle is given. Use the fact that the perimeter is 32 feet to find the length of each rectangle.

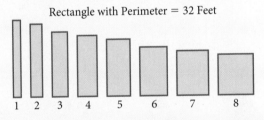

Rectangle with Perimeter = 32 Feet

2. Use the lengths you found in Step 1 to fill in the length column in the table.

3. Using the fact that the area of a rectangle is the product of the length and width, fill in the area column in the table.

4. Use the information in the table to construct a line graph on the template below.

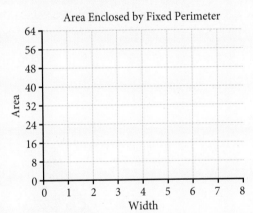

5. Make a conjecture about the type of rectangle to enclose the greatest area for a fixed perimeter.

RESEARCH PROJECT

The image shown to the right is from the Mandelbrot Set, a fractal named after the Polish mathematician Benoit Mandelbrot. A fractal is a geometric shape with self-similarity: if you magnify part of it, the details will be similar to the whole.

Sierpinksi's Triangle (below) is a fractal studied by the Polish mathematician Waclaw Sierpinski. It consists of three triangles, each of which consists of three smaller triangles, and so on.

One way to construct Sierpinski's Triangle is to start with an equilateral triangle, draw the triangle joining the midpoints of the three sides, and cut out this middle triangle. Then repeat this process on the three remaining triangles to get nine triangles. Repeat this process infinitely, and you get Sierpinski's triangle.

Courtesy of David Dewey

Introduction to Algebra

9

Introduction

The Grand Canyon, located in the state of Arizona, is a large gorge created by the Colorado River over millions of years. Much of the Grand Canyon is located in the Grand Canyon National Park, which receives over four million visitors per year. Visitors come to hike trails and view the magnificent rock formations.

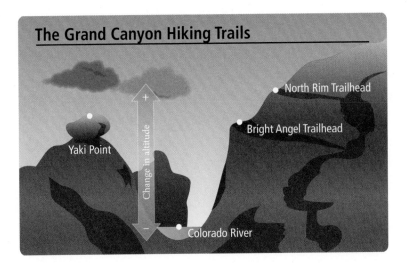

Many of the hiking trails in the Grand Canyon have significant changes in altitude. We sometimes represent changes in altitude with negative numbers. In this chapter we will work problems which refer to some of the trails found in the Grand Canyon and which involve negative numbers.

Chapter Pretest

The pretest below contains problems that are representative of the problems you will find in the chapter.

Give the opposite of each number.

1. 10
-10

2. -3
3

Place either < or > between the numbers so that the resulting statement is true.

3. $\dfrac{6}{5} > -\dfrac{5}{6}$

4. $2 < |-4|$

Simplify each expression.

5. $-|-8|$
-8

6. $-(-1)$
1

Perform the indicated operations.

7. $9 - 19$
-10

8. $3.42 + (-6.89)$
-3.47

9. $-\dfrac{3}{5} - \dfrac{2}{5}$
-1

10. $\dfrac{1}{10} + \left(-\dfrac{4}{5}\right) + \left(-\dfrac{3}{20}\right)$
$-\dfrac{17}{20}$

11. $-40 - (-7)$
-33

12. $5(-4)$
-20

13. $-\dfrac{2}{3}\left(-\dfrac{3}{5}\right)$
$\dfrac{2}{5}$

14. $21 \div (-7)$
-3

15. $\dfrac{-40}{-5}$
8

16. $\dfrac{0}{-1}$
0

Simplify the following expressions as much as possible.

17. $(-2)^3$
-8

18. $-10 + 2(1 - 3)$
-14

19. $\dfrac{7 + 4(-1)}{2 - 3}$
-3

20. $(3x + 4) + 9$
$3x + 13$

21. $5(3y - 2)$
$15y - 10$

22. $-4b + 3b$
$-b$

23. On a certain day, the temperature reaches a high of 30° above 0 and a low of 5° below 0. What is the difference between the high and low temperatures for the day?   35°

Getting Ready for Chapter 9

The problems below review material covered previously that you need to know in order to be successful in Chapter 9. If you have any difficulty with the problems here, you need to go back and review before going on to Chapter 9.

1. Use the associative property to rewrite the expression: $5(3 \cdot 2)$ $(5 \cdot 3)2$
2. Use the distributive property to rewrite the expression: $4 \cdot 7 - 4 \cdot 2$ $4(7 - 2)$

Perform the indicated operation.

3. $60.3 + 49.8$
110.1

4. $9 - 0$
9

5. $0.4(0.8)$
0.32

6. $7 - 7$
0

7. 5^3
125

8. $\dfrac{1}{10} + \dfrac{4}{5}$ $\dfrac{9}{10}$

9. $14 - 8$
6

10. $6 \div 3$
2

11. $60 \div 20$
3

12. $8 \div 8$
1

13. $\dfrac{7}{8} \cdot \dfrac{5}{14}$ $\dfrac{5}{16}$

14. $12\left(\dfrac{2}{3}\right)$
8

15. $12 \div 4$
3

16. $12 \div 3$
4

17. Find the perimeter of the square.   24 in.

6 in.

6 in.

18. Find the area of the rectangle.   7,500 ft²

75 ft

100 ft

Positive and Negative Numbers

Objectives

A Use the number line and inequality symbols to compare numbers.

B Find the absolute value of a number.

C Find the opposite of a number.

D Create displays with negative numbers.

Introduction . . .

Before the late nineteenth century, time zones did not exist. Each town would set its clocks according to the motions of the Sun. It was not until the late 1800s that a system of worldwide time zones was developed. This system divides the earth into 24 time zones with Greenwich, England, designated as the center of the time zones (GMT). This location is assigned a value of zero. Each of the World Time Zones is assigned a number ranging from −12 to +12 depending on its position east or west of Greenwich, England.

If New York is 5 time zones to the left of GMT, this would be noted as −5:00 GMT.

A Comparing Numbers

To see the relationship between negative and positive numbers, we can extend the number line as shown in Figure 1. We first draw a straight line and label a convenient point with 0. This is called the *origin*, and it is usually in the middle of the line. We then label positive numbers to the right (as we have done previously), and negative numbers to the left.

FIGURE 1

Note A number, other than 0, with no sign (+ or −) in front of it is assumed to be positive. That is, 5 = +5.

The numbers increase going from left to right. If we move to the right, we are moving in the positive direction. If we move to the left, we are moving in the negative direction. *Any number to the left of another number is considered to be less than the number to its right.*

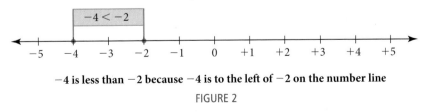

−4 is less than −2 because −4 is to the left of −2 on the number line

FIGURE 2

We see from the line that every negative number is less than every positive number.

In algebra we can use inequality symbols when comparing numbers.

> **Notation**
> If a and b are any two numbers on the number line, then
> $a < b$ is read "a is less than b".
> $a > b$ is read "a is greater than b".

As you can see, the inequality symbols always point to the smaller of the two numbers being compared. Here are some examples that illustrate how we use the inequality symbols.

EXAMPLE 1 $3 < 5$ is read "3 is less than 5." Note that it would also be correct to write $5 > 3$. Both statements, "3 is less than 5" and "5 is greater than 3," have the same meaning. The inequality symbols always point to the smaller number.

EXAMPLE 2 $0 > 100$ is a false statement, because 0 is less than 100, not greater than 100. To write a true inequality statement using the numbers 0 and 100, we would have to write either $0 < 100$ or $100 > 0$.

EXAMPLE 3 $-3 < 5$ is a true statement, because -3 is to the left of 5 on the number line, and, therefore, it must be less than 5. Another statement that means the same thing is $5 > -3$.

EXAMPLE 4 $-5 < -2$ is a true statement, because -5 is to the left of -2 on the number line, meaning that -5 is less than -2. Both statements $-5 < -2$ and $-2 > -5$ have the same meaning; they both say that -5 is a smaller number than -2.

B Absolute Value

It is sometimes convenient to talk about only the numerical part of a number and disregard the sign (+ or −) in front of it. The following definition gives us a way of doing this.

> **Definition**
> The **absolute value** of a number is its distance from 0 on the number line. We denote the absolute value of a number with vertical lines. For example, the absolute value of -3 is written $|-3|$.

The absolute value of a number is never negative because it is a distance, and a distance is always measured in positive units (unless it happens to be 0).

Here are some examples of absolute value problems.

EXAMPLE 5 $|5| = 5$ The number 5 is 5 units from 0.

EXAMPLE 6 $|-3| = 3$ The number -3 is 3 units from 0.

PRACTICE PROBLEMS

Write each statement in words.
1. $2 < 8$

2. $5 > 10$ (Is this a true statement?)

3. $-4 < 4$

4. $-7 < -2$

Give the absolute value of each of the following.
5. $|6|$

6. $|-5|$

Answers
1. 2 is less than 8.
2. 5 is greater than 10. (No.)
3. -4 is less than 4.
4. -7 is less than -2.
5. 6 6. 5

EXAMPLE 7 $|-7| = 7$ The number -7 is 7 units from 0.

Give the absolute value.
7. $|-8|$

C Opposites

Definition
Two numbers that are the same distance from 0 but in opposite directions from 0 are called **opposites**.* The notation for the opposite of a is $-a$.

EXAMPLE 8   Give the opposite of each of the following numbers:

$5, 7, 1, -5, -8$

8. Give the opposite of each of the following numbers: 8, 10, 0, −4.

SOLUTION   The opposite of 5 is -5.
The opposite of 7 is -7.
The opposite of 1 is -1.
The opposite of -5 is $-(-5)$, or 5.
The opposite of -8 is $-(-8)$, or 8.

We see from the previous example that the opposite of every positive number is a negative number, and likewise, the opposite of every negative number is a positive number. The last two parts of Example 8 illustrate the following property:

Property
If a represents any positive number, then it is always true that
$$-(-a) = a$$

In other words, this property states that the opposite of a negative number is a positive number.

It should be evident now that the symbols + and − can be used to indicate several different ideas in mathematics. In the past we have used them to indicate addition and subtraction. They can also be used to indicate the direction a number is from 0 on the number line. For instance, the number +3 (read "positive 3") is the number that is 3 units from zero in the positive direction. On the other hand, the number −3 (read "negative 3") is the number that is 3 units from 0 in the negative direction. The symbol − can also be used to indicate the opposite of a number, as in $-(-2) = 2$. The interpretation of the symbols + and − depends on the situation in which they are used. For example:

$3 + 5$ The + sign indicates addition.
$7 - 2$ The − sign indicates subtraction.
-7 The − sign is read "negative" 7.
$-(-5)$ The first − sign is read "the opposite of." The second − sign is read "negative" 5.

This may seem confusing at first, but as you work through the problems in this chapter you will get used to the different interpretations of the symbols + and −.

We should mention here that the set of whole numbers along with their opposites forms the set of *integers*. That is:

$$\text{Integers} = \{ \ldots, -3, -2, -1, 0, 1, 2, 3, \ldots \}$$

*In some books opposites are called *additive inverses*.

Answers
7. 8 **8.** −8, −10, 0, 4

9. Use the information in the table below to make both a scatter diagram and a line graph.

AVERAGE MONTHLY PRECIPITATION SAN LUIS OBISPO, CALIFORNIA	
Month	Precipitation (mm)
Jan	134.1
Mar	113.8
May	11.9
July	0.8
Sept	11.2
Nov	55.1

DESCRIPTIVE STATISTICS

D Displaying Negative Numbers

In the table below, the temperatures below zero are represented by negative numbers.

EXAMPLE 9   Use the information in Table 1 and the template below to draw a scatter diagram and a line graph representing the information in Table 1.

TABLE 1	
RECORD LOW TEMPERATURES FOR JACKSON HOLE, WYOMING	
Month	Temperature
January	−50°F
February	−44°F
March	−32°F
April	−5°F
May	12°F
June	19°F
July	24°F
August	18°F
September	14°F
October	2°F
November	−27°F
December	−49°F

SOLUTION   Notice that the vertical axis in the template looks like the number line we have been using. To produce the scatter diagram, we place a dot above each month, across from the temperature for that month. For example, the dot above July will be across from 24°. Doing the same for each of the months, we have the scatter diagram shown in Figure 3. To produce the line graph in Figure 4, we simply connect the dots in Figure 3 with line segments.

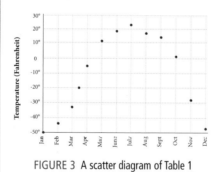

FIGURE 3 A scatter diagram of Table 1

FIGURE 4 A line graph of Table 1

Getting Ready for Class

After reading through the preceding section, respond in your own words and in complete sentences.

1. Write the statement "3 is less than 5" in symbols.
2. What is the absolute value of a number?
3. Describe what we mean by numbers that are "opposites" of each other.
4. If you locate two different numbers on the number line, which one will be the smaller number?

Answer
9. See solutions section.

Problem Set 9.1

A Write each of the following in words. [Example 1]

1. $4 < 7$
4 is less than 7.

2. $0 < 10$
0 is less than 10.

3. $5 > -2$
5 is greater than -2.

4. $8 > -8$
8 is greater than -8.

5. $-10 < -3$.
-10 is less than -3.

6. $-20 < -5$
-20 is less than -5.

7. $0 > -4$
0 is greater than -4.

8. $0 > -100$
0 is greater than -100.

Write each of the following in symbols.

▶ **9.** 30 is greater than -30.
$30 > -30$

10. -30 is less than 30.
$-30 < 30$

▶ **11.** -10 is less than 0.
$-10 < 0$

12. 0 is greater than -10.
$0 > -10$

13. -3 is greater than -15.
$-3 > -15$

▶ **14.** -15 is less than -3.
$-15 < -3$

A Place either $<$ or $>$ between each of the following pairs of numbers so that the resulting statement is true. [Examples 2–4]

15. $3 < 7$

16. $17 > 0$

▶ **17.** $7 > -5$

18. $2 > -13$

19. $-6 < 0$

20. $-14 < 0$

21. $-12 < -2$

▶ **22.** $-20 < -1$

▶ **23.** $-\dfrac{1}{2} > -\dfrac{3}{4}$

▶ **24.** $-\dfrac{6}{7} < \dfrac{5}{6}$

25. $-0.75 < -0.25$

▶ **26.** $-1 > -3.5$

▶ **27.** $-0.1 < -0.01$

28. $-0.04 > -0.4$

29. $-3 < |6|$

▶ **30.** $|8| > -2$

31. $15 > |-4|$

32. $20 > |-6|$

▶ **33.** $|-2| < |-7|$

▶ **34.** $|-3| > |-1|$

B Find each of the following absolute values. [Examples 5–7]

35. $|2|$
2

36. $|7|$
7

37. $|100|$
100

▶ **38.** $|10,000|$
10,000

39. $|-8|$
8

40. $|-9|$
9

41. $|-231|$
231

▶ **42.** $|-457|$
457

▶ **43.** $\left|-\dfrac{3}{4}\right|$
$\dfrac{3}{4}$

44. $\left|-\dfrac{1}{10}\right|$
$\dfrac{1}{10}$

45. $|-200|$
200

46. $|-350|$
350

47. $|8|$
8

48. $|9|$
9

49. $|231|$
231

50. $|457|$
457

▶ Selected exercises available online at www.webassign.net/brookscole

C Give the opposite of each of the following numbers. [Example 8]

51. 3
  −3

52. −5
  5

▶ **53.** −2
  2

54. 15
  −15

▶ **55.** 75
  −75

56. −32
  32

▶ **57.** 0
  0

58. 1
  −1

59. −0.123
  0.123

▶ **60.** −3.45
  3.45

61. $\dfrac{7}{8}$
  $-\dfrac{7}{8}$

▶ **62.** $\dfrac{1}{100}$
  $-\dfrac{1}{100}$

Simplify each of the following.

63. −(−2)
  2

64. −(−5)
  5

▶ **65.** −(−8)
  8

66. −(−3)
  3

67. −|−2|
  −2

68. −|−5|
  −5

▶ **69.** −|−8|
  −8

70. −|−3|
  −3

71. What number is its own opposite?
  0

72. Is |a| = a always a true statement?
  No

73. If n is a negative number, is −n positive or negative?
  Positive

74. If n is a positive number, is −n positive or negative?
  Negative

■ Estimating

Work Problems 75–80 mentally, without pencil and paper or a calculator.

▶ **75.** Is −60 closer to 0 or −100?
  −100

76. Is −20 closer to 0 or −30?
  −30

▶ **77.** Is −10 closer to −20 or 20?
  −20

78. Is −20 closer to −40 or 10?
  −40

79. Is −362 closer to −360 or −370?
  −360

▶ **80.** Is −368 closer to −360 or −370?
  −370

D **Applying the Concepts** [Example 9]

81. The London Eye has a height of 450 feet. Describe the location of someone standing on the ground in relation to someone at the top of the London Eye.

—450 feet

82. The Eiffel Tower has several levels visitors can walk around on. The first is 57 meters above the ground, the second is 115 meters high, and the third level is 276 meters high. What is the location of someone standing on the first level in relation to someone standing on the third level?

—219 meters

83. The Bright Angel trail at Grand Canyon National Park ends at Indian Garden, 3,060 feet below the trailhead. Write this as a negative number with respect to the trailhead.

—3,060 feet

84. The South Kaibab Trail at Grand Canyon National Park ends at Cedar Ridge, 1,140 feet below the trailhead. Write this as a negative number with respect to the trailhead.

—1,140 feet

85. Car Depreciation Depreciation refers to the decline in a car's market value during the time you own the car. According to sources such as Kelley Blue Book and Edmunds.com, not all cars depreciate at the same rate. Suppose you pay $25,000 for a new car which has a high rate of depreciation. Your car loses about $5,000 in value per year. Represent this loss in value as a negative number. A car with a low rate of depreciation loses about $2,750 in value each year. Represent this loss as a negative number.

—$5,000; —$2,750

86. Census Figures In June, 2007 the U.S. Census Bureau released population estimates for the twenty-five cities with the largest population loss between July 1, 2005 and July 1, 2006. New Orleans had the largest population loss. The city's population fell by 228,782 people. Detroit, Michigan experienced a population loss of 12,344 people during the same time period. Represent the loss of population for New Orleans and for Detroit as a negative number.

—228,782; —12,344

87. Temperature and Altitude Yamina is flying from Phoenix to San Francisco on a Boeing 737 jet. When the plane reaches an altitude of 33,000 feet, the temperature outside the plane is 61 degrees below zero Fahrenheit. Represent this temperature with a negative number. If the temperature outside the plane gets warmer by 10 degrees, what will the new temperature be?

—61°F, —51°F

88. Temperature Change At 11:00 in the morning in Superior, Wisconsin, Jim notices the temperature is 15 degrees below zero Fahrenheit. Write this temperature as a negative number. At noon it has warmed up by 8 degrees. What is the temperature at noon?

—15°F, —7°F

89. Temperature Change At 10:00 in the morning in White Bear Lake, Minnesota, Zach notices the temperature is 5 degrees below zero Fahrenheit. Write this temperature as a negative number. By noon the temperature has dropped another 10 degrees. What is the temperature at noon?

−5°F, −15°F

▶ **90. Snorkeling** Steve is snorkeling in the ocean near his home in Maui. At one point he is 6 feet below the surface. Represent this situation with a negative number. If he descends another 6 feet, what negative number will represent his new position?

−6 feet, −12 feet

91. Time Zones New Orleans, Louisiana, is 1 time zone west of New York City. Represent this time zone as a negative number, as discussed in the introduction to this chapter.

New Orleans: −6:00 GMT

92. Time Zones Seattle, Washington, is 2 time zones west of New Orleans, Louisiana. Represent this time zone as a negative number, as discussed in the introduction to this chapter.

Seattle: −8:00 GMT

Table 2 lists various wind chill temperatures. The top row gives air temperature, while the first column gives wind speed in miles per hour. The numbers within the table indicate how cold the weather will feel. For example, if the thermometer reads 30°F and the wind is blowing at 15 miles per hour, the wind chill temperature is 9°F.

TABLE 2								
WIND CHILL TEMPERATURES								
Air temperatures (°F)								
Wind Speed	30°	25°	20°	15°	10°	5°	0°	−5°
10 mph	16°	10°	3°	−3°	−9°	−15°	−22°	−27°
15 mph	9°	2°	−5°	−11°	−18°	−25°	−31°	−38°
20 mph	4°	−3°	−10°	−17°	−24°	−31°	−39°	−46°
25 mph	1°	−7°	−15°	−22°	−29°	−36°	−44°	−51°
30 mph	−2°	−10°	−18°	−25°	−33°	−41°	−49°	−56°

93. Wind Chill Find the wind chill temperature if the thermometer reads 25°F and the wind is blowing at 25 miles per hour.

−7°F

94. Wind Chill Find the wind chill temperature if the thermometer reads 10°F and the wind is blowing at 25 miles per hour.

−29°F

95. Wind Chill Which will feel colder: a day with an air temperature of 10°F and a 25-mph wind, or a day with an air temperature of −5°F and a 10-mph wind?

10°F and 25-mph wind

96. Wind Chill Which will feel colder: a day with an air temperature of 15°F and a 20-mph wind, or a day with an air temperature of 5°F and a 10-mph wind?

15°F and 20-mph wind

Table 3 lists the record low temperatures for each month of the year for Lake Placid, New York. Table 4 lists the record high temperatures for the same city.

TABLE 3	
RECORD LOW TEMPERATURES FOR LAKE PLACID, NEW YORK	
Month	Temperature
January	−36°F
February	−30°F
March	−14°F
April	−2°F
May	19°F
June	22°F
July	35°F
August	30°F
September	19°F
October	15°F
November	−11°F
December	−26°F

TABLE 4	
RECORD HIGH TEMPERATURES FOR LAKE PLACID, NEW YORK	
Month	Temperature
January	54°F
February	59°F
March	69°F
April	82°F
May	90°F
June	93°F
July	97°F
August	93°F
September	90°F
October	87°F
November	67°F
December	60°F

97. **Temperature** Figure 5 is a bar chart of the information in Table 3. Use the template in Figure 6 to construct a scatter diagram of the same information. Then connect the dots in the scatter diagram to obtain a line graph of that same information. (Notice that we have used the numbers 1 through 12 to represent the months January through December.)

FIGURE 5 A bar chart of Table 3

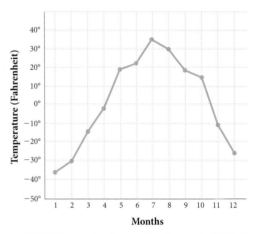

FIGURE 6 A scatter diagram, then line graph of Table 3

98. **Temperature** Figure 7 is a bar chart of the information in Table 4. Use the template in Figure 8 to construct a scatter diagram of the same information. Then connect the dots in the scatter diagram to obtain a line graph of that same information. (Again, we have used the numbers 1 through 12 to represent the months January through December.)

FIGURE 7 A bar chart of Table 4

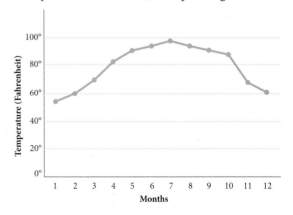

FIGURE 8 A scatter diagram, then line graph of Table 4

■ Getting Ready for the Next Section

Add or subtract.

99. 10 + 15
25

100. 12 + 15
27

101. 15 − 10
5

102. 15 − 12
3

103. 10 − 5 − 3 + 4
6

104. 12 − 3 − 7 + 5
7

105. [3 + 10] + [8 − 2]
19

106. [2 + 12] + [7 − 5]
16

107. 276 + 32 + 4,005
4,313

108. 17 + 3 + 152 + 1,200
1,372

109. 635 − 579
56

110. 2,987 − 1,130
1,857

■ Maintaining Your Skills

Complete each statement using the commutative property of addition.

111. 3 + 5 =
5 + 3

112. 9 + x =
x + 9

Complete each statement using the associative property of addition.

113. 7 + (2 + 6) =
(7 + 2)+ 6

114. (x + 3) + 5 =
x + (3 + 5)

Write each of the following in symbols.

115. The sum of x and 4
x + 4

116. The sum of x and 4 is 9.
x + 4 = 9

117. 5 more than y
y + 5

118. x increased by 8
x + 8

■ Extending the Concepts

119. There are two numbers that are 5 units from 2 on the number line. One of them is 7. What is the other one?
−3

120. There are two numbers that are 5 units from −2 on the number line. One of them is 3. What is the other one?
−7

121. In your own words and in complete sentences, explain what the opposite of a number is.
The opposite of a number is the number that is the same distance from 0, but on the opposite side of 0.

122. In your own words and in complete sentences, explain what the absolute value of a number is.
The absolute value of a number is the distance between the number and 0 on the number line.

123. The expression −(−3) is read "the opposite of negative 3," and it simplifies to just 3. Give a similar written description of the expression −|−3|, and then simplify it.
The opposite of the absolute value of −3. It simplifies to −3.

124. Give written descriptions of the expressions −(−4) and −|−4| and then simplify each of them.
The expression −(−4) is read "the opposite of −4," and it simplifies to 4. The expression −|−4| is read "the opposite of the absolute value of −4," and it simplifies to −4.

Addition with Negative Numbers

9.2

Objectives

A Use the number line to add positive and negative numbers.

B Add positive and negative numbers using a rule.

Introduction . . .

Suppose you are in Las Vegas playing blackjack and you lose $3 on the first hand and then you lose $5 on the next hand. If you represent winning with positive numbers and losing with negative numbers, how will you represent the results from your first two hands? Since you lost $3 and $5 for a total of $8, one way to represent the situation is with addition of negative numbers:

$$(-\$3) + (-\$5) = -\$8$$

From this example we see that the sum of two negative numbers is a negative number. To generalize addition of positive and negative numbers, we can use the number line.

A Adding with a Number Line

We can think of each number on the number line as having two characteristics: (1) a *distance* from 0 (absolute value) and (2) a *direction* from 0 (positive or negative). The distance from 0 is represented by the numerical part of the number (like the 5 in the number −5), and its direction is represented by the + or − sign in front of the number.

We can visualize addition of numbers on the number line by thinking in terms of distance and direction from 0. Let's begin with a simple problem we know the answer to. We interpret the sum 3 + 5 on the number line as follows:

1. The first number is 3, which tells us "start at the origin, and move 3 units in the positive direction."
2. The + sign is read "and then move."
3. The 5 means "5 units in the positive direction."

Note This method of adding numbers may seem a little complicated at first, but it will allow us to add numbers we couldn't otherwise add.

FIGURE 1

Figure 1 shows these steps. To summarize, 3 + 5 means to start at the origin (0), move 3 units in the *positive* direction, and then move 5 units in the *positive* direction. We end up at 8, which is the sum we are looking for: 3 + 5 = 8.

EXAMPLE 1 Add 3 + (−5) using the number line.

SOLUTION We start at the origin, move 3 units in the positive direction, and then move 5 units in the negative direction, as shown in Figure 2. The last arrow ends at −2, which must be the sum of 3 and −5. That is:

$$3 + (-5) = -2$$

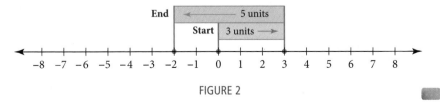

FIGURE 2

PRACTICE PROBLEMS

1. Add: 2 + (−5)

Answer
1. −3

9.2 Addition with Negative Numbers

529

2. Add: $-2 + 5$

EXAMPLE 2   Add $-3 + 5$ using the number line.

SOLUTION   We start at the origin, move 3 units in the negative direction, and then move 5 units in the positive direction, as shown in Figure 3. We end up at 2, which is the sum of -3 and 5. That is:

$$-3 + 5 = 2$$

FIGURE 3

3. Add: $-2 + (-5)$

EXAMPLE 3   Add $-3 + (-5)$ using the number line.

SOLUTION   We start at the origin, move 3 units in the negative direction, and then move 5 more units in the negative direction. This is shown on the number line in Figure 4. As you can see, the last arrow ends at -8. We must conclude that the sum of -3 and -5 is -8. That is:

$$-3 + (-5) = -8$$

FIGURE 4

Adding numbers on the number line as we have done in these first three examples gives us a way of visualizing addition of positive and negative numbers. We eventually want to be able to write a rule for addition of positive and negative numbers that doesn't involve the number line. The number line is a way of justifying the rule we will eventually write. Here is a summary of the results we have so far:

$$3 + \quad 5 = 8 \qquad -3 + \quad 5 = \quad 2$$
$$3 + (-5) = -2 \qquad -3 + (-5) = -8$$

Examine these results to see if you notice any pattern in the answers.

4. Add: $2 + 6$

EXAMPLE 4 $4 + 7 = 11$

EXAMPLE 5 $4 + (-7) = -3$

5. Add: $2 + (-6)$

EXAMPLE 6 $-4 + 7 = 3$

6. Add: $-2 + 6$

EXAMPLE 7 $-4 + (-7) = -11$

7. Add: $-2 + (-6)$

B A Rule for Addition

A summary of the results of these last four examples looks like this:

$$\begin{aligned}
4 + 7 &= 11 \\
4 + (-7) &= -3 \\
-4 + 7 &= 3 \\
-4 + (-7) &= -11
\end{aligned}$$

Looking over all the examples in this section, and noticing how the results in the problems are related, we can write the following rule for adding any two numbers:

> **Note** This rule covers all possible addition problems involving positive and negative numbers. You *must* memorize it. After you have worked some problems, the rule will seem almost automatic.

Rule
1. To add two numbers with the *same* sign: Simply add their absolute values, and use the common sign. If both numbers are positive, the answer is positive. If both numbers are negative, the answer is negative.
2. To add two numbers with *different* signs: Subtract the smaller absolute value from the larger absolute value. The answer will have the sign of the number with the larger absolute value.

Answers
5. −4 **6.** 4 **7.** −8

The following examples show how the rule is used. You will find that the rule for addition is consistent with all the results obtained using the number line.

EXAMPLE 8   Add all combinations of positive and negative 10 and 15.

SOLUTION
$$10 + 15 = 25$$
$$10 + (-15) = -5$$
$$-10 + 15 = 5$$
$$-10 + (-15) = -25$$

8. Add all combinations of positive and negative 12 and 15.

Notice that when we add two numbers with the same sign, the answer also has that sign. When the signs are not the same, the answer has the sign of the number with the larger absolute value.

Once you have become familiar with the rule for adding positive and negative numbers, you can apply it to more complicated sums.

EXAMPLE 9   Simplify: $10 + (-5) + (-3) + 4$

9. Simplify: $12 + (-3) + (-7) + 5$

SOLUTION   Adding left to right, we have:
$$10 + (-5) + (-3) + 4 = 5 + (-3) + 4 \qquad 10 + (-5) = 5$$
$$= 2 + 4 \qquad\qquad 5 + (-3) = 2$$
$$= 6$$

EXAMPLE 10   Simplify: $[-3 + (-10)] + [8 + (-2)]$

10. Simplify:
$[-2 + (-12)] + [7 + (-5)]$

SOLUTION   We begin by adding the numbers inside the brackets.
$$[-3 + (-10)] + [8 + (-2)] = [-13] + [6]$$
$$= -7$$

EXAMPLE 11   Add: $-4.75 + (-2.25)$

11. Add: $-5.76 + (-3.24)$

SOLUTION   Because both signs are negative, we add absolute values. The answer will be negative.
$$-4.75 + (-2.25) = -7.00$$

EXAMPLE 12   Add: $3.42 + (-6.89)$

12. Add: $6.88 + (-8.55)$

SOLUTION   The signs are different, so we subtract the smaller absolute value from the larger absolute value. The answer will be negative, because 6.89 is larger than 3.42 and the sign in front of 6.89 is $-$.
$$3.42 + (-6.89) = -3.47$$

EXAMPLE 13   Add: $\dfrac{3}{8} + \left(-\dfrac{1}{8}\right)$

13. Add: $\dfrac{5}{6} + \left(-\dfrac{2}{6}\right)$

SOLUTION   We subtract absolute values. The answer will be positive, because $\dfrac{3}{8}$ is positive.
$$\frac{3}{8} + \left(-\frac{1}{8}\right) = \frac{2}{8}$$
$$= \frac{1}{4} \qquad \text{Reduce to lowest terms}$$

Answers
8. See solutions section.
9. 7 **10.** -12 **11.** -9.00
12. -1.67 **13.** $\dfrac{1}{2}$

EXAMPLE 14 Add: $\frac{1}{10} + \left(-\frac{4}{5}\right) + \left(-\frac{3}{20}\right)$

SOLUTION To begin, change each fraction to an equivalent fraction with an LCD of 20.

$$\frac{1}{10} + \left(-\frac{4}{5}\right) + \left(-\frac{3}{20}\right) = \frac{1 \cdot \mathbf{2}}{10 \cdot \mathbf{2}} + \left(-\frac{4 \cdot \mathbf{4}}{5 \cdot \mathbf{4}}\right) + \left(-\frac{3}{20}\right)$$

$$= \frac{2}{20} + \left(-\frac{16}{20}\right) + \left(-\frac{3}{20}\right)$$

$$= -\frac{14}{20} + \left(-\frac{3}{20}\right)$$

$$= -\frac{17}{20}$$

USING TECHNOLOGY

Calculators

There are a number of different ways in which calculators display negative numbers. Some calculators use a key labeled $\boxed{+/-}$, whereas others use a key labeled $\boxed{(-)}$. You will need to consult with the manual that came with your calculator to see how your calculator does the job.

Here are a couple of ways to find the sum $-10 + (-15)$ on a calculator:

Scientific Calculator: $10 \boxed{+/-} \boxed{+} 15 \boxed{+/-} \boxed{=}$

Graphing Calculator: $\boxed{(-)} 10 \boxed{+} \boxed{(-)} 15 \boxed{ENT}$

Getting Ready for Class

After reading through the preceding section, respond in your own words and in complete sentences.

1. Explain how you would use the number line to add 3 and 5.

2. If two numbers are negative, such as -3 and -5, what sign will their sum have?

3. If you add two numbers with different signs, how do you determine the sign of the answer?

4. With respect to addition with positive and negative numbers, does the phrase "two negatives make a positive" make any sense?

---

14. Add: $\frac{1}{2} + \left(-\frac{3}{4}\right) + \left(-\frac{5}{8}\right)$

Answer

14. $-\frac{7}{8}$

Problem Set 9.2

A   Draw a number line from −10 to +10 and use it to add the following numbers. [Examples 1–7]

1. 2 + 3
5

2. 2 + (−3)
−1

▶ **3.** −2 + 3
1

4. −2 + (−3)
−5

5. 5 + (−7)
−2

6. −5 + 7
2

7. −4 + (−2)
−6

8. −8 + (−2)
−10

9. 10 + (−6)
4

10. −9 + 3
−6

11. 7 + (−3)
4

12. −7 + 3
−4

▶ **13.** −4 + (−5)
−9

▶ **14.** −2 + (−7)
−9

B   Combine the following by using the rule for addition of positive and negative numbers. (Your goal is to be fast and accurate at addition, with the latter being more important.) [Example 8]

15. 7 + 8
15

16. 9 + 12
21

▶ **17.** 5 + (−8)
−3

18. 4 + (−11)
−7

19. −6 + (−5)
−11

▶ **20.** −7 + (−2)
−9

21. −10 + 3
−7

22. −14 + 7
−7

23. −1 + (−2)
−3

24. −5 + (−4)
−9

▶ **25.** −11 + (−5)
−16

26. −16 + (−10)
−26

27. 4 + (−12)
−8

28. 9 + (−1)
8

▶ **29.** −85 + (−42)
−127

30. −96 + (−31)
−127

31. −121 + 170
49

32. −130 + 158
28

33. −375 + 409
34

34. −765 + 213
−552

Complete the following tables.

35.

First Number a	Second Number b	Their Sum $a+b$
5	−3	2
5	−4	1
5	−5	0
5	−6	−1
5	−7	−2

36.

First Number a	Second Number b	Their Sum $a+b$
−5	3	−2
−5	4	−1
−5	5	0
−5	6	1
−5	7	2

▶ **37.**

First Number x	Second Number y	Their Sum $x+y$
−5	−3	−8
−5	−4	−9
−5	−5	−10
−5	−6	−11
−5	−7	−12

38.

First Number x	Second Number y	Their Sum $x+y$
30	−20	10
−30	20	−10
−30	−20	−50
30	20	50
−30	0	−30

B Add the following numbers left to right. [Example 9]

39. $24 + (-6) + (-8)$
10

40. $35 + (-5) + (-30)$
0

▶ **41.** $-201 + (-143) + (-101)$
−445

42. $-27 + (-56) + (-89)$
−172

43. $-321 + 752 + (-324)$
107

▶ **44.** $-571 + 437 + (-502)$
−636

45. $-2 + (-5) + (-6) + (-7)$
−20

46. $-8 + (-3) + (-4) + (-7)$
−22

▶ **47.** $15 + (-30) + 18 + (-20)$
−17

48. $20 + (-15) + 30 + (-18)$
17

49. $-78 + (-42) + 57 + 13$
−50

▶ **50.** $-89 + (-51) + 65 + 17$
−58

B Use the rule for order of operations to simplify each of the following. [Example 10]

▶ **51.** $(-8 + 5) + (-6 + 2)$
−7

52. $(-3 + 1) + (-9 + 4)$
−7

53. $(-10 + 4) + (-3 + 12)$
3

54. $(-11 + 5) + (-3 + 2)$
−7

55. $20 + (-30 + 50) + 10$
50

56. $30 + (-40 + 20) + 50$
60

▶ **57.** $108 + (-456 + 275)$
−73

58. $106 + (-512 + 318)$
−88

59. $[5 + (-8)] + [3 + (-11)]$
−11

60. $[8 + (-2)] + [5 + (-7)]$
4

61. $[57 + (-35)] + [19 + (-24)]$
17

▶ **62.** $[63 + (-27)] + [18 + (-24)]$
30

B Use the rule for addition of numbers to add the following fractions and decimals. [Examples 11–14]

63. $-1.3 + (-2.5)$
−3.8

64. $-9.1 + (-4.5)$
−13.6

65. $24.8 + (-10.4)$
14.4

66. $29.5 + (-21.3)$
8.2

67. $-5.35 + 2.35 + (-6.89)$
−9.89

68. $-9.48 + 5.48 + (-4.28)$
−8.28

69. $-\dfrac{5}{6} + \left(-\dfrac{1}{6}\right)$
−1

70. $-\dfrac{7}{9} + \left(-\dfrac{2}{9}\right)$
−1

71. $\dfrac{3}{7} + \left(-\dfrac{5}{7}\right)$
$-\dfrac{2}{7}$

▶ **72.** $\dfrac{11}{13} + \left(-\dfrac{12}{13}\right)$
$-\dfrac{1}{13}$

73. $-\dfrac{2}{5} + \dfrac{3}{5} + \left(-\dfrac{4}{5}\right)$
$-\dfrac{3}{5}$

▶ **74.** $-\dfrac{6}{7} + \dfrac{4}{7} + \left(-\dfrac{1}{7}\right)$
$-\dfrac{3}{7}$

75. −3.8 + 2.54 + 0.4
−0.86

76. −9.6 + 5.15 + 0.8
−3.65

77. −2.89 + (−1.4) + 0.09
−4.2

▶ **78.** −3.99 + (−1.42) + 0.06
−5.35

79. $\frac{1}{2} + \left(-\frac{3}{4}\right)$
$-\frac{1}{4}$

80. $\frac{3}{5} + \left(-\frac{7}{10}\right)$
$-\frac{1}{10}$

▶ **81.** Find the sum of −8, −10, and −3.
−21

82. Find the sum of −4, 17, and −6.
7

▶ **83.** What number do you add to 8 to get 3?
−5

84. What number do you add to 10 to get 4?
−6

85. What number do you add to −3 to get −7?
−4

86. What number do you add to −5 to get −8?
−3

87. What number do you add to −4 to get 3?
7

88. What number do you add to −7 to get 2?
9

▶ **89.** If the sum of −3 and 5 is increased by 8, what number results?
10

90. If the sum of −9 and −2 is increased by 10, what number results?
−1

■ Applying the Concepts

91. One of the trails at the Grand Canyon starts at Bright Angel Trailhead and then drops 4,060 feet to the Colorado River and then climbs 4,440 feet to Yaki Point. What is the trail's ending position in relation to the Bright Angel Trailhead? If the trail ends below the starting position write the answer as a negative number.
380 feet above the trailhead

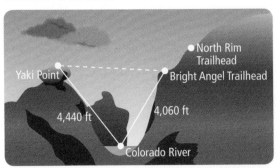

92. One of the trails in the Grand Canyon starts at the North Rim trailhead and drops 5,490 feet to the Colorado River. The trail then climbs 4,060 feet to the Bright Angel Trailhead. What is the Bright Angel Trailhead's position in relation to the North Rim Trailhead? If the trail ends below the starting position write the answer as a negative number.
1,430 feet below the trailhead, −1,430 feet

93. Checkbook Balance Ethan has a balance of −$40 in his checkbook. If he deposits $100 and then writes a check for $50, what is the new balance in his checkbook?

		RECORD ALL CHARGES OR CREDITS THAT AFFECT YOUR ACCOUNT			
			PAYMENT/DEBIT (−)	DEPOSIT/CREDIT (+)	BALANCE −$40 00
				$100 00	
	9/20	Deposit			
1502	9/21	Vons Market	$50 00		

$10

94. Checkbook Balance Kendra has a balance of −$20 in her checkbook. If she deposits $45 and then writes a check for $15, what is the new balance in her checkbook?

		RECORD ALL CHARGES OR CREDITS THAT AFFECT YOUR ACCOUNT			
			PAYMENT/DEBIT (−)	DEPOSIT/CREDIT (+)	BALANCE −$20 00
				$45 00	
	9/25	Deposit			
1501	9/28	SLO Soccer	$15 00		

$10

■ Getting Ready for the Next Section

Give the opposite of each number.

95. 2
−2

96. 3
−3

97. −4
4

98. −5
5

99. $\frac{2}{5}$
$-\frac{2}{5}$

100. $\frac{3}{8}$
$-\frac{3}{8}$

101. −30
30

102. −15
15

103. 60.3
−60.3

104. 70.4
−70.4

105. Subtract 3 from 5.
2

106. Subtract 2 from 8.
6

107. Find the difference of 7 and 4.
3

108. Find the difference of 8 and 6.
2

■ Maintaining Your Skills

The problems below review subtraction with whole numbers.

Subtract.

109. $763 - 159$
604

110. $1,007 - 136$
871

111. $465 - 462 - 3$
0

112. $481 - 479 - 2$
0

Write each of the following statements in symbols.

113. The difference of 10 and x.
$10 - x$

114. The difference of x and 10.
$x - 10$

115. 17 subtracted from y.
$y - 17$

116. y subtracted from 17.
$17 - y$

Subtraction with Negative Numbers

Objectives

A Subtract numbers by thinking of subtraction as addition of the opposite.

B Solve applications involving subtraction with positive and negative numbers.

Introduction . . .

How would we represent the final balance in a checkbook if the original balance was $20 and we wrote a check for $30? The final balance would be −$10. We can summarize the whole situation with subtraction:

$$\$20 - \$30 = -\$10$$

NUMBER	DATE	DESCRIPTION OF TRANSACTION	PAYMENT/DEBIT (−)	DEPOSIT/CREDIT (+)	BALANCE $20 00	
					-$10 00	
1501	9/15	Campus Bookstore	$30 00			

RECORD ALL CHARGES OR CREDITS THAT AFFECT YOUR ACCOUNT

From this we see that subtracting 30 from 20 gives us −10. Another example that gives the same answer but involves addition is this:

$$20 + (-30) = -10$$

A Subtraction

From the two examples above, we find that subtracting 30 gives the same result as adding −30. We use this kind of reasoning to give a definition for subtraction that will allow us to use the rules we developed for addition to do our subtraction problems. Here is that definition:

> **Definition**
> **Subtraction** If a and b represent any two numbers, then it is always true that
>
> $$a - b = a + (-b)$$
>
> To subtract b Add its opposite, $-b$
>
> *In words:* Subtracting a number is equivalent to adding its opposite.

Let's see if this definition conflicts with what we already know to be true about subtraction.

EXAMPLE 1 Subtract: $5 - 2$

SOLUTION From previous experience we know that

$$5 - 2 = 3$$

We can get the same answer by using the definition we just gave for subtraction. Instead of subtracting 2, we can add its opposite, −2. Here is how it looks:

$$5 - 2 = 5 + (-2)$$ Change subtraction to addition of the opposite

$$\qquad = 3$$ Apply the rule for addition of positive and negative numbers

The result in Example 1 is the same whether we use our previous knowledge of subtraction or the new definition. The new definition is essential when the problems begin to get more complicated.

Instructor's Note
Of the four operations with negative numbers, my students have the most trouble with subtraction, especially with problems such as $5 - (-3)$. Their intuition tells them the answer should be 2. I tell them this is one time they can't trust their intuition. (Sometimes they tell me they have been in other classes where the answer was 2. I tell them the answer was never 2 and never will be 2.) I try to have them think in terms of addition, rather than subtraction. I always go back to the definition for help with problems like this.

Note This definition of subtraction may seem a little strange at first. In Example 1 you will notice that using the definition gives us the same results we are used to getting with subtraction. As we progress further into the section, we will use the definition to subtract numbers we haven't been able to subtract before.

PRACTICE PROBLEMS

1. Subtract: $7 - 3$

Answer
1. 4

539

2. Subtract: $-7 - 3$

 Note A real-life analogy to Example 2 would be: "If the temperature were 7° below 0 and then it dropped another 2°, what would the temperature be then?"

3. Subtract: $-8 - 6$

4. Subtract: $10 - (-6)$

5. Subtract: $-10 - (-15)$

 Note Examples 4 and 5 may give results you are not used to getting. But you must realize that the results are correct. That is, $12 - (-6)$ is 18, and $-20 - (-30)$ is 10. If you think these results should be different, then you are not thinking of subtraction correctly.

6. Subtract each of the following.
 a. $8 - 5$
 b. $-8 - 5$
 c. $8 - (-5)$
 d. $-8 - (-5)$
 e. $12 - 10$
 f. $-12 - 10$
 g. $12 - (-10)$
 h. $-12 - (-10)$

Answers
2. -10 **3.** -14 **4.** 16 **5.** 5
6. a. 3 **b.** -13 **c.** 13 **d.** -3
   e. 2 **f.** -22 **g.** 22 **h.** -2

EXAMPLE 2 Subtract: $-7 - 2$

SOLUTION We have never subtracted a positive number from a negative number before. We must apply our definition of subtraction:

$$-7 - 2 = -7 + (-2) \quad \text{Instead of subtracting 2, we add its opposite, } -2$$
$$= -9 \quad \text{Apply the rule for addition}$$

EXAMPLE 3 Subtract: $-10 - 5$

SOLUTION We apply the definition of subtraction (if you don't know the definition of subtraction yet, go back and read it) and add as usual.

$$-10 - 5 = -10 + (-5) \quad \text{Definition of subtraction}$$
$$= -15 \quad \text{Addition}$$

EXAMPLE 4 Subtract: $12 - (-6)$

SOLUTION The first $-$ sign is read "subtract," and the second one is read "negative." The problem in words is "12 subtract negative 6." We can use the definition of subtraction to change this to the addition of positive 6:

$$12 - (-6) = 12 + 6 \quad \text{Subtracting } -6 \text{ is equivalent to adding } +6$$
$$= 18 \quad \text{Addition}$$

EXAMPLE 5 Subtract: $-20 - (-30)$

SOLUTION Instead of subtracting -30, we can use the definition of subtraction to write the problem again as the addition of 30:

$$-20 - (-30) = -20 + 30 \quad \text{Definition of subtraction}$$
$$= 10 \quad \text{Addition}$$

Examples 1–5 illustrate all the possible combinations of subtraction with positive and negative numbers. There are no new rules for subtraction. We apply the definition to change each subtraction problem into an equivalent addition problem. The rule for addition can then be used to obtain the correct answer.

EXAMPLE 6 The following table shows the relationship between subtraction and addition:

Subtraction	Addition of the Opposite	Answer
$7 - 9$	$7 + (-9)$	-2
$-7 - 9$	$-7 + (-9)$	-16
$7 - (-9)$	$7 + 9$	16
$-7 - (-9)$	$-7 + 9$	2
$15 - 10$	$15 + (-10)$	5
$-15 - 10$	$-15 + (-10)$	-25
$15 - (-10)$	$15 + 10$	25
$-15 - (-10)$	$-15 + 10$	-5

EXAMPLE 7 Combine: $-3 + 6 - 2$

SOLUTION The first step is to change subtraction to addition of the opposite. After that has been done, we add from left to right.

$$-3 + 6 - 2 = -3 + 6 + (-2) \quad \text{Subtracting 2 is equivalent to adding } -2$$
$$= 3 + (-2) \quad \text{Add left to right}$$
$$= 1$$

EXAMPLE 8 Combine: $10 - (-4) - 8$

SOLUTION Changing subtraction to addition of the opposite, we have

$$10 - (-4) - 8 = 10 + 4 + (-8)$$
$$= 14 + (-8)$$
$$= 6$$

EXAMPLE 9 Subtract 3 from -5.

SOLUTION Subtracting 3 is equivalent to adding -3.

$$-5 - 3 = -5 + (-3) = -8$$

Subtracting 3 from -5 gives us -8.

EXAMPLE 10 Subtract -4 from 9.

SOLUTION Subtracting -4 is the same as adding $+4$:

$$9 - (-4) = 9 + 4 = 13$$

Subtracting -4 from 9 gives us 13.

EXAMPLE 11 Find the difference of -7 and -4.

SOLUTION Subtracting -4 from -7 looks like this:

$$-7 - (-4) = -7 + 4 = -3$$

The difference of -7 and -4 is -3.

EXAMPLE 12 Subtract 60.3 from -49.8.

SOLUTION $-49.8 - 60.3 = -49.8 + (-60.3)$
$$= -110.1$$

EXAMPLE 13 Find the difference of $-\dfrac{3}{5}$ and $\dfrac{2}{5}$.

SOLUTION $-\dfrac{3}{5} - \dfrac{2}{5} = -\dfrac{3}{5} + \left(-\dfrac{2}{5}\right)$
$$= -\dfrac{5}{5}$$
$$= -1$$

7. Combine: $-4 + 6 - 7$

8. Combine: $15 - (-5) - 8$

9. Subtract 2 from -8.

10. Subtract -5 from 7.

11. Find the difference of -8 and -6.

Subtract.
12. $-57.8 - 70.4$

13. $-\dfrac{5}{8} - \dfrac{3}{8}$

Answers
7. -5 8. 12 9. -10 10. 12
11. -2 12. -128.2 13. -1

14. Suppose the temperature is 42°F at takeoff and then drops to −42°F when the plane reaches its cruising altitude. Find the difference in temperature at takeoff and at cruising altitude.

B Application

EXAMPLE 14 Many of the planes used by the United States during World War II were not pressurized or sealed from outside air. As a result, the temperature inside these planes was the same as the surrounding air temperature outside. Suppose the temperature inside a B-17 Flying Fortress is 50°F at takeoff and then drops to −30°F when the plane reaches its cruising altitude of 28,000 feet. Find the difference in temperature inside this plane at takeoff and at 28,000 feet.

Courtesy of the U.S. Air Force Museum

SOLUTION The temperature at takeoff is 50°F, whereas the temperature at 28,000 feet is −30°F. To find the difference we subtract, with the numbers in the same order as they are given in the problem:

$$50 - (-30) = 50 + 30 = 80$$

The difference in temperature is 80°F.

Subtraction and Taking Away

Some people may believe that the answer to −5 − 9 should be −4 or 4, not −14. If this is happening to you, you are probably thinking of subtraction in terms of taking one number away from another. Thinking of subtraction in this way works well with positive numbers if you always subtract the smaller number from the larger. In algebra, however, we encounter many situations other than this. The definition of subtraction, that $a - b = a + (-b)$ clearly indicates the correct way to use subtraction. That is, when working subtraction problems, you should think "addition of the opposite," not "taking one number away from another."

USING TECHNOLOGY

Calculators

Here is how we work the subtraction problem shown in Example 11 on a calculator.

Scientific Calculator: 7 | +/− | | − | 4 | +/− | | = |

Graphing Calculator: | (−) | 7 | − | | (−) | 4 | ENT |

Getting Ready for Class

After reading through the preceding section, respond in your own words and in complete sentences.

1. Write the subtraction problem 5 − 3 as an equivalent addition problem.
2. Explain the process you would use to subtract 2 from −7.
3. Write an addition problem that is equivalent to the subtraction problem −20 − (−30).
4. To find the difference of −7 and −4 we subtract what number from −7?

Problem Set 9.3

A Subtract. [Examples 1–5, 12, 13]

▶ **1.** $7 - 5$
2

▶ **2.** $5 - 7$
-2

3. $8 - 6$
2

4. $6 - 8$
-2

▶ **5.** $-3 - 5$
-8

6. $-5 - 3$
-8

7. $-4 - 1$
-5

8. $-1 - 4$
-5

▶ **9.** $5 - (-2)$
7

10. $2 - (-5)$
7

▶ **11.** $3 - (-9)$
12

12. $9 - (-3)$
12

▶ **13.** $-4 - (-7)$
3

14. $-7 - (-4)$
-3

15. $-10 - (-3)$
-7

▶ **16.** $-3 - (-10)$
7

17. $15 - 18$
-3

18. $20 - 32$
-12

▶ **19.** $100 - 113$
-13

20. $121 - 21$
100

▶ **21.** $-30 - 20$
-50

22. $-50 - 60$
-110

23. $-79 - 21$
-100

24. $-86 - 31$
-117

▶ **25.** $156 - (-243)$
399

▶ **26.** $292 - (-841)$
1,133

27. $-35 - (-14)$
-21

28. $-29 - (-4)$
-25

29. $-9.01 - 2.4$
-11.41

30. $-8.23 - 5.4$
-13.63

31. $-0.89 - 1.01$
-1.9

32. $-0.42 - 2.04$
-2.46

33. $-\dfrac{1}{6} - \dfrac{5}{6}$
-1

34. $-\dfrac{4}{7} - \dfrac{3}{7}$
-1

▶ **35.** $\dfrac{5}{12} - \dfrac{5}{6}$
$-\dfrac{5}{12}$

36. $\dfrac{7}{15} - \dfrac{4}{5}$
$-\dfrac{1}{3}$

37. $-\dfrac{13}{70} - \dfrac{23}{42}$
$-\dfrac{11}{15}$

38. $-\dfrac{17}{60} - \dfrac{17}{90}$
$-\dfrac{17}{36}$

▶ Selected exercises available online at www.webassign.net/brookscole

A Simplify as much as possible by first changing all subtractions to addition of the opposite and then adding left to right. [Examples 7, 8]

▶ **39.** $4 - 5 - 6$
-7

40. $7 - 3 - 2$
2

41. $-8 + 3 - 4$
-9

42. $-10 - 1 + 16$
5

▶ **43.** $-8 - 4 - 2$
-14

44. $-7 - 3 - 6$
-16

45. $12 - 30 - 47$
-65

46. $-29 - 53 - 37$
-119

▶ **47.** $33 - (-22) - 66$
-11

48. $44 - (-11) + 55$
110

49. $101 - (-95) + 6$
202

50. $-211 - (-207) + 3$
-1

▶ **51.** $-900 + 400 - (-100)$
-400

52. $-300 + 600 - (-200)$
500

53. $-3.4 - 5.6 - 8.5$
-17.5

54. $-2.1 - 3.1 - 4.1$
-9.3

▶ **55.** $\dfrac{1}{2} - \dfrac{1}{3} - \dfrac{1}{4}$
$-\dfrac{1}{12}$

56. $\dfrac{1}{5} - \dfrac{1}{6} - \dfrac{1}{7}$
$-\dfrac{23}{210}$

A Translate each of the following and simplify the result. [Examples 9–11]

▶ **57.** Subtract -6 from 5.
11

58. Subtract 8 from -2.
-10

▶ **59.** Find the difference of -5 and -1.
-4

60. Find the difference of -7 and -3.
-4

▶ **61.** Subtract -4 from the sum of -8 and 12.
8

62. Subtract -7 from the sum of 7 and -12.
2

▶ **63.** What number do you subtract from -3 to get -9?
6

64. What number do you subtract from 5 to get 8?
-3

■ Estimating

Work Problems 65–70 mentally, without pencil and paper or a calculator.

▶ **65.** The answer to the problem $52 - 49$ is closest to which of the following numbers?
   a. 100   **b.** 0   **c.** -100
   b

66. The answer to the problem $-52 - 49$ is closest to which of the following numbers?
   a. 100   **b.** 0   **c.** -100
   c

67. The answer to the problem $52 - (-49)$ is closest to which of the following numbers?
   a. 100   **b.** 0   **c.** -100
   a

68. The answer to the problem $-52 - (-49)$ is closest to which of the following numbers?
   a. 100   **b.** 0   **c.** -100
   b

69. Is $-161 - (-62)$ closer to -200 or -100?
-100

70. Is $-553 - 50$ closer to -600 or -500?
-600

B **Applying the Concepts** [Example 14]

71. The graph shows the record low temperatures for the Grand Canyon. What is the temperature difference between January and July?

    −16 degrees

Source: National Park Service

72. The graph shows the lowest and highest points in the Grand Canyon and Death Valley. What is the difference between the lowest point in the Grand Canyon and the lowest point in Death Valley?

    1,482 feet

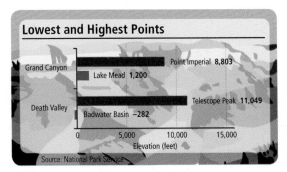

Source: National Park Service

73. The highest point in Grand Canyon National Park is at Point Imperial with an elevation of 8,803 feet. The lowest point in the park is at Lake Mead at 1,200 feet. What is the difference between the highest and the lowest points?

    7,603 feet

▶ 74. **Temperature** On Monday the temperature reached a high of 28° above 0. That night it dropped to 16° below 0. What is the difference between the high and the low temperatures for Monday?

    44°

75. **Tracking Inventory** By definition, inventory is the total amount of goods contained in a store or warehouse at any given time. It is helpful for store owners to know the number of items they have available for sale in order to accommodate customer demand. This table shows the beginning inventory on May 1st and tracks the number of items bought and sold for one month. Determine the number of items in inventory at the end of the month.

    −100 items

Date	Transaction	Number of Units Available	Number of Units Sold
May 1	Beginning Inventory	400	
May 3	Purchase	100	
May 8	Sale		700
May 15	Purchase	600	
May 19	Purchase	200	
May 25	Sale		400
May 27	Sale		300
May 31	Ending Inventory		

76. **Profit and Loss** You own a small business which provides computer support to homeowners who wish to create their own in-house computer network. In addition to setting up the network you also maintain and troubleshoot home PCs. Business gets off to a slow start. You record a profit of $2,298 during the first quarter of the year, a loss of $2,854 during the second quarter, a profit of $3,057 during the third quarter, and a profit of $1,250 for the last quarter of the year. Do you end the year with a net profit or a net loss? Represent that profit or loss as a positive or negative value.

    Profit; +$3,751

Tuition Cost The chart shows the cost of college tuition and fees at public four-year universities. Because of tax breaks, along with federal and state grants, the actual cost per student is much less than the total cost of tuition and fees. Use the information in this chart to answer Questions 77–80.

77. Find the difference in student grants in 1998 and student grants and tax deductions in 2008.

$1,760

78. Find the difference in actual costs in 1998 and actual costs in 2008.

$1,249

79. Find the difference in total costs in 1998 and total costs in 2008.

$3,009

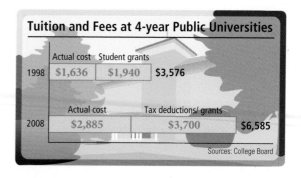

Tuition and Fees at 4-year Public Universities

	Actual cost	Student grants	
1998	$1,636	$1,940	$3,576

	Actual cost	Tax deductions/ grants	
2008	$2,885	$3,700	$6,585

Sources: College Board

80. What has increased more from 1998 to 2008, student grants and tax deductions or actual student costs?

Student grants and tax deductions

Repeated below is the table of wind chill temperatures that we used previously. Use it for Problems 81–84.

	Air Temperature (°F)							
Wind speed	30°	25°	20°	15°	10°	5°	0°	−5°
10 mph	16°	10°	3°	−3°	−9°	−15°	−22°	−27°
15 mph	9°	2°	−5°	−11°	−18°	−25°	−31°	−38°
20 mph	4°	−3°	−10°	−17°	−24°	−31°	−39°	−46°
25 mph	1°	−7°	−15°	−22°	−29°	−36°	−44°	−51°
30 mph	−2°	−10°	−18°	−25°	−33°	−41°	−49°	−56°

81. Wind Chill If the temperature outside is 15°F, what is the difference in wind chill temperature between a 15-mile-per-hour wind and a 25-mile-per-hour wind?

$-11 - (-22) = 11°F$

82. Wind Chill If the temperature outside is 0°F, what is the difference in wind chill temperature between a 15-mile-per-hour wind and a 25-mile-per-hour wind?

$-31 - (-44) = 13°F$

83. Wind Chill Find the difference in temperature between a day in which the air temperature is 20°F and the wind is blowing at 10 miles per hour and a day in which the air temperature is 10°F and the wind is blowing at 20 miles per hour.

$3 - (-24) = 27°F$

84. Wind Chill Find the difference in temperature between a day in which the air temperature is 0°F and the wind is blowing at 10 miles per hour and a day in which the air temperature is −5°F and the wind is blowing at 20 miles per hour.

$-22 - (-46) = 24°F$

Use the tables below to work Problems 85–88.

RECORD LOW TEMPERATURES FOR LAKE PLACID, NEW YORK	
Month	Temperature
January	−36°F
February	−30°F
March	−14°F
April	−2°F
May	19°F
June	22°F
July	35°F
August	30°F
September	19°F
October	15°F
November	−11°F
December	−26°F

RECORD HIGH TEMPERATURES FOR LAKE PLACID, NEW YORK	
Month	Temperature
January	54°F
February	59°F
March	69°F
April	82°F
May	90°F
June	93°F
July	97°F
August	93°F
September	90°F
October	87°F
November	67°F
December	60°F

85. Temperature Difference Find the difference between the record high temperature and the record low temperature for the month of December.

$60 - (-26) = 86°F$

86. Temperature Difference Find the difference between the record high temperature and the record low temperature for the month of March.

$69 - (-14) = 83°F$

87. Temperature Difference Find the difference between the record low temperatures of March and December.

$-14 - (-26) = 12°F$

88. Temperature Difference Find the difference between the record high temperatures of March and December.

$69 - 60 = 9°F$

▬ Getting Ready for the Next Section

Perform the indicated operations.

89. $3(2)(5)$

30

90. $5(2)(4)$

40

91. 6^2

36

92. 8^2

64

93. 4^3

64

94. 3^3

27

95. $6(3 + 5)$

48

96. $2(5 + 8)$

26

97. $3(9 - 2) + 4(7 - 2)$

41

98. $2(5 - 3) - 7(4 - 2)$

−10

99. $(3 + 7)(6 - 2)$

40

100. $(6 + 1)(9 - 4)$

35

Simplify each of the following.

101. $2 + 3(4 + 1)$

17

102. $6 + 5(2 + 3)$

31

103. $(6 + 2)(6 - 2)$

32

104. $(7 + 1)(7 - 1)$

48

105. 5^2

25

106. 2^3

8

107. $2^3 \cdot 3^2$

72

108. $2^3 + 3^2$

17

Maintaining Your Skills

Write each of the following in symbols.

109. The product of 3 and 5.

$3 \cdot 5$

110. The product of 5 and 3.

$5 \cdot 3$

111. The product of 7 and x.

$7x$

112. The product of 2 and y.

$2y$

Rewrite the following using the commutative property of multiplication.

113. $3(5) =$

$5(3)$

114. $7(x) =$

$x(7)$

Rewrite the following using the associative property of multiplication.

115. $5(7 \cdot 8) =$

$(5 \cdot 7) \cdot 8$

116. $4(6 \cdot y)$

$(4 \cdot 6)y$

Apply the distributive property to each expression and then simplify the result.

117. $2(3 + 4)$

$2(3) + 2(4) = 6 + 8 = 14$

118. $5(6 + 7)$

$5(6) + 5(7) = 30 + 35 = 65$

Extending the Concepts

119. Give an example that shows that subtraction is not a commutative operation.

$3 - 5 \neq 5 - 3$

120. Why is the expression "two negatives make a positive" not correct?

Because, with addition, the sum of two negatives is a negative. For example, $-3 + (-4) = -7$.

121. Give an example of an everyday situation that is modeled by the subtraction problem
$\$10 - \$12 - -\$2.$

You have a balance of $10 in your checkbook, and you write a check for $12. Your new balance is −$2.

122. Give an example of an everyday situation that is modeled by the subtraction problem
$-\$10 - \$12 = -\$22.$

You have a balance of −$10 in your checkbook, and you write a check for $12. Your new balance is −$22.

In Chapter 2 we defined an arithmetic sequence as a sequence of numbers in which each number, after the first number, is obtained from the previous number by adding the same amount each time.

Find the next two numbers in each arithmetic sequence below.

123. $10, 5, 0, \ldots$

$-5, -10$

124. $8, 3, -2, \ldots$

$-7, -12$

125. $-10, -6, -2, \ldots$

$2, 6$

126. $-4, -1, 2, \ldots$

$5, 8$

Multiplication with Negative Numbers

Objectives

A Multiply positive and negative numbers.

B Apply the rule for order of operations to expressions containing positive and negative numbers.

Introduction . . .

Suppose you buy three shares of a certain stock on Monday, and by Friday the price per share has dropped $5. How much money have you lost? The answer is $15. Because it is a loss, we can express it as −$15. The multiplication problem below can be used to describe the relationship among the numbers.

SUPERIOR SHIPPING COMPANY
THREE SHARES

AND IF YOU BELIEVE THAT WITH THREE SHARES OF STOCK YOU CAN ACTUALLY MAKE SOME MONEY IN TODAY'S STOCK MARKET REGARDLESS OF WHAT YOU MIGHT THINK OR WHAT YOUR BROKER TELLS YOU THEN I HAVE A BRIDGE I WANT TO SELL YOU.

3 shares   each loses $5   for a total of −$15

$$3(-5) = -15$$

From this we conclude that it is reasonable to say that the product of a positive number and a negative number is a negative number.

A Multiplication

In order to generalize multiplication with negative numbers, recall that we first defined multiplication by whole numbers to be repeated addition. That is:

$$3 \cdot 5 = 5 + 5 + 5$$

↑   ↑   ↑

Multiplication   Repeated addition

This concept is very helpful when it comes to developing the rule for multiplication problems that involve negative numbers. For the first example we look at what happens when we multiply a negative number by a positive number.

EXAMPLE 1   Multiply: 3(−5)

SOLUTION   Writing this product as repeated addition, we have

$$3(-5) = (-5) + (-5) + (-5)$$
$$= -10 + (-5)$$
$$= -15$$

The result, −15, is obtained by adding the three negative 5's.

EXAMPLE 2   Multiply: −3(5)

SOLUTION   In order to write this multiplication problem in terms of repeated addition, we will have to reverse the order of the two numbers. This is easily done, because multiplication is a commutative operation.

$$-3(5) = 5(-3)$$ Commutative property
$$= (-3) + (-3) + (-3) + (-3) + (-3)$$ Repeated addition
$$= -15$$ Addition

The product of −3 and 5 is −15.

EXAMPLE 3   Multiply: −3(−5)

SOLUTION   It is impossible to write this product in terms of repeated addition. We will find the answer to −3(−5) by solving a different problem. Look at the following problem:

$$-3[5 + (-5)] = -3[0] = 0$$

PRACTICE PROBLEMS

1. Multiply: 2(−6)

2. Multiply: −2(6)

3. Multiply: −2(−6)

Answers
1. −12   2. −12

Note The discussion here explains why $-3(-5) = 15$. We want to be able to justify everything we do in mathematics. The discussion tells *why* $-3(-5) = 15$.

The result is 0, because multiplying by 0 always produces 0. Now we can work the same problem another way, and in the process find the answer to $-3(-5)$. Applying the distributive property to the same expression, we have

$$-3[5 + (-5)] = -3(5) + (-3)(-5) \qquad \text{Distributive property}$$
$$= -15 + (?) \qquad\qquad -3(5) = -15$$

The question mark must be $+15$, because we already know that the answer to the problem is 0, and $+15$ is the only number we can add to -15 to get 0. So, our problem is solved:

$$-3(-5) = +15$$

Table 1 gives a summary of what we have done so far in this section.

TABLE 1

Original Numbers Have	For Example	The Answer Is
Same signs	$3(5) = 15$	Positive
Different signs	$-3(5) = -15$	Negative
Different signs	$3(-5) = -15$	Negative
Same signs	$-3(-5) = 15$	Positive

From the examples we have done so far in this section and their summaries in Table 1, we write the following rule for multiplication of positive and negative numbers:

Rule

To multiply any two numbers, we multiply their absolute values.
1. The answer is *positive* if both the original numbers have the same sign. That is, the product of two numbers with the same sign is positive.
2. The answer is *negative* if the original two numbers have different signs. The product of two numbers with different signs is negative.

This rule should be memorized. By the time you have finished reading this section and working the problems at the end of the section, you should be fast and accurate at multiplication with positive and negative numbers.

EXAMPLE 4 $\quad 2(4) = 8 \quad$ Like signs; positive answer

EXAMPLE 5 $\quad -2(-4) = 8 \quad$ Like signs; positive answer

EXAMPLE 6 $\quad 2(-4) = -8 \quad$ Unlike signs; negative answer

EXAMPLE 7 $\quad -2(4) = -8 \quad$ Unlike signs; negative answer

EXAMPLE 8 $\quad 7(-6) = -42 \quad$ Unlike signs; negative answer

EXAMPLE 9 $\quad -5(-8) = 40 \quad$ Like signs; positive answer

EXAMPLE 10
$$-3(2)(-5) = -6(-5) \quad \text{Multiply } -3 \text{ and } 2 \text{ to get } -6$$
$$= 30$$

Multiply.
4. $3(2)$

5. $-3(-2)$

6. $3(-2)$

7. $-3(2)$

8. $8(-9)$

9. $-6(-4)$

10. $-5(2)(-4)$

Answers
3. 12 4. 6 5. 6 6. -6 7. -6
8. -72 9. 24 10. 40

EXAMPLE 11 Use the definition of exponents to expand each expression. Then simplify by multiplying.

a. $(-6)^2 = (-6)(-6)$ Definition of exponents
       $= 36$ Multiply

b. $-6^2 = -6 \cdot 6$ Definition of exponents
       $= -36$ Multiply

c. $(-4)^3 = (-4)(-4)(-4)$ Definition of exponents
       $= -64$ Multiply

d. $-4^3 = -4 \cdot 4 \cdot 4$ Definition of exponents
       $= -64$ Multiply

In Example 11, the base is a negative number in Parts a and c, but not in Parts b and d. We know this is true because of the use of parentheses.

B   Order of Operations

EXAMPLE 12 Simplify: $-6[3 + (-5)]$

SOLUTION We begin inside the brackets and work our way out:

$$-6[3 + (-5)] = -6[-2]$$
$$= 12$$

EXAMPLE 13 Simplify: $-4 + 5(-6 + 2)$

SOLUTION Simplifying inside the parentheses first, we have

$$-4 + 5(-6 + 2) = -4 + 5(-4)$$ Simplify inside parentheses
$$= -4 + (-20)$$ Multiply
$$= -24$$ Add

EXAMPLE 14 Simplify: $-2(7) + 3(-6)$

SOLUTION Multiplying left to right before we add gives us

$$-2(7) + 3(-6) = -14 + (-18)$$
$$= -32$$

EXAMPLE 15 Simplify: $-3(2 - 9) + 4(-7 - 2)$

SOLUTION We begin by subtracting inside the parentheses:

$$-3(2 - 9) + 4(-7 - 2) = -3(-7) + 4(-9)$$
$$= 21 + (-36)$$
$$= -15$$

EXAMPLE 16 Simplify: $(-3 - 7)(2 - 6)$

SOLUTION Again, we begin by simplifying inside the parentheses:

$$(-3 - 7)(2 - 6) = (-10)(-4)$$
$$= 40$$

---

11. Use the definition of exponents to expand each expression. Then simplify by multiplying.
a. $(-8)^2$

b. -8^2

c. $(-3)^3$

d. -3^3

12. Simplify: $-2[5 + (-8)]$

13. Simplify: $-3 + 4(-7 + 3)$

14. Simplify: $-3(5) + 4(-4)$

15. Simplify: $-2(3 - 5) - 7(-2 - 4)$

16. Simplify: $(-6 - 1)(4 - 9)$

Answers
11. a. 64 **b.** -64 **c.** -27 **d.** -27
12. 6 **13.** -19 **14.** -31 **15.** 46
16. 35

17. $\frac{3}{4}\left(-\frac{4}{7}\right)$

18. $\left(-\frac{5}{6}\right)\left(-\frac{9}{20}\right)$

19. $(-3)(6.7)$

20. $(-0.6)(-0.5)$

Here are a few more multiplication problems involving fractions and decimals.

EXAMPLE 17 $\left(\frac{2}{3}\right)\left(-\frac{3}{5}\right) = -\frac{6}{15} = -\frac{2}{5}$ The rule for multiplication also holds for fractions

EXAMPLE 18 $\left(-\frac{7}{8}\right)\left(-\frac{5}{14}\right) = \frac{35}{112} = \frac{5}{16}$

EXAMPLE 19 $(-5)(3.4) = -17.0$ The rule for multiplication also holds for decimals

EXAMPLE 20 $(-0.4)(-0.8) = 0.32$

Getting Ready for Class

After reading through the preceding section, respond in your own words and in complete sentences.

1. Write the multiplication problem $3(-5)$ as an addition problem.
2. Write the multiplication problem $2(4)$ as an addition problem.
3. If two numbers have the same sign, then their product will have what sign?
4. If two numbers have different signs, then their product will have what sign?

Answers

17. $-\frac{3}{7}$ **18.** $\frac{3}{8}$ **19.** -20.1
20. 0.30

Problem Set 9.4

A Find each of the following products. (Multiply.) [Examples 1–10, 17–20]

▶ **1.** 7(−8)
−56

2. −3(5)
−15

3. −6(10)
−60

4. 4(−8)
−32

▶ **5.** −7(−8)
56

6. −4(−7)
28

7. −9(−9)
81

8. −6(−3)
18

▶ **9.** −2.1(4.3)
−9.03

10. −6.8(5.7)
−38.76

11. $-\dfrac{4}{5}\left(-\dfrac{15}{28}\right)$
$\dfrac{3}{7}$

12. $-\dfrac{8}{9}\left(-\dfrac{27}{32}\right)$
$\dfrac{3}{4}$

13. $-12\left(\dfrac{2}{3}\right)$
−8

▶ **14.** $-18\left(\dfrac{5}{6}\right)$
−15

15. 3(−2)(4)
−24

▶ **16.** 5(−1)(3)
−15

▶ **17.** −4(3)(−2)
24

18. −4(5)(−6)
120

19. −1(−2)(−3)
−6

▶ **20.** −2(−3)(−4)
−24

A Use the definition of exponents to expand each of the following expressions. Then multiply according to the rule for multiplication. [Example 11]

▶ **21. a.** $(-4)^2$
16

22. a. $(-5)^2$
25

▶ **23. a.** $(-5)^3$
−125

24. a. $(-4)^3$
−64

25. a. $(-2)^4$
16

26. a. $(-1)^4$
1

b. -4^2
−16

b. -5^2
−25

b. -5^3
−125

b. -4^3
−64

b. -2^4
−16

b. -1^4
−1

Complete the following tables. Remember, if $x = -5$, then $x^2 = (-5)^2 = 25$. [Example 11]

▶ **27.**

Number x	Square x^2
−3	9
−2	4
−1	1
0	0
1	1
2	4
3	9

28.

Number x	Cube x^3
−3	−27
−2	−8
−1	−1
0	0
1	1
2	8
3	27

29.

First Number x	Second Number y	Their Product xy
6	2	12
6	1	6
6	0	0
6	−1	−6
6	−2	−12

30.

First Number a	Second Number b	Their Product ab
−5	3	−15
−5	2	−10
−5	1	−5
−5	0	0
−5	−1	5
−5	−2	10
−5	−3	15

B Use the rule for order of operations along with the rules for addition, subtraction, and multiplication to simplify each of the following expressions. [Examples 12–16]

▶ **31.** $4(-3 + 2)$
  -4

32. $7(-6 + 3)$
  -21

▶ **33.** $-10(-2 - 3)$
  50

34. $-5(-6 - 2)$
  40

35. $-3 + 2(5 - 3)$
  1

36. $-7 + 3(6 - 2)$
  5

▶ **37.** $-7 + 2[-5 - 9]$
  -35

38. $-8 + 3[-4 - 1]$
  -23

39. $2(-5) + 3(-4)$
  -22

40. $6(-1) + 2(-7)$
  -20

41. $3(-2)4 + 3(-2)$
  -30

▶ **42.** $2(-1)(-3) + 4(-6)$
  -18

▶ **43.** $(8 - 3)(2 - 7)$
  -25

44. $(9 - 3)(2 - 6)$
  -24

45. $(2 - 5)(3 - 6)$
  9

▶ **46.** $(3 - 7)(2 - 8)$
  24

47. $3(5 - 8) + 4(6 - 7)$
  -13

48. $2(3 - 7) + 3(5 - 6)$
  -11

49. $-2(8 - 10) + 3(4 - 9)$
  -11

50. $-3(6 - 9) + 2(3 - 8)$
  -1

▶ **51.** $-3(4 - 7) - 2(-3 - 2)$
  19

▶ **52.** $-5(-2 - 8) - 4(6 - 10)$
  66

53. $3(-2)(6 - 7)$
  6

54. $4(-3)(2 - 5)$
  36

55. Find the product of -3, -2, and -1.
  -6

56. Find the product of -7, -1, and 0.
  0

▶ **57.** What number do you multiply by -3 to get 12?
  -4

58. What number do you multiply by -7 to get -21?
  3

▶ **59.** Subtract -3 from the product of -5 and 4.
  -17

60. Subtract 5 from the product of -8 and 1.
  -13

Work Problems 61–68 mentally, without pencil and paper or a calculator.

61. The product $-32(-522)$ is closest to which of the following numbers?
  a. $15,000$ **b.** -500 **c.** $-1,500$ **d.** $-15,000$
  a

62. The product $32(-522)$ is closest to which of the following numbers?
  a. $15,000$ **b.** -500 **c.** $-1,500$ **d.** $-15,000$
  d

▶ **63.** The product $-47(470)$ is closest to which of the following numbers?
  a. $25,000$ **b.** 420 **c.** $-2,500$ **d.** $-25,000$
  d

64. The product $-47(-470)$ is closest to which of the following numbers?
  a. $25,000$ **b.** 420 **c.** $-2,500$ **d.** $-25,000$
  a

65. The product $-222(-987)$ is closest to which of the following numbers?
  a. $200,000$ **b.** 800 **c.** -800 **d.** $-1,200$
  a

66. The sum $-222 + (-987)$ is closest to which of the following numbers?
  a. $200,000$ **b.** 800 **c.** -800 **d.** $-1,200$
  d

67. The difference $-222 - (-987)$ is closest to which of the following numbers?
  a. $200,000$ **b.** 800 **c.** -800 **d.** $-1,200$
  b

68. The difference $-222 - 987$ is closest to which of the following numbers?
  a. $200,000$ **b.** 800 **c.** -800 **d.** $-1,200$
  d

◼ Applying the Concepts

69. The chart shows the record low temperatures for Grand Canyon National Park, by month. Write the record low temperature for March.

Record Low Temperatures

Source: National Park Service

−6°C

70. The chart shows the cities with the highest annual insurance rates.

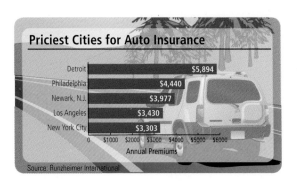

Priciest Cities for Auto Insurance

Detroit	$5,894
Philadelphia	$4,440
Newark, N.J.	$3,977
Los Angeles	$3,430
New York City	$3,303

Annual Premiums

Source: Runzheimer International

a. What is the monthly payment for a driver in Philadelphia? $370

b. Use negative numbers to write an expression for the cost of three months of auto insurance for a driver living in Philadelphia.   3(−$370) = −$1,110

71. Temperature Change A hot-air balloon is rising to its cruising altitude. Suppose the air temperature around the balloon drops 4 degrees each time the balloon rises 1,000 feet. What is the net change in air temperature around the balloon as it rises from 2,000 feet to 6,000 feet?

6,000 ft

2,000 ft

−16 degrees

72. Temperature Change A small airplane is rising to its cruising altitude. Suppose the air temperature around the plane drops 4 degrees each time the plane increases its altitude by 1,000 feet. What is the net change in air temperature around the plane as it rises from 5,000 feet to 12,000 feet?

12,000 ft

5,000 ft

−28 degrees

73. Expense Account A business woman has a travel expense account of $1,000. If she spends $75 a week for 8 weeks what will the balance of her expense account be at the end of this time.

$400 remains

74. Gas Prices Two local gas stations offer different prices for a gallon of regular gasoline. The Exxon Mobil station is currently selling their gas at $3.99 per gallon. The Getty station is currently selling their gas for $3.85 per gallon. Represent the net savings to you on a purchase of 15 gallons of regular gas if you buy gas from the Getty gas station.

$2.10

■ Getting Ready for the Next Section

Perform the indicated operations.

75. $35 \div 5$
7

76. $32 \div 4$
8

77. $\dfrac{20}{4}$
5

78. $\dfrac{30}{5}$
6

79. $12 - 17$
-5

80. $7 - 11$
-4

81. $(6 \cdot 3) \div 2$
9

82. $(8 \cdot 5) \div 4$
10

83. $80 \div 10 \div 2$
4

84. $80 \div 2 \div 10$
4

85. $15 + 5(4) \div 10$
17

86. $[20 + 6(2)] \div (11 - 7)$
8

87. $4(10^2) + 20 \div 4$
405

88. $3(4^2) + 10 \div 5$
50

■ Maintaining Your Skills

Write each of the following statements in symbols.

89. The quotient of 12 and 6
$12 \div 6$ or $\dfrac{12}{6}$

90. The quotient of x and 5
$\dfrac{x}{5}$ or $x \div 5$

Rewrite each of the following multiplication problems as an equivalent division problem.

91. $2(3) = 6$
$6 \div 3 = 2$

92. $5 \cdot 4 = 20$
$20 \div 4 = 5$

Rewrite each of the following division problems as an equivalent multiplication problem.

93. $10 \div 5 = 2$
$5 \cdot 2 = 10$

94. $\dfrac{63}{9} = 7$
$9 \cdot 7 = 63$

Divide.

95. $4{,}984 \div 56$
89

96. $4{,}994 \div 56$
89 R 10

■ Extending the Concepts

In Chapter 1 we defined a geometric sequence to be a sequence of numbers in which each number, after the first number, is obtained from the previous number by multiplying by the same amount each time.

Find the next two terms in each of the following geometric sequences.

97. $2, -6, 18, \ldots$
$-54, 162$

98. $1, -4, 16, \ldots$
$-64, 256$

99. $-2, 6, -18, \ldots$
$54, -162$

100. $-1, 4, -16, \ldots$
$64, -256$

Simplify each of the following according to the rule for order of operations.

101. $5(-2)^2 - 3(-2)^3$
44

102. $8(-1)^3 - 6(-3)^2$
-62

103. $7 - 3(4 - 8)$
19

104. $6 - 2(9 - 11)$
10

105. $5 - 2[3 - 4(6 - 8)]$
-17

106. $7 - 4[6 - 3(2 - 9)]$
-101

Division with Negative Numbers

Objectives

A Divide positive and negative numbers.

B Apply the rule for order of operations to expressions that contain positive and negative numbers.

Introduction . . .

Suppose four friends invest equal amounts of money in a moving truck to start a small business. After 2 years the truck has dropped $10,000 in value. If we represent this change with the number −$10,000, then the loss to each of the four partners can be found with division:

$10,000 drop in 2 years

$$(-\$10,000) \div 4 = -\$2,500$$

From this example it seems reasonable to assume that a negative number divided by a positive number will give a negative answer.

To cover all the possible situations we can encounter with division of negative numbers, we use the relationship between multiplication and division. If we let n be the answer to the problem $12 \div (-2)$, then we know that

$$12 \div (-2) = n \quad \text{and} \quad -2(n) = 12$$

From our work with multiplication, we know that n must be −6 in the multiplication problem above, because −6 is the only number we can multiply −2 by to get 12. Because of the relationship between the two problems above, it must be true that 12 divided by −2 is −6.

The following pairs of problems show more quotients of positive and negative numbers. In each case the multiplication problem on the right justifies the answer to the division problem on the left.

$$6 \div 3 = 2 \quad \text{because} \quad 3(2) = 6$$
$$6 \div (-3) = -2 \quad \text{because} \quad -3(-2) = 6$$
$$-6 \div 3 = -2 \quad \text{because} \quad 3(-2) = -6$$
$$-6 \div (-3) = 2 \quad \text{because} \quad -3(2) = -6$$

The results given above can be used to write the rule for division with negative numbers.

A Division

> **Rule**
>
> To divide two numbers, we divide their absolute values.
> **1.** The answer is *positive* if both the original numbers have the same sign. That is, the quotient of two numbers with the same signs is positive.
> **2.** The answer is *negative* if the original two numbers have different signs. That is, the quotient of two numbers with different signs is negative.

EXAMPLE 1 $-12 \div 4 = -3$ Unlike signs, negative answer

EXAMPLE 2 $12 \div (-4) = -3$ Unlike signs; negative answer

EXAMPLE 3 $-12 \div (-4) = 3$ Like signs; positive answer

EXAMPLE 4 $\dfrac{12}{-4} = -3$ Unlike signs; negative answer

EXAMPLE 5 $\dfrac{-20}{-4} = 5$ Like signs; positive answer

From the examples we have done so far, we can make the following generalization about quotients that contain negative signs:

If a and b are numbers and b is not equal to 0, then
$$-\frac{a}{b} = \frac{a}{-b} = \frac{-a}{b} \quad \text{and} \quad \frac{-a}{-b} = \frac{a}{b}$$

B Order of Operations

The last examples in this section involve more than one operation. We use the rules developed previously in this chapter and the rule for order of operations to simplify each.

6. Simplify: $\dfrac{8(-5)}{-4}$

EXAMPLE 6 Simplify: $\dfrac{6(-3)}{-2}$

SOLUTION We begin by multiplying 6 and -3:

$$\frac{6(-3)}{-2} = \frac{-18}{-2} \qquad \text{Multiplication; } 6(-3) = -18$$
$$= 9 \qquad \text{Like signs; positive answer}$$

7. Simplify: $\dfrac{-20 + 6(-2)}{7 - 11}$

EXAMPLE 7 Simplify: $\dfrac{-15 + 5(-4)}{12 - 17}$

SOLUTION Simplifying above and below the fraction bar, we have

$$\frac{-15 + 5(-4)}{12 - 17} = \frac{-15 + (-20)}{-5} = \frac{-35}{-5} = 7$$

8. Simplify: $-3(4^2) + 10 \div (-5)$

EXAMPLE 8 Simplify: $-4(10^2) + 20 \div (-4)$

SOLUTION Applying the rule for order of operations, we have

$$\begin{aligned} -4(10^2) + 20 \div (-4) &= -4(100) + 20 \div (-4) & \text{Exponents first} \\ &= -400 + (-5) & \text{Multiply and divide} \\ &= -405 & \text{Add} \end{aligned}$$

9. Simplify: $-80 \div 2 \div 10$

EXAMPLE 9 Simplify: $-80 \div 10 \div 2$

SOLUTION In a situation like this, the rule for order of operations states that we are to divide left to right.

$$\begin{aligned} -80 \div 10 \div 2 &= -8 \div 2 & \text{Divide } -80 \text{ by } 10 \\ &= -4 \end{aligned}$$

Getting Ready for Class

After reading through the preceding section, respond in your own words and in complete sentences.

1. Write a multiplication problem that is equivalent to the division problem $-12 \div 4 = -3$.

2. Write a multiplication problem that is equivalent to the division problem $-12 \div (-4) = 3$.

3. If two numbers have the same sign, then their quotient will have what sign?

4. Dividing a negative number by 0 always results in what kind of expression?

Answers
6. 10 **7.** 8 **8.** −50 **9.** −4

Problem Set 9.5

A Find each of the following quotients. (Divide.) [Examples 1–5]

▶ **1.** $-15 \div 5$
-3

2. $15 \div (-3)$
-5

3. $20 \div (-4)$
-5

4. $-20 \div 4$
-5

▶ **5.** $-30 \div (-10)$
3

6. $-50 \div (-25)$
2

▶ **7.** $\dfrac{-14}{-7}$
2

8. $\dfrac{-18}{-6}$
3

▶ **9.** $\dfrac{12}{-3}$
-4

10. $\dfrac{12}{-4}$
-3

▶ **11.** $-22 \div 11$
-2

12. $-35 \div 7$
-5

▶ **13.** $\dfrac{0}{-3}$
0

14. $\dfrac{0}{-5}$
0

▶ **15.** $125 \div (-25)$
-5

16. $-144 \div (-9)$
16

Complete the following tables.

▶ **17.**

First Number a	Second Number b	The Quotient of a and b $\dfrac{a}{b}$
100	−5	−20
100	−10	−10
100	−25	−4
100	−50	−2

18.

First Number a	Second Number b	The Quotient of a and b $\dfrac{a}{b}$
24	−4	−6
24	−3	−8
24	−2	−12
24	−1	−24

19.

First Number a	Second Number b	The Quotient of a and b $\dfrac{a}{b}$
−100	−5	20
−100	5	−20
100	−5	−20
100	5	20

20.

First Number a	Second Number b	The Quotient of a and b $\dfrac{a}{b}$
−24	−2	12
−24	−4	6
−24	−6	4
−24	−8	3

▶ **21.** Find the quotient of -25 and 5.
-5

22. Find the quotient of -38 and -19.
2

▶ **23.** What number do you divide by -5 to get -7?
35

24. What number do you divide by 6 to get -7?
-42

▶ **25.** Subtract -3 from the quotient of 27 and 9.
6

26. Subtract -7 from the quotient of -72 and -9.
15

B Use any of the rules developed in this chapter and the rule for order of operations to simplify each of the following expressions as much as possible. [Examples 6–9]

▶ **27.** $\dfrac{4(-7)}{-28}$
1

28. $\dfrac{6(-3)}{-18}$
1

▶ **29.** $\dfrac{-3(-10)}{-5}$
−6

30. $\dfrac{-4(-12)}{-6}$
−8

▶ **31.** $\dfrac{2(-3)}{6-3}$
−2

32. $\dfrac{2(-3)}{3-6}$
2

▶ **33.** $\dfrac{4-8}{8-4}$
−1

34. $\dfrac{9-5}{5-9}$
−1

▶ **35.** $\dfrac{2(-3)+10}{-4}$
−1

36. $\dfrac{7(-2)-6}{-10}$
2

▶ **37.** $\dfrac{2+3(-6)}{4-12}$
2

38. $\dfrac{3+9(-1)}{5-7}$
3

▶ **39.** $\dfrac{6(-7)+3(-2)}{20-4}$
−3

40. $\dfrac{9(-8)+5(-1)}{12-1}$
−7

▶ **41.** $\dfrac{3(-7)(-4)}{6(-2)}$
−7

42. $\dfrac{-2(4)(-8)}{(-2)(-2)}$
16

▶ **43.** $(-5)^2 + 20 \div 4$
30

44. $6^2 + 36 \div 9$
40

45. $100 \div (-5)^2$
4

46. $400 \div (-4)^2$
25

▶ **47.** $-100 \div 10 \div 2$
−5

48. $-500 \div 50 \div 10$
−1

▶ **49.** $-100 \div (10 \div 2)$
−20

▶ **50.** $-500 \div (50 \div 10)$
−100

▶ **51.** $(-100 \div 10) \div 2$
−5

52. $(-500 \div 50) \div 10$
−1

■ Estimating

Work Problems 53–60 mentally, without pencil and paper or a calculator.

53. Is $397 \div (-401)$ closer to 1 or −1?
−1

54. Is $-751 \div (-749)$ closer to 1 or −1?
1

▶ **55.** The quotient $-121 \div 27$ is closest to which of the following numbers?
   a. −150   **b.** −100   **c.** −4   **d.** 6
   c

56. The quotient $1,000 \div (-337)$ is closest to which of the following numbers?
   a. 663   **b.** −3   **c.** −30   **d.** −663
   b

57. Which number is closest to the sum $-151 + (-49)$?
   a. −200   **b.** −100   **c.** 3   **d.** 7,500
   a

58. Which number is closest to $-151 - (-49)$?
   a. −200   **b.** −100   **c.** 3   **d.** 7,500
   b

59. Which number is closest to the product $-151(-49)$?
   a. −200   **b.** −100   **c.** 3   **d.** 7,500
   d

60. Which number is closest to the quotient $-151 \div (-49)$?
   a. −200   **b.** −100   **c.** 3   **d.** 7,500
   c

◼ Applying the Concepts

61. The chart shows the most expensive cities to live in. Expenses can also be written as negative numbers. Find the monthly cost to live in Los Angeles. Use negative numbers.

−$9,810.50

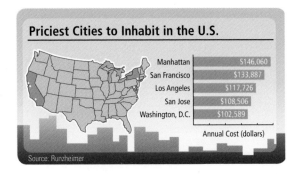

Priciest Cities to Inhabit in the U.S.

Manhattan	$146,060
San Francisco	$133,887
Los Angeles	$117,726
San Jose	$108,506
Washington, D.C.	$102,589

Annual Cost (dollars)

Source: Runzheimer

62. The chart shows the average annual premiums of the cities with the most expensive auto insurance. Because insurance is an expense, it can be written as a negative number. What is the monthly cost of insurance in New York City? Use negative numbers and round to the nearest cent.

−$275.25

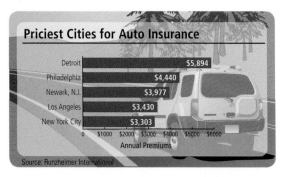

Priciest Cities for Auto Insurance

Detroit	$5,894
Philadelphia	$4,440
Newark, N.J.	$3,977
Los Angeles	$3,430
New York City	$3,303

0   $1000 $2000 $3000 $4000 $5000 $6000
Annual Premiums

Source: Runzheimer International

63. Temperature Line Graph The table below gives the low temperature for each day of one week in White Bear Lake, Minnesota. Use the diagram in the figure to draw a line graph of the information in the table.

LOW TEMPERATURES IN WHITE BEAR LAKE, MINNESOTA	
Day	Temperature
Monday	10 °F
Tuesday	8 °F
Wednesday	−5 °F
Thursday	−3 °F
Friday	−8 °F
Saturday	5 °F
Sunday	7 °F

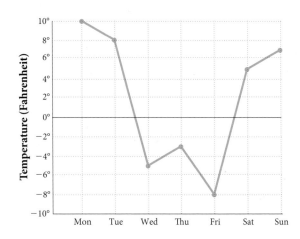

64. Temperature Line Graph The table below gives the low temperature for each day of one week in Fairbanks, Alaska. Use the diagram in the figure to draw a line graph of the information in the table.

LOW TEMPERATURES IN FAIRBANKS, ALASKA	
Day	Temperature
Monday	−26 °F
Tuesday	−5 °F
Wednesday	9 °F
Thursday	12 °F
Friday	3 °F
Saturday	−15 °F
Sunday	−20 °F

■ Getting Ready for the Next Section

The problems below review some of the properties of addition and multiplication we covered in Chapter 1.

Rewrite each expression using the commutative property of addition or multiplication.

65. $3 + x$

$x + 3$

66. $4y$

$y \cdot 4$

Rewrite each expression using the associative property of addition or multiplication.

67. $5 + (7 + a)$

$(5 + 7) + a$

68. $(x + 4) + 6$

$x + (4 + 6)$

69. $3(4y)$

$(3 \cdot 4)y$

70. $(3y)8$

$3(y \cdot 8)$

Apply the distributive property to each expression.

71. $5(3 + 7)$

$5(3) + 5(7)$

72. $8(4 + 2)$

$8(4) + 8(2)$

Simplify.

73. 6^2

36

74. 12^2

144

75. 4^3

64

76. 5^2

25

77. $2(100) + 2(75)$

350

78. $2(100) + 2(53)$

306

79. $100(75)$

7,500

80. $100(53)$

5,300

■ Maintaining Your Skills

The problems below review addition, subtraction, multiplication, and division of positive and negative numbers, as covered in this chapter.

Perform the indicated operations.

81. $8 + (-4)$

4

82. $-8 + 4$

-4

83. $-8 + (-4)$

-12

84. $-8 - 4$

-12

85. $8 - (-4)$

12

86. $-8 - (-4)$

-4

87. $8(-4)$

-32

88. $-8(4)$

-32

89. $-8(-4)$

32

90. $8 \div (-4)$

-2

91. $-8 \div 4$

-2

92. $-8 \div (-4)$

2

■ Extending the Concepts

Find the next term in each sequence below.

93. $32, -16, 8, \ldots$

-4

94. $243, -81, 27, \ldots$

-9

95. $-32, 16, -8, \ldots$

4

96. $-243, 81, -27, \ldots$

9

Simplify each of the following expressions.

97. $\dfrac{6 - 3(2 - 11)}{6 - 3(2 + 11)}$

-1

98. $\dfrac{8 + 4(3 - 5)}{8 - 4(3 + 5)}$

0

99. $\dfrac{6 - (3 - 4) - 3}{1 - 2 - 3}$

-1

100. $\dfrac{7 - (3 - 6) - 4}{-1 - 2 - 3}$

-1

Simplifying Algebraic Expressions

Introduction . . .

The woodcut shown here depicts Queen Dido of Carthage around 900 B.C., having an ox hide cut into small strips that will be tied together to make a long rope. The rope will be used to enclose her territory. The question is: what shape will enclose the largest territory? This has become known as the Queen Dido problem.

Objectives

A Simplify expressions by using the associative property.

B Apply the distributive property to expressions containing numbers and variables.

C Use the distributive property to combine similar terms.

D Use the formulas for area and perimeter of squares and rectangles.

To translate the problem into something we are more familiar with, suppose we have 24 yards of fencing that we are to use to build a rectangular dog run. If we want the dog run to have the largest area possible then we want the rectangle, with perimeter 24 yards, that encloses the largest area. The diagram below shows six dog runs, each of which has a perimeter of 24 yards. Notice how the length decreases as the width increases.

Dog Runs with Perimeter = 24 yards

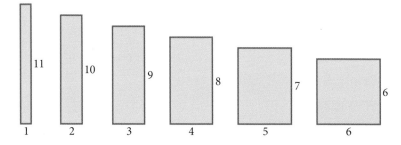

Since area is length times width, we can build a table and a line graph that show how the area changes as we change the width of the dog run.

AREA ENCLOSED BY RECTANGLE OF PERIMETER 24 YARDS	
Width (Yards)	Area (Square Yards)
1	11
2	20
3	27
4	32
5	35
6	36

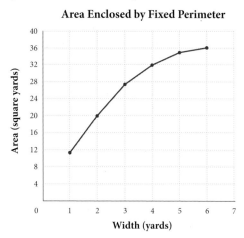

Area Enclosed by Fixed Perimeter

In this section we want to simplify expressions containing variables—that is, algebraic expressions. An algebraic expression is a combination of constants and variables joined by arithmetic operations such as addition, subtraction, multiplication and division.

A Using the Associative Property

To begin let's review how we use the associative properties for addition and multiplication to simplify expressions.

Consider the expression $4(5x)$. We can apply the associative property of multiplication to this expression to change the grouping so that the 4 and the 5 are grouped together, instead of the 5 and the x. Here's how it looks:

$$4(5x) = (4 \cdot 5)x \qquad \text{Associative property}$$
$$= 20x \qquad \text{Multiplication: } 4 \cdot 5 = 20$$

We have simplified the expression to $20x$, which in most cases in algebra will be easier to work with than the original expression.

Here are some more examples.

EXAMPLE 1
$$7(3a) = (7 \cdot 3)a \qquad \text{Associative property}$$
$$= 21a \qquad \text{7 times 3 is 21}$$

EXAMPLE 2
$$-2(5x) = (-2 \cdot 5)x \qquad \text{Associative property}$$
$$= -10x \qquad \text{The product of } -2 \text{ and 5 is } -10$$

EXAMPLE 3
$$3(-4y) = [3(-4)]y \qquad \text{Associative property}$$
$$= -12y \qquad \text{3 times } -4 \text{ is } -12$$

We can use the associative property of addition to simplify expressions also.

EXAMPLE 4
$$3 + (8 + x) = (3 + 8) + x \qquad \text{Associative property}$$
$$= 11 + x \qquad \text{The sum of 3 and 8 is 11}$$

EXAMPLE 5
$$(2x + 5) + 10 = 2x + (5 + 10) \qquad \text{Associative property}$$
$$= 2x + 15 \qquad \text{Addition}$$

B Using the Distributive Property

In Chapter 1 we introduced the distributive property. In symbols it looks like this:
$$a(b + c) = ab + ac$$

Because subtraction is defined as addition of the opposite, the distributive property holds for subtraction as well as addition. That is,
$$a(b - c) = ab - ac$$

We say that multiplication distributes over addition and subtraction. Here are some examples that review how the distributive property is applied to expressions that contain variables.

EXAMPLE 6
$$4(x + 5) = 4(x) + 4(5) \qquad \text{Distributive property}$$
$$= 4x + 20 \qquad \text{Multiplication}$$

PRACTICE PROBLEMS

Multiply.
1. $5(7a)$

2. $-3(9x)$

3. $5(-8y)$

Simplify.
4. $6 + (9 + x)$

5. $(3x + 7) + 4$

Apply the distributive property.
6. $6(x + 4)$

Answers
1. $35a$ 2. $-27x$ 3. $-40y$
4. $15 + x$ 5. $3x + 11$ 6. $6x + 24$

EXAMPLE 7
$$2(a - 3) = 2(a) - 2(3) \quad \text{Distributive property}$$
$$= 2a - 6 \quad \text{Multiplication}$$

In Examples 1–3 we simplified expressions such as 4(5x) by using the associative property. Here are some examples that use a combination of the associative property and the distributive property.

EXAMPLE 8
$$4(5x + 3) = 4(5x) + 4(3) \quad \text{Distributive property}$$
$$= (4 \cdot 5)x + 4(3) \quad \text{Associative property}$$
$$= 20x + 12 \quad \text{Multiplication}$$

EXAMPLE 9
$$7(3a - 6) = 7(3a) - 7(6) \quad \text{Distributive property}$$
$$= 21a - 42 \quad \text{Associative property and multiplication}$$

EXAMPLE 10
$$5(2x + 3y) = 5(2x) + 5(3y) \quad \text{Distributive property}$$
$$= 10x + 15y \quad \text{Associative property and multiplication}$$

C Similar Terms

We can also use the distributive property to simplify expressions like $4x + 3x$. Because multiplication is a commutative operation, we can also rewrite the distributive property like this:

$$b \cdot a + c \cdot a = (b + c)a$$

Applying the distributive property in this form to the expression $4x + 3x$, we have

$$4x + 3x = (4 + 3)x \quad \text{Distributive property}$$
$$= 7x \quad \text{Addition}$$

Expressions like $4x$ and $3x$ are called *similar terms* because the variable parts are the same. Some other examples of similar terms are $5y$ and $-6y$ and the terms $7a$, $-13a$, and $\frac{3}{4}a$. To simplify an algebraic expression (an expression that involves both numbers and variables), we combine similar terms by applying the distributive property. Table 1 shows several pairs of similar terms and how they can be combined using the distributive property.

TABLE 1

Original Expression		Apply Distributive Property		Simplified Expression
$4x + 3x$	=	$(4 + 3)x$	=	$7x$
$7a + a$	=	$(7 + 1)a$	=	$8a$
$-5x + 7x$	=	$(-5 + 7)x$	=	$2x$
$8y - y$	=	$(8 - 1)y$	=	$7y$
$-4a - 2a$	=	$(-4 - 2)a$	=	$-6a$
$3x - 7x$	=	$(3 - 7)x$	=	$-4x$

As you can see from the table, the distributive property can be applied to any combination of positive and negative terms so long as they are similar terms.

7. $7(a - 5)$

8. $6(4x + 5)$

9. $3(8a - 4)$

10. $8(3x + 4y)$

Instructor Note
In Table 1, students have the most trouble with the problems on lines 2 and 4. When I work these problems in class, I always put in an extra step and write $7a + a$ as $7a + 1a$.

Answers
7. $7a - 35$ **8.** $24x + 30$
9. $24a - 12$ **10.** $24x + 32y$

D Algebraic Expressions Representing Area and Perimeter

Below are a square with a side of length s and a rectangle with a length of l and a width of w. The table that follows the figures gives the formulas for the area and perimeter of each.

Square

Rectangle

w

s

ℓ

	Square	Rectangle
Area A	s^2	ℓw
Perimeter P	$4s$	$2\ell + 2w$

11. Find the area and perimeter of a square if its side is 12 feet long.

EXAMPLE 11 Find the area and perimeter of a square with a side 6 inches long.

SOLUTION Substituting 6 for s in the formulas for area and perimeter of a square, we have

$$\text{Area} = A = s^2 = 6^2 = 36 \text{ square inches}$$

$$\text{Perimeter} = P = 4s = 4(6) = 24 \text{ inches}$$

12. A football field is 100 yards long and approximately 53 yards wide. Find the area and perimeter.

EXAMPLE 12 A soccer field is 100 yards long and 75 yards wide. Find the area and perimeter.

100 yd

75 yd

SOLUTION Substituting 100 for l and 75 for w in the formulas for area and perimeter of a rectangle, we have

$$\text{Area} = A = lw = 100(75) = 7{,}500 \text{ square yards}$$

$$\text{Perimeter} = P = 2l + 2w = 2(100) + 2(75) = 200 + 150 = 350 \text{ yards}$$

Getting Ready for Class

After reading through the preceding section, respond in your own words and in complete sentences.

1. Without actually multiplying, how do you apply the associative property to the expression $4(5x)$?

2. What are similar terms?

3. Explain why $2a - a$ is a, rather than 1.

4. Can two rectangles with the same perimeter have different areas? Explain your answer.

Answers
11. $A = 144$ sq ft, $P = 48$ ft
12. $A = 5{,}300$ sq yd, $P = 306$ yd

Problem Set 9.6

A Apply the associative property to each expression, and then simplify the result. [Examples 1–5]

▶ **1.** $5(4a)$
20a

2. $8(9a)$
72a

3. $6(8a)$
48a

4. $3(2a)$
6a

5. $-6(3x)$
−18x

▶ **6.** $-2(7x)$
−14x

7. $-3(9x)$
−27x

▶ **8.** $-4(6x)$
−24x

9. $5(-2y)$
−10y

▶ **10.** $3(-8y)$
−24y

11. $6(-10y)$
−60y

12. $5(-5y)$
−25y

▶ **13.** $2 + (3 + x)$
5 + x

14. $9 + (6 + x)$
15 + x

15. $5 + (8 + x)$
13 + x

16. $3 + (9 + x)$
12 + x

▶ **17.** $4 + (6 + y)$
10 + y

18. $2 + (8 + y)$
10 + y

▶ **19.** $7 + (1 + y)$
8 + y

20. $4 + (1 + y)$
5 + y

▶ **21.** $(5x + 2) + 4$
5x + 6

22. $(8x + 3) + 10$
8x + 13

23. $(6y + 4) + 3$
6y + 7

▶ **24.** $(3y + 7) + 8$
3y + 15

25. $(12a + 2) + 19$
12a + 21

▶ **26.** $(6a + 3) + 14$
6a + 17

27. $(7x + 8) + 20$
7x + 28

▶ **28.** $(14x + 3) + 15$
14x + 18

B Apply the distributive property to each expression, and then simplify. [Examples 6–10]

29. $7(x + 5)$
7x + 35

▶ **30.** $8(x + 3)$
8x + 24

▶ **31.** $6(a - 7)$
6a − 42

32. $4(a - 9)$
4a − 36

▶ **33.** $2(x - y)$
2x − 2y

34. $5(x - a)$
5x − 5a

35. $4(5 + x)$
20 + 4x

▶ **36.** $8(3 + x)$
24 + 8x

▶ **37.** $3(2x + 5)$
6x + 15

38. $8(5x + 4)$
40x + 32

39. $6(3a + 1)$
18a + 6

40. $4(8a + 3)$
32a + 12

▶ **41.** $2(6x - 3y)$
12x − 6y

42. $7(5x - y)$
35x − 7y

▶ **43.** $5(7 - 4y)$
35 − 20y

▶ **44.** $8(6 - 3y)$
48 − 24y

C Use the distributive property to combine similar terms. [Table 1]

45. $3x + 5x$
8x

46. $7x + 8x$
15x

47. $3a + a$
4a

48. $8a + a$
9a

▶ **49.** $-2x + 6x$
4x

50. $-3x + 9x$
6x

51. $6y - y$
5y

▶ **52.** $3y - y$
2y

53. $-8a - 2a$
−10a

▶ **54.** $-7a - 5a$
−12a

55. $4x - 9x$
−5x

▶ **56.** $5x - 11x$
−6x

■ Applying the Concepts

57. A farmer is replacing several turbines on his windmills. He plans to replace x turbines, and he is going to get $300 off each turbine he buys. Also, he'll get a $250 rebate on his entire purchase. Write an expression that describes this situation and then simplify.

$x(\$3{,}300 - \$300) - \$250 = \$3{,}000x - \$250$

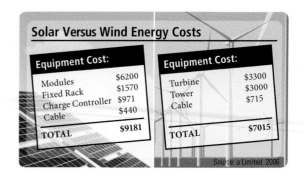

Solar Versus Wind Energy Costs

Equipment Cost:	
Modules	$6200
Fixed Rack	$1570
Charge Controller	$971
Cable	$440
TOTAL	**$9181**

Equipment Cost:	
Turbine	$3300
Tower	$3000
Cable	$715
TOTAL	**$7015**

Source: a Limited. 2006

58. A homeowner is replacing 4 solar modules. She is going to receive a discount of some amount x off each module and a $350 mail-in rebate. Write an expression that describes this situation and then simplify.

$4(\$6{,}200 - x) - \$350 = \$24{,}450 - 4x$

D **Area and Perimeter** Find the area and perimeter of each square if the length of each side is as given below. [Example 11]

59. $s = 6$ feet
$A = 36\ \text{ft}^2, P = 24\ \text{ft}$

60. $s = 14$ yards
$A = 196\ \text{yd}^2, P = 56\ \text{yd}$

61. $s = 9$ inches
$A = 81\ \text{in}^2, P = 36\ \text{in.}$

▶ **62.** $s = 15$ meters
$A = 225\ \text{m}^2, P = 60\ \text{m}$

D **Area and Perimeter** Find the area and perimeter for a rectangle if the length and width are as given below. [Example 12]

63. $l = 20$ inches, $w = 10$ inches
$A = 200\ \text{in}^2, P = 60\ \text{in.}$

64. $l = 40$ yards, $w = 20$ yards
$A = 800\ \text{yd}^2, P = 120\ \text{yd}$

65. $l = 25$ feet, $w = 12$ feet
$A = 300\ \text{ft}^2, P = 74\ \text{ft}$

▶ **66.** $l = 210$ meters, $w = 120$ meters
$A = 25{,}200\ m^2, P = 660\ \text{m}$

Temperature Scales In the metric system, the scale we use to measure temperature is the Celsius scale. On this scale water boils at 100 degrees and freezes at 0 degrees. When we write 100 degrees measured on the Celsius scale, we use the notation 100°C, which is read "100 degrees Celsius." If we know the temperature in degrees Fahrenheit, we can convert to degrees Celsius by using the formula

$$C = \frac{5(F - 32)}{9}$$

where F is the temperature in degrees Fahrenheit. Use this formula to find the temperature in degrees Celsius for each of the following Fahrenheit temperatures.

67. 68°F
20°C

68. 59°F
15°C

▶ **69.** 41°F
5°C

▶ **70.** 23°F
−5°C

71. 14°F
−10°C

72. 32°F
0°C

Chapter 9 Summary

◼ Absolute Value [9.1]

The absolute value of a number is its distance from 0 on the number line. It is the numerical part of a number. The absolute value of a number is never negative.

EXAMPLES

1. $|3| = 3$ and $|-3| = 3$

◼ Opposites [9.1]

Two numbers are called opposites if they are the same distance from 0 on the number line but in opposite directions from 0. The opposite of a positive number is a negative number, and the opposite of a negative number is a positive number.

2. $-(5) = -5$ and $-(-5) = 5$

◼ Addition of Positive and Negative Numbers [9.2]

1. To add two numbers with *the same sign:* Simply add absolute values and use the common sign. If both numbers are positive, the answer is positive. If both numbers are negative, the answer is negative.
2. To add two numbers with *different signs:* Subtract the smaller absolute value from the larger absolute value. The answer has the same sign as the number with the larger absolute value.

3. $3 + 5 = 8$
 $-3 + (-5) = -8$

 $5 + (-3) = 2$
 $-5 + 3 = -2$

◼ Subtraction [9.3]

Subtracting a number is equivalent to adding its opposite. If a and b represent numbers, then subtraction is defined in terms of addition as follows:

$$\underset{\underset{\text{Subtraction}}{\uparrow}}{a} - b = a + \underset{\underset{\text{Addition of the opposite}}{\uparrow}}{(-b)}$$

4. $3 - 5 = 3 + (-5) = -2$
 $-3 - 5 = -3 + (-5) = -8$
 $3 - (-5) = 3 + 5 = 8$
 $-3 - (-5) = -3 + 5 = 2$

◼ Multiplication with Positive and Negative Numbers [9.4]

To multiply two numbers, multiply their absolute values.
1. The answer is *positive* if both numbers have the same sign.
2. The answer is *negative* if the numbers have different signs.

5. $3(5) = 15$
 $3(-5) = -15$
 $-3(5) = -15$
 $-3(-5) = 15$

◼ Division [9.5]

The rule for assigning the correct sign to the answer in a division problem is the same as the rule for multiplication. That is, like signs give a positive answer, and unlike signs give a negative answer.

6. $\dfrac{12}{4} = 3$

 $\dfrac{-12}{4} = -3$

 $\dfrac{12}{-4} = -3$

 $\dfrac{-12}{-4} = 3$

Simplifying Expressions [9.6] ⬛

7. Simplify.
  a. $-2(5x) = (-2 \cdot 5)x = -10x$
  b. $4(2a - 8) = 4(2a) - 4(8)$
       $= 8a - 32$

We simplify algebraic expressions by applying the commutative, associative, and distributive properties.

Combining Similar Terms [9.6] ⬛

8. Combine similar terms.
  a. $5x + 7x = (5 + 7)x = 12x$
  b. $2y - 8y = (2 - 8)y = -6y$

We combine similar terms by applying the distributive property.

Give the opposite of each number. [9.1]

1. 17
  −17

2. −32
  32

3. −4.6
  4.6

4. $\dfrac{3}{5}$

  $-\dfrac{3}{5}$

For each pair of numbers, name the smaller number. [9.1]

5. 6; −6
  −6

6. −8; −3
  −8

7. $|-3|$; 2
  2

8. $|-4|$; $|6|$
  $|-4|$

Simplify each expression. [9.1]

9. −(−4)
  4

10. −$|-4|$
  −4

11. $|-6|$
  6

12. $|19|$
  19

Perform the indicated operations. [9.2, 9.3, 9.4, 9.5]

13. 5 + (−7)
  −2

14. −3 + 8
  5

15. −345 + (−626)
  −971

16. −23 + 58
  35

17. 7 − 9 − 4 − 6
  −12

18. −7 − 5 − 2 − 3
  −17

19. 4 − (−3)
  7

20. 30 − 42
  −12

21. 5(−4)
  −20

22. −4(−3)
  12

23. (56)(−31)
  −1,736

24. (20)(−4)
  −80

25. $\dfrac{48}{-16}$
  −3

26. $\dfrac{-20}{5}$
  −4

27. $\dfrac{-14}{-7}$
  2

28. $\dfrac{-25}{5}$
  −5

Simplify the following expressions as much as possible. [9.2, 9.3, 9.4, 9.5]

29. $(-6)^2$
  36

30. $\left(-\dfrac{3}{4}\right)^2$

  $\dfrac{9}{16}$

31. $(-2)^3$
  −8

32. $(-0.2)^4$
  0.0016

33. 7 + 4(6 − 9)
  −5

34. (−3)(−4) + 2(−5)
  2

35. (7 − 3)(7 − 9)
  −8

36. 3(−6) + 8(2 − 5)
  −42

37. $\dfrac{8-4}{-8+4}$
  −1

38. $\dfrac{-4+2(-5)}{6-4}$
  −7

39. $\dfrac{8(-2)+5(-4)}{12-3}$
  −4

40. $\dfrac{-2(5)+4(-3)}{10-8}$
  −11

41. Give the sum of -19 and -23. [9.2]
-42

42. Give the sum of -78 and -51. [9.2]
-129

43. Find the difference of -6 and 5. [9.3]
-11

44. Subtract -8 from -10. [9.3]
-2

45. What is the product of -9 and 3? [9.4]
-27

46. What is -3 times the sum of -9 and -4? [9.2, 9.4]
39

47. Divide the product of 8 and -4 by -16. [9.4, 9.5]
2

48. Give the quotient of -38 and 2. [9.5]
-19

Indicate whether each statement is *True* or *False*. [9.2, 9.3, 9.4, 9.5]

49. $\dfrac{-10}{-5} = -2$
False

50. $10 - (-5) = 15$
True

51. $2(-3) = -3 + (-3)$
True

52. $-6 - (-2) = -8$
False

53. $3 - 5 = 5 - 3$
False

54. Reaction Distance The table below shows how many feet your car will travel from the time you decide you want to stop to the time it takes you to hit the brake pedal. Use the template to construct a line graph of the information in the table. [9.1]

REACTION DISTANCES	
Speed (mi/hr)	Distance (ft)
0	0
10	11
20	22
30	33
40	44
50	55
60	66
70	77
80	88

55. Gambling A gambler wins $58 Saturday night and then loses $86 on Sunday. Use positive and negative numbers to describe this situation. Then give the gambler's net loss or gain as a positive or negative number. [9.2]
$58 + (-$86) = -28

56. Name two numbers that are 7 units from -8 on the number line. [9.1]
-1 and -15

57. Temperature On Wednesday, the temperature reaches a high of 17° above 0 and a low of 7° below 0. What is the difference between the high and low temperatures for Wednesday? [9.3]
24°

58. If the difference between two numbers is -3, and one of the numbers is 5, what is the other number? [9.3]
8 or 2

Use the associative properties to simplify each expression. [9.6]

59. $(3x + 4) + 8$
$3x + 12$

60. $8(3x)$
$24x$

61. $-3(7a)$
$-21a$

62. $6(-5y)$
$-30y$

Apply the distributive property and then simplify if possible. [9.6]

63. $4(x + 3)$
$4x + 12$

64. $2(x - 5)$
$2x - 10$

65. $7(3y - 8)$
$21y - 56$

66. $3(2a + 5b)$
$6a + 15b$

Combine similar terms. [9.6]

67. $7x - 4x$
$3x$

68. $-8a + 10a$
$2a$

69. $5y - y$
$4y$

70. $12x + 4x$
$16x$

Simplify.

1. $\frac{3}{5} + \frac{2}{7}$ $\frac{31}{35}$

2. $\frac{7}{6} - \frac{5}{6}$ $\frac{1}{3}$

3. $613 - 297$ 316

4. $\left(3\frac{1}{2} + \frac{1}{3}\right)\left(4\frac{1}{6} - \frac{2}{3}\right)$ $13\frac{5}{12}$

5. $\left(\frac{2}{3}\right)^4$ $\frac{16}{81}$

6. $53(807)$ $42,771$

7. $\frac{5}{8} \div (-10)$ $-\frac{1}{16}$

8. $6 - 3^2 + (6 - 9)$ -6

9. Round 37.6451 to the nearest hundredth. 37.65

10. Change $4\frac{7}{8}$ to an improper fraction. $\frac{39}{8}$

11. Write the number 38,609 in words.
Thirty-eight thousand, six hundred nine

12. Identify the property or properties used in the following: $5(x + 9) = 5(x) + 5(9)$
Distributive property of multiplication

Simplify.

13. $6(3)^3 - 9(2)^2$ 126

14. $\sqrt{\frac{36}{49}}$ $\frac{6}{7}$

15. $\frac{3}{8} - \frac{1}{4} + \frac{5}{6}$ $\frac{23}{24}$

16. $(0.2)^3 + (0.3)^2$ 0.098

17. $\frac{9 - 5}{-9 + 5}$ -1

18. $-(-6)$ 6

Write each ratio as a fraction in lowest terms.

19. 24 seconds to 1 minute $\frac{2}{5}$

20. $\frac{2}{3}$ to $\frac{3}{4}$ $\frac{8}{9}$

21. Change $\frac{49}{6}$ to a mixed number. $8\frac{1}{6}$

22. Write $4\frac{7}{8}$ as a decimal. 4.875

23. Change $\frac{3}{8}$ to a percent. 37.5%

24. Change 76% to a fraction. $\frac{19}{25}$

25. What is 2.5% of 40? 1

26. 17 is what percent of 42.5? 40%

Make the following conversions.

27. 350 m to kilometers 0.35 km

28. 14 gal to liters 53.06 L

29. Write $\frac{14}{25}$ as a decimal. 0.56

30. 10 is 50% of what number? 20

31. Reduce $\frac{99}{36}$. $\frac{11}{4}$

32. Sale Price A dress that normally sells for $129 is on sale for 20% off the normal price. What is the sale price of the dress?
$103.20

33. Ratio If the ratio of men to women in a self-defense class is 3 to 4, and there are 15 men in the class, how many women are in the class?
20 women

34. Surfboard Length A surfing company decides that a surfboard would be more efficient if its length were reduced by $3\frac{5}{8}$ inches. If the original length was 7 feet $\frac{3}{16}$ inches, what will be the new length of the board (in inches)?
$80\frac{9}{16}$ in.

35. Average Distance A bicyclist on a cross-country trip travels 72 miles the first day, 113 miles the second day, 108 miles the third day, and 95 miles the fourth day. What is her average distance traveled during the four days?
97 mi.

36. Area and Perimeter Find the area and perimeter of the triangle below.

$9\frac{5}{6}$ ft $7\frac{1}{3}$ ft   6 ft   11 ft

Area = 33 ft² Perimeter = $28\frac{1}{6}$ ft

37. Cost of Chocolate If white chocolate sells for $4.32 per pound, how much will 2.5 pounds cost?
$10.80

38. Number Line The distance between two numbers on the number line is 9. If one of the numbers is −4, what are the two possibilities for the other number?
−13 and 5

Use the illustration to answer Problems 39 and 40.

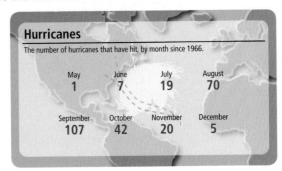

Hurricanes
The number of hurricanes that have hit, by month since 1966.

May	June	July	August
1	7	19	70

September	October	November	December
107	42	20	5

39. How many more hurricanes were there in September than in October?   65 more

40. What is the ratio of hurricanes in August to hurricanes in November? $\frac{7}{2}$

Give the opposite of each number.

1. 14 -14

2. $-\dfrac{2}{3}$ $\frac{2}{3}$

Place an inequality symbol ($<$ or $>$) between each pair of numbers so that the resulting statement is true.

3. $-1 > -4$

4. $|-4| > |2|$

Simplify each expression.

5. $-(-7)$ 7

6. $-|-2|$ -2

Perform the indicated operations.

7. $8 + (-17)$ -9

8. $-4.2 - 1.7$ -5.9

9. $-\dfrac{2}{3} + \left(-\dfrac{4}{5}\right)$ $-\frac{22}{15}$

10. $-65 - (-29)$ -36

11. $(-6)(-7)$ 42

12. $-\dfrac{1}{3}(-18)$ 6

13. $\dfrac{-80}{16}$ -5

14. $\dfrac{-35}{-7}$ 5

15. $-4.3 + 0.7$ -3.6

16. $-\dfrac{4}{9} \div \dfrac{16}{21}$ $-\frac{7}{12}$

17. $-\dfrac{7}{3}(6)$ -14

18. $-\dfrac{42}{6}$ -7

19. $\dfrac{3}{5} - \dfrac{9}{10}$ $-\frac{3}{10}$

20. $\left(-3\dfrac{1}{16}\right)\left(-\dfrac{8}{21}\right)$ $\frac{7}{6}$

Simplify the following expressions as much as possible.

21. $(-3)^2$ 9

22. $(-2)^3$ -8

23. $(-7)(3) + (-2)(-5)$ -11

24. $(8 - 5)(6 - 11)$ -15

25. $\dfrac{-5 + 3(-3)}{5 - 7}$ 7

26. $\dfrac{-3(2) + 5(-2)}{7 - 3}$ -4

27. $(-4)^3 - (6 + 4)$ -74

28. $(-3)(8) - (-7)(-3)$ -45

29. $3 - 2(5 - 3^2)$ 11

30. $\dfrac{5}{3}(-6) - 7(-2)$ 4

31. $\dfrac{-7 + 3(4)}{16 + 2(-3)}$ $\frac{1}{2}$

32. $3(5 - 9) + 4^2$ 4

33. $(-5)^2 - 3(5 - 3)$ 19

34. $\dfrac{8(-2) - 6(7 - 3)}{2(5 + 3)}$ $-\frac{5}{2}$

35. Give the sum of -15 and -46.
-61

36. Subtract -5 from -12.
-7

37. What is the product of -8 and -3?
24

38. Give the quotient of 45 and -9.
-5

39. Two times the sum of 6 and -13.
-14

40. Three times the difference of 5 and 9 is increased by 7.
-5

41. **Gambling** A gambler loses $100 Saturday night and wins $65 on Sunday. Give the gambler's net loss or gain as a negative or positive number.
$-\$35$

42. **Temperature** On Friday, the temperature reaches a high of 21° above 0 and a low of 4° below 0. What is the difference between the high and low temperatures for Friday?
25°

43. **National Parks** Use negative numbers to describe the difference in the number of visits from 1999 to 2003.

National Park Visitors

Number of visitors in National Parks in millions

Source: nps.gov

-21 million visitors

Chapter 9 Projects

INTRODUCTION TO ALGEBRA

Random Motion

Number of People 3

Time Needed 15 minutes

Equipment Coins, dice, pencil, and paper

Background Microscopic atoms and molecules move randomly. We use random movement models to help us understand their motion. Random motion also helps us understand things like the stock market and computer science.

In a random walk, an ant starts at a lamppost and takes steps of equal length along the street. We can think of the lamppost as the origin. The ant either takes a step in the negative or positive direction. Mathematicians have studied questions such as where the ant is likely to end up after taking a certain number of steps.

Stage	Coin	Die	Position of Ant
0	—	—	0
1			
2			
3			
4			
5			
6			
7			
8			
9			
10			

Procedure You will use a coin and die to simulate random motion. The ant will start at 0 on the number line. Roll the die and flip the coin. The ant will move the number of steps shown on the die. If the coin comes up heads, the ant moves in the positive direction. If the coin comes up tails, the ant moves in the negative direction. Repeat this process 10 times. Start each stage from the ending position of the previous stage. For example, if the ant ends up at −3 after Stage 1, then in Stage 2 the ant starts at −3. Record your results in the table.

RESEARCH PROJECT

David Harold Blackwell

At age 22, David Blackwell earned his doctorate, becoming the seventh African American to earn a Ph.D. in mathematics. In high school, Blackwell did not care for algebra and trigonometry. When he took a course in analysis, he really became interested in math. Although Blackwell faced a good deal of racism during his career, he became a successful teacher, author, and mathematician. Research the life and work of Dr. Blackwell, and then present your results in an essay.

Courtesy of David Harold Blackwell

Solving Equations

Introduction

Central Park in New York City was the first landscaped public park in the United States. More than 25 million people visit the park each year. Central Park is $\frac{1}{2}$ mile wide and covers an area of 1.4 square miles. A person who jogs around the perimeter of the park will cover approximately 6.6 miles. Because the park can be modeled with a rectangle, we can use these numbers to find the length of the park. In fact, solving either of the two equations below will give us the length.

$$\frac{1}{2}x = 1.4 \qquad 2x + 2 \cdot \frac{1}{2} = 6.6$$

In this chapter, we will learn how to take the numbers and relationships given in the paragraph above and translate them into equations like the ones above. Before we do that, we will learn how to solve these equations, and many others as well.

Comparing Parks

Park	Acres
Central Park (New York)	843 acres
Stanley Park (Vancouver)	1,000 acres
Richmond Park (London)	2,360 acres
Griffith Park (Los Angeles)	4,210 acres

The illustration here shows the area of Central Park compared to other prominent parks in large cities.

The pretest below contains problems that are representative of the problems you will find in the chapter.

Simplify.

1. $4a - 1 - 5a + 8$
   $-a + 7$

2. $2(5y - 6) + 4y$
   $14y - 12$

Solve each equation.

3. $a + 4 = -2$
   -6

4. $5y + 9 - 4y = -7 + 11$
   -5

5. $\frac{1}{5}x = 3$ 15

6. $-2x + 9 = 11$
   -1

7. $2a + 1 = 5(a - 2) - 1$
   4

8. $\frac{x}{3} - \frac{x}{4} = 5$ 60

9. Find the value of $3x - 4$ when $x = -2$. -10

10. Is $x = 5$ a solution to the equation $6x - 28 = 1$?   No

11. The sum of a number and 6 is -17. Find the number.
   -23

12. If four times a number is decreased by 7, the result is 25. Find the number.   8

The problems below review material covered previously that you need to know in order to be successful in Chapter 10. If you have any difficulty with the problems here, you need to go back and review before going on to Chapter 10.

Simplify.

1. $-2 + 7$ 5

2. $180 - 45$ 135

3. $-2 + (-4)$ -6

4. $\frac{5}{8} + \frac{3}{4}$ $\frac{11}{8}$

5. $(-4)(5)$ -20

6. $\frac{6}{-3}$ -2

7. $\frac{3}{2}(12)$ 18

8. $\left(-\frac{5}{4}\right)\left(-\frac{4}{5}\right)$ 1

9. $\left(-\frac{5}{4}\right)\left(\frac{8}{15}\right)$ $-\frac{2}{3}$

10. $-4(-1) + 9$ 13

11. $\frac{1}{3}(15) + 2$ 7

12. $\frac{5}{9}(95 - 32)$ 35

13. $3x + 7x$ $10x$

14. $-4(3x)$ $-12x$

15. $4(x - 5)$ $4x - 20$

16. $2\left(\frac{1}{2}x\right)$ x

17. Write in symbols: the sum of x and 2. $x + 2$

18. Find the perimeter. $P = 8x$

$3x$

We recall that the distributive property from Section 1.5 can be used to find the area of a rectangle using two different methods.

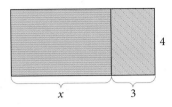

Area = 4(x) + 4(3)
     = 4x + 12

Area = 4(x + 3)
     = 4x + 12

Since the areas are equal, the equation $4(x + 3) = 4(x) + 4(3)$ is a true statement.

A The Distributive Property

 EXAMPLE 1 Apply the distributive property to the expression:

$$5(x + 3)$$

SOLUTION Distributing the 5 over x and 3, we have

$5(x + 3) = 5(x) + 5(3)$	Distributive property
$= 5x + 15$	Multiplication

Remember, $5x$ means "5 times x."

The distributive property can be applied to more complicated expressions involving negative numbers.

EXAMPLE 2 Multiply: $-4(3x + 5)$

SOLUTION Multiplying both the $3x$ and the 5 by -4, we have

$-4(3x + 5) = -4(3x) + (-4)5$	Distributive property
$= -12x + (-20)$	Multiplication
$= -12x - 20$	Definition of subtraction

Notice, first of all, that when we apply the distributive property here, we multiply through by -4. It is important to include the sign with the number when we use the distributive property. Second, when we multiply -4 and $3x$, the result is $-12x$ because

$-4(3x) = (-4 \cdot 3)x$	Associative property
$= -12x$	Multiplication

PRACTICE PROBLEMS

1. Apply the distributive property to the expression $6(x + 4)$.

2. Multiply: $-3(2x + 4)$

Instructor Note
A number of the problems shown in the examples here have been solved previously in the text. Even so, I have included them here to give students a good start in this chapter.

Answers
1. $6x + 24$ **2.** $-6x - 12$

3. Multiply: $\frac{1}{2}(2x - 4)$

EXAMPLE 3 Multiply: $\frac{1}{3}(3x - 12)$

SOLUTION

$$\frac{1}{3}(3x - 12) = \frac{1}{3}(3x) - \frac{1}{3}(12) \quad \text{Distributive property}$$

$$= 1x - \frac{12}{3} \quad \text{Simplify}$$

$$= x - 4 \quad \text{Divide}$$

We can also use the distributive property to simplify expressions like $4x + 3x$. Because multiplication is a commutative operation, we can rewrite the distributive property like this:

$$b \cdot a + c \cdot a = (b + c)a$$

Applying the distributive property in this form to the expression $4x + 3x$, we have:

$$4x + 3x = (4 + 3)x \quad \text{Distributive property}$$
$$= 7x \quad \text{Addition}$$

B Similar Terms

Recall that expressions like $4x$ and $3x$ are called *similar terms* because the variable parts are the same. Some other examples of similar terms are $5y$ and $-6y$, and the terms $7a$, $-13a$, $\frac{3}{4}a$. To simplify an algebraic expression (an expression that involves both numbers and variables), we combine similar terms by applying the distributive property. Table 1 reviews how we combine similar terms using the distributive property.

Note We are using the word *term* in a different sense here than we did with fractions. (The terms of a fraction are the numerator and the denominator.)

TABLE 1

Original Expression		Apply Distribution Property		Simplified Expression
$4x + 3x$	=	$(4 + 3)x$	=	$7x$
$7a + a$	=	$(7 + 1)a$	=	$8a$
$-5x + 7x$	=	$(-5 + 7)x$	=	$2x$
$8y - y$	=	$(8 - 1)y$	=	$7y$
$-4a - 2a$	=	$(-4 - 2)a$	=	$-6a$
$3x - 7x$	=	$(3 - 7)x$	=	$-4x$

As you can see from the table, the distributive property can be applied to any combination of positive and negative terms so long as they are similar terms.

4. Simplify: $6x - 2 + 3x + 8$

EXAMPLE 4 Simplify: $5x - 2 + 3x + 7$

SOLUTION We begin by changing subtraction to addition of the opposite and applying the commutative property to rearrange the order of the terms. We want similar terms to be written next to each other.

$$5x - 2 + 3x + 7 = 5x + 3x + (-2) + 7 \quad \text{Commutative property}$$
$$= (5 + 3)x + (-2) + 7 \quad \text{Distributive property}$$
$$= 8x + 5 \quad \text{Addition}$$

Notice that we take the negative sign in front of the 2 with the 2 when we rearrange terms. How do we justify doing this?

Answers
3. $x - 2$ **4.** $9x + 6$

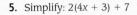

EXAMPLE 5 Simplify: $3(4x + 5) + 6$

SOLUTION We begin by distributing the 3 across the sum of $4x$ and 5. Then we combine similar terms.

$$3(4x + 5) + 6 = 12x + 15 + 6 \quad \text{Distributive property}$$
$$= 12x + 21 \quad \text{Add 15 and 6}$$

EXAMPLE 6 Simplify: $2(3x + 1) + 4(2x - 5)$

SOLUTION Again, we apply the distributive property first; then we combine similar terms. Here is the solution showing only the essential steps:

$$2(3x + 1) + 4(2x - 5) = 6x + 2 + 8x - 20 \quad \text{Distributive property}$$
$$= 14x - 18 \quad \text{Combine similar terms}$$

C The Value of an Algebraic Expression

An expression such as $3x + 5$ will take on different values depending on what x is. If we were to let x equal 2, the expression $3x + 5$ would become 11. On the other hand, if x is 10, the same expression has a value of 35:

When	$x = 2$	When	$x = 10$
the expression	$3x + 5$	the expression	$3x + 5$
becomes	$3(2) + 5$	becomes	$3(10) + 5$
	$= 6 + 5$		$= 30 + 5$
	$= 11$		$= 35$

EXAMPLES Find the value of each of the following expressions by replacing the variable with the given number.

Original Expression	Value of the Variable	Value of the Expression
7. $3x - 1$	$x = 2$	$3(2) - 1 = 6 - 1 = 5$
8. $2x - 3 + 4x$	$x = -1$	$2(-1) - 3 + 4(-1) = -2 - 3 + (-4) = -9$
9. $y^2 - 6y + 9$	$y = 4$	$4^2 - 6(4) + 9 = 16 - 24 + 9 = 1$

EXAMPLE 10 Find the area of a 30-W solar panel shown here with a length of 15 inches and a width of $10 + 3x$ inches.

SOLUTION Previously we worked with area, so we know that Area = (length) (width). Using the values for length and width, we have:

$$A = lw$$
$$A = 15(10 + 3x) \quad \text{length} = 15; \text{width} = 10 + 3x$$
$$= 150 + 45x \text{ in}^2 \quad \text{Distributive property}$$

15"

$10 + 3x$

5. Simplify: $2(4x + 3) + 7$

6. Simplify: $3(2x + 1) + 5(4x - 3)$

7. Find the value of $4x - 7$ when $x = 3$.

8. Find the value of $2x - 5 + 6x$ when $x = -2$.

9. Find the value of $y^2 - 10y + 25$ when $y = -2$.

10. Find the area of a 30-W solar panel with a length of 25 cm and a width of $8 + 2x$ cm.

Answers
5. $8x + 13$ **6.** $26x - 12$ **7.** 5
8. -21 **9.** 49 **10.** $200 + 50x$ cm^2

FACTS FROM GEOMETRY   Angles

An angle is formed by two rays with the same endpoint. The common end-point is called the *vertex* of the angle, and the rays are called the *sides* of the angle.

In Figure 1, angle θ (theta) is formed by the two rays *OA* and *OB*. The vertex of θ is *O*. Angle θ is also denoted as angle *AOB*, where the letter associated with the vertex is always the middle letter in the three letters used to denote the angle.

Degree Measure The angle formed by rotating a ray through one complete revolution about its endpoint (Figure 2) has a measure of 360 degrees, which we write as 360°.

FIGURE 1   FIGURE 2

One complete revolution = 360°

One degree of angle measure, written 1°, is $\frac{1}{360}$ of a complete rotation of a ray about its endpoint; there are 360° in one full rotation. (The number 360 was decided upon by early civilizations because it was believed that the Earth was at the center of the universe and the Sun would rotate once around the Earth every 360 days.) Similarly, 180° is half of a complete rotation, and 90° is a quarter of a full rotation. Angles that measure 90° are called *right angles*, and angles that measure 180° are called *straight angles*. If an angle measures between 0° and 90° it is called an *acute angle*, and an angle that measures between 90° and 180° is an *obtuse angle*. Figure 3 illustrates further.

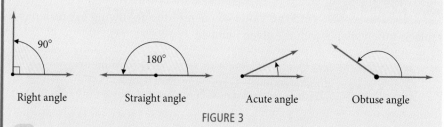

Right angle   Straight angle   Acute angle   Obtuse angle

FIGURE 3

D   **Complementary Angles and Supplementary Angles** If two angles add up to 90°, we call them *complementary angles*, and each is called the *complement* of the other. If two angles have a sum of 180°, we call them *supplementary angles*, and each is called the supplement of the other. Figure 4 illustrates the relationship between angles that are complementary and angles that are supplementary.

Complementary angles: α + β = 90°   Supplementary angles: α + β = 180°

FIGURE 4

EXAMPLE 11   Find *x* in each of the following diagrams.

a.

Complementary angles

b.

Supplementary angles

11. Find *x* in each of the following diagrams.

a.

Complementary angles

b.

Supplementary angles

SOLUTION   We use subtraction to find each angle.

a. Because the two angles are complementary, we can find *x* by subtracting 30° from 90°:

$$x = 90° - 30° = 60°$$

We say 30° and 60° are complementary angles. The complement of 30° is 60°.

b. The two angles in the diagram are supplementary. To find *x*, we subtract 45° from 180°:

$$x = 180° - 45° = 135°$$

We say 45° and 135° are supplementary angles. The supplement of 45° is 135°.

USING TECHNOLOGY

Calculators

When we think of technology, we think of computers and calculators. However, some simpler devices are also in the category of technology, because they help us do things that would be difficult to do without them. The protractor below can be used to draw and measure angles. In the diagram below, the protractor is being used to measure an angle of 120°. It can also be used to draw angles of any size.

If you have a protractor, use it to draw the following angles: 30°, 45°, 60°, 120°, 135°, and 150°. Then imagine how you would draw these angles without a protractor.

Answer
11. a. 45°   **b.** 120°

Getting Ready for Class

After reading through the preceding section, respond in your own words and in complete sentences.

1. What is the distributive property?

2. What property allows $5(x + 3)$ to be rewritten as $5x + 5(3)$?

3. What property allows $3x + 4x$ to be rewritten as $7x$?

4. True or false? The expression $3x$ means 3 multiplied by x.

Problem Set 10.1

A For review, use the distributive property to combine each of the following pairs of similar terms. [Examples 1–3]

▶ **1.** $2x + 8x$
$10x$

2. $3x + 7x$
$10x$

3. $-4y + 5y$
y

4. $-3y + 10y$
$7y$

5. $4a - a$
$3a$

6. $9a - a$
$8a$

7. $8(x + 2)$
$8x + 16$

8. $8(x - 2)$
$8x - 16$

9. $2(3a + 7)$
$6a + 14$

10. $5(3a + 2)$
$15a + 10$

▶ **11.** $\dfrac{1}{3}(3x + 6)$
$x + 2$

12. $\dfrac{1}{2}(2x + 4)$
$x + 2$

B Simplify the following expressions by combining similar terms. In some cases the order of the terms must be rearranged first by using the commutative property. [Examples 4–6]

▶ **13.** $4x + 2x + 3 + 8$
$6x + 11$

14. $7x + 5x + 2 + 9$
$12x + 11$

15. $7x - 5x + 6 - 4$
$2x + 2$

▶ **16.** $10x - 7x + 9 - 6$
$3x + 3$

17. $-2a + a + 7 + 5$
$-a + 12$

18. $-8a + 3a + 12 + 1$
$-5a + 13$

19. $6y - 2y - 5 + 1$
$4y - 4$

20. $4y - 3y - 7 + 2$
$y - 5$

▶ **21.** $4x + 2x - 8x + 4$
$-2x + 4$

22. $6x + 5x - 12x + 6$
$-x + 6$

23. $9x - x - 5 - 1$
$8x - 6$

24. $2x - x - 3 - 8$
$x - 11$

▶ **25.** $2a + 4 + 3a + 5$
$5a + 9$

26. $9a + 1 + 2a + 6$
$11a + 7$

27. $3x + 2 - 4x + 1$
$-x + 3$

28. $7x + 5 - 2x + 6$
$5x + 11$

▶ **29.** $12y + 3 + 5y$
$17y + 3$

30. $8y + 1 + 6y$
$14y + 1$

▶ **31.** $4a - 3 - 5a + 2a$
$a - 3$

32. $6a - 4 - 2a + 6a$
$10a - 4$

Apply the distributive property to each expression and then simplify.

33. $2(3x + 4) + 8$
  $6x + 16$

34. $2(5x + 1) + 10$
  $10x + 12$

35. $5(2x - 3) + 4$
  $10x - 11$

▶ **36.** $6(4x - 2) + 7$
  $24x - 5$

▶ **37.** $8(2y + 4) + 3y$
  $19y + 32$

38. $2(5y + 1) + 2y$
  $12y + 2$

▶ **39.** $6(4y - 3) + 6y$
  $30y - 18$

40. $5(2y - 6) + 4y$
  $14y - 30$

▶ **41.** $2(x + 3) + 4(x + 2)$
  $6x + 14$

42. $3(x + 1) + 2(x + 5)$
  $5x + 13$

43. $3(2a + 4) + 7(3a - 1)$
  $27a + 5$

▶ **44.** $7(2a + 2) + 4(5a - 1)$
  $34a + 10$

C Find the value of each of the following expressions when $x = 5$. [Examples 7–9]

45. $2x + 4$
  14

46. $3x + 2$
  17

▶ **47.** $7x - 8$
  27

48. $8x - 9$
  31

▶ **49.** $-4x + 1$
  -19

50. $-3x + 7$
  -8

51. $-8 + 3x$
  7

▶ **52.** $-7 + 2x$
  3

Find the value of each of the following expressions when $a = -2$.

▶ **53.** $2a + 5$
  1

54. $3a + 4$
  -2

55. $-7a + 4$
  18

56. $-9a + 3$
  21

▶ **57.** $-a + 10$
  12

58. $-a + 8$
  10

59. $-4 + 3a$
  -10

▶ **60.** $-6 + 5a$
  -16

Find the value of each of the following expressions when $x = 3$. You may substitute 3 for x in each expression the way it is written, or you may simplify each expression first and then substitute 3 for x.

▶ **61.** $3x + 5x + 4$
28

62. $6x + 8x + 7$
49

▶ **63.** $9x + x + 3 + 7$
40

64. $5x + 3x + 2 + 4$
30

65. $4x + 3 + 2x + 5$
26

66. $7x + 6 + 2x + 9$
42

▶ **67.** $3x - 8 + 2x - 3$
4

68. $7x - 2 + 4x - 1$
30

Find the value of each of $12x - 3$ for each of the following values of x.

▶ **69.** $\dfrac{1}{2}$
3

70. $\dfrac{1}{3}$
1

71. $\dfrac{1}{4}$
0

72. $\dfrac{1}{6}$
−1

▶ **73.** $\dfrac{3}{2}$
15

74. $\dfrac{2}{3}$
5

75. $\dfrac{3}{4}$
6

76. $\dfrac{5}{6}$
7

Use the distributive property to write two equivalent expressions for the area of each figure.

77.

$6(x + 4) = 6x + 24$

78.

$7(x + 5) = 7x + 35$

Write an expression for the perimeter of each figure.

79.

Square $x + 1$

$4x + 4$

80.

$3x + 2$

Rectangle $2x - 1$

$10x + 2$

▶ **81.**

$3x + 1$

Parallelogram $2x - 3$

$10x - 4$

82.

$4x + 1$ Triangle $4x + 1$

$5x + 4$

$13x + 6$

D Applying the Concepts

83. **Buildings** This Google Earth image shows the Leaning Tower of Pisa. Most buildings stand at a right angle, but the tower is sinking on one side. The angle of inclination is the angle between the vertical and the tower. If the angle between the tower and the ground is 85° what is the angle of inclination?   5°

84. **Geometry** This Google Earth image shows the Pentagon. The interior angles of a regular pentagon are all the same and sum to 540°. Find the size of each angle.

108°

Find x in each figure and decide if the two angles are complementary or supplementary. [Example 11]

85.

55°; complementary angles

86.

145°; supplementary angles

▶ 87.

20°; complementary angles

▶ 88.

110°; supplementary angles

89. Luke earns $12 per hour working as a math tutor. We can express the amount he earns each week for working x hours with the expression 12x. Indicate with a yes or no, which of the following could be one of Luke's paychecks. If you answer no, explain your answer.
    a. $60 for working five hours
       Yes
    b. $100 for working nine hours
       No, he should earn $108 for working 9 hours
    c. $80 for working seven hours
       No, he should earn $84 for working 7 hours
    d. $168 for working 14 hours
       Yes

90. Kelly earns $15 per hour working as a graphic designer. We can express the amount she earns each week for working x hours with the expression 15x. Indicate with a yes or no which of the following could be one of Kelly's paychecks. If you answer no, explain your answer.
    a. $75 for working five hours
       Yes
    b. $125 for working nine hours
       No, she should earn $135 for working 9 hours
    c. $90 for working six hours
       Yes
    d. $500 for working 35 hours
       No, she should earn $525 for working 35 hours

▶ **91. Temperature and Altitude** On a certain day, the temperature on the ground is 72 degrees Fahrenheit, and the temperature at an altitude of A feet above the ground is found from the expression $72 - \frac{A}{300}$. Find the temperature at the following altitudes.

    a. 12,000 feet   **b.** 15,000 feet   **c.** 27,000 feet

       32°F   22°F   −18°F

92. Perimeter of a Rectangle As you know, the expression $2l + 2w$ gives the perimeter of a rectangle with length l and width w. The garden below has a width of $3\frac{1}{2}$ feet and a length of 8 feet. What is the length of the fence that surrounds the garden?

23 ft

3.5 ft

8 ft

▶ **93. Cost of Bottled Water** A water bottling company charges $7 per month for their water dispenser and $2 for each gallon of water delivered. If you have g gallons of water delivered in a month, then the expression $7 + 2g$ gives the amount of your bill for that month. Find the monthly bill for each of the following deliveries.

    a. 10 gallons   **b.** 20 gallons

      $27 $47

(WBC) **WATER BOTTLE CO.**		
MONTHLY BILL		
234 5th Street Glendora, CA 91740		DUE 07/23/10
Water dispenser	1	$7.00
Gallons of water	8	$16.00
		$23.00

94. Cellular Phone Rates A cellular phone company charges $35 per month plus 25 cents for each minute, or fraction of a minute, that you use one of their cellular phones. The expression $\frac{3500 + 25t}{100}$ gives the amount of money, in dollars, you will pay for using one of their phones for t minutes a month. Find the monthly bill for using one of their phones:

    a. 20 minutes in a month   **b.** 40 minutes in a month

      $40 $45

Cell Phone Company Grover Beach, CA		
August 2010		DUE 08/15/10
Monthly Access per Phone:	1	$35.00
Charges: $0.25/minute	50	$12.50
		$47.50

■ Getting Ready for the Next Section

Add.

95. $4 + (-4)$

    0

96. $2 + (-2)$

    0

97. $-2 + (-4)$

    −6

98. $-2 + (-5)$

    −7

99. $-5 + 2$

    −3

100. $-3 + 12$

    9

101. $\frac{5}{8} + \frac{3}{4}$

    $\frac{11}{8}$

102. $\frac{5}{6} + \frac{2}{3}$

    $\frac{3}{2}$

103. $-\frac{3}{4} + \frac{3}{4}$

    0

104. $-\frac{2}{3} + \frac{2}{3}$

    0

Simplify.

105. $x + 0$

x

106. $y + 0$

y

107. $y + 4 - 6$

$y - 2$

108. $y + 6 - 2$

$y + 4$

■ Maintaining Your Skills

Give the opposite of each number.

109. 9

-9

110. 12

-12

111. -6

6

112. -5

5

Problems 113–118 review material we covered in Chapter 1. Match each statement on the left with the property that justifies it on the right.

113. $2(6 + 5) = 2(6) + 2(5)$

a

114. $3 + (4 + 1) = (3 + 4) + 1$

b

115. $x + 5 = 5 + x$

c

116. $(a + 3) + 2 = a + (3 + 2)$

b

117. $(x + 5) + 1 = 1 + (x + 5)$

c

118. $(a + 4) + 2 = (4 + 2) + a$

d

a. Distributive property

b. Associative property

c. Commutative property

d. Commutative and associative properties

Perform the indicated operation.

119. $-\dfrac{5}{4}\left(\dfrac{8}{15}\right)$

$-\dfrac{2}{3}$

120. $-\dfrac{4}{3}\left(\dfrac{6}{5}\right)$

$-\dfrac{8}{5}$

121. $12 \div \dfrac{2}{3}$

18

122. $6 \div \dfrac{3}{5}$

10

123. $\dfrac{2}{3} - \dfrac{3}{4}$

$-\dfrac{1}{12}$

124. $\dfrac{3}{5} - \dfrac{5}{8}$

$-\dfrac{1}{40}$

The Addition Property of Equality

Objectives

A Identify a solution to an equation.

B Use the addition property of equality to solve linear equations.

Introduction . . .

Previously we defined complementary angles as two angles whose sum is 90°. If A and B are complementary angles, then

$$A + B = 90°$$

Complementary angles

If we know that $A = 30°$, then we can substitute 30° for A in the formula above to obtain the equation

$$30° + B = 90°$$

In this section we will learn how to solve equations like this one that involve addition and subtraction with one variable.

In general, solving an equation involves finding all replacements for the variable that make the equation a true statement.

A Solutions to Equations

> **Note** Although an equation may have many solutions, the equations we work with in the first part of this chapter will always have a single solution.

Definition

A **solution** for an equation is a number that when used in place of the variable makes the equation a true statement.

For example, the equation $x + 3 = 7$ has as its solution the number 4, because replacing x with 4 in the equation gives a true statement:

When	$x = 4$
the equation	$x + 3 = 7$
becomes	$4 + 3 = 7$
or	$7 = 7$ A true statement

EXAMPLE 1 Is $x = 5$ the solution to the equation $3x + 2 = 17$?

SOLUTION To see if it is, we replace x with 5 in the equation and find out if the result is a true statement:

When	$x = 5$
the equation	$3x + 2 = 17$
becomes	$3(5) + 2 = 17$
	$15 + 2 = 17$
	$17 = 17$ A true statement

Because the result is a true statement, we can conclude that $x = 5$ is the solution to $3x + 2 = 17$.

PRACTICE PROBLEMS

1. Show that $x = 3$ is the solution to the equation $5x - 4 = 11$.

2. Is $a = -3$ the solution to the equation $6a - 3 = 2a + 4$?

EXAMPLE 2   Is $a = -2$ the solution to the equation $7a + 4 = 3a - 2$?

SOLUTION   When the equation becomes

$$a = -2$$
$$7a + 4 = 3a - 2$$
$$7(-2) + 4 = 3(-2) - 2$$
$$-14 + 4 = -6 - 2$$
$$-10 = -8 \qquad \text{A false statement}$$

Because the result is a false statement, we must conclude that $a = -2$ is *not* the solution to the equation $7a + 4 = 3a - 2$.

Instructor Note
As you know, the addition property of equality can be extended to include subtracting the same number from both sides of an equation. I don't mention this in class, nor do I work examples using subtraction, because I have found that my students will make fewer mistakes if they think in terms of addition. However, in the next section we cover the multiplication property of equality, and we do extend that property to include dividing both sides of an equation by the same number.

B   Addition Property of Equality

We want to develop a process for solving equations with one variable. The most important property needed for solving the equations in this section is called the *addition property of equality.* The formal definition looks like this:

> **Addition Property of Equality**
> Let A, B, and C represent algebraic expressions.
>
> $$\text{If} \qquad A = B$$
> $$\text{then} \qquad A + C = B + C$$
>
> *In words:* Adding the same quantity to both sides of an equation never changes the solution to the equation.

This property is extremely useful in solving equations. Our goal in solving equations is to isolate the variable on one side of the equation. We want to end up with an equation of the form

$$x = \text{a number}$$

To do so we use the addition property of equality. Remember to follow this basic rule of algebra: *Whatever is done to one side of an equation must be done to the other side in order to preserve the equality.*

3. Solve for x: $x + 5 = -2$

 Note   With some of the equations in this section, you will be able to see the solution just by looking at the equation. But it is important that you show all the steps used to solve the equations anyway. The equations you come across in the future will not be as easy to solve, so you should learn the steps involved very well.

EXAMPLE 3   Solve for x: $x + 4 = -2$

SOLUTION   We want to isolate x on one side of the equation. If we add -4 to both sides, the left side will be $x + 4 + (-4)$, which is $x + 0$ or just x.

$$x + 4 = -2$$
$$x + 4 + (\mathbf{-4}) = -2 + (\mathbf{-4}) \qquad \text{Add } -4 \text{ to both sides}$$
$$x + 0 = -6 \qquad \text{Addition}$$
$$x = -6 \qquad x + 0 = x$$

The solution is -6. We can check it if we want to by replacing x with -6 in the original equation:

$$\text{When} \qquad x = -6$$
$$\text{the equation} \qquad x + 4 = -2$$
$$\text{becomes} \qquad -6 + 4 = -2$$
$$-2 = -2 \qquad \text{A true statement}$$

Answers
2. No   **3.** -7

EXAMPLE 4 Solve for a: $a - 3 = 5$

SOLUTION
$$a - 3 = 5$$
$$a - 3 + \mathbf{3} = 5 + \mathbf{3} \quad \text{Add 3 to both sides}$$
$$a + 0 = 8 \quad \text{Addition}$$
$$a = 8 \quad a + 0 = a$$

The solution to $a - 3 = 5$ is $a = 8$.

EXAMPLE 5 Solve for y: $y + 4 - 6 = 7 - 1$

SOLUTION Before we apply the addition property of equality, we must simplify each side of the equation as much as possible:

$$y + 4 - 6 = 7 - 1$$
$$y - 2 = 6 \quad \text{Simplify each side}$$
$$y - 2 + \mathbf{2} = 6 + \mathbf{2} \quad \text{Add 2 to both sides}$$
$$y + 0 = 8 \quad \text{Addition}$$
$$y = 8 \quad y + 0 = y$$

EXAMPLE 6 Solve for x: $3x - 2 - 2x = 4 - 9$

SOLUTION Simplifying each side as much as possible, we have

$$3x - 2 - 2x = 4 - 9$$
$$x - 2 = -5 \quad 3x - 2x = x$$
$$x - 2 + \mathbf{2} = -5 + \mathbf{2} \quad \text{Add 2 to both sides}$$
$$x + 0 = -3 \quad \text{Addition}$$
$$x = -3 \quad x + 0 = x$$

EXAMPLE 7 Solve for x: $-3 - 6 = x + 4$

SOLUTION The variable appears on the right side of the equation in this problem. This makes no difference; we can isolate x on either side of the equation. We can leave it on the right side if we like:

$$-3 - 6 = x + 4$$
$$-9 = x + 4 \quad \text{Simplify the left side}$$
$$-9 + \mathbf{(-4)} = x + 4 + \mathbf{(-4)} \quad \text{Add } -4 \text{ to both sides}$$
$$-13 = x + 0 \quad \text{Addition}$$
$$-13 = x \quad x + 0 = x$$

The statement $-13 = x$ is equivalent to the statement $x = -13$. In either case the solution to our equation is -13.

EXAMPLE 8 Solve: $a - \dfrac{3}{4} = \dfrac{5}{8}$

SOLUTION To isolate a we add $\dfrac{3}{4}$ to each side:

$$a - \frac{3}{4} = \frac{5}{8}$$
$$a - \frac{3}{4} + \frac{\mathbf{3}}{\mathbf{4}} = \frac{5}{8} + \frac{\mathbf{3}}{\mathbf{4}}$$
$$a = \frac{11}{8}$$

When solving equations we will leave answers like $\dfrac{11}{8}$ as improper fractions, rather than change them to mixed numbers.

4. Solve for a: $a - 2 = 7$

5. Solve for y: $y + 6 - 2 = 8 - 9$

6. Solve for x: $5x - 3 - 4x = 4 - 7$

7. Solve for x: $-5 - 7 = x + 2$

8. Solve: $a - \dfrac{2}{3} = \dfrac{5}{6}$

Instructor Note
I have my students write solutions to equations as improper fractions rather than as mixed numbers.

Answers
4. 9 **5.** -5 **6.** 0 **7.** -14
8. $\dfrac{3}{2}$

9. Solve: $5(3a - 4) - 14a = 25$

EXAMPLE 9 Solve: $4(2a - 3) - 7a = 2 - 5$.

SOLUTION We must begin by applying the distributive property to separate terms on the left side of the equation. Following that, we combine similar terms and then apply the addition property of equality.

$4(2a - 3) - 7a = 2 - 5$	Original equation
$8a - 12 - 7a = 2 - 5$	Distributive property
$a - 12 = -3$	Simplify each side
$a - 12 + \mathbf{12} = -3 + \mathbf{12}$	Add 12 to each side
$a = 9$	Addition

A Note on Subtraction

Although the addition property of equality is stated for addition only, we can subtract the same number from both sides of an equation as well. Because subtraction is defined as addition of the opposite, subtracting the same quantity from both sides of an equation will not change the solution. If we were to solve the equation in Example 3 using subtraction instead of addition, the steps would look like this:

$x + 4 = -2$	Original equation
$x + 4 - \mathbf{4} = -2 - \mathbf{4}$	Subtract 4 from each side
$x = -6$	Subtraction

In my experience teaching algebra, I find that students make fewer mistakes if they think in terms of addition rather than subtraction. So, you are probably better off if you continue to use the addition property just the way we have used it in the examples in this section. But, if you are curious as to whether you can subtract the same number from both sides of an equation, the answer is yes.

Getting Ready for Class

After reading through the preceding section, respond in your own words and in complete sentences. An answer of true or false should be accompanied by a sentence explaining why the answer is true or false.

1. What is a solution to an equation?
2. True or false? According to the addition property of equality, adding the same value to both sides of an equation will never change the solution to the equation.
3. Show that $x = 5$ is a solution to the equation $3x + 2 = 17$ without solving the equation.
4. True or false? The equations below have the same solution.

   Equation 1: $7x + 5 = 19$
   Equation 2: $7x + 5 + 3 = 19 + 3$

Answer
9. 45

Problem Set 10.2

A Check to see if the number to the right of each of the following equations is the solution to the equation. [Examples 1, 2]

▶ **1.** $2x + 1 = 5$; 2
Yes

2. $4x + 3 = 7$; 1
Yes

3. $3x + 4 = 19$; 5
Yes

4. $3x + 8 = 14$; 2
Yes

5. $2x - 4 = 2$; 4
No

6. $5x - 6 = 9$; 3
Yes

7. $2x + 1 = 3x + 3$; -2
Yes

8. $4x + 5 = 2x - 1$; -6
No

▶ **9.** $x - 4 = 2x + 1$; -4
No

10. $x - 8 = 3x + 2$; -5
Yes

B Solve each equation. [Examples 3, 4, 8]

11. $x + 2 = 8$
6

▶ **12.** $x + 3 = 5$
2

▶ **13.** $x - 4 = 7$
11

14. $x - 6 = 2$
8

▶ **15.** $a + 9 = -6$
-15

16. $a + 3 = -1$
-4

17. $x - 5 = -4$
1

18. $x - 8 = -3$
5

▶ **19.** $y - 3 = -6$
-3

20. $y - 5 = -1$
4

▶ **21.** $a + \dfrac{1}{3} = -\dfrac{2}{3}$
-1

22. $a + \dfrac{1}{4} = -\dfrac{3}{4}$
-1

▶ **23.** $x - \dfrac{3}{5} = \dfrac{4}{5}$
$\dfrac{7}{5}$

24. $x - \dfrac{7}{8} = \dfrac{3}{8}$
$\dfrac{5}{4}$

▶ **25.** $y + 7.3 = -2.7$
-10

▶ **26.** $y + 8.2 = -2.8$
-11

▶ Selected exercises available online at www.webassign.net/brookscole

B Simplify each side of the following equations before applying the addition property. [Examples 5–7]

▶ **27.** $x + 4 - 7 = 3 - 10$
-4

28. $x + 6 - 2 = 5 - 12$
-11

29. $x - 6 + 4 = -3 - 2$
-3

30. $x - 8 + 2 = -7 - 1$
-2

▶ **31.** $3 - 5 = a - 4$
2

32. $2 - 6 = a - 1$
-3

▶ **33.** $3a + 7 - 2a = 1$
-6

34. $5a + 6 - 4a = 4$
-2

▶ **35.** $6a - 2 - 5a = -9 + 1$
-6

36. $7a - 6 - 6a = -3 + 1$
4

▶ **37.** $8 - 5 = 3x - 2x + 4$
-1

▶ **38.** $10 - 6 = 8x - 7x + 6$
-2

B The following equations contain parentheses. Apply the distributive property to remove the parentheses, then simplify each side before using the addition property of equality. [Example 9]

39. $2(x + 3) - x = 4$
-2

40. $5(x + 1) - 4x = 2$
-3

▶ **41.** $-3(x - 4) + 4x = 3 - 7$
-16

42. $-2(x - 5) + 3x = 4 - 9$
-15

43. $5(2a + 1) - 9a = 8 - 6$
-3

▶ **44.** $4(2a - 1) - 7a = 9 - 5$
8

▶ **45.** $-(x + 3) + 2x - 1 = 6$
10

46. $-(x - 7) + 2x - 8 = 4$
5

Find the value of x for each of the figures, given the perimeter.

47. $P = 36$ $x = 4$

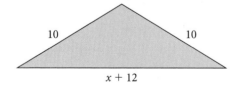

48. $P = 30$ $x - 13$

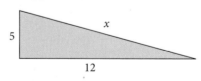

▶ **49.** $P = 16$ $x = 12$

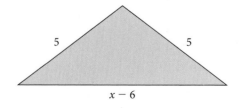

50. $P = 60$ $x = 24$

■ Applying the Concepts

Temperature The chart shows the temperatures for some of the world's hottest places. To convert from Celsius to Kelvin we use the formula $y = x + 273$, where y is the temperature in Kelvin and x is the temperature in Celsius. Use the formula to answer Questions 51 and 52.

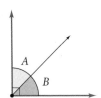

Heating Up

		160
137°F	Al'Aziziyah, Libya	140
134°F	Greenland Ranch, Death Valley, United States	120
131°F	Ghudamis, Libya	100
131°F	Kebili, Tunisia	80
130°F	Tombouctou, Mali	60
Source: Aneki.com		40

51. The hottest temperature in Al'Aziziyah was 331 Kelvin. Convert this to Celsius.

58° Celsius

52. The hottest temperature in Kebili, Tunisia, was 328 Kelvin. Convert this to Celsius.

55° Celsius

53. Geometry Two angles are complementary angles. If one of the angles is 23°, then solving the equation $x + 23° = 90°$ will give you the other angle. Solve the equation.

67°

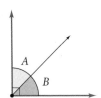

Complementary angles

▶ **54. Geometry** Two angles are supplementary angles. If one of the angles is 23°, then solving the equation $x + 23° = 180°$ will give you the other angle. Solve the equation.

157°

55. Theater Tickets The El Portal Center for the Arts in North Hollywood, California, holds a maximum of 400 people. The two balconies hold 86 and 89 people each; the rest of the seats are at the stage level. Solving the equation $x + 86 + 89 = 400$ will give you the number of seats on the stage level.

a. Solve the equation for x.

225

b. If tickets on the stage level are $30 each, and tickets in either balcony are $25 each, what is the maximum amount of money the theater can bring in for a show?

$11,125

▶ **56. Geometry** The sum of the angles in the triangle on the swing set is 180°. Use this fact to write an equation containing x. Then solve the equation.

$x + 67° + 67° = 180°$; 46°

■ Getting Ready for the Next Section

Find the reciprocal of each number.

57. 4

$\frac{1}{4}$

58. 3

$\frac{1}{3}$

59. $\frac{1}{2}$

2

60. $\frac{1}{3}$

3

61. $\frac{2}{3}$

$\frac{3}{2}$

62. $\frac{3}{5}$

$\frac{5}{3}$

Multiply.

63. $2 \cdot \frac{1}{2}$

1

64. $\frac{1}{4} \cdot 4$

1

65. $-\frac{1}{3}(-3)$

1

66. $-\frac{1}{4}(-4)$

1

67. $\frac{3}{2}\left(\frac{2}{3}\right)$

1

68. $\frac{5}{3}\left(\frac{3}{5}\right)$

1

69. $\left(-\frac{5}{4}\right)\left(-\frac{4}{5}\right)$

1

70. $\left(-\frac{4}{3}\right)\left(-\frac{3}{4}\right)$

1

Simplify.

71. $1 \cdot x$

x

72. $1 \cdot a$

a

73. $4x - 11 + 3x$

$7x - 11$

74. $2x - 11 + 3x$

$5x - 11$

■ Maintaining Your Skills

75. $\frac{3}{2} + \frac{5}{10}$

2

76. $\frac{1}{3} + \frac{4}{12}$

$\frac{2}{3}$

77. $\frac{2}{7} + \frac{1}{14}$

$\frac{5}{14}$

78. $\frac{3}{8} + \frac{1}{16}$

$\frac{7}{16}$

79. $\frac{1}{3} - \frac{2}{5}$

$-\frac{1}{15}$

80. $\frac{3}{4} - \frac{3}{7}$

$\frac{9}{28}$

81. $\frac{1}{6} - \frac{4}{3}$

$-\frac{7}{6}$

82. $\frac{2}{5} - \frac{5}{10}$

$-\frac{1}{10}$

Translating Translate each of the following into an equation, and then solve the equation.

83. The sum of x and 12 is 30.

Equation: $x + 12 = 30$; solution: 18

84. The difference of x and 12 is 30.

Equation: $x - 12 = 30$; solution: 42

85. The difference of 8 and 5 is equal to the sum of x and 7.

Equation: $8 - 5 = x + 7$; solution: -4

86. The sum of 8 and 5 is equal to the difference of x and 7.

Equation: $8 + 5 = x - 7$; solution: 20

Objectives

A Use the multiplication property of equality to solve equations.

In this section we will continue to solve equations in one variable. We will again use the addition property of equality, but we will also use another property—the *multiplication property of equality*—to solve the equations in this section. We will state the multiplication property of equality and then see how it is used by looking at some examples.

The most popular Internet video download of all time was a *Star Wars* movie trailer. The video was compressed so it would be small enough for people to download over the Internet. In movie theaters, a film plays at 24 frames per second. Over the Internet, that number is sometimes cut in half, to 12 frames per second, to make the file size smaller.

We can use the equation $240 = \frac{x}{12}$ to find the number of total frames, x, in a 240-second movie clip that plays at 12 frames per second.

A   Multiplication Property of Equality

Multiplication Property of Equality

Let A, B, and C represent algebraic expressions, with C not equal to 0.

$$\text{If} \quad A = B$$
$$\text{then} \quad AC = BC$$

In words: Multiplying both sides of an equation by the same nonzero quantity never changes the solution to the equation.

Now, because division is defined as multiplication by the reciprocal, we are also free to divide both sides of an equation by the same nonzero quantity and always be sure we have not changed the solution to the equation.

EXAMPLE 1   Solve for x: $\frac{1}{2}x = 3$

SOLUTION   Our goal here is the same as it was in Section 4.2. We want to isolate x (that is, $1x$) on one side of the equation. We have $\frac{1}{2}x$ on the left side. If we multiply both sides by 2, we will have $1x$ on the left side. Here is how it looks:

$$\frac{1}{2}x = 3$$

$$\mathbf{2}\left(\frac{1}{2}x\right) = \mathbf{2}(3) \qquad \text{Multiply both sides by 2}$$

$$x = 6 \qquad \text{Multiplication}$$

To see why $2\left(\frac{1}{2}x\right)$ is equivalent to x, we use the associative property:

$$2\left(\frac{1}{2}x\right) = \left(2 \cdot \frac{1}{2}\right)x \qquad \text{Associative property}$$

$$= 1 \cdot x \qquad 2 \cdot \frac{1}{2} = 1$$

$$= x \qquad 1 \cdot x = x$$

Although we will not show this step when solving problems, it is implied.

1. Solve for x: $\frac{1}{3}x = 5$

Instructor Note
As you can see, we do allow for dividing both sides of an equation by the same number. Example 5, along with the note in the margin next to it, justifies using division to solve equations. However, you may want to give some further explanation in class.

Answer
1. 15

2. Solve for a: $\frac{1}{5}a + 3 = 7$

3. Solve for y: $\frac{3}{5}y = 6$

Instructor Note
When I work a problem similar to the one shown in Example 3, I always show a few extra steps in order to point out how the associative property is used to simplify the left side of the equation to just y.

Answers
2. 20 **3.** 10

EXAMPLE 2 Solve for a: $\frac{1}{3}a + 2 = 7$

SOLUTION We begin by adding -2 to both sides to get $\frac{1}{3}a$ by itself. We then multiply by 3 to solve for a.

$$\frac{1}{3}a + 2 = 7$$

$$\frac{1}{3}a + 2 + (-2) = 7 + (-2) \quad \text{Add } -2 \text{ to both sides}$$

$$\frac{1}{3}a = 5 \quad \text{Addition}$$

$$3 \cdot \frac{1}{3}a = 3 \cdot 5 \quad \text{Multiply both sides by 3}$$

$$a = 15 \quad \text{Multiplication}$$

We can check our solution to see that it is correct:

When $a = 15$

the equation $\frac{1}{3}a + 2 = 7$

becomes $\frac{1}{3}(15) + 2 = 7$

$$5 + 2 = 7$$

$$7 = 7 \quad \text{A true statement}$$

EXAMPLE 3 Solve for y: $\frac{2}{3}y = 12$

SOLUTION In this case we multiply each side of the equation by the reciprocal of $\frac{2}{3}$, which is $\frac{3}{2}$.

$$\frac{2}{3}y = 12$$

$$\frac{3}{2}\left(\frac{2}{3}y\right) = \frac{3}{2}(12)$$

$$y = 18$$

The solution checks because $\frac{2}{3}$ of 18 is 12.

Note The reciprocal of a negative number is also a negative number. Remember, reciprocals are two numbers that have a product of 1. Since 1 is a positive number, any two numbers we multiply to get 1 must both have the same sign. Here are some negative numbers and their reciprocals:

The reciprocal of -2 is $-\frac{1}{2}$.

The reciprocal of -7 is $-\frac{1}{7}$.

The reciprocal of $-\frac{1}{3}$ is -3.

The reciprocal of $-\frac{3}{4}$ is $-\frac{4}{3}$.

The reciprocal of $-\frac{9}{5}$ is $-\frac{5}{9}$.

EXAMPLE 4 Solve for x: $-\frac{4}{5}x = \frac{8}{15}$

SOLUTION The reciprocal of $-\frac{4}{5}$ is $-\frac{5}{4}$.

$$-\frac{4}{5}x = \frac{8}{15}$$

$$-\frac{5}{4}\left(-\frac{4}{5}x\right) = -\frac{5}{4}\left(\frac{8}{15}\right)$$

$$x = -\frac{2}{3}$$

Many times, it is convenient to divide both sides by a nonzero number to solve an equation, as the next example shows.

EXAMPLE 5 Solve for x: $4x = -20$

SOLUTION If we divide both sides by 4, the left side will be just x, which is what we want. It is okay to divide both sides by 4 because division by 4 is equivalent to multiplication by $\frac{1}{4}$, and the multiplication property of equality states that we can multiply both sides by any number so long as it isn't 0.

$$4x = -20$$

$$\frac{4x}{4} = \frac{-20}{4} \qquad \text{Divide both sides by 4}$$

$$x = -5 \qquad \text{Division}$$

Because $4x$ means "4 times x," the factors in the numerator of $\frac{4x}{4}$ are 4 and x.

Because the factor 4 is common to the numerator and the denominator, we divide it out to get just x.

EXAMPLE 6 Solve for x: $-3x + 7 = -5$

SOLUTION We begin by adding -7 to both sides to reduce the left side to $-3x$.

$$-3x + 7 = -5$$

$$-3x + 7 + (-7) = -5 + (-7) \qquad \text{Add } -7 \text{ to both sides}$$

$$-3x = -12 \qquad \text{Addition}$$

$$\frac{-3x}{-3} = \frac{-12}{-3} \qquad \text{Divide both sides by } -3$$

$$x = 4 \qquad \text{Division}$$

With more complicated equations we simplify each side separately before applying the addition or multiplication properties of equality. The examples below illustrate.

EXAMPLE 7 Solve for x: $5x - 8x + 3 = 4 - 10$

SOLUTION We combine similar terms to simplify each side and then solve as usual.

$$5x - 8x + 3 = 4 - 10$$

$$-3x + 3 = -6 \qquad \text{Simplify each side}$$

$$-3x + 3 + (-3) = -6 + (-3) \qquad \text{Add } -3 \text{ to both sides}$$

$$-3x = -9 \qquad \text{Addition}$$

$$\frac{-3x}{-3} = \frac{-9}{-3} \qquad \text{Divide both sides by } -3$$

$$x = 3 \qquad \text{Division}$$

4. Solve for x: $-\frac{3}{4}x = \frac{6}{5}$

5. Solve for x: $6x = -42$

Note If we multiply each side by $\frac{1}{4}$, the solution looks like this:

$$\frac{1}{4}(4x) = \frac{1}{4}(-20)$$

$$\left(\frac{1}{4} \cdot 4\right)x = -5$$

$$1x = -5$$

$$x = -5$$

6. Solve for x: $-5x + 6 = -14$

7. Solve for x: $3x - 7x + 5 = 3 - 18$

Answers

4. $-\frac{8}{5}$ **5.** -7 **6.** 4 **7.** 5

8. Solve for x:
$-5 + 4 = 2x - 11 + 3x$

EXAMPLE 8   Solve for x: $-8 + 11 = 4x - 11 + 3x$

SOLUTION   We begin by simplifying each side separately.

$$-8 + 11 = 4x - 11 + 3x$$

$3 = 7x - 11$	Simplify both sides
$3 + \mathbf{11} = 7x - 11 + \mathbf{11}$	Add 11 to both sides
$14 = 7x$	Addition
$\dfrac{14}{7} = \dfrac{7x}{7}$	Divide both sides by 7
$2 = x$ or $x = 2$	

Again, it makes no difference which side of the equation x ends up on, so long as it is just one x.

⃠ COMMON MISTAKES

Before we end this section, we should mention a very common mistake made by students when they first begin to solve equations. It involves trying to subtract away the number in front of the variable—like this:

$7x = 21$	
$7x - \mathbf{7} = 21 - \mathbf{7}$	Add -7 to both sides
$x = 14$ ⟵ ——— Mistake	

The mistake is not in trying to subtract 7 from both sides of the equation. The mistake occurs when we say $7x - 7 = x$. It just isn't true. We can add and subtract only similar terms. The terms $7x$ and 7 are not similar, because one contains x and the other doesn't. The correct way to do the problem is like this:

$7x = 21$	
$\dfrac{7x}{7} = \dfrac{21}{7}$	Divide both sides by 7
$x = 3$	Division

Getting Ready for Class

After reading through the preceding section, respond in your own words and in complete sentences.

1. True or false? Multiplying both sides of an equation by the same non-zero quantity will never change the solution to the equation.

2. If we were to multiply the right side of an equation by 2, then the left side should be multiplied by _____.

3. Dividing both sides of the equation $4x = -20$ by 4 is the same as multiplying both sides by what number?

Answer

8. 2

Problem Set 10.3

A Use the multiplication property of equality to solve each of the following equations. In each case, show all the steps. [Examples 1, 3–5]

1. $\frac{1}{4}x = 2$

8

▶ **2.** $\frac{1}{3}x = 7$

21

3. $\frac{1}{2}x = -3$

-6

4. $\frac{1}{5}x = -6$

-30

▶ **5.** $-\frac{1}{3}x = 2$

-6

6. $-\frac{1}{3}x = 5$

-15

▶ **7.** $-\frac{1}{6}x = -1$

6

8. $-\frac{1}{2}x = -4$

8

▶ **9.** $\frac{3}{4}y = 12$

16

10. $\frac{2}{3}y = 18$

27

▶ **11.** $3a = 48$

16

12. $2a = 28$

14

13. $-\frac{3}{5}x = \frac{9}{10}$

$-\frac{3}{2}$

▶ **14.** $-\frac{4}{5}x = -\frac{8}{15}$

$\frac{2}{3}$

15. $5x = -35$

-7

16. $7x = -35$

-5

▶ **17.** $-8y = 64$

-8

18. $-9y = 27$

-3

▶ **19.** $-7x = -42$

6

20. $-6x = -42$

7

▶ Selected exercises available online at www.webassign.net/brookscole

A Using the addition property of equality first, solve each of the following equations. [Examples 2, 6]

21. $3x - 1 = 5$
2

▶ **22.** $2x + 4 = 6$
1

23. $-4a + 3 = -9$
3

▶ **24.** $-5a + 10 = 50$
−8

25. $6x - 5 = 19$
4

26. $7x - 5 = 30$
5

27. $\frac{1}{3}a + 3 = -5$
−24

▶ **28.** $\frac{1}{2}a + 2 = -7$
−18

29. $-\frac{1}{4}a + 5 = 2$
12

30. $-\frac{1}{5}a + 3 = 7$
−20

31. $2x - 4 = -20$
−8

▶ **32.** $3x - 5 = -26$
−7

33. $\frac{2}{3}x - 4 = 6$
15

▶ **34.** $\frac{3}{4}x - 2 = 7$
12

▶ **35.** $-11a + 4 = -29$
3

36. $-12a + 1 = -47$
4

▶ **37.** $-3y - 2 = 1$
−1

38. $-2y - 8 = 2$
−5

▶ **39.** $-2x - 5 = -7$
1

40. $-3x - 6 = -36$
10

A Simplify each side of the following equations first, then solve. [Examples 7, 8]

41. $2x + 3x - 5 = 7 + 3$
3

42. $4x + 5x - 8 = 6 + 4$
2

▶ **43.** $4x - 7 + 2x = 9 - 10$
1

44. $5x - 6 + 3x = -6 - 8$
−1

▶ **45.** $3a + 2a + a = 7 - 13$
−1

46. $8a - 6a + a = 8 - 14$
−2

47. $5x + 4x + 3x = 4 - 8$
$-\frac{1}{3}$

▶ **48.** $4x + 8x - 2x = 15 - 10$
$\frac{1}{2}$

49. $5 - 18 = 3y - 2y + 1$
−14

▶ **50.** $7 - 16 = 4y - 3y + 2$
−11

Find the value of *x* for each of the figures, given the perimeter.

51. *P* = 72   *x* = 9

2x

52. *P* = 96   *x* = 8

3x

▶ **53.** *P* = 80   *x* = 8

3x

2x

▶ **54.** *P* = 64   *x* = 4

5x

3x

Applying the Concepts

55. Cars The chart shows the fastest cars in America. To convert miles per hour to feet per second we use the formula $y = \frac{15}{22}x$ where *x* is the car's speed in feet per second and *y* is the speed in miles per hour. Find the speed of the Ford GT in feet per second. Round to the nearest tenth.

300.7 ft/sec

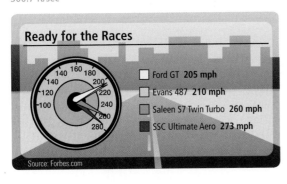

56. Mountains The map shows the heights of the tallest mountains in the world. To convert the heights of the mountains into miles, we use the formula $y = 5{,}280x$, where *y* is in feet and *x* is in miles. Find the height of K2 in miles. Round to the nearest tenth of a mile.

5.3 miles

57. MP3 Players Southwest Electronics tracked the number of MP3 players it sold each month for a year. The store manager found that when he raised the price of the MP3 players just slightly, sales went down. He used the equation $60 = -2x + 130$ to determine the price x he needs to charge if he wants to sell 60 MP3 players a month. Solve this equation.

$35.00

58. Part-time Tuition Costs Many two-year colleges have a large number of students who take courses on a part-time basis. Students pay a charge for each credit hour taken plus an activity fee. Suppose the equation $\$1960 = \$175x + \$35$ can be used to determine the number of credit hours a student is taking during the upcoming semester. Solve this equation.

11 credit hours

59. Super Bowl XLII According to Nielsen Media Research, the New York Giants' victory over the New England Patriots in Super Bowl XLII was the most watched Super Bowl ever, with 3 million more viewers than the previous record for Super Bowl XXX in 1996. The equation $192,000,000 = 2x - 3,000,000$ shows that the total number of viewers for both Super Bowl games was 192 million. Solve for x to determine how many viewers watched Super Bowl XLII.

97,500,000 or 97.5 million viewers

60. Blending Gasoline In an attempt to save money at the gas pump, customers will combine two different octane gasolines to get a blend that is slightly higher in octane than regular gas but not as expensive as premium gas. The equation $14x + 120 - 6x = 200$ can be used to find out how many gallons of one octane are needed. Solve this equation.

10 gallons

192,000,000 viewers total

$$14x + 120 - 6x = 200$$

■ Maintaining Your Skills

Translations Translate each sentence below into an equation, then solve the equation.

▶ **61.** The sum of $2x$ and 5 is 19.

$2x + 5 = 19; x = 7$

▶ **62.** The sum of 8 and $3x$ is 2.

$8 + 3x = 2; x = -2$

63. The difference of $5x$ and 6 is -9.

$5x - 6 = -9; x = -\dfrac{3}{5}$

▶ **64.** The difference of 9 and $6x$ is 21.

$9 - 6x = 21; x = -2$

■ Getting Ready for the Next Section

Apply the distributive property to each of the following expressions.

65. $2(3a - 8)$

$6a - 16$

66. $4(2a - 5)$

$8a - 20$

67. $-3(5x - 1)$

$-15x + 3$

68. $-2(7x - 3)$

$-14x + 6$

Simplify each of the following expressions as much as possible.

69. $3(y - 5) + 6$

$3y - 9$

70. $5(y + 3) + 7$

$5y + 22$

71. $6(2x - 1) + 4x$

$16x - 6$

72. $8(3x - 2) + 4x$

$28x - 16$

Linear Equations in One Variable

Introduction . . .

The Rhind Papyrus is an ancient Egyptian document, created around 1650 BC, that contains some mathematical riddles. One problem on the Rhind Papyrus asked the reader to find a quantity such that when it is added to one-fourth of itself the sum is 15. The equation that describes this situation is

$$x + \frac{1}{4}x = 15$$

Bridgeman Art Library/Getty Images

As you can see, this equation contains a fraction. One of the topics we will discuss in this section is how to solve equations that contain fractions.

In this chapter we have been solving what are called *linear equations in one variable*. They are equations that contain only one variable, and that variable is always raised to the first power and never appears in a denominator. Here are some examples of linear equations in one variable:

$$3x + 2 = 17, \quad 7a + 4 = 3a - 2, \quad 2(3y - 5) = 6$$

Because of the work we have done in the first three sections of this chapter, we are now able to solve any linear equation in one variable. The steps outlined below can be used as a guide to solving these equations.

A Solving Linear Equations with One Variable

> **Strategy**   Solving a Linear Equation with One Variable
>
> **Step 1:** Simplify each side of the equation as much as possible. This step is done using the commutative, associative, and distributive properties.
>
> **Step 2:** Use the addition property of equality to get all *variable terms* on one side of the equation and all *constant terms* on the other, and then combine like terms. A *variable term* is any term that contains the variable. A *constant term* is any term that contains only a number.
>
> **Step 3:** Use the multiplication property of equality to get the variable by itself on one side of the equation.
>
> **Step 4:** Check your solution in the original equation if you think it is necessary.

Note   Once you have some practice at solving equations, these steps will seem almost automatic. Until that time, it is a good idea to pay close attention to these steps.

Instructor Note
Using division on the last step in solving equations is always shown in the examples in this section. However, if I were working Example 1 in class, when I reached the last step I would say, "We can multiply both sides by 1/3 or we can divide both sides by 3," just to remind them that the two processes are equivalent.

PRACTICE PROBLEMS

1. Solve: $4(x + 3) = -8$

EXAMPLE 1   Solve: $3(x + 2) = -9$

SOLUTION   We begin by applying the distributive property to the left side:

Step 1 $\begin{cases} 3(x + 2) = -9 \\ 3x + 6 = -9 \end{cases}$ Distributive property

Step 2 $\begin{cases} 3x + 6 + (-6) = -9 + (-6) \\ 3x = -15 \end{cases}$ Add -6 to both sides

Addition

Step 3 $\begin{cases} \dfrac{3x}{3} = \dfrac{-15}{3} \\ x = -5 \end{cases}$ Divide both sides by 3

Division

Answer
1. -5

10.4 Linear Equations in One Variable

This general method of solving linear equations involves using the two properties developed in Sections 10.2 and 10.3. We can add any number to both sides of an equation or multiply (or divide) both sides by the same nonzero number and always be sure we have not changed the solution to the equation. The equations may change in form, but the solution to the equation stays the same. Looking back to Example 1, we can see that each equation looks a little different from the preceding one. What is interesting, and useful, is that each of the equations says the same thing about x. They all say that x is -5. The last equation, of course, is the easiest to read. That is why our goal is to end up with x isolated on one side of the equation.

2. Solve: $6a + 7 = 4a - 3$

EXAMPLE 2

Solve: $4a + 5 = 2a - 7$

SOLUTION Neither side can be simplified any further. What we have to do is get the variable terms ($4a$ and $2a$) on the same side of the equation. We can eliminate the variable term from the right side by adding $-2a$ to both sides:

$$4a + 5 = 2a - 7$$

Step 2
$$4a + (\mathbf{-2a}) + 5 = 2a + (\mathbf{-2a}) - 7 \quad \text{Add } -2a \text{ to both sides}$$
$$2a + 5 = -7 \quad \text{Addition}$$
$$2a + 5 + (\mathbf{-5}) = -7 + (\mathbf{-5}) \quad \text{Add } -5 \text{ to both sides}$$
$$2a = -12 \quad \text{Addition}$$

Step 3
$$\frac{2a}{2} = \frac{-12}{2} \quad \text{Divide by 2}$$
$$a = -6 \quad \text{Division}$$

3. Solve: $5(x - 2) + 3 = -12$

EXAMPLE 3

Solve: $2(x - 4) + 5 = -11$

SOLUTION We begin by applying the distributive property to multiply 2 and $x - 4$:

$$2(x - 4) + 5 = -11$$

Step 1
$$2x - 8 + 5 = -11 \quad \text{Distributive property}$$
$$2x - 3 = -11 \quad \text{Addition}$$

Step 2
$$2x - 3 + \mathbf{3} = -11 + \mathbf{3} \quad \text{Add 3 to both sides}$$
$$2x = -8 \quad \text{Addition}$$

Step 3
$$\frac{2x}{2} = \frac{-8}{2} \quad \text{Divide by 2}$$
$$x = -4 \quad \text{Division}$$

4. Solve: $3(4x - 5) + 6 = 3x + 9$

EXAMPLE 4

Solve: $5(2x - 4) + 3 = 4x - 5$

SOLUTION We apply the distributive property to multiply 5 and $2x - 4$. We then combine similar terms and solve as usual:

$$5(2x - 4) + 3 = 4x - 5$$

Step 1
$$10x - 20 + 3 = 4x - 5 \quad \text{Distributive property}$$
$$10x - 17 = 4x - 5 \quad \text{Simplify the left side}$$

Step 2
$$10x + (\mathbf{-4x}) - 17 = 4x + (\mathbf{-4x}) - 5 \quad \text{Add } -4x \text{ to both sides}$$
$$6x - 17 = -5 \quad \text{Addition}$$
$$6x - 17 + \mathbf{17} = -5 + \mathbf{17} \quad \text{Add 17 to both sides}$$
$$6x = 12 \quad \text{Addition}$$

Step 3
$$\frac{6x}{6} = \frac{12}{6} \quad \text{Divide by 6}$$
$$x = 2 \quad \text{Division}$$

Answers
2. -5 **3.** -1 **4.** 2

B Equations Involving Fractions

We will now solve some equations that involve fractions. Because integers are usually easier to work with than fractions, we will begin each problem by clearing the equation we are trying to solve of all fractions. To do this, we will use the multiplication property of equality to multiply each side of the equation by the LCD for all fractions appearing in the equation. Here is an example.

EXAMPLE 5 Solve the equation $\frac{x}{2} + \frac{x}{6} = 8$.

SOLUTION The LCD for the fractions $\frac{x}{2}$ and $\frac{x}{6}$ is 6. It has the property that both 2 and 6 divide it evenly. Therefore, if we multiply both sides of the equation by 6, we will be left with an equation that does not involve fractions.

$$\mathbf{6}\left(\frac{x}{2} + \frac{x}{6}\right) = \mathbf{6}(8) \qquad \text{Multiply each side by 6}$$

$$6\left(\frac{x}{2}\right) + 6\left(\frac{x}{6}\right) = 6(8) \qquad \text{Apply the distributive property}$$

$$3x + x = 48 \qquad \text{Multiplication}$$

$$4x = 48 \qquad \text{Combine similar terms}$$

$$x = 12 \qquad \text{Divide each side by 4}$$

We could check our solution by substituting 12 for x in the original equation. If we do so, the result is a true statement. The solution is 12.

As you can see from Example 5, the most important step in solving an equation that involves fractions is the first step. In that first step we multiply both sides of the equation by the LCD for all the fractions in the equation. After we have done so, the equation is clear of fractions because the LCD has the property that all the denominators divide it evenly.

EXAMPLE 6 Solve the equation $2x + \frac{1}{2} = \frac{3}{4}$.

SOLUTION This time the LCD is 4. We begin by multiplying both sides of the equation by 4 to clear the equation of fractions.

$$\mathbf{4}\left(2x + \frac{1}{2}\right) = \mathbf{4}\left(\frac{3}{4}\right) \qquad \text{Multiply each side by the LCD, 4}$$

$$4(2x) + 4\left(\frac{1}{2}\right) = 4\left(\frac{3}{4}\right) \qquad \text{Apply the distributive property}$$

$$8x + 2 = 3 \qquad \text{Multiplication}$$

$$8x = 1 \qquad \text{Add } -2 \text{ to each side}$$

$$x = \frac{1}{8} \qquad \text{Divide each side by 8}$$

EXAMPLE 7 Solve for x: $\frac{3}{x} + 2 = \frac{1}{2}$. (Assume x is not 0.)

SOLUTION This time the LCD is $2x$. Following the steps we used in Examples 5 and 6, we have

$$\mathbf{2x}\left(\frac{3}{x} + 2\right) = \mathbf{2x}\left(\frac{1}{2}\right) \qquad \text{Multiply through by the LCD, } 2x$$

$$2x\left(\frac{3}{x}\right) + 2x(2) = 2x\left(\frac{1}{2}\right) \qquad \text{Distributive property}$$

$$6 + 4x = x \qquad \text{Multiplication}$$

$$6 = -3x \qquad \text{Add } -4x \text{ to each side}$$

$$-2 = x \qquad \text{Divide each side by } -3$$

5. Solve: $\frac{x}{3} + \frac{x}{6} = 9$

Instructor Note
Examples 5–7 are different from the previous examples in that we use the multiplication property first to clear the equations of fractions. I sometimes take two days to cover this section and wait until the second day to cover these problems.

6. Solve: $3x + \frac{1}{4} = \frac{5}{8}$

7. Solve: $\frac{4}{x} + 3 = \frac{11}{5}$

Instructor Note
The equation shown in Example 7 is not a linear equation in one variable. Sometimes I point this out to my classes. If I were doing this kind of problem in my algebra classes, I would mention the possibility of obtaining extraneous solutions. However, I never mention this fact in prealgebra or basic math.

Answers
5. 18 **6.** $\frac{1}{8}$ **7.** -5

Equations Containing Decimals

8. Solve: $\frac{1}{5}x - 2.4 = 8.3$

> **EXAMPLE 8**   Solve: $\frac{1}{2}x - 3.78 = 2.52$
>
> **SOLUTION**   We begin by adding 3.78 to each side of the equation. Then we multiply each side by 2.
>
> $$\frac{1}{2}x - 3.78 = 2.52$$
>
> $$\frac{1}{2}x - 3.78 + \mathbf{3.78} = 2.52 + \mathbf{3.78} \qquad \text{Add 3.78 to each side}$$
>
> $$\frac{1}{2}x = 6.30$$
>
> $$\mathbf{2}\left(\frac{1}{2}x\right) = \mathbf{2}(6.30) \qquad \text{Multiply each side by 2}$$
>
> $$x = 12.6$$

9. Solve: $7a - 0.18 = 2a + 0.77$

> **EXAMPLE 9**   Solve: $5a - 0.42 = -3a + 0.98$
>
> **SOLUTION**   We can isolate a on the left side of the equation by adding $3a$ to each side.
>
> $$5a + \mathbf{3a} - 0.42 = -3a + \mathbf{3a} + 0.98 \qquad \text{Add } 3a \text{ to each side}$$
>
> $$8a - 0.42 = 0.98$$
>
> $$8a - 0.42 + \mathbf{0.42} = 0.98 + \mathbf{0.42} \qquad \text{Add 0.42 to each side}$$
>
> $$8a = 1.40$$
>
> $$\frac{8a}{\mathbf{8}} = \frac{1.40}{\mathbf{8}} \qquad \text{Divide each side by 8}$$
>
> $$a = 0.175$$

Getting Ready for Class

After reading through the preceding section, respond in your own words and in complete sentences.

1. Apply the distributive property to the expression $3(x + 4)$.
2. Write the equation that results when $-4a$ is added to both sides of the equation below.

   $$6a + 9 = 4a - 3$$

3. Solve the equation $2x + \frac{1}{2} = \frac{3}{4}$ by first adding $-\frac{1}{2}$ to each side.

   Compare your answer with the solution to the equation shown in Example 6.

Problem Set 10.4

A Solve each equation using the methods shown in this section. [Examples 1–4]

▶ **1.** $5(x + 1) = 20$
3

2. $4(x + 2) = 24$
4

3. $6(x - 3) = -6$
2

4. $7(x - 2) = -7$
1

▶ **5.** $2x + 4 = 3x + 7$
−3

6. $5x + 3 = 2x + (-3)$
−2

7. $7y - 3 = 4y - 15$
−4

▶ **8.** $3y + 5 = 9y + 8$
$-\dfrac{1}{2}$

9. $12x + 3 = -2x + 17$
1

10. $15x + 1 = -4x + 20$
1

▶ **11.** $6x - 8 = -x - 8$
0

12. $7x - 5 = -x - 5$
0

▶ **13.** $7(a - 1) + 4 = 11$
2

14. $3(a - 2) + 1 = 4$
3

15. $8(x + 5) - 6 = 18$
−2

16. $7(x + 8) - 4 = 10$
−6

▶ **17.** $2(3x - 6) + 1 = 7$
3

18. $5(2x - 4) + 8 = 38$
5

▶ **19.** $10(y + 1) + 4 = 3y + 7$
−1

20. $12(y + 2) + 5 = 2y - 1$
−3

▶ **21.** $4(x - 6) + 1 = 2x - 9$
7

22. $7(x - 4) + 3 = 5x - 9$
8

23. $2(3x + 1) = 4(x - 1)$
−3

▶ **24.** $7(x - 8) = 2(x - 13)$
6

25. $3a + 4 = 2(a - 5) + 15$
1

26. $10a + 3 = 4(a - 1) + 1$
−1

▶ **27.** $9x - 6 = -3(x + 2) - 24$
−2

28. $8x - 10 = -4(x + 3) + 2$
0

▶ **29.** $3x - 5 = 11 + 2(x - 6)$
4

30. $5x - 7 = -7 + 2(x + 3)$
2

B Solve each equation by first finding the LCD for the fractions in the equation and then multiplying both sides of the equation by it. (Assume x is not 0 in Problems 39–46.) [Examples 5–7]

▶ **31.** $\dfrac{x}{3} + \dfrac{x}{6} = 5$
10

32. $\dfrac{x}{2} - \dfrac{x}{4} = 3$
12

▶ **33.** $\dfrac{x}{5} - x = 4$
-5

34. $\dfrac{x}{3} + x = 8$
6

▶ **35.** $3x + \dfrac{1}{2} = \dfrac{1}{4}$
$-\dfrac{1}{12}$

36. $3x - \dfrac{1}{3} = \dfrac{1}{6}$
$\dfrac{1}{6}$

▶ **37.** $\dfrac{x}{3} + \dfrac{1}{2} = -\dfrac{1}{2}$
-3

38. $\dfrac{x}{2} + \dfrac{4}{3} = -\dfrac{2}{3}$
-4

39. $\dfrac{4}{x} = \dfrac{1}{5}$
20

▶ **40.** $\dfrac{2}{3} = \dfrac{6}{x}$
9

41. $\dfrac{3}{x} + 1 = \dfrac{2}{x}$
-1

42. $\dfrac{4}{x} + 3 = \dfrac{1}{x}$
-1

▶ **43.** $\dfrac{3}{x} - \dfrac{2}{x} = \dfrac{1}{5}$
5

▶ **44.** $\dfrac{7}{x} + \dfrac{1}{x} = 2$
4

45. $\dfrac{1}{x} - \dfrac{1}{2} = -\dfrac{1}{4}$
4

▶ **46.** $\dfrac{3}{x} - \dfrac{4}{5} = -\dfrac{1}{5}$
5

Solve each equation.

▶ **47.** $4x - 4.7 = 3.5$
2.05

48. $2x + 3.8 = -7.7$
-5.75

49. $0.02 + 5y = -0.3$
-0.064

50. $0.8 + 10y = -0.7$
-0.15

51. $\dfrac{1}{3}x - 2.99 = 1.02$
12.03

▶ **52.** $\dfrac{1}{7}x + 2.87 = -3.01$
-41.16

53. $7n - 0.32 = 5n + 0.56$
0.44

54. $6n + 0.88 = 2n - 0.77$
-0.4125

55. $3a + 4.6 = 7a + 5.3$
-0.175

56. $2a - 3.3 = 7a - 5.2$
0.38

57. $0.5x + 0.1(x + 20) = 3.2$
2

58. $0.1x + 0.5(x + 8) = 7$
5

Find the value of x for each of the figures, given the perimeter.

59. $P = 36$ $x = 10$

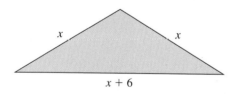

x x

$x + 6$

60. $P = 30$ $x = 5$

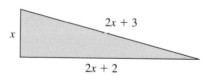

x $2x + 3$

$2x + 2$

▶ **61.** $P = 16$ $x = 5$

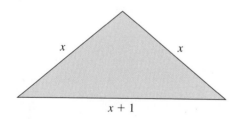

x x

$x + 1$

62. $P = 60$ $x = 10$

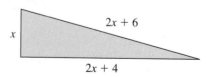

x $2x + 6$

$2x + 4$

Applying the Concepts

63. Skyscrapers The chart shows the heights of the three tallest buildings in the world. The height of the Empire State Building relative to the Petronas Towers can be given by the equation $1483 = 233 + x$. What is the height of the Empire State Building?

1,250 feet

Such Great Heights

Taipei 101
Taipei, Taiwan
1,670 ft

Petronas Tower 1 & 2
Kuala Lumpur, Malaysia
1,483 ft

Sears Tower
Chicago, USA
1,450 ft

Source: www.tenmojo.com

64. Sound The chart shows the decibel level of various sounds. The human threshold of pain relative to the decibel level at a football stadium is given by the equation $117 = x - 3$. What is the human threshold of pain?

120 dB

Sounds Around Us

Normal Conversation))))) **60 dB**

Football Stadium))))))))) **117 dB**

Blue Whale))))))))))))) **188 dB**

Source: www.4to40.com

▶ **65. Geometry** The figure shows part of a room. From a point on the floor, the angle of elevation to the top of the window is 45°, while the angle of elevation to the ceiling above the window is 58°. Solving either of the equations $58 - x = 45$ or $45 + x = 58$ will give us the number of degrees in the angle labeled $x°$. Solve both equations.

13

Ceiling

Window

58°

45°

Floor

▶ **66. Rhind Papyrus** As we mentioned in the introduction to this section, the Rhind Papyrus was created around 1650 BC and contains the riddle, "What quantity when added to one-fourth of itself becomes 15?" This riddle can be solved by finding x in the equation below. Solve this equation.

$$x + \frac{1}{4}x = 15 \quad x = 12$$

Bridgeman Art Library/ Getty Images

67. Math Tutoring Several students on campus decide to start a small business that offers tutoring services to students enrolled in mathematics courses. The following equation shows the amount of money they collected at the end of the month, assuming expenses of $400 and a charge of $30 an hour per student. Solve the equation $\$500 = \$30x - 400$ to determine the number of hours students came in for tutoring in one month.

30 hours

68. Shopping for a Calculator You find that you need to purchase a specific calculator for your college mathematics class. The equation $\$18.75 = p + \frac{1}{4}p$ shows the price charged by the college bookstore for a calculator after it has been marked up. How much did the bookstore pay the manufacturer for the calculator?

$15.00

■ Getting Ready for the Next Section

Write the mathematical expressions that are equivalent to each of the following English phrases.

69. The sum of a number and 2

$x + 2$

70. The sum of a number and 5

$x + 5$

71. Twice a number

$2x$

72. Three times a number

$3x$

73. Twice the sum of a number and 6

$2(x + 6)$

74. Three times the sum of a number and 8

$3(x + 8)$

75. The difference of x and 4

$x - 4$

76. The difference of 4 and x

$4 - x$

77. The sum of twice a number and 5

$2x + 5$

78. The sum of three times a number and 4

$3x + 4$

■ Maintaining Your Skills

Place the correct symbol, $<$ or $>$, between the numbers.

79. $0.02 \quad < \quad 0.2$

80. $0.3 \quad > \quad 0.03$

81. $0.45 \quad > \quad 0.4$

82. $0.5 \quad < \quad 0.56$

Write the numbers in order from smallest to largest.

83. $0.01 \quad 0.013 \quad 0.03 \quad 0.003 \quad 0.031 \quad 0.001$

$0.001, 0.003, 0.01, 0.013, 0.03, 0.031$

84. $0.062 \quad 0.006 \quad 0.002 \quad 0.02 \quad 0.06 \quad 0.026$

$0.002, 0.006, 0.02, 0.026, 0.06, 0.062$

■ Extending the Concepts

85. Admission to the school basketball game is $4 for students and $6 for general admission. For the first game of the season, 100 more student tickets than general admission tickets were sold. The total amount of money collected was $2,400.

   a. Write an equation that will help us find the number of students in attendance.

   $4x + 6(x - 100) = 2,400$

   b. Solve this equation for x.

   $x = 300$

   c. What was the total attendance for the game?

   500 people

Objectives

A Set up and solve number problems using linear equations.

B Set up and solve geometry problems using linear equations.

C Set up and solve age problems using linear equations.

Introduction . . .

As you begin reading through the examples in this section, you may find yourself asking why some of these problems seem so contrived. The title of the section is "Applications," but many of the problems here don't seem to have much to do with real life. You are right about that. Example 5 is what we refer to as an "age problem." Realistically, it is not the kind of problem you would expect to find if you choose a career in which you use algebra. However, solving age problems is good practice for someone with little experience with application problems, because the solution process has a form that can be applied to all similar age problems.

To begin this section we list the steps used in solving application problems. We call this strategy the *Blueprint for Problem Solving*. It is an outline that will overlay the solution process we use on all application problems.

Blueprint for Problem Solving

Step 1: **Read** the problem, and then mentally **list** the items that are known and the items that are unknown.

Step 2: **Assign a variable** to one of the unknown items. (In most cases this will amount to letting x equal the item that is asked for in the problem.) Then **translate** the other **information** in the problem to expressions involving the variable.

Step 3: **Reread** the problem, and then **write an equation**, using the items and variables listed in Steps 1 and 2, that describes the situation.

Step 4: **Solve the equation** found in Step 3.

Step 5: **Write** your **answer** using a complete sentence.

Step 6: **Reread** the problem, and **check** your solution with the original words in the problem.

There are a number of substeps within each of the steps in our blueprint. For instance, with Steps 1 and 2 it is always a good idea to draw a diagram or picture if it helps you to visualize the relationship between the items in the problem.

It is important for you to remember that solving application problems is more of an art than a science. Be flexible. No one strategy works all of the time. Try to stay away from looking for the "one way" to set up and solve a problem. Think of the blueprint for problem solving as guidelines that will help you organize your approach to these problems, rather than as a set of rules.

A Number Problems

 EXAMPLE 1 The sum of a number and 2 is 8. Find the number.

SOLUTION Using our blueprint for problem solving as an outline, we solve the problem as follows:

Step 1 *Read* the problem, and then mentally *list* the items that are known and the items that are unknown.

> *Known items:* The numbers 2 and 8
> *Unknown item:* The number in question

PRACTICE PROBLEMS

1. The sum of a number and 3 is 10. Find the number.

Step 2 *Assign a variable* to one of the unknown items. Then *translate* the other *information* in the problem to expressions involving the variable.

> Let x = the number asked for in the problem
> Then "The sum of a number and 2" translates to $x + 2$.

Step 3 *Reread* the problem, and then *write an equation,* using the items and variables listed in Steps 1 and 2, that describes the situation.

> With all word problems, the word "is" translates to = .

> The sum of x and 2 is 8.
> $x + 2 = 8$

Step 4 *Solve the equation* found in Step 3.

$$x + 2 = 8$$
$$x + 2 + (-2) = 8 + (-2) \qquad \text{Add } -2 \text{ to each side}$$
$$x = 6$$

Step 5 *Write* your *answer* using a complete sentence.

> The number is 6.

Step 6 *Reread* the problem, and *check* your solution with the original words in the problem.

> The sum of **6** and 2 is 8. A true statement

To help with other problems of the type shown in Example 1, here are some common English words and phrases and their mathematical translations.

English	Algebra
The sum of a and b	$a + b$
The difference of a and b	$a - b$
The product of a and b	$a \cdot b$
The quotient of a and b	$\dfrac{a}{b}$
Of	$\cdot$ (multiply)
Is	$=$ (equals)
A number	x
4 more than x	$x + 4$
4 times x	$4x$
4 less than x	$x - 4$

You may find some examples and problems in this section and the problem set that follows that you can solve without using algebra or our blueprint. It is very important that you solve those problems using the methods we are showing here. The purpose behind these problems is to give you experience using the blueprint as a guide to solving problems written in words. Your answers are much less important than the work that you show in obtaining your answer.

EXAMPLE 2 If 5 is added to the sum of twice a number and three times the number, the result is 25. Find the number.

SOLUTION

Step 1 *Read and list.*

> *Known items:* The numbers 5 and 25, twice a number, and three times a number
> *Unknown item:* The number in question

---

2. If 4 is added to the sum of twice a number and three times the number, the result is 34. Find the number.

Answer

1. The number is 7.

Step 2 *Assign a variable and translate the information.*

Let x = the number asked for in the problem.
Then "The sum of twice a number and three times the number" translates to $2x + 3x$.

Step 3 *Reread and write an equation.*

Step 4 *Solve the equation.*

$$5 + 2x + 3x = 25$$

$5x + 5 = 25$	Simplify the left side
$5x + 5 + (-5) = 25 + (-5)$	Add -5 to both sides
$5x = 20$	Addition
$\dfrac{5x}{5} = \dfrac{20}{5}$	Divide by 5
$x = 4$	

Step 5 *Write your answer.*

The number is 4.

Step 6 *Reread and check.*

Twice **4** is 8, and three times **4** is 12. Their sum is $8 + 12 = 20$. Five added to this is 25. Therefore, 5 added to the sum of twice **4** and three times **4** is 25.

B Geometry Problems

EXAMPLE 3 The length of a rectangle is three times the width. The perimeter is 72 centimeters. Find the width and the length.

SOLUTION

Step 1 *Read and list.*

Known items: The length is three times the width.
The perimeter is 72 centimeters.

Unknown items: The length and the width

Step 2 *Assign a variable, and translate the information.* We let x = the width. Because the length is three times the width, the length must be $3x$. A picture will help.

$3x$ (length)

FIGURE 1

3. The length of a rectangle is twice the width. The perimeter is 42 centimeters. Find the length and the width.

Answer

2. The number is 6.

Step 3 *Reread and write an equation.* Because the perimeter is the sum of the sides, it must be $x + x + 3x + 3x$ (the sum of the four sides). But the perimeter is also given as 72 centimeters. Hence,

$$x + x + 3x + 3x = 72$$

Step 4 *Solve the equation.*

$$x + x + 3x + 3x = 72$$
$$8x = 72$$
$$x = 9$$

Step 5 *Write your answer.* The width, x, is 9 centimeters. The length, $3x$, must be 27 centimeters.

Step 6 *Reread and check.* From the diagram below, we see that these solutions check:

Perimeter is 72   Length $= 3 \times$ Width

$$9 + 9 + 27 + 27 = 72 \qquad\qquad 27 = 3 \cdot 9$$

FIGURE 2

Next we review some facts about triangles that we introduced in a previous chapter.

FACTS FROM GEOMETRY   **Labeling Triangles and the Sum of the Angles in a Triangle**

One way to label the important parts of a triangle is to label the vertices with capital letters and the sides with small letters, as shown in Figure 3.

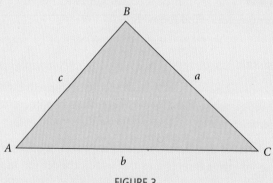

FIGURE 3

In Figure 3, notice that side a is opposite vertex A, side b is opposite vertex B, and side c is opposite vertex C. Also, because each vertex is the vertex of one of the angles of the triangle, we refer to the three interior angles as A, B, and C.

In any triangle, the sum of the interior angles is $180°$. For the triangle shown in Figure 3, the relationship is written

$$A + B + C = 180°$$

Answer
3. The width is 7 cm, and the length is 14 cm.

EXAMPLE 4 The angles in a triangle are such that one angle is twice the smallest angle, while the third angle is three times as large as the smallest angle. Find the measure of all three angles.

SOLUTION

Step 1 *Read and list.*

Known items: The sum of all three angles is 180°; one angle is twice the smallest angle; and the largest angle is three times the smallest angle.

Unknown items: The measure of each angle

Step 2 *Assign a variable and translate information.* Let x be the smallest angle, then $2x$ will be the measure of another angle, and $3x$ will be the measure of the largest angle.

Step 3 *Reread and write an equation.* When working with geometric objects, drawing a generic diagram will sometimes help us visualize what it is that we are asked to find. In Figure 4, we draw a triangle with angles A, B, and C.

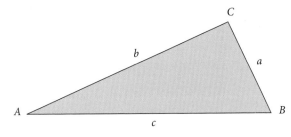

FIGURE 4

We can let the value of $A = x$, the value of $B = 2x$, and the value of $C = 3x$. We know that the sum of angles A, B, and C will be 180°, so our equation becomes

$$x + 2x + 3x = 180°$$

Step 4 *Solve the equation.*

$$x + 2x + 3x = 180°$$
$$6x = 180°$$
$$x = 30°$$

Step 5 *Write the answer.*

The smallest angle A measures 30°.
Angle B measures $2x$, or $2(30°) = 60°$.
Angle C measures $3x$, or $3(30°) = 90°$.

Step 6 *Reread and check.* The angles must add to 180°:

$$A + B + C = 180°$$
$$30° + 60° + 90° = 180°$$
$$180° = 180° \qquad \text{Our answers check}$$

4. The angles in a triangle are such that one angle is three times the smallest angle, while the largest angle is five times the smallest angle. Find the measure of all three angles.

Answer

4. The angles are 20°, 60°, and 100°.

5. Joyce is 21 years older than her son Travis. In six years the sum of their ages will be 49. How old are they now?

C Age Problem

EXAMPLE 5 Jo Ann is 22 years older than her daughter Stacey. In six years the sum of their ages will be 42. How old are they now?

SOLUTION

Step 1 *Read and list:*

Known items:	Jo Ann is 22 years older than Stacey. Six years from now their ages will add to 42.
Unknown items:	Their ages now

Step 2 *Assign a variable and translate the information.* Let x = Stacey's age now. Because Jo Ann is 22 years older than Stacey, her age is $x + 22$.

Step 3 *Reread and write an equation.* As an aid in writing the equation we use the following table:

	Now	In Six years
Stacey	x	$x + 6$
Jo Ann	$x + 22$	$x + 28$

Their ages in six years will be their ages now plus 6

Because the sum of their ages six years from now is 42, we write the equation as

$$(x + 6) + (x + 28) = 42$$

Stacey's age in 6 years Jo Ann's age in 6 years

Step 4 *Solve the equation.*

$$x + 6 + x + 28 = 42$$
$$2x + 34 = 42$$
$$2x = 8$$
$$x = 4$$

Step 5 *Write your answer.* Stacey is now 4 years old, and Jo Ann is $4 + 22 = 26$ years old.

Step 6 *Reread and check.* To check, we see that in six years, Stacey will be 10, and Jo Ann will be 32. The sum of 10 and 32 is 42, which checks.

Car Rental Problem

6. If a car were rented from the company in Example 6 for 2 days and the total charge was $41, how many miles was the car driven?

EXAMPLE 6 A car rental company charges $11 per day and 16 cents per mile for their cars. If a car were rented for 1 day and the charge was $25.40, how many miles was the car driven?

SOLUTION

Step 1 *Read and list.*

Known items:	Charges are $11 per day and 16 cents per mile. Car is rented for 1 day. Total charge is $25.40.
Unknown items:	How many miles the car was driven

Answer

5. Travis is 8; Joyce is 29.

Step 2 *Assign a variable and translate information.* If we let x = the number of miles driven, then the charge for the number of miles driven will be $0.16x$, the cost per mile times the number of miles.

Step 3 *Reread and write an equation.* To find the total cost to rent the car, we add 11 to $0.16x$. Here is the equation that describes the situation:

$$\underbrace{\$11 \text{ per day}}_{11} + \underbrace{16 \text{ cents per mile}}_{0.16x} = \underbrace{\text{Total cost}}_{25.40}$$

Step 4 *Solve the equation.* To solve the equation, we add −11 to each side and then divide each side by 0.16.

$$11 + (\mathbf{-11}) + 0.16x = 25.40 + (\mathbf{-11}) \qquad \text{Add} -11 \text{ to each side}$$
$$0.16x = 14.40$$
$$\frac{0.16x}{\mathbf{0.16}} = \frac{14.40}{\mathbf{0.16}} \qquad \text{Divide each side by 0.16}$$
$$x = 90 \qquad 14.40 \div 0.16 = 90$$

Step 5 *Write the answer.* The car was driven 90 miles.

Step 6 *Reread and check.* The charge for 1 day is $11. The 90 miles adds $90(\$0.16) = \$14.40$ to the 1-day charge. The total is $\$11 + \$14.40 = \$25.40$, which checks with the total charge given in the problem.

Coin Problem

EXAMPLE 7 Diane has $1.60 in dimes and nickels. If she has 7 more dimes than nickels, how many of each coin does she have?

SOLUTION
Step 1 *Read and list.*

Known items:	We have dimes and nickels. There are 7 more dimes than nickels, and the total value of the coins is $1.60.
Unknown items:	How many of each type of coin Diane has

Step 2 *Assign a variable and translate information.* If we let x = the number of nickels, then the number of dimes must be $x + 7$, because Diane has 7 more dimes than nickels. Because each nickel is worth 5 cents, the amount of money she has in nickels is $0.05x$. Similarly, because each dime is worth 10 cents, the amount of money she has in dimes is $0.10(x + 7)$. Here is a table that summarizes what we have so far:

	Nickels	Dimes
Number of	x	$x + 7$
Value of	$0.05x$	$0.10(x + 7)$

7. Amy has $1.75 in dimes and quarters. If she has 7 more dimes than quarters, how many of each coin does she have?

Step 3 *Reread and write an equation.* Because the total value of all the coins is $1.60, the equation that describes this situation is

$$\underbrace{\text{Amount of money in nickels}}_{0.05x} + \underbrace{\text{Amount of money in dimes}}_{0.10(x+7)} = \underbrace{\text{Total amount of money}}_{1.60}$$

Step 4 *Solve the equation.* This time, let's show only the essential steps in the solution.

$0.05x + 0.10x + 0.70 = 1.60$	Distributive property
$0.15x + 0.70 = 1.60$	Add $0.05x$ and $0.10x$ to get $0.15x$
$0.15x = 0.90$	Add -0.70 to each side
$x = 6$	Divide each side by 0.15

Step 5 *Write the answer.* Because $x = 6$, Diane has 6 nickels. To find the number of dimes, we add 7 to the number of nickels (she has 7 more dimes than nickels). The number of dimes is $6 + 7 = 13$.

Step 6 *Reread and check.* Here is a check of our results.

$$\begin{array}{l} \text{6 nickels are worth } 6(\$0.05) = \$0.30 \\ \underline{\text{13 dimes are worth } 13(\$0.10) = \$1.30} \\ \text{The total value is} \qquad\qquad\qquad \$1.60 \end{array}$$

Getting Ready for Class

After reading through the preceding section, respond in your own words and in complete sentences.

1. What is the first step in solving a word problem?
2. Write a mathematical expression equivalent to the phrase "the sum of x and ten."
3. Write a mathematical expression equivalent to the phrase "twice the sum of a number and ten."
4. Suppose the length of a rectangle is three times the width. If we let x represent the width of the rectangle, what expression do we use to represent the length?

Problem Set 10.5

Write each of the following English phrases in symbols using the variable x.

▶ **1.** The sum of x and 3
$x + 3$

2. The difference of x and 2
$x - 2$

▶ **3.** The sum of twice x and 1
$2x + 1$

4. The sum of three times x and 4
$3x + 4$

▶ **5.** Five x decreased by 6
$5x - 6$

6. Twice the sum of x and 5
$2(x + 5)$

▶ **7.** Three times the sum of x and 1
$3(x + 1)$

8. Four times the sum of twice x and 1
$4(2x + 1)$

▶ **9.** Five times the sum of three x and 4
$5(3x + 4)$

10. Three x added to the sum of twice x and 1
$(2x + 1) + 3x$

Use the six steps in the "Blueprint for Problem Solving" to solve the following word problems. You may recognize the solution to some of them by just reading the problem. In all cases, be sure to assign a variable and write the equation used to describe the problem. Write your answer using a complete sentence.

A Number Problems [Examples 1, 2]

▶ **11.** The sum of a number and 3 is 5. Find the number.
The number is 2.

12. If 2 is subtracted from a number, the result is 4. Find the number.
The number is 6.

▶ **13.** The sum of twice a number and 1 is −3. Find the number.
The number is −2.

14. If three times a number is increased by 4, the result is −8. Find the number.
The number is −4.

▶ **15.** When 6 is subtracted from five times a number, the result is 9. Find the number.
The number is 3.

16. Twice the sum of a number and 5 is 4. Find the number.
The number is −3.

▶ **17.** Three times the sum of a number and 1 is 18. Find the number.
The number is 5.

18. Four times the sum of twice a number and 6 is −8. Find the number.
The number is −4.

▶ **19.** Five times the sum of three times a number and 4 is −10. Find the number.
The number is −2.

20. If the sum of three times a number and two times the same number is increased by 1, the result is 16. Find the number.
The number is 3.

▶ Selected exercises available online at www.webassign.net/brookscole

B   Geometry Problems   [Examples 3, 4]

▶ **21.** The length of a rectangle is twice its width. The perimeter is 30 meters. Find the length and the width.

    The length is 10 m and the width is 5 m.

22. The width of a rectangle is 3 feet less than its length. If the perimeter is 22 feet, what is the width?

    The width is 4 ft.

▶ **23.** The perimeter of a square is 32 centimeters. What is the length of one side?

    The length of one side is 8 cm.

24. Two sides of a triangle are equal in length, and the third side is 10 inches. If the perimeter is 26 inches, how long are the two equal sides?

    The two equal sides are each 8 in. long.

▶ **25.** Two angles in a triangle are equal, and their sum is equal to the third angle in the triangle. What are the measures of each of the three interior angles?

    The measures of the angles are 45°, 45°, and 90°.

26. One angle in a triangle measures twice the smallest angle, while the largest angle is six times the smallest angle. Find the measures of all three angles.

    The measures of the angles are 20°, 40°, and 120°.

▶ **27.** The smallest angle in a triangle is $\frac{1}{3}$ as large as the largest angle. The third angle is twice the smallest angle. Find the three angles.

    The angles are 30°, 60°, and 90°.

28. One angle in a triangle is half the largest angle, but three times the smallest. Find all three angles.

    The angles are 18°, 54°, and 108°.

C   Age Problems   [Example 5]

▶ **29.** Pat is 20 years older than his son Patrick. In 2 years, the sum of their ages will be 90. How old are they now?   Patrick is 33 years old, and Pat is 53 years old.

	Now	In 2 Years
Patrick	x	
Pat		

30. Diane is 23 years older than her daughter Amy. In 5 years, the sum of their ages will be 91. How old are they now?   Amy is 29 years old, and Diane is 52 years old.

	Now	In 5 Years
Amy	x	
Diane		

▶ **31.** Dale is 4 years older than Sue. Five years ago the sum of their ages was 64. How old are they now?

    Sue is 35 years old, and Dale is 39 years old.

32. Pat is 2 years younger than his wife, Wynn. Ten years ago the sum of their ages was 48. How old are they now?

    Wynn is 35 years old, and Pat is 33 years old.

▬   Renting a Car   [Example 6]

33. A car rental company charges $10 a day and 16 cents per mile for their cars. If a car were rented for 1 day for a total charge of $23.92, how many miles was it driven?

    87 mi

34. A car rental company charges $12 a day and 18 cents per mile to rent their cars. If the total charge for a 1-day rental were $33.78, how many miles was the car driven?

    121 mi

▶ **35.** A rental company charges $9 per day and 15 cents a mile for their cars. If a car were rented for 2 days for a total charge of $40.05, how many miles was it driven?

    147 mi

▶ **36.** A car rental company charges $11 a day and 18 cents per mile to rent their cars. If the total charge for a 2-day rental were $61.60, how many miles was it driven?

    220 mi

■ Coin Problems [Example 7]

▶ **37.** Mary has $2.20 in dimes and nickels. If she has 10 more dimes than nickels, how many of each coin does she have?

8 nickels, 18 dimes

▶ **38.** Bob has $1.65 in dimes and nickels. If he has 9 more nickels than dimes, how many of each coin does he have?

17 nickels, 8 dimes

39. Suppose you have $9.60 in dimes and quarters. How many of each coin do you have if you have twice as many quarters as dimes?

16 dimes, 32 quarters

40. A collection of dimes and quarters has a total value of $2.75. If there are 3 times as many dimes as quarters, how many of each coin is in the collection?

5 quarters, 15 dimes

■ Miscellaneous Problems

▶ **41. Magic Square** The sum of the numbers in each row, each column, and each diagonal of the square below is 15. Use this fact, along with the information in the first column of the square, to write an equation containing the variable x, then solve the equation to find x. Next, write and solve equations that will give you y and z.

$x = 8, y = 6, z = 9$

x	1	y
3	5	7
4	z	2

42. Magic Square The sum of the numbers in each row, each column, and each diagonal of the square below is 3. Use this fact, along with the information in the second row of the square, to write an equation containing the variable a, then solve the equation to find a. Next, write and solve an equation that will allow you to find the value of b. Next, write and solve equations that will give you c and d.

$a = -1, b = 2, c = 5, d = -3$

4	d	b
a	1	3
0	c	-2

▶ **43. Wages** JoAnn works in the publicity office at the state university. She is paid $14 an hour for the first 35 hours she works each week and $21 an hour for every hour after that. If she makes $574 one week, how many hours did she work?

39 hours

▶ **44. Ticket Sales** Stacey is selling tickets to the school play. The tickets are $6 for adults and $4 for children. She sells twice as many adult tickets as children's tickets and brings in a total of $112. How many of each kind of ticket did she sell?

7 children's tickets, 14 adult tickets

45. Cars The chart shows the fastest cars in America. The maximum speed of an Evans 487 is twice the sum of the speed of a trucker and 45 miles per hour. What is the speed of the trucker?

60 miles per hour

▶ **46. Skyscrapers** The chart shows the heights of the three tallest buildings in the world. The Sears Tower is 80 feet less than 5 times the height of the Statue of Liberty. What is the height of the Statue of Liberty?

306 feet

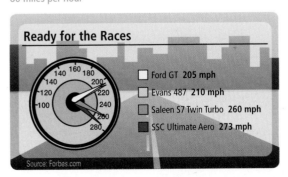

Ready for the Races

☐ Ford GT **205 mph**
☐ Evans 487 **210 mph**
☐ Saleen S7 Twin Turbo **260 mph**
■ SSC Ultimate Aero **273 mph**

Source: Forbes.com

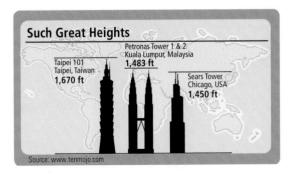

Such Great Heights

Taipei 101
Taipei, Taiwan
1,670 ft

Petronas Tower 1 & 2
Kuala Lumpur, Malaysia
1,483 ft

Sears Tower
Chicago, USA
1,450 ft

Source: www.tenmojo.com

■ Getting Ready for the Next Section

Simplify.

47. $\frac{5}{9}(95 - 32)$

35

48. $\frac{5}{9}(77 - 32)$

25

49. Find the value of $90 - x$ when $x = 25$.

65

50. Find the value of $180 - x$ when $x = 25$.

155

51. Find the value of $2x + 6$ when $x = -2$

2

52. Find the value of $2x + 6$ when $x = 0$.

6

Solve.

53. $40 = 2l + 12$

14

54. $80 = 2l + 12$

34

55. $6 + 3y = 4$

$-\frac{2}{3}$

56. $8 + 3y = 4$

$-\frac{4}{3}$

■ Maintaining Your Skills

The problems below review some of the work you have done with percents.

Change each fraction to a decimal and then to a percent.

57. $\frac{3}{4}$

0.75, 75%

58. $\frac{5}{8}$

0.625, 62.5%

59. $1\frac{1}{5}$

1.2, 120%

60. $\frac{7}{10}$

0.7, 70%

Change each percent to a fraction and a decimal.

61. 37%

$\frac{37}{100}$, 0.37

62. 18%

$\frac{9}{50}$, 0.18

63. 3.4%

$\frac{17}{500}$, 0.034

64. 125%

$\frac{5}{4}$, 1.25

65. What number is 15% of 135?

20.25

66. 19 is what percent of 38?

50%

67. 12 is 16% of what number?

75

10.6

Introduction . . .

In mathematics a formula is an equation that contains more than one variable. The equation $P = 2w + 2l$ is an example of a formula. This formula tells us the relationship between the perimeter P of a rectangle, its length l, and its width w.

There are many formulas with which you may be familiar already. Perhaps you have used the formula $d = r \cdot t$ to find out how far you would go if you traveled at 50 miles an hour for 3 hours. If you take a chemistry class while you are in college, you will certainly use the formula that gives the relationship between the two temperature scales, Fahrenheit and Celsius:

$$F = \frac{9}{5}C + 32$$

Although there are many kinds of problems we can work using formulas, we will limit ourselves to those that require only substitutions. The examples that follow illustrate this type of problem.

A Formulas

EXAMPLE 1 The perimeter P of a rectangular livestock pen is 40 feet. If the width w is 6 feet, find the length.

6 feet

l

SOLUTION First we substitute 40 for P and 6 for w in the formula $P = 2l + 2w$. Then we solve for l:

When $P = 40$ and $w = 6$
the formula $P = 2l + 2w$
becomes $40 = 2l + 2(6)$
or $40 = 2l + 12$ Multiply 2 and 6
             $28 = 2l$ Add -12 to each side
             $14 = l$ Multiply each side by $\frac{1}{2}$

To summarize our results, if a rectangular pen has a perimeter of 40 feet and a width of 6 feet, then the length must be 14 feet.

PRACTICE PROBLEMS

1. Suppose the livestock pen in Example 1 has a perimeter of 80 feet. If the width is still 6 feet, what is the new length?

Answer
1. 34 feet

2. Use the formula in Example 2 to find C when F is 77 degrees.

Note The formula we are using here,

$$C = \frac{5}{9}(F - 32),$$

is an alternative form of the formula we mentioned in the introduction to this section:

$$F = \frac{9}{5}C + 32$$

Both formulas describe the same relationship between the two temperature scales. If you go on to take an algebra class, you will learn how to convert one formula into the other.

3. Use the formula in Example 3 to find y when x is 0.

4. Use the formula in Example 4 to find y when x is -3.

EXAMPLE 2 Use the formula $C = \frac{5}{9}(F - 32)$ to find C when F is 95 degrees.

SOLUTION Substituting 95 for F in the formula gives us the following:

When $\qquad F = 95$

the formula $\quad C = \frac{5}{9}(F - 32)$

becomes $\qquad C = \frac{5}{9}(95 - 32)$

$\qquad\qquad\qquad = \frac{5}{9}(63)$

$\qquad\qquad\qquad = \frac{5}{9} \cdot \frac{63}{1}$

$\qquad\qquad\qquad = \frac{315}{9}$

$\qquad\qquad\qquad = 35$

A temperature of 95 degrees Fahrenheit is the same as a temperature of 35 degrees Celsius.

EXAMPLE 3 Use the formula $y = 2x + 6$ to find y when x is -2.

SOLUTION Proceeding as we have in the previous examples, we have:

When $\qquad x = -2$

the formula $\quad y = 2x + 6$

becomes $\qquad y = 2(-2) + 6$

$\qquad\qquad\qquad = -4 + 6$

$\qquad\qquad\qquad = 2$

In some cases evaluating a formula also involves solving an equation, as the next example illustrates.

EXAMPLE 4 Find y when x is 3 in the formula $2x + 3y = 4$.

SOLUTION First we substitute 3 for x; then we solve the resulting equation for y.

When $\qquad\qquad\quad x = 3$

the equation $\quad 2x + 3y = 4$

becomes $\qquad 2(3) + 3y = 4$

$\qquad\qquad\qquad 6 + 3y = 4$

$\qquad\qquad\qquad\qquad 3y = -2 \qquad$ Add -6 to each side

$\qquad\qquad\qquad\qquad y = -\frac{2}{3} \qquad$ Divide each side by 3

B Rate Equation

Now we will look at some problems that use what is called the *rate equation*. You use this equation on an intuitive level when you are estimating how long it will take you to drive long distances. For example, if you drive at 50 miles per hour for 2 hours, you will travel 100 miles. Here is the rate equation:

$$\text{Distance} = \text{rate} \cdot \text{time, or } d = r \cdot t$$

Answers

2. 25 degrees Celsius **3.** 6

4. $\frac{10}{3}$

The rate equation has two equivalent forms, one of which is obtained by solving for r, while the other is obtained by solving for t. Here they are:

$$r = \frac{d}{t} \text{ and } t = \frac{d}{r}$$

The rate in this equation is also referred to as *average speed*.

EXAMPLE 5   At 1 P.M., Jordan leaves her house and drives at an average speed of 50 miles per hour to her sister's house. She arrives at 4 P.M.

> **a.** How many hours was the drive to her sister's house?
> **b.** How many miles from her sister does Jordan live?

SOLUTION

> **a.** If she left at 1:00 P.M. and arrived at 4:00 P.M., we simply subtract 1 from 4 for an answer of 3 hours.
>
> **b.** We are asked to find a distance in miles given a rate of 50 miles per hour and a time of 3 hours. We will use the rate equation, $d = r \cdot t$, to solve this. We have:
>
> $d = 50 \text{ miles per hour} \cdot 3 \text{ hours}$
> $d = 50(3)$
> $d = 150 \text{ miles}$

Notice that we were asked to find a distance in miles, so our answer has a unit of miles. When we are asked to find a time, our answer will include a unit of time, like days, hours, minutes, or seconds.

When we are asked to find a rate, our answer will include units of rate, like miles per hour, feet per second, problems per minute, and so on.

FACTS FROM GEOMETRY

Earlier we defined complementary angles as angles that add to 90°. That is, if x and y are complementary angles, then

$$x + y = 90°$$

If we solve this formula for y, we obtain a formula equivalent to our original formula:

$$y = 90° - x$$

Because y is the complement of x, we can generalize by saying that the complement of angle x is the angle $90° - x$. By a similar reasoning process, we can say that the supplement of angle x is the angle $180° - x$. To summarize, if x is an angle, then

> the complement of x is $90° - x$, and
> the supplement of x is $180° - x$

If you go on to take a trigonometry class, you will see these formulas again.

---

5. At 9 A.M. Maggie leaves her house and drives at an average speed of 60 miles per hour to her sister's house. She arrives at 11 A.M.
   a. How many hours was the drive to her sister's house?
   b. How many miles from her sister does Maggie live?

Complementary angles

Supplementary angles

Answer
5. a. 2 hours **b.** 120 miles

6. Find the complement and the supplement of 35°.

EXAMPLE 6   Find the complement and the supplement of 25°.

SOLUTION   We can use the formulas above with $x = 25°$.

The complement of 25° is $90° - 25° = 65°$.
The supplement of 25° is $180° - 25° = 155°$.

Getting Ready for Class

After reading through the preceding section, respond in your own words and in complete sentences.

1. What is a formula?
2. How do you solve a formula for one of its variables?
3. What are complementary angles?
4. What is the formula that converts temperature on the Celsius scale to temperature on the Fahrenheit scale?

Answer

6. Complement = 55°;
    Supplement = 145°

Problem Set 10.6

A The formula for the area A of a rectangle with length l and width w is $A = l \cdot w$. Find A if: [Examples 1–4]

▶ **1.** $l = 32$ feet and $w = 22$ feet
704 ft²

▶ **2.** $l = 22$ feet and $w = 12$ feet
264 ft²

▶ **3.** $l = \dfrac{3}{2}$ inch and $w = \dfrac{3}{4}$ inch
$\dfrac{9}{8}$ in²

4. $l = \dfrac{3}{5}$ inch and $w = \dfrac{3}{10}$ inch
$\dfrac{9}{50}$ in²

The formula $G = H \cdot R$ tells us how much gross pay G a person receives for working H hours at an hourly rate of pay R. In Problems 5-8, find G.

▶ **5.** $H = 40$ hours and $R = \$6$
$240

6. $H = 36$ hours and $R = \$8$
$288

▶ **7.** $H = 30$ hours and $R = \$9\dfrac{1}{2}$
$285

8. $H = 20$ hours and $R = \$6\dfrac{3}{4}$
$135

Because there are 3 feet in every yard, the formula $F = 3 \cdot Y$ will convert Y yards into F feet. In Problems 9-12, find F.

▶ **9.** $Y = 4$ yards
12 ft

10. $Y = 8$ yards
24 ft

▶ **11.** $Y = 2\dfrac{2}{3}$ yards
8 ft

12. $Y = 6\dfrac{1}{3}$ yards
19 ft

If you invest P dollars (P is for *principal*) at simple interest rate R for T years, the amount of interest you will earn is given by the formula $I = P \cdot R \cdot T$. In Problems 13 and 14, find I.

▶ **13.** $P = \$1,000$, $R = \dfrac{7}{100}$, and $T = 2$ years
$140

14. $P = \$2,000$, $R = \dfrac{6}{100}$, and $T = 2\dfrac{1}{2}$ years
$300

In Problems 15-18, use the formula $P = 2w + 2l$ to find P.

▶ **15.** $w = 10$ inches and $l = 19$ inches
58 in.

16. $w = 12$ inches and $l = 22$ inches
68 in.

▶ **17.** $w = \dfrac{3}{4}$ foot and $l = \dfrac{7}{8}$ foot
$3\dfrac{1}{4} = \dfrac{13}{4}$ ft

18. $w = \dfrac{1}{2}$ foot and $l = \dfrac{3}{2}$ feet
4 ft

We have mentioned the two temperature scales, Fahrenheit and Celsius. Table 1 is intended to give you a more intuitive idea of the relationship between the two temperatures scales.

TABLE 1

COMPARING TWO TEMPERATURE SCALES

Situation	Temperature (Fahrenheit)	Temperature (Celsius)
Water freezes	32°F	0°C
Room temperature	68°F	20°C
Normal body temperature	$98\frac{3}{5}$°F	37°C
Water boils	212°F	100°C
Bake cookies	365°F	185°C

Table 2 gives the formulas, in both symbols and words, that are used to convert between the two scales.

TABLE 2

FORMULAS FOR CONVERTING BETWEEN TEMPERATURE SCALES

To Convert From	Formula In Symbols	Formula In Words
Fahrenheit to Celsius	$C = \frac{5}{9}(F - 32)$	Subtract 32, then multiply by $\frac{5}{9}$.
Celsius to Fahrenheit	$F = \frac{9}{5}C + 32$	Multiply by $\frac{9}{5}$, then add 32.

19. Let $F = 212$ in the formula $C = \frac{5}{9}(F - 32)$, and solve for C. Does the value of C agree with the information in Table 1?

$C = 100°C$; yes

20. Let $C = 100$ in the formula $F = \frac{9}{5}C + 32$, and solve for F. Does the value of F agree with the information in Table 1?

$F = 212°F$; yes

21. Let $F = 68$ in the formula $C = \frac{5}{9}(F - 32)$, and solve for C. Does the value of C agree with the information in Table 1?

$C = 20°C$; yes

22. Let $C = 37$ in the formula $F = \frac{9}{5}C + 32$, and solve for F. Does the value of F agree with the information in Table 1?

$F = 98\frac{3}{5}°F$; yes

▶ **23.** Find C when F is 32°.

0°C

▶ **24.** Find C when F is −4°.

−20°C

▶ **25.** Find F when C is −15°.

5°F

▶ **26.** Find F when C is 35°.

95°F

B Maximum Heart Rate In exercise physiology, a person's maximum heart rate, in beats per minute, is found by subtracting his age in years from 220. So, if A represents your age in years, then your maximum heart rate is

$$M = 220 - A$$

Use this formula to complete the following tables.

27.

Age (years)	Maximum Heart Rate (beats per minute)
18	202
19	201
20	200
21	199
22	198
23	197

28.

Age (years)	Maximum Heart Rate (beats per minute)
15	205
20	200
25	195
30	190
35	185
40	180

Training Heart Rate A person's training heart rate, in beats per minute, is the person's resting heart rate plus 60% of the difference between maximum heart rate and his resting heart rate. If resting heart rate is R and maximum heart rate is M, then the formula that gives training heart rate is

$$T = R + \frac{3}{5}(M - R)$$

Use this formula along with the results of Problems 27 and 28 to fill in the following two tables.

29. For a 20-year-old person

Resting Heart Rate (beats per minute)	Training Heart Rate (beats per minute)
60	144
65	146
70	148
75	150
80	152
85	154

30. For a 40-year-old person

Resting Heart Rate (beats per minute)	Training Heart Rate (beats per minute)
60	132
65	134
70	136
75	138
80	140
85	142

B Use the rate equation $d = r \cdot t$ to solve Problems 31 and 32. [Example 5]

▶ **31.** At 2:30 P.M. Shelly leaves her house and drives at an average speed of 55 miles per hour to her sister's house. She arrives at 6:30 P.M.

   a. How many hours was the drive to her sister's house?

     4 hr

   b. How many miles from her sister does Shelly live?

     220 mi

32. At 1:30 P.M. Cary leaves his house and drives at an average speed of 65 miles per hour to his brother's house. He arrives at 5:30 P.M.

   a. How many hours was the drive to his brother's house?

     4 hr

   b. How many miles from his brother's house does Cary live?

     260 mi

Use the rate equation $r = \dfrac{d}{t}$ to solve Problems 33 and 34.

33. At 2:30 P.M. Brittney leaves her house and drives 260 miles to her sister's house. She arrives at 6:30 P.M.
   a. How many hours was the drive to her sister's house?
      4 hr
   ▶ **b.** What was Brittney's average speed?
      65 mi/hr

34. At 8:30 A.M. Ethan leaves his house and drives 220 miles to his brother's house. He arrives at 12:30 P.M.
   a. How many hours was the drive to his brother's house?
      4 hr
   b. What was Ethan's average speed?
      55 mi/hr

As you know, the volume V enclosed by a rectangular solid with length l, width w, and height h is $V = l \cdot w \cdot h$. In Problems 35-38, find V if:

▶ **35.** $l = 6$ inches, $w = 12$ inches, and $h = 5$ inches
   360 in³

36. $l = 16$ inches, $w = 22$ inches, and $h = 15$ inches
   5,280 in³

37. $l = 6$ yards, $w = \dfrac{1}{2}$ yard, and $h = \dfrac{1}{3}$ yard
   1 yd³

38. $l = 30$ yards, $w = \dfrac{5}{2}$ yards, and $h = \dfrac{5}{3}$ yards
   125 yd³

Suppose $y = 3x - 2$. In Problems 39–44, find y if:

▶ **39.** $x = 3$
   $y = 7$

▶ **40.** $x = -5$
   $y = -17$

41. $x = -\dfrac{1}{3}$
   $y = -3$

42. $x = \dfrac{2}{3}$
   $y = 0$

▶ **43.** $x = 0$
   $y = -2$

44. $x = 5$
   $y = 13$

Suppose $x + y = 5$. In Problems 45–50, find x if:

▶ **45.** $y = 2$
   $x = 3$

46. $y = -2$
   $x = 7$

47. $y = 0$
   $x = 5$

48. $y = 5$
   $x = 0$

▶ **49.** $y = -3$
   $x = 8$

50. $y = 3$
   $x = 2$

Suppose $x + y = 3$. In Problems 51–56, find y if:

▶ **51.** $x = 2$
   $y = 1$

52. $x = -2$
   $y = 5$

53. $x = 0$
   $y = 3$

54. $x = 3$
   $y = 0$

▶ **55.** $x = \dfrac{1}{2}$
   $y = \dfrac{5}{2}$

56. $x = -\dfrac{1}{2}$
   $y = \dfrac{7}{2}$

Suppose $4x + 3y = 12$. In Problems 57–62, find y if:

▶ **57.** $x = 3$
   $y = 0$

58. $x = -5$
   $y = \dfrac{32}{3}$

59. $x = -\dfrac{1}{4}$
   $y = \dfrac{13}{3}$

60. $x = \dfrac{3}{2}$
   $y = 2$

▶ **61.** $x = 0$
   $y = 4$

62. $x = -3$
   $y = 8$

Suppose $4x + 3y = 12$. In Problems 63-68, find x if:

▶ **63.** $y = 4$
   $x = 0$

64. $y = -4$
   $x = 6$

▶ **65.** $y = -\dfrac{1}{3}$
   $x = \dfrac{13}{4}$

66. $y = \dfrac{5}{3}$
   $x = \dfrac{7}{4}$

▶ **67.** $y = 0$
   $x = 3$

68. $y = -3$
   $x = \dfrac{21}{4}$

Find the complement and supplement of each angle. [Example 6]

▶ **69.** 45°
   Complement is 45°, supplement is 135°

70. 75°
   Complement is 15°, supplement is 105°

71. 31°
   Complement is 59°, supplement is 149°

72. 59°
   Complement is 31°, supplement is 121°

Applying the Concepts

73. Digital Video The most popular video download of all time was a *Star Wars* movie trailer. The video was compressed so it would be small enough for people to download over the Internet. A formula for estimating the size, in kilobytes, of a compressed video is

$$S = \frac{height \cdot width \cdot fps \cdot time}{35{,}000}$$

where *height* and *width* are in pixels, *fps* is the number of frames per second the video is to play (television plays at 30 fps), and *time* is given in seconds.

a. Estimate the size in kilobytes of the *Star Wars* trailer that has a height of 480 pixels, has a width of 216 pixels, plays at 30 fps, and runs for 150 seconds.

13,330 kilobytes

b. Estimate the size in kilobytes of the *Star Wars* trailer that has a height of 320 pixels, has a width of 144 pixels, plays at 15 fps, and runs for 150 seconds.

2,962 kilobytes

74. Vehicle Weight If you can measure the area that the tires on your car contact the ground, and you know the air pressure in the tires, then you can estimate the weight of your car, in pounds, with the following formula:

$$W = APN$$

where *W* is the vehicle's weight in pounds, *A* is the average tire contact area with a hard surface in square inches, *P* is the air pressure in the tires in pounds per square inch (psi, or lb/in^2), and *N* is the number of tires.

Tire Pressure **P**
Contact Area **A**

a. What is the approximate weight of a car if the average tire contact area is a rectangle 6 inches by 5 inches and if the air pressure in the tires is 30 psi?

3,600 pounds

b. What is the approximate weight of a car if the average tire contact area is a rectangle 5 inches by 4 inches, and the tire pressure is 30 psi?

2,400 pounds

75. Temperature The chart shows the temperatures for some of the world's hottest places.

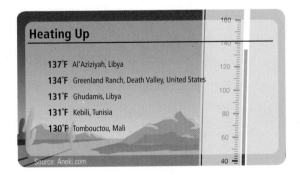

Heating Up

137°F Al'Aziziyah, Libya
134°F Greenland Ranch, Death Valley, United States
131°F Ghudamis, Libya
131°F Kebili, Tunisia
130°F Tombouctou, Mali

Source: Aneki.com

a. Use the formula $C = \frac{5}{9}(F - 32)$ to find the temperature in Celsius for Al'Aziziyah.

About 58° Celsius

b. Use the formula $K = \frac{5}{9}(F - 32) + 273$ to find the temperature in Ghudamis, Libya, in Kelvin.

328 K

76. Fermat's Last Theorem The postage stamp shows Fermat's last theorem, which states that if *n* is an integer greater than 2, then there are no positive integers *x*, *y*, and *z* that will make the formula $x^n + y^n = z^n$ true.

Use the formula $x^n + y^n = z^n$ to

a. Find *x* if $n = 1$, $y = 7$, and $z = 15$.

8

b. Find *y* if $n = 1$, $x = 23$, and $z = 37$.

14

■ Maintaining Your Skills

Simplify.

77. $\dfrac{\dfrac{3}{5}}{\dfrac{4}{5}}$

$\frac{3}{4}$

78. $\dfrac{\dfrac{5}{7}}{\dfrac{6}{7}}$

$\frac{5}{6}$

79. $\dfrac{1 + \dfrac{1}{2}}{1 - \dfrac{1}{2}}$

3

80. $\dfrac{1 + \dfrac{1}{3}}{1 - \dfrac{1}{3}}$

2

81. $\dfrac{\dfrac{1}{2} + \dfrac{1}{4}}{\dfrac{1}{4} + \dfrac{1}{8}}$

2

82. $\dfrac{\dfrac{1}{2} - \dfrac{1}{4}}{\dfrac{1}{4} - \dfrac{1}{8}}$

2

83. $\dfrac{\dfrac{3}{5} + \dfrac{3}{7}}{\dfrac{3}{5} - \dfrac{3}{7}}$

6

84. $\dfrac{\dfrac{5}{7} + \dfrac{5}{8}}{\dfrac{5}{7} - \dfrac{5}{8}}$

15

Objectives

A Plot ordered pairs on a coordinate system.

B Name the coordinates of a point on the rectangular coordinate system.

C Graph a line given two points.

Introduction . . .

The table and line graph below are similar to those that we have used previously to discuss temperature. Note that we have extended both the table and the line graph to show some temperatures below zero on both scales.

TABLE 1

COMPARING TEMPERATURES ON TWO SCALES

Temperature In Degrees Celsius	Temperature In Degrees Fahrenheit
−100°C	−148°F
−75°C	−103°F
−50°C	−58°F
−25°C	−13°F
0°C	32°F
25°C	77°F
50°C	122°F
75°C	167°F
100°C	212°F

FIGURE 1   A line graph of the data in Table 1

The data in Table 1 are called *paired data* because it is organized so that each number in the first column is paired with a specific number in the second column: a Celsius temperature of 100°C (first column) corresponds to a Fahrenheit temperature of 212°F (second column). The information in Figure 1 is also paired data because each dot on the line graph comes from one of the pairs of numbers in the table: The upper rightmost dot on the line graph corresponds to 100°C and 212°F. In order to standardize the way in which we present paired data visually, we use the *rectangular coordinate system*.

A The Rectangular Coordinate System

The rectangular coordinate system can be used to plot (or graph) pairs of numbers (see Figure 2 on the following page). It consists of two number lines, called *axes*, which intersect at right angles. (A right angle is a 90° angle.) The point at which the axes intersect is called the *origin*.

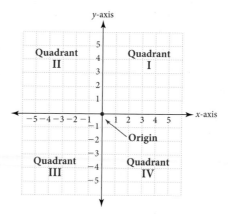

FIGURE 2

The horizontal number line is exactly the same as the real number line and is called the *x-axis*. The vertical number line is also the same as the real number line with the positive direction up and the negative direction down. It is called the *y-axis*. As you can see, the axes divide the plane into four regions, called *quadrants*, which are numbered 1 through IV in a counterclockwise direction.

Because the rectangular coordinate system consists of two number lines, one called the *x-axis* and the other called the *y-axis*, we can plot pairs of numbers such as $x = 2$ and $y = 3$. As a matter of fact, each point in the rectangular coordinate system is named by exactly one pair of numbers. We call the pair of numbers that name a point the *coordinates* of that point. To find the point that is associated with the pair of numbers $x = 2$ and $y = 3$, we start at the origin and move 2 units horizontally to the right and then 3 units vertically up (see Figure 3). The place where we end up is the point named by the pair of numbers $x = 2$, $y = 3$, which we write in shorthand form as the ordered pair (2, 3).

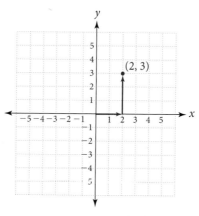

FIGURE 3

In general, to graph an ordered pair (a, b) on the rectangular coordinate system, we start at the origin and move a units right or left (right if a is positive, left if a is negative). From there we move b units up or down (up if b is positive, down if b is negative). The point where we end up is the graph of the ordered pair (a, b).

PRACTICE PROBLEMS

1. Plot the ordered pairs (3, 2), (3, −2), (−3, −2), and (−3, 2) on the coordinate system used in Example 1.

EXAMPLE 1   Plot (graph) the ordered pairs (2, 3), (−2, 3), (−2, −3), and (2, −3).

SOLUTION   To graph the ordered pair (2, 3), we start at the origin and move 2 units to the right, then 3 units up. We are now at the point whose coordinates are

(2, 3). We plot the other three ordered pairs in the same manner (Figure 4).

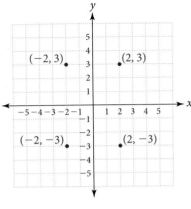

FIGURE 4

Note Looking at Example 1, we see that any point in quadrant I must have positive x- and y-coordinates, $(+, +)$. In quadrant II, x-coordinates are negative and y-coordinates are positive, $(-, +)$. In quadrant III, both coordinates are negative, $(-, -)$. Finally, in quadrant IV, all ordered pairs must have the form $(+, -)$.

EXAMPLE 2 Plot the ordered pairs $(1, -4)$, $\left(\frac{1}{2}, 3\right)$, $(2, 0)$, $(0, -2)$, and $(-3, 0)$.

SOLUTION

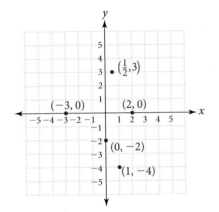

B Points on a Rectangular Coordinate System

EXAMPLE 3 Give the coordinates of each point in Figure 5.

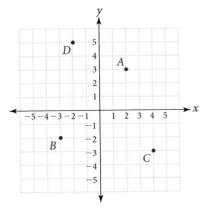

FIGURE 5

2. Plot the ordered pairs $(-1, -4)$, $\left(-\frac{1}{2}, 3\right)$, $(0, 2)$, $(5, 0)$, $(0, -5)$, and $(-1, 0)$ on the coordinate system used in Example 2.

3. Give the coordinates of each point in the figure below.

Answers
1. See solutions section.
2. See solutions section.

SOLUTION *A* is named by the ordered pair (2, 3). *B* is named by the ordered pair (−3, −2). *C* is named by the ordered pair (4, −3). *D* is named by the ordered pair (−2, 5).

EXAMPLE 4   Where are all the points that have coordinates of the form (*x*, 0)?

SOLUTION   Because the *y*-coordinate is 0, these points must lie on the *x*-axis. Remember, the *y*-coordinate tells us how far up or down we move to find the point in question. If the *y*-coordinate is 0, then we don't move up or down at all. Therefore, we must stay on the *x*-axis.

C   Graphing Lines

EXAMPLE 5   Graph the points (1, 2) and (3, 4), and draw a line through them. Then use your result to answer these questions.

   a. Does the graph of (2, 3) lie on this line?
   b. Does the graph of (−3, −5) lie on this line?

SOLUTION   Figure 6 shows the graphs of (1, 2) and (3, 4) and the line that connects them. The line does not pass through the point (−3, −5) but does pass through (2, 3).

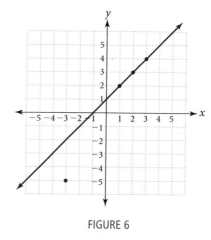

FIGURE 6

Getting Ready for Class

After reading the preceding section and working the practice problems in the margin, answer the following questions.
   1. What is an ordered pair of numbers?
   2. Explain in words how you would graph the ordered pair (2, 3).
   3. How do you construct a rectangular coordinate system?
   4. Where is the origin on a rectangular coordinate system?

4. The points (2, 0), (−3, 0), $\left(\frac{5}{2}, 0\right)$, and (−8, 0) all lie on which axis?

5. **a.** Does the point (−3, −2) lie on the line shown in Example 5?
   b. Does the point (3, 2) lie on the line shown in Example 5?

Answers
3. *A* is (3, 0); *B* is (0, −3); *C* is (3, −3); *D* is (−3, 3).
4. The *x*-axis   5. **a.** Yes   **b.** No

Problem Set 10.7

A Graph each of the following ordered pairs. [Examples 1, 2]

▶ **1.** (4, 2)   **2.** (4, −2)   **3.** (−4, 2)   ▶ **4.** (−4, −2)   ▶ **5.** (3, 4)   **6.** (−3, 4)

▶ **7.** (−3, −4)   **8.** (3, −4)   ▶ **9.** (4, 3)   **10.** (−4, 3)   **11.** $\left(5, \dfrac{1}{2}\right)$ ▶ **12.** $\left(-5, -\dfrac{1}{2}\right)$

▶ **13.** $\left(1, -\dfrac{3}{2}\right)$ **14.** $\left(-\dfrac{3}{2}, 1\right)$ **15.** (2, 0)   **16.** (0, −5)   ▶ **17.** (−2, 0)   **18.** (0, 5)

USE FOR ODD-NUMBERED PROBLEMS

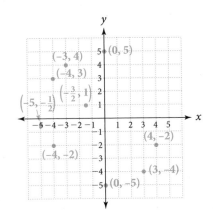

USE FOR EVEN-NUMBERED PROBLEMS

B **19–25.** Give the coordinates of each point in the figure below. [Examples 3, 4]

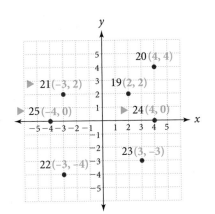

19.   (2, 2)
20.   (4, 4)
21.   (−3, 2)
22.   (−3, −4)
23.   (3, −3)
24.   (4, 0)
25.   (−4, 0)

▶ **26.** Where will you find all the ordered pairs of the form (0, *y*)?

On the *y*-axis

C Graph the points (1, 3) and (2, 4), and draw a line through them. Use that graph to answer Problems 27–30. [Example 5]

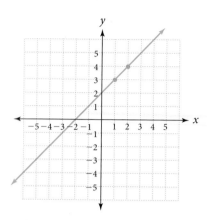

▶ **27.** Does the ordered pair (−1, 1) lie on this line?

Yes

28. Does the ordered pair (3, 4) lie on this line?

No

29. Does the ordered pair (−3, −5) lie on this line?

No

30. Does the ordered pair (3, 5) lie on this line?

Yes

Graph the points (−3, 2) and (1, 3), and draw a line through them. Use that graph to answer Problems 31–34.

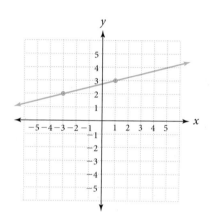

▶ **31.** Does the ordered pair (5, 4) lie on this line?

Yes

32. Does the ordered pair (3, −1) lie on this line?

No

▶ **33.** Does the ordered pair (4, 5) lie on this line?

No

▶ **34.** Does the ordered pair (−7, 1) lie on this line?

Yes

■ Applying the Concepts

35. Horse Racing The graph shows the total amount of money wagered on the Kentucky Derby over the years. List three ordered pairs that lie on the graph.
(1985, 20), (1990, 34), (1995, 45)

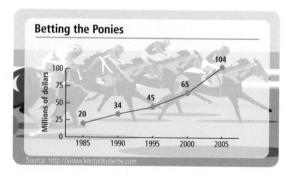

▶ **36. Solar Energy** The graph shows the annual number of solar thermal collector shipments in the United States. Use the graph to answer the following questions.

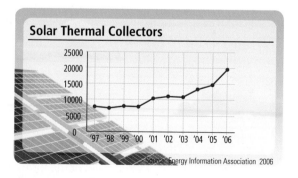

a.   Does the graph contain the point (2000, 7,500)? Yes

b.   Does the graph contain the point (2004, 15,000)? No

c.   Does the graph contain the point (2005, 15,000)? Yes

▶ **37. Hourly Wages** Jane takes a job at the local Marcy's department store. Her job pays $8.00 per hour. The graph shows how much Jane earns for working from 0 to 40 hours in a week.

a. List three ordered pairs that lie on the line graph.
(5, 40), (10, 80), (20, 160)

b. How much will she earn for working 40 hours?
$320

c. If her check for one week is $240, how many hours did she work?
30 hours

d. She works 35 hours one week, but her paycheck before deductions are subtracted out is for $260. Is this correct? Explain
No, if she works 35 hours, she should be paid $280.

▶ **38. Hourly Wages** Judy takes a job at Gigi's boutique. Her job pays $6.00 per hour plus $50 per week in commission. The graph shows how much Judy earns for working from 0 to 40 hours in a week.

a. List three ordered pairs that lie on the line graph.
(5, 80), (10, 110), (20, 170)

b. How much will she earn for working 40 hours?
$290

c. If her check for one week is $230, how many hours did she work?
30 hours

d. She works 35 hours one week, but her paycheck before deductions are subtracted out is for $260. Is this correct? Explain.
Yes, this is the correct amount.

▬ Maintaining Your Skills

Multiply or divide as indicated.

39. $\dfrac{x^2}{y} \cdot \dfrac{y^3}{x}$

xy^2

40. $\dfrac{a^3}{15} \cdot \dfrac{12}{a^2}$

$\dfrac{4a}{5}$

41. $\dfrac{x^2}{y^3} \div \dfrac{x^3}{y^2}$

$\dfrac{1}{xy}$

42. $\dfrac{a^2b}{c^3} \div \dfrac{ab^2}{c^3}$

$\dfrac{a}{b}$

Add or subtract as indicated.

43. $\dfrac{x}{5} + \dfrac{3}{4}$

$\dfrac{4x + 15}{20}$

44. $5 + \dfrac{2}{x}$

$\dfrac{5x + 2}{x}$

45. $3 - \dfrac{1}{x}$

$\dfrac{3x - 1}{x}$

46. $\dfrac{x}{8} - \dfrac{5}{6}$

$\dfrac{3x - 20}{24}$

■ Extending the Concepts

47. Right triangle *ABC* has legs of length 5. Point *C* is the ordered pair (6, 2). Find the coordinates of *A* and *B*.

$A = (1, 2), B = (6, 7)$

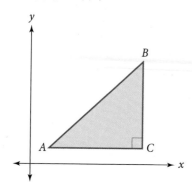

48. Right triangle *ABC* has legs of length 7. Point *C* is the ordered pair (−8, −3). Find the coordinates of *A* and *B*.

$A = (−1, −3), B = (−8, −10)$

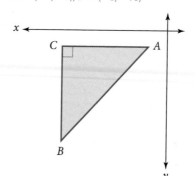

49. Rectangle *ABCD* has a length of 5 and a width of 3. Point *D* is the ordered pair (7, 2). Find points *A*, *B*, and *C*.

$A = (2, 2), B = (2, 5), C = (7, 5)$

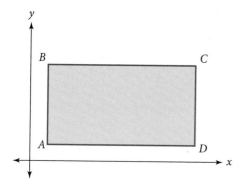

50. Rectangle *ABCD* has a length of 5 and a width of 3. Point *D* is the ordered pair (−1, 1). Find points *A*, *B*, and *C*.

$A = (−6, 1), B = (−6, 4), C = (−1, 4)$

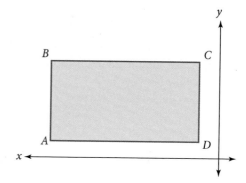

Chapter 10 Summary

Combining Similar Terms [10.1]

Two terms are similar terms if they have the same variable part. The expressions $7x$ and $2x$ are similar because the variable part in each is the same. Similar terms are combined by using the distributive property.

EXAMPLES

1. $7x + 2x = (7 + 2)x$
   $= 9x$

Finding the Value of an Algebraic Expression [10.1]

An algebraic expression is a mathematical expression that contains numbers and variables. Expressions that contain a variable will take on different values depending on the value of the variable.

2. When $x = 5$, the expression $2x + 7$ becomes
   $2(5) + 7 = 10 + 7 = 17$

The Solution to an Equation [10.2]

A solution to an equation is a number that, when used in place of the variable, makes the equation a true statement.

The Addition Property of Equality [10.2]

Let A, B, and C represent algebraic expressions.

> If $\quad A = B$
> then $\quad A + C = B + C$

In words: Adding the same quantity to both sides of an equation will not change the solution.

3. We solve $x - 4 = 9$ by adding 4 to each side.
$$x - 4 = 9$$
$$x - 4 + \mathbf{4} = 9 + \mathbf{4}$$
$$x + 0 = 13$$
$$x = 13$$

The Multiplication Property of Equality [10.3]

Let A, B, and C represent algebraic expressions, with C not equal to 0.

> If $\quad A = B$
> then $\quad AC = BC$

In words: Multiplying both sides of an equation by the same nonzero number will not change the solution to the equation. This property holds for division as well.

4. Solve $\frac{1}{3}x = 5$.
$$\frac{1}{3}x = 5$$
$$\mathbf{3} \cdot \frac{1}{3}x = \mathbf{3} \cdot 5$$
$$x = 15$$

Steps Used to Solve a Linear Equation in One Variable [10.4]

Step 1 Simplify each side of the equation.

Step 2 Use the addition property of equality to get all variable terms on one side and all constant terms on the other side.

5. $2(x - 4) + 5 = -11$
$$2x - 8 + 5 = -11$$
$$2x - 3 = -11$$
$$2x - 3 + \mathbf{3} = -11 + \mathbf{3}$$
$$2x = -8$$
$$\frac{2x}{2} = \frac{-8}{2}$$
$$x = -4$$

Step 3 Use the multiplication property of equality to get just one x isolated on either side of the equation.

Step 4 Check the solution in the original equation if necessary.

If the original equation contains fractions, you can begin by multiplying each side by the LCD for all fractions in the equation.

Evaluating Formulas [10.6]

6. When the formula becomes

$w = 8$ and $l = 13$
$P = 2w + 2l$
$P = 2 \cdot 8 + 2 \cdot 13$
$= 16 + 26$
$= 42$

In mathematics, a formula is an equation that contains more than one variable. For example, the formula for the perimeter of a rectangle is $P = 2l + 2w$. We evaluate a formula by substituting values for all but one of the variables and then solving the resulting equation for that variable.

The Rectangular Coordinate System [10.7]

The rectangular coordinate system consists of two number lines, called axes, which intersect at right angles. The point at which the axes intersect is called the origin.

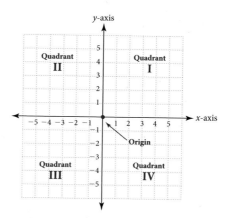

Graphing Ordered Pairs [10.7]

To graph an ordered pair (a, b) on the rectangular coordinate system, we start at the origin and move a units right or left (right if a is positive, left if a is negative). From there we move b units up or down (up if b is positive, down if b is negative). The point where we end up is the graph of the ordered pair (a, b).

Simplify the expressions by combining similar terms. [10.1]

1. $10x + 7x$
$17x$

2. $8x - 12x$
$-4x$

3. $2a + 9a + 3 - 6$
$11a - 3$

4. $4y - 7y + 8 - 10$
$-3y - 2$

5. $6x - x + 4$
$5x + 4$

6. $-5a + a + 4 - 3$
$-4a + 1$

7. $2a - 6 + 8a + 2$
$10a - 4$

8. $12y - 4 + 3y - 9$
$15y - 13$

Find the value of each expression when x is 4. [10.1]

9. $10x + 2$
42

10. $5x - 12$
8

11. $-2x + 9$
1

12. $-x + 8$
4

Find the value of each expression when x is -5.

13. $3y + 6$
-9

14. $9 - 2y$
19

15. $12 + y$
7

16. $-6y - 20$
10

17. Is $x = -3$ a solution to $5x - 2 = -17$? [10.2]
Yes

18. Is $x = 4$ a solution to $3x - 2 = 2x + 1$? [10.2]
No

Solve the equations. [10.2, 10.3, 10.4]

19. $x - 5 = 4$
9

20. $-x + 3 + 2x = 6 - 7$
-4

21. $2x + 1 = 7$
3

22. $3x - 5 = 1$
2

23. $2x + 4 = 3x - 5$
9

24. $4x + 8 = 2x - 10$
-9

25. $3(x - 2) = 9$
5

26. $4(x - 3) = -20$
-2

27. $3(2x + 1) - 4 = -7$
-1

28. $4(3x + 1) = -2(5x - 2)$
0

29. $5x + \dfrac{3}{8} = -\dfrac{1}{4}$
$-\dfrac{1}{8}$

30. $\dfrac{7}{x} - \dfrac{2}{5} = 1$
5

31. $3(2x - 5) = 4x + 3$
9

32. $\dfrac{2}{3}(6x - 9) = 6x - 2$
-2

33. $3x - 11 = 2(x - 2)$
7

34. $4(3x - 9) = 2(4x + 6)$
12

35. $5x + 9 = 4x - 7$
-16

36. $4(x - 6) = 8$
8

37. $5x - 7 = 3$
2

38. $\dfrac{3}{x} - \dfrac{1}{4} = 2$
$\dfrac{4}{3}$

39. Number Problem The sum of a number and -3 is -5. Find the number. [10.5]

The number is -2.

40. Number Problem If twice a number is added to 3, the result is 7. Find the number. [10.5]

The number is 2.

41. Number Problem Three times the sum of a number and 2 is -6. Find the number. [10.5]

The number is -4.

42. Number Problem If 7 is subtracted from twice a number, the result is 5. Find the number. [10.5]

The number is 6.

43. Geometry The length of a rectangle is twice its width. If the perimeter is 42 meters, find the length and the width. [10.5]

The length is 14 m, and the width is 7 m.

44. Age Problem Patrick is 3 years older than Amy. In 5 years the sum of their ages will be 31. How old are they now? [10.5]

Amy is 9 years old; and Patrick is 12 years old.

45. Geometry Two angles are complementary angles. If one angle is 5 times larger than the other angle, find the two angles. [10.5]

15° and 75°

46. Geometry Two angles are supplementary. If one angle is 85°, what is the other angle? [10.5]

95°

47. Geometry The biggest angle in a triangle is 6 times bigger than the smallest angle. The third angle is half the largest angle. Find the three angles. [10.5]

18°, 54°, 108°

48. Number Problem If two times the sum of a number and 6 is increased by 12, the result is 16. Find the number. [10.5]

-4

In Problems 49–52, use the equation $3x + 2y = 6$ to find y. [10.6]

49. $x = -2$

$y = 6$

50. $x = 6$

$y = -6$

51. $x = 0$

$y = 3$

52. $x = \dfrac{1}{3}$

$y = \dfrac{5}{2}$

In Problems 53–55, use the equation $3x + 2y = 6$ to find x when y has the given value. [10.6]

53. $y = 3$

$x = 0$

54. $y = -3$

$x = 4$

55. $y = 0$

$x = 2$

In Problems 56–59, use the equation $y = \dfrac{2}{3}x - 4$ to find x when y has the given value. [10.6]

56. $y = 0$

$x = 6$

57. $y = -6$

$x = -3$

58. $y = 4$

$x = 12$

59. $y = -10$

$x = -9$

In Problems 9–16, plot the points. [10.7]

60. $(4, 2)$

61. $(4, -2)$

62. $(-4, 2)$

63. $(-4, -2)$

64. $(4, 0)$

65. $(0, 4)$

66. $(0, -4)$

67. $(-4, 0)$

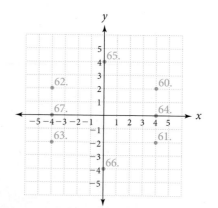

Simplify.

1. $5{,}309 + 687$ 5,996

2. $\dfrac{7}{11} + \dfrac{4}{5}$ $\dfrac{79}{55} = 1\dfrac{24}{55}$

3. $11.09 - 6.531$ 4.559

4. $4\dfrac{1}{8} - 1\dfrac{3}{4}$ $2\dfrac{3}{8}$

5. $2305(407)$ 938,135

6. $0.002(230)$ 0.46

7. $314\overline{)13{,}188}$ 42

8. $\dfrac{6}{32} \div \dfrac{9}{48}$ 1

9. Round the number 435,906 to the nearest ten thousand.   440,000

10. Write 0.48 as a fraction in lowest terms.
$\dfrac{12}{25}$

11. Change $\dfrac{76}{12}$ to a mixed number in lowest terms.
$6\dfrac{1}{3}$

12. Find the difference of 0.45 and $\dfrac{2}{5}$.
0.05

13. Write the decimal 0.8 as a percent.
80%

Use the table given in Chapter 7 to make the following conversion.

14. 7 kilograms to pounds
15.4 lb

15. Write 124% as a fraction or mixed number in lowest terms. $1\dfrac{6}{25}$

16. What percent of 60 is 21?
35%

Simplify.

17. $\left(\dfrac{1}{3}\right)^3 + \left(\dfrac{1}{9}\right)^2$ $\dfrac{4}{81}$

18. $8x + 9 - 9x - 14$ $-x - 5$

19. $-|-7|$ -7

20. $\dfrac{-3(-8) + 4(-2)}{11 - 9}$ 8

21. $19 - 5(7 - 4)$ 4

22. $\sqrt{25} + \sqrt{16}$ 9

Solve.

23. $\dfrac{3}{8}y = 21$ 56

24. $-3(2x - 1) = 3(x + 5)$ $-\dfrac{4}{3}$

25. $\dfrac{3.6}{4} = \dfrac{4.5}{x}$ 5

26. Write the following ratio as a fraction in lowest terms: 0.04 to 0.32 $\dfrac{1}{8}$

27. Subtract -3 from 5.
8

28. **Surface Area** Find the surface area of a rectangular solid with length 7 inches, width 3 inches, and height 2 inches.   82 in²

29. **Age** Ben is 8 years older than Ryan. In 6 years the sum of their ages will be 38. How old are they now?
Ben is 17, Ryan is 9

30. **Gas Mileage** A truck travels 432 miles on 27 gallons of gas. What is the rate of gas mileage in miles per gallon.
16 mpg

31. **Discount** A surfboard that usually sells for $400 is marked down to $320. What is the discount? What is the discount rate?
$80, 20%

32. **Geometry** Find the length of the hypotenuse of a right triangle with sides of 5 and 12 meters.
13 m

33. **Cost of Coffee** If coffee costs $6.40 per pound, how much will 2 lb 4 oz, cost?
$14.40

34. **Interest** If $1,400 is invested at 6% simple interest for 90 days, how much interest is earned?
$21

35. **Wildflower Seeds** C.J. works in a nursery, and one of his tasks is filling packets of wildflower seeds. If each packet is to contain $\dfrac{1}{4}$ pound of seeds, how many packets can be filled from 16 pounds of seeds?
64

36. **Commission** A car stereo salesperson receives a commission of 8% on all units he sells. If his total sales for March are $9,800, how much money in commission will he make?
$784

37. **Volume** How many 8 fluid ounce glasses of water will it take to fill a 15-gallon aquarium?
240

Internet Access Speed The graph below gives the speed of the most common modems used for Internet access.

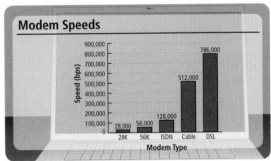

38. How much faster is cable than a 56K modem?
456,000 bps

39. What is the ratio of the speed of cable to the speed of an ISDN modem?
$\dfrac{4}{1}$

Simplify each expression by combining similar terms.

1. $9x - 3x + 7 - 12$
$6x - 5$

2. $4b - 1 - b - 3$
$3b - 4$

3. $3(2x - 6) - 4x$
$2x - 18$

4. $4(5x - 6) - 6x + 12$
$14x - 12$

Find the value of each expression when $x = 3$.

5. $3x - 12$
-3

6. $-x + 12$
9

7. Is $x = -1$ a solution to $4x - 3 = -7$?
Yes

8. Is $x = 3$ a solution to $3x - 7 = -2$?
No

9. Use the equation $4x + 3y = 12$ to find y when $x = -3$.
8

10. Use the equation $y = \frac{4}{3}x + 7$ to find x when $y = -1$.
-6

Solve each equation.

11. $x - 7 = -3$ 4

12. $a - 2.9 = -7.8$ -4.9

13. $\frac{2}{3}y = 18$ 27

14. $\frac{7}{x} - \frac{1}{6} = 1$ 6

15. $3x - 7 = 5x + 1$ -4

16. $2(x - 5) = -8$ 1

17. $3(2x + 3) = -3(x - 5)$ $\frac{2}{3}$

18. $6(3x - 2) - 8 = 4x - 6$ 1

19. $\frac{4}{3}(6x - 9) = 2(4x - 6)$
all real numbers

20. $3(x - 7) = -6$ 5

21. Number Problem Twice the sum of a number and 3 is -10. Find the number.
The number is -8.

22. Hot Air Balloon The first successful crossing of the Atlantic in a hot air balloon was made in August 1978 by Maxie Anderson, Ben Abruzzo, and Larry Newman of the United States. The 3,100 mile trip took approximately 140 hours. Use the formula $r = \frac{d}{t}$ to find their average speed to the nearest whole number.
22 mi/hr

23. Geometry The length of a rectangle is 4 centimeters longer than its width. If the perimeter is 28 centimeters, find the length and the width.
The length is 9 cm, and the width is 5 cm.

24. Age problem Karen is 5 years younger than Susan. Three years ago, the sum of their ages was 11. How old are they now?
Susan is 11 years old, and Karen is 6 years old.

25. Geometry The largest angle in a triangle is 3 times bigger than another angle, which is twice as big as the smallest angle. Find the three angles.
$20°$, $40°$, $120°$

26. Coin Problem A coin collection has seven more dimes than quarters. If the collection has a value of $2.10, how many quarters and dimes are in the collection?
4 quarters, 11 dimes

27. Geometry Two angles are complementary. If one angle is 3 times bigger than the other angle, find the two angles.
$22.5°$, and $67.5°$

28. Perimeter of a Rectangle If a rectangle has a length of 13 meters and a perimeter of 35 meters, find the width of the rectangle.
4.5 m

29. Google Earth The length of the base of the Sphinx is 12 times longer than the width. If the perimeter of the base is 520 feet. Find the length and the width.

20 ft, 240 ft

30. Plot the following points: $(3, 2)$, $(-3, 2)$, $(3, 0)$, $(0, -2)$.

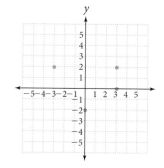

Chapter 10 Projects

SOLVING EQUATIONS

The Equation Game

Number of People 2–5

Time Needed 30 minutes

Equipment Per group: deck of cards, timer or clock, pencil and paper, copy of rules.

Background The Equation Game is a fun way to practice working with equations.

Procedure Remove all the face cards from the deck. Aces will be 1's. The dealer deals four cards face up, a fifth card face down. Each player writes down the four numbers that are face up. Set the timer for 5 minutes, then flip the fifth card. Each player writes down equations that use the numbers on the first four cards to equal the number on the fifth card. When the five minutes are up, figure out the scores. An equation that uses

1 of the four cards scores 0 points
2 of the four cards scores 4 points
3 of the four cards scores 9 points
4 of the four cards scores 16 points

Check the other players' equations. If you find an error, you get 7 points. The person with the mistake gets no points for that equation.

Example The first four cards are a four, a nine, an ace, and a two. The fifth card is a seven. Here are some equations you could make:

$$9 - 2 = 7$$
$$4 + 2 + 1 = 7$$
$$\frac{9 - (4 - 2)}{1} = 7$$

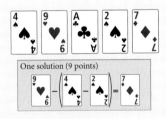

This project was adapted from www.exploratorium.edu/math_explorer/fantasticFour.html.

Algebraic Symbolism

Algebra made a beginning as early as 1850 B.C. in Egypt. However, the symbols we use in algebra today took some time to develop. For example, the algebraic use of letters for numbers began much later with Diophantus, a mathematician famous for studying *Diophantine equations*. In the early centuries, the full words *plus, minus, multiplied by, divided by,* and *equals* were written out. Imagine how much more difficult your homework would be if you had to write out all these words instead of using symbols. Algebraists began to come up with a system of symbols to make writing algebra easier. At first, not everyone agreed on the symbols to be used. For example, the present division sign ÷ was often used for subtraction. People in different countries used different symbols: the Italians preferred to use p and m for plus and minus, while the less traditional Germans were starting to use + and −.

Research the history of algebraic symbolism. Find out when the algebraic symbols we use today (such as letters to represent variables, +, −, ÷, ·, a/b and $\left(\frac{a}{b}\right)$ came into common use. Summarize your results in an essay.

Appendix A
RESOURCES

By gathering resources early in the term, before you need help, the information about these resources will be available to you when they are needed.

Instructor

Knowing the contact information for your instructor is very important. You may already have this information from the course syllabus. It is a good idea to write it down again.

Name _____ Office Location _____

Available Hours: M _____ T _____ W _____ TH _____ F _____

Phone Number _____ ext. _____ E-mail Address _____ @ _____

Tutoring Center

Many schools offer tutoring, free of charge to their students. If this is the case at your school, find out when and where tutoring is offered.

Tutoring Location _____ Phone Number _____ ext. _____

Available Hours: M _____ T _____ W _____ TH _____ F _____

Computer Lab

Many schools offer a computer lab where students can use the online resources and software available with their textbook. Other students using the same software and websites as you can be very helpful. Find out where the computer lab at your school is located.

Computer Lab Location _____ Phone Number _____ ext. _____

Available Hours: M _____ T _____ W _____ TH _____ F _____

Videos

A complete set of videos is available to your school. These videos feature the author of your textbook presenting full-length, 15- to 20-minute lessons from every section of your textbook. If you miss class, or find yourself behind, these tapes will prove very useful.

Videotape Location _____ Phone Number _____ ext. _____

Available Hours: M _____ T _____ W _____ TH _____ F _____

Classmates

Form a study group and meet on a regular basis. When you meet try to speak to each other using proper mathematical language. That is, use the words that you see in the definition and property boxes in your textbook.

Name _____ Phone _____ E-mail _____

Name _____ Phone _____ E-mail _____

Name _____ Phone _____ E-mail _____

Appendix B

ONE HUNDRED ADDITION FACTS

The following 100 problems should be done mentally. You should be able to find these sums quickly and accurately. Do all 100 problems, and then check your answers. Make a list of each problem you missed, and then go over the list as many times as it takes to memorize the correct answers. Once this has been done, go back and work all 100 problems again. Repeat this process until you get all 100 problems correct.

Add.

1. $\begin{array}{r}0\\+4\\\hline\end{array}$	**2.** $\begin{array}{r}1\\+9\\\hline\end{array}$	**3.** $\begin{array}{r}2\\+7\\\hline\end{array}$	**4.** $\begin{array}{r}0\\+3\\\hline\end{array}$	**5.** $\begin{array}{r}4\\+1\\\hline\end{array}$
6. $\begin{array}{r}2\\+5\\\hline\end{array}$	**7.** $\begin{array}{r}5\\+6\\\hline\end{array}$	**8.** $\begin{array}{r}2\\+6\\\hline\end{array}$		

6. $\begin{array}{r}2\\+5\\\hline\end{array}$ **7.** $\begin{array}{r}5\\+6\\\hline\end{array}$ **8.** $\begin{array}{r}2\\+6\\\hline\end{array}$

9. $\begin{array}{r}9\\+8\\\hline\end{array}$ **10.** $\begin{array}{r}4\\+9\\\hline\end{array}$ **11.** $\begin{array}{r}3\\+7\\\hline\end{array}$ **12.** $\begin{array}{r}9\\+4\\\hline\end{array}$ **13.** $\begin{array}{r}4\\+5\\\hline\end{array}$ **14.** $\begin{array}{r}1\\+4\\\hline\end{array}$ **15.** $\begin{array}{r}0\\+1\\\hline\end{array}$ **16.** $\begin{array}{r}6\\+4\\\hline\end{array}$

17. $\begin{array}{r}5\\+3\\\hline\end{array}$ **18.** $\begin{array}{r}9\\+5\\\hline\end{array}$ **19.** $\begin{array}{r}5\\+8\\\hline\end{array}$ **20.** $\begin{array}{r}0\\+7\\\hline\end{array}$ **21.** $\begin{array}{r}5\\+1\\\hline\end{array}$ **22.** $\begin{array}{r}1\\+0\\\hline\end{array}$ **23.** $\begin{array}{r}6\\+5\\\hline\end{array}$ **24.** $\begin{array}{r}5\\+2\\\hline\end{array}$

25. $\begin{array}{r}5\\+7\\\hline\end{array}$ **26.** $\begin{array}{r}3\\+6\\\hline\end{array}$ **27.** $\begin{array}{r}7\\+0\\\hline\end{array}$ **28.** $\begin{array}{r}4\\+6\\\hline\end{array}$ **29.** $\begin{array}{r}1\\+5\\\hline\end{array}$ **30.** $\begin{array}{r}3\\+1\\\hline\end{array}$ **31.** $\begin{array}{r}1\\+7\\\hline\end{array}$ **32.** $\begin{array}{r}7\\+6\\\hline\end{array}$

33. $\begin{array}{r}3\\+3\\\hline\end{array}$ **34.** $\begin{array}{r}8\\+0\\\hline\end{array}$ **35.** $\begin{array}{r}1\\+8\\\hline\end{array}$ **36.** $\begin{array}{r}5\\+4\\\hline\end{array}$ **37.** $\begin{array}{r}2\\+8\\\hline\end{array}$ **38.** $\begin{array}{r}0\\+5\\\hline\end{array}$ **39.** $\begin{array}{r}5\\+9\\\hline\end{array}$ **40.** $\begin{array}{r}9\\+9\\\hline\end{array}$

41. $\begin{array}{r}0\\+0\\\hline\end{array}$ **42.** $\begin{array}{r}6\\+9\\\hline\end{array}$ **43.** $\begin{array}{r}7\\+4\\\hline\end{array}$ **44.** $\begin{array}{r}8\\+2\\\hline\end{array}$ **45.** $\begin{array}{r}7\\+3\\\hline\end{array}$ **46.** $\begin{array}{r}8\\+5\\\hline\end{array}$ **47.** $\begin{array}{r}8\\+4\\\hline\end{array}$ **48.** $\begin{array}{r}6\\+7\\\hline\end{array}$

49. $\begin{array}{r}8\\+1\\\hline\end{array}$ **50.** $\begin{array}{r}1\\+3\\\hline\end{array}$ **51.** $\begin{array}{r}7\\+5\\\hline\end{array}$ **52.** $\begin{array}{r}0\\+1\\\hline\end{array}$ **53.** $\begin{array}{r}8\\+3\\\hline\end{array}$ **54.** $\begin{array}{r}6\\+6\\\hline\end{array}$ **55.** $\begin{array}{r}9\\+6\\\hline\end{array}$ **56.** $\begin{array}{r}8\\+9\\\hline\end{array}$

57. $\begin{array}{r}3\\+0\\\hline\end{array}$ **58.** $\begin{array}{r}6\\+2\\\hline\end{array}$ **59.** $\begin{array}{r}2\\+1\\\hline\end{array}$ **60.** $\begin{array}{r}6\\+0\\\hline\end{array}$ **61.** $\begin{array}{r}4\\+8\\\hline\end{array}$ **62.** $\begin{array}{r}6\\+1\\\hline\end{array}$ **63.** $\begin{array}{r}2\\+0\\\hline\end{array}$ **64.** $\begin{array}{r}7\\+9\\\hline\end{array}$

65. $\begin{array}{r}2\\+9\\\hline\end{array}$ **66.** $\begin{array}{r}9\\+3\\\hline\end{array}$ **67.** $\begin{array}{r}3\\+8\\\hline\end{array}$ **68.** $\begin{array}{r}7\\+2\\\hline\end{array}$ **69.** $\begin{array}{r}8\\+8\\\hline\end{array}$ **70.** $\begin{array}{r}4\\+4\\\hline\end{array}$ **71.** $\begin{array}{r}8\\+7\\\hline\end{array}$ **72.** $\begin{array}{r}2\\+4\\\hline\end{array}$

73. $\begin{array}{r}3\\+2\\\hline\end{array}$ **74.** $\begin{array}{r}4\\+7\\\hline\end{array}$ **75.** $\begin{array}{r}9\\+7\\\hline\end{array}$ **76.** $\begin{array}{r}1\\+2\\\hline\end{array}$ **77.** $\begin{array}{r}6\\+3\\\hline\end{array}$ **78.** $\begin{array}{r}2\\+2\\\hline\end{array}$ **79.** $\begin{array}{r}9\\+2\\\hline\end{array}$ **80.** $\begin{array}{r}9\\+1\\\hline\end{array}$

81. $\begin{array}{r}3\\+5\\\hline\end{array}$ **82.** $\begin{array}{r}1\\+1\\\hline\end{array}$ **83.** $\begin{array}{r}5\\+5\\\hline\end{array}$ **84.** $\begin{array}{r}7\\+7\\\hline\end{array}$ **85.** $\begin{array}{r}0\\+8\\\hline\end{array}$ **86.** $\begin{array}{r}7\\+8\\\hline\end{array}$ **87.** $\begin{array}{r}2\\+3\\\hline\end{array}$ **88.** $\begin{array}{r}3\\+9\\\hline\end{array}$

89. $\begin{array}{r}6\\+8\\\hline\end{array}$ **90.** $\begin{array}{r}4\\+0\\\hline\end{array}$ **91.** $\begin{array}{r}0\\+6\\\hline\end{array}$ **92.** $\begin{array}{r}4\\+3\\\hline\end{array}$ **93.** $\begin{array}{r}7\\+1\\\hline\end{array}$ **94.** $\begin{array}{r}0\\+9\\\hline\end{array}$ **95.** $\begin{array}{r}9\\+0\\\hline\end{array}$ **96.** $\begin{array}{r}8\\+6\\\hline\end{array}$

97. $\begin{array}{r}3\\+4\\\hline\end{array}$ **98.** $\begin{array}{r}5\\+0\\\hline\end{array}$ **99.** $\begin{array}{r}1\\+6\\\hline\end{array}$ **100.** $\begin{array}{r}4\\+2\\\hline\end{array}$

Appendix C

ONE HUNDRED MULTIPLICATION FACTS

The following 100 problems should be done mentally. You should be able to find these products quickly and accurately. Do all 100 problems, and then check your answers. Make a list of each problem you missed, and then go over the list as many times as it takes to memorize the correct answers. Once this has been done, go back and work all 100 problems again. Repeat this process until you get all 100 problems correct.

Multiply.

1. 3 ×4	**2.** 5 ×4	**3.** 0 ×5	**4.** 0 ×6	**5.** 2 ×5	**6.** 1 ×7	**7.** 4 ×4	**8.** 7 ×2
9. 7 ×1	**10.** 5 ×9	**11.** 2 ×6	**12.** 5 ×3	**13.** 3 ×5	**14.** 4 ×5	**15.** 8 ×1	**16.** 3 ×7
17. 5 ×8	**18.** 0 ×3	**19.** 6 ×0	**20.** 0 ×4	**21.** 4 ×6	**22.** 8 ×2	**23.** 5 ×7	**24.** 0 ×9
25. 2 ×7	**26.** 6 ×1	**27.** 1 ×8	**28.** 4 ×7	**29.** 3 ×8	**30.** 6 ×8	**31.** 5 ×4	**32.** 7 ×3
33. 0 ×8	**34.** 4 ×8	**35.** 2 ×9	**36.** 5 ×6	**37.** 1 ×9	**38.** 2 ×8	**39.** 0 ×7	**40.** 6 ×2
41. 4 ×9	**42.** 8 ×0	**43.** 3 ×0	**44.** 9 ×6	**45.** 3 ×4	**46.** 8 ×3	**47.** 7 ×9	**48.** 1 ×9
49. 1 ×3	**50.** 9 ×9	**51.** 2 ×4	**52.** 8 ×7	**53.** 5 ×2	**54.** 7 ×8	**55.** 1 ×4	**56.** 0 ×2
57. 9 ×8	**58.** 2 ×3	**59.** 9 ×5	**60.** 7 ×7	**61.** 6 ×5	**62.** 0 ×1	**63.** 9 ×3	**64.** 8 ×9
65. 9 ×7	**66.** 6 ×4	**67.** 3 ×1	**68.** 1 ×5	**69.** 9 ×6	**70.** 1 ×2	**71.** 4 ×1	**72.** 2 ×2
73. 6 ×3	**74.** 5 ×1	**75.** 9 ×2	**76.** 6 ×9	**77.** 7 ×0	**78.** 4 ×0	**79.** 7 ×6	**80.** 5 ×0
81. 0 ×0	**82.** 3 ×9	**83.** 1 ×1	**84.** 8 ×6	**85.** 9 ×0	**86.** 7 ×4	**87.** 8 ×4	**88.** 2 ×0
89. 9 ×1	**90.** 8 ×5	**91.** 4 ×2	**92.** 8 ×3	**93.** 7 ×5	**94.** 2 ×1	**95.** 6 ×6	**96.** 3 ×2
97. 4 ×3	**98.** 1 ×6	**99.** 6 ×7	**100.** 1 ×0				

Negative Exponents

Up to this point, all the exponents we have worked with have been positive numbers. We want to extend the type of numbers we can use for exponents to include negative numbers as well. The definition that follows allows us to work with exponents that are negative numbers.

Negative Exponents

> **Definition**
>
> **Negative Exponents** If r is a positive integer and a is any number other than zero, then
> $$a^{-r} = \frac{1}{a^r}$$

The definition indicates that negative exponents give us reciprocals, as the following examples illustrate.

Note Because division by 0 is undefined, our definition includes the restriction $a \neq 0$.

EXAMPLE 1   Simplify: 2^{-3}

SOLUTION   The first step is to rewrite the expression with a positive exponent, by using our definition. After that, we simplify.

$$2^{-3} = \frac{1}{2^3} \quad \text{Definition of negative exponents}$$

$$= \frac{1}{8} \quad \text{The cube of 2 is 8}$$

EXAMPLE 2   Simplify: 5^{-2}

SOLUTION   First we write the expression with a positive exponent, then we simplify.

$$5^{-2} = \frac{1}{5^2} \quad \text{Definition of negative exponents}$$

$$= \frac{1}{25} \quad \text{The square of 5 is 25}$$

As you can see from our first two examples, when we apply the definition for negative exponents to expressions containing negative exponents, we end up with reciprocals.

EXAMPLE 3   Simplify: $(-3)^{-2}$

SOLUTION   The fact that the base in this problem is negative does not change the procedure we use to simplify:

$$(-3)^{-2} = \frac{1}{(-3)^2} \quad \text{Definition of negative exponents}$$

$$= \frac{1}{9} \quad \text{The square of } -3 \text{ is 9}$$

To check your understanding of negative exponents, look over the two lines below.

$$2^1 = 2 \qquad 2^2 = 4 \qquad 2^3 = 8 \qquad 2^4 = 16$$

$$2^{-1} = \frac{1}{2} \qquad 2^{-2} = \frac{1}{4} \qquad 2^{-3} = \frac{1}{8} \qquad 2^{-4} = \frac{1}{16}$$

PRACTICE PROBLEMS

1. Simplify: 2^{-4}

2. Simplify: 4^{-2}

3. Simplify: $(-2)^{-3}$

Answers

1. $\frac{1}{16}$ 2. $\frac{1}{16}$ 3. $-\frac{1}{8}$

Appendix D Negative Exponents

The properties of exponents we have developed so far hold for negative exponents as well as positive exponents. For example, Property 1, our multiplication property for exponents, is still written as

$$a^r \cdot a^s = a^{r+s}$$

but now r and s can be negative numbers also.

4. Simplify: $3^4 \cdot 3^{-7}$

EXAMPLE 4   Simplify: $2^5 \cdot 2^{-7}$

SOLUTION   This is multiplication with the same base, so we add exponents.

$$2^5 \cdot 2^{-7} = 2^{5+(-7)} \quad \text{Property 1 for exponents}$$
$$= 2^{-2} \quad \text{Addition}$$
$$= \frac{1}{2^2} \quad \text{Definition of negative exponents}$$
$$= \frac{1}{4} \quad \text{The square of 2 is 4}$$

When we simplify expressions containing negative exponents, let's agree that the final expression contains only positive exponents.

5. Simplify: $x^6 \cdot x^{-10}$

EXAMPLE 5   Simplify: $x^9 \cdot x^{-12}$

SOLUTION   Again, because we have the product of two expressions with the same base, we use Property 1 for exponents to add exponents.

$$x^9 \cdot x^{-12} = x^{9+(-12)} \quad \text{Property 1 for exponents}$$
$$= x^{-3} \quad \text{Add exponents}$$
$$= \frac{1}{x^3} \quad \text{Definition of negative exponents}$$

Division with Exponents

To develop our next property of exponents, we use the definition for positive exponents. Consider the expression $\frac{x^6}{x^4}$. We can simplify by expanding the numerator and denominator and then reducing to lowest terms by dividing out common factors.

$$\frac{x^6}{x^4} = \frac{x \cdot x \cdot x \cdot x \cdot x \cdot x}{x \cdot x \cdot x \cdot x} \quad \text{Expand numerator and denominator}$$

$$= \frac{\cancel{x} \cdot \cancel{x} \cdot \cancel{x} \cdot \cancel{x} \cdot x \cdot x}{\cancel{x} \cdot \cancel{x} \cdot \cancel{x} \cdot \cancel{x}} \quad \text{Divide out common factors}$$

$$= x \cdot x$$
$$= x^2 \quad \left. \right\} \quad \text{Write answer with exponent 2}$$

Note that the exponent in the answer is the difference of the exponents in the original problem. More specifically, if we subtract the exponent in the denominator from the exponent in the numerator, we obtain the exponent in the answer. This discussion leads us to another property of exponents.

Division Property for Expressions Containing Exponents

If a is any number other than zero, and r and s are integers, then

$$\frac{a^r}{a^s} = a^{r-s}$$

In words: To divide two numbers with the same base, subtract the exponent in the denominator from the exponent in the numerator, and use the common base as the base in the answer.

EXAMPLE 6   Simplify: $\dfrac{2^5}{2^8}$

SOLUTION   Using our new property, we subtract the exponent in the denominator from the exponent in the numerator. The result is an expression containing a negative exponent.

$$\frac{2^5}{2^8} = 2^{5-8} \qquad \text{Division property for exponents}$$

$$= 2^{-3} \qquad \text{Subtraction}$$

$$= \frac{1}{2^3} \qquad \text{Definition of negative exponents}$$

$$= \frac{1}{8} \qquad \text{The cube of 2 is 8}$$

To further justify our new property of exponents, we can rework the problem shown in Example 6, without using the division property for exponents, to see that we obtain the same answer.

$$\frac{2^5}{2^8} = \frac{2 \cdot 2 \cdot 2 \cdot 2 \cdot 2}{2 \cdot 2 \cdot 2 \cdot 2 \cdot 2 \cdot 2 \cdot 2 \cdot 2} \qquad \text{Expand numerator and denominator}$$

$$= \frac{\cancel{2} \cdot \cancel{2} \cdot \cancel{2} \cdot \cancel{2} \cdot \cancel{2}}{\cancel{2} \cdot \cancel{2} \cdot \cancel{2} \cdot \cancel{2} \cdot \cancel{2} \cdot 2 \cdot 2 \cdot 2} \left. \vphantom{\begin{array}{c} 1 \\ 1 \\ 1 \end{array}} \right\} \quad \text{Divide out common factors}$$

$$= \frac{1}{2 \cdot 2 \cdot 2}$$

$$= \frac{1}{8} \qquad \text{Multiply}$$

As you can see, the answer matches the answer obtained by using the division property for exponents.

EXAMPLE 7   Divide: $10^{-3} \div 10^5$

SOLUTION   We begin by writing the division problem in fractional form. Then we apply our division property.

$$10^{-3} \div 10^5 = \frac{10^{-3}}{10^5} \qquad \text{Write problem in fractional form}$$

$$= 10^{-3-5} \qquad \text{Division property for exponents}$$

$$= 10^{-8} \qquad \text{Subtraction}$$

$$= \frac{1}{10^8} \qquad \text{Definition of negative exponents}$$

We can leave the answer in exponential form, as it is, or we can expand the denominator to obtain

$$= \frac{1}{100,000,000}$$

6. Simplify: $\dfrac{2^6}{2^8}$

7. Divide: $10^{-5} \div 10^3$

Answers

6. $\frac{1}{4}$ **7.** $\frac{1}{10^8}$

8. Simplify: $\dfrac{10^{-6}}{10^{-8}}$

EXAMPLE 8 Simplify: $\dfrac{10^{-8}}{10^{-6}}$

SOLUTION Again, we are dividing expressions that have the same base. To find the exponent on the answer, we subtract the exponent in the denominator from the exponent in the numerator.

$$\dfrac{10^{-8}}{10^{-6}} = 10^{-8-(-6)} \quad \text{Division property for exponents}$$

$$= 10^{-2} \quad \text{Subtraction}$$

$$= \dfrac{1}{10^2} \quad \text{Definition of negative exponents}$$

$$= \dfrac{1}{100} \quad \text{Answer in expanded form}$$

9. Simplify: $4x^{-3} \cdot 7x$

EXAMPLE 9 Simplify: $3x^{-4} \cdot 5x$

SOLUTION To begin to simplify this expression, we regroup using the commutative and associative properties. That way, the numbers 3 and 5 are grouped together, as are the powers of x. Note also how we write x as x^1, so we can see the exponent.

$$3x^{-4} \cdot 5x = 3x^{-4} \cdot 5x^1 \quad \text{Write } x \text{ as } x^1$$

$$= (3 \cdot 5)(x^{-4} \cdot x^1) \quad \text{Commutative and associative properties}$$

$$= 15x^{-4+1} \quad \text{Multiply 3 and 5, then add exponents}$$

$$= 15x^{-3} \quad \text{The sum of } -4 \text{ and } 1 \text{ is } -3$$

$$= \dfrac{15}{x^3} \quad \text{Definition of negative exponents}$$

10. Simplify: $\dfrac{x^{-5} \cdot x^2}{x^{-8}}$

EXAMPLE 10 Simplify: $\dfrac{x^{-4} \cdot x^7}{x^{-2}}$

SOLUTION We simplify the numerator first by adding exponents.

$$\dfrac{x^{-4} \cdot x^7}{x^{-2}} = \dfrac{x^{-4+7}}{x^{-2}} \quad \text{Multiplication property for exponents}$$

$$= \dfrac{x^3}{x^{-2}} \quad \text{The sum of } -4 \text{ and } 7 \text{ is } 3$$

$$= x^{3-(-2)} \quad \text{Division property for exponents}$$

$$= x^5 \quad \text{Subtracting } -2 \text{ is equivalent to adding } +2$$

Getting Ready for Class

After reading through the preceding section, respond in your own words and in complete sentences.

1. Negative exponents are _____.
2. Do negative exponents result in negative numbers?
3. How do you divide exponents with the same base?
4. The problem below is wrong. Correct the right-hand side.

$$\dfrac{x^7}{x^8} = x$$

Answers

8. 100 **9.** $\dfrac{28}{x^2}$ **10.** x^5

Problem Set D

Write each expression with positive exponents, then simplify. [Examples 1–5]

1. 2^{-5}

$\frac{1}{32}$

2. 3^{-4}

$\frac{1}{81}$

3. 10^{-2}

$\frac{1}{100}$

4. 10^{-3}

$\frac{1}{1000}$

5. x^{-3}

$\frac{1}{x^3}$

6. x^{-4}

$\frac{1}{x^4}$

7. $(-4)^{-2}$

$\frac{1}{16}$

8. $(-2)^{-4}$

$\frac{1}{16}$

9. $(-5)^{-3}$

$-\frac{1}{125}$

10. $(-4)^{-3}$

$-\frac{1}{64}$

11. $2^6 \cdot 2^{-8}$

$\frac{1}{4}$

12. $3^5 \cdot 3^{-8}$

$\frac{1}{27}$

13. $10^{-2} \cdot 10^5$

$1,000$

14. $10^{-3} \cdot 10^6$

$1,000$

15. $x^{-4} \cdot x^{-3}$

$\frac{1}{x^7}$

16. $x^{-3} \cdot x^{-7}$

$\frac{1}{x^{10}}$

17. $3^8 \cdot 3^{-6}$

9

18. $2^9 \cdot 2^{-6}$

8

19. $2 \cdot 2^{-4}$

$\frac{1}{8}$

20. $3^{-5} \cdot 3$

$\frac{1}{81}$

21. $10^{-3} \cdot 10^8 \cdot 10^{-2}$

$1,000$

22. $10^{-3} \cdot 10^9 \cdot 10^{-4}$

100

23. $x^{-5} \cdot x^{-4} \cdot x^{-3}$

$\frac{1}{x^{12}}$

24. $x^{-7} \cdot x^{-9} \cdot x^{-6}$

$\frac{1}{x^{22}}$

25. $2^{-3} \cdot 2 \cdot 2^3$

2

26. $3 \cdot 3^5 \cdot 3^{-5}$

3

Divide as indicated. Write your answer using only positive exponents. [Examples 6–10]

27. $\dfrac{2^9}{2^7}$

4

28. $\dfrac{3^8}{3^4}$

81

29. $\dfrac{2^7}{2^9}$

$\frac{1}{4}$

30. $\dfrac{3^5}{3^7}$

$\frac{1}{9}$

31. $\dfrac{x^4}{x^3}$

x

32. $\dfrac{x^7}{x^5}$

x^2

33. $\dfrac{x^3}{x^4}$

$\frac{1}{x}$

34. $\dfrac{x^5}{x^7}$

$\frac{1}{x^2}$

35. $10^{-2} \div 10^5$

$\frac{1}{10^7}$

36. $10^{-4} \div 10^2$

$\frac{1}{10^6}$

37. $10^{-5} \div 10^2$

$\frac{1}{10^7}$

38. $10^{-3} \div 10$

$\frac{1}{10^4}$

39. $\dfrac{10^{-2}}{10^{-5}}$

$1,000$

40. $\dfrac{10^{-4}}{10^{-7}}$

$1,000$

41. $x^{12} \div x^{-12}$

x^{24}

42. $x^6 \div x^{-6}$

x^{12}

43. $2^{12} \div 2^{10}$

4

44. $3^{11} \div 3^9$

9

45. $\dfrac{10}{10^{-3}}$

$10,000$

46. $\dfrac{10^2}{10^{-5}}$

10^7

Simplify each expression. Write your answer using only positive exponents.

47. $3x^{-2} \cdot 5x^7$

$15x^5$

48. $5x^{-3} \cdot 8x^6$

$40x^3$

49. $2x^{-2} \cdot 3x^{-3}$

$\frac{6}{x^5}$

50. $4x^{-6} \cdot 5x^{-4}$

$\frac{20}{x^{10}}$

51. $(4x^{-4})(-3x^{-3})$

$-\frac{12}{x^7}$

52. $(3x^2)(-4x^{-1})$

$-12x$

53. $7x \cdot 3x^{-4} \cdot 2x^5$

$42x^2$

54. $6x \cdot 2x^{-3} \cdot 3x^4$

$36x^2$

55. $\dfrac{x^{-3} \cdot x^7}{x^{-1}}$

x^5

56. $\dfrac{x^{-4} \cdot x^6}{x^{-2}}$

x^4

57. $\dfrac{x^{-2} \cdot x^{-8}}{x^{-12}}$

x^2

58. $\dfrac{x^{-5} \cdot x^{-7}}{x^{-15}}$

x^3

There are many disciplines that deal with very large numbers and others that deal with very small numbers. For example, in astronomy, distances commonly are given in light-years. A light-year is the distance that light will travel in one year. It is approximately

> 5,880,000,000,000 miles

It can be difficult to perform calculations with numbers in this form because of the number of zeros present. Scientific notation provides a way of writing very large, or very small, numbers in a more manageable form.

Scientific Notation

> **Definition**
> A number is in scientific notation when it is written as the product of a number between 1 and 10 and an integer power of 10. A number written in scientific notation has the form
>
> $$n \times 10^r$$
>
> where $1 \leq n < 10$ and $r =$ an integer.

PRACTICE PROBLEMS

EXAMPLE 1   The speed of light is 186,000 miles per second. Write 186,000 in scientific notation.

SOLUTION   To write this number in scientific notation, we rewrite it as the product of a number between 1 and 10 and a power of 10. To do so, we move the decimal point 5 places to the left so that it appears between the 1 and the 8, giving us 1.86. Then we multiply this number by 10^5. The number that results has the same value as our original number but is written in scientific notation. Here is our result:

> $$186,000 = 1.86 \times 10^5$$

Both numbers have exactly the same value. The number on the left is written in *standard form*, while the number on the right is written in scientific notation.

1. Write 27,500 in scientific notation.

Converting to Standard Form

EXAMPLE 2   If your pulse rate is 60 beats per minute, then your heart will beat 8.64×10^4 times each day. Write 8.64×10^4 in standard form.

SOLUTION   Because 10^4 is 10,000, we can think of this as simply a multiplication problem. That is,

> $$8.64 \times 10^4 = 8.64 \times 10,000 = 86,400$$

Looking over our result, we can think of the exponent 4 as indicating the number of places we need to move the decimal point to write our number in standard form. Because our exponent is positive 4, we move the decimal point from its original position, between the 8 and the 6, four places to the right. If we need to add any zeros on the right we do so. The result is the standard form of our number, 86,400.

2. Write 7.89×10^5 in standard form.

Answers
1. 2.75×10^4 **2.** 789,000

Next, we turn our attention to writing small numbers in scientific notation. To do so, we use the negative exponents developed in the previous section. For example, the number 0.00075, when written in scientific notation, is equivalent to 7.5×10^{-4}. Here's why:

$$7.5 \times 10^{-4} = 7.5 \times \frac{1}{10^4} = 7.5 \times \frac{1}{10,000} = \frac{7.5}{10,000} = 0.00075$$

The table below lists some other numbers both in scientific notation and in standard form.

EXAMPLE 3   Each pair of numbers in the table below is equal.

Standard Form		Scientific Notation
376,000	=	3.76×10^5
49,500	=	4.95×10^4
3,200	=	3.2×10^3
591	=	5.91×10^2
46	=	4.6×10^1
8	=	8×10^0
0.47	=	4.7×10^{-1}
0.093	=	9.3×10^{-2}
0.00688	=	6.88×10^{-3}
0.0002	=	2×10^{-4}
0.000098	=	9.8×10^{-5}

As we read across the table, for each pair of numbers, notice how the decimal point in the number on the right is placed so that the number containing the decimal point is always a number between 1 and 10. Correspondingly, the exponent on 10 keeps track of how many places the decimal point was moved in converting from standard form to scientific notation. In general, when the exponent is positive, we are working with a large number. On the other hand, when the exponent is negative, we are working with a small number. (By small number, we mean a number that is less than 1, but larger than 0.)

We end this section with a diagram that shows two numbers, one large and one small, that are converted to scientific notation.

3. Fill in the missing numbers in the table below:

Standard Form		Scientific Notation
a. 24,500	=	
b.	=	5.6×10^5
c. 0.000789	=	
d.	=	4.8×10^{-3}

Answer
3. **a.** 2.45×10^4
   b. 560,000
   c. 7.89×10^{-4}
   d. 0.0048

Getting Ready for Class

After reading through the preceding section, respond in your own words and in complete sentences.

1. What is scientific notation?

2. What types of numbers are frequently written with scientific notation?

3. In writing the distance, in miles, to the sun, would we use a positive power of ten or a negative power of ten?

4. In writing the weight, in kilograms, of a paper clip, would we use a positive power of ten or a negative power of ten?

Problem Set E

Write each number in scientific notation. [Examples 1, 3]

1. 425,000
4.25×10^5

2. 635,000
6.35×10^5

3. 6,780,000
6.78×10^6

4. 5,490,000
5.49×10^6

5. 11,000
1.1×10^4

6. 29,000
2.9×10^4

7. 89,000,000
8.9×10^7

8. 37,000,000
3.7×10^7

Write each number in standard form. [Examples 2, 3]

9. 3.84×10^4
38,400

10. 3.84×10^7
38,400,000

11. 5.71×10^7
57,100,000

12. 5.71×10^5
571,000

13. 3.3×10^3
3,300

14. 3.3×10^2
330

15. 8.913×10^7
89,130,000

16. 8.913×10^5
891,300

Write each number in scientific notation. [Examples 1, 3]

17. 0.00035
3.5×10^{-4}

18. 0.0000035
3.5×10^{-6}

19. 0.0007
7×10^{-4}

20. 0.007
7×10^{-3}

21. 0.06035
6.035×10^{-2}

22. 0.0006035
6.035×10^{-4}

23. 0.1276
1.276×10^{-1}

24. 0.001276
1.276×10^{-3}

Write each number in standard form. [Examples 2, 3]

25. 8.3×10^{-4}
0.00083

26. 8.3×10^{-7}
0.00000083

27. 6.25×10^{-2}
0.0625

28. 7.83×10^{-4}
0.000783

29. 3.125×10^{-1}
0.3125

30. 3.125×10^{-2}
0.03125

31. 5×10^{-3}
0.005

32. 5×10^{-5}
0.00005

▶ Selected exercises available online at www.webassign.net/brookscole

■ Applying the Concepts

Super Bowl Advertising and Viewers The cost of a 30-second television ad along with the approximate number of viewers for four different Super Bowls is shown below. Complete the table by writing the ad cost in scientific notation, and the number of viewers in standard form.

	Year	Super Bowl	Ad Cost	Ad Cost in Scientific Notation	Viewers in Scientific Notation	Number of Viewers
33.	1967	I	$42,000	4.2×10^4	4.0×10^6	4,000,000
34.	1977	XI	$162,000	1.62×10^5	6.2×10^7	62,000,000
35.	1987	XXI	$575,000	5.75×10^5	8.7×10^7	87,000,000
36.	1997	XXXI	$1,200,000	1.2×10^6	8.8×10^7	88,000,000

Galilean Moons The planet Jupiter has about 60 known moons. In the year 1610 Galileo first discovered the four largest moons of Jupiter, Io, Europa, Ganymede, and Callisto. These moons are known as the Galilean moons. Each moon has a unique period, or the time it takes to make a trip around Jupiter. Fill in the tables below.

NASA

37.

Jupiter's Moon	Period (seconds)	
Io	153,000	1.53×10^5
Europa	307,000	3.07×10^5
Ganymede	618,000	6.18×10^5
Callisto	1,440,000	1.44×10^6

38.

Jupiter's Moon	Distance from Jupiter (kilometers)	
Io	422,000	4.22×10^5
Europa	617,000	6.17×10^5
Ganymede	1,070,000	1.07×10^6
Callisto	1,880,000	1.88×10^6

Computer Science The smallest amount of data that a computer can hold is measured in bits. A byte is the next largest unit and is equal to 8, or 2^3, bits. Fill in the table below.

	Unit	Number of Bytes	
		Exponential Form	Scientific Notation
39.	Kilobyte	$2^{10} = 1{,}024$	1.024×10^3
40.	Megabyte	$2^{20} \approx 1{,}048{,}000$	1.048×10^6
41.	Gigabyte	$2^{30} \approx 1{,}074{,}000{,}000$	1.074×10^9
42.	Terabyte	$2^{40} \approx 1{,}099{,}500{,}000{,}000$	1.0995×10^{12}

Multiplication and Division with Numbers Written in Scientific Notation

In this section, we extend our work with scientific notation to include multiplication and division with numbers written in scientific notation. To work the problems in this section, we use the material presented in the previous two sections, along with the commutative and associative properties of multiplication and the rule for multiplication with fractions. Here is our first example.

 EXAMPLE 1   Multiply: $(3.5 \times 10^8)(2.2 \times 10^{-5})$

SOLUTION   First we apply the commutative and associative properties to rearrange the numbers, so that the decimal numbers are grouped together and the powers of 10 are also.

$$(3.5 \times 10^8)(2.2 \times 10^{-5}) = (3.5)(2.2) \times (10^8)(10^{-5})$$

Next, we multiply the decimal numbers together and then the powers of ten. To multiply the powers of ten, we add exponents.

$$= 7.7 \times 10^{8+(-5)}$$
$$= 7.7 \times 10^3$$

EXAMPLE 2   Find the product of 130,000,000 and 0.000005. Write your answer in scientific notation.

SOLUTION   We begin by writing both numbers in scientific notation. Then we proceed as we did in Example 1: We group the numbers between 1 and 10 separately from the powers of 10.

$$(130,000,000)(0.000005) = (1.3 \times 10^8)(5 \times 10^{-6})$$
$$= (1.3)(5) \times (10^8)(10^{-6})$$
$$= 6.5 \times 10^2$$

Our next examples involve division with numbers in scientific notation.

EXAMPLE 3   Divide: $\dfrac{8 \times 10^3}{4 \times 10^{-6}}$

SOLUTION   To separate the numbers between 1 and 10 from the powers of 10, we "undo" the multiplication and write the problem as the product of two fractions. Doing so looks like this:

$$\frac{8 \times 10^3}{4 \times 10^{-6}} = \frac{8}{4} \times \frac{10^3}{10^{-6}} \quad \text{Write as two separate fractions}$$

Next, we divide 8 by 4 to obtain 2. Then we divide 10^3 by 10^{-6} by subtracting exponents.

$$= 2 \times 10^{3-(-6)} \quad \text{Divide}$$
$$= 2 \times 10^9$$

PRACTICE PROBLEMS

1. Multiply: $(2.5 \times 10^6)(1.4 \times 10^2)$

2. Find the product of 2,200,000 and 0.00015.

3. Divide: $\dfrac{6 \times 10^5}{2 \times 10^{-4}}$

Answers
1. 3.5×10^8 2. 3.3×10^2
3. 3.0×10^9

4. Divide: $\dfrac{0.0038}{19,000,000}$

EXAMPLE 4 Divide: $\dfrac{0.00045}{1,500,000}$

SOLUTION To begin, write each number in scientific notation.

$$\frac{0.00045}{1,500,000} = \frac{4.5 \times 10^{-4}}{1.5 \times 10^{6}} \qquad \text{Write numbers in scientific notation}$$

Next, as in the previous example, we write the problem as two separate fractions in order to group the numbers between 1 and 10 together, as well as the powers of 10.

$$= \frac{4.5}{1.5} \times \frac{10^{-4}}{10^{6}} \qquad \text{Write as two separate fractions}$$

$$= 3 \times 10^{-4-6} \qquad \text{Divide}$$

$$= 3 \times 10^{-10} \qquad -4 - 6 = -4 + (-6) = -10$$

5. Simplify: $\dfrac{(6.8 \times 10^{-4})(3.9 \times 10^{2})}{7.8 \times 10^{-6}}$

EXAMPLE 5 Simplify: $\dfrac{(6.8 \times 10^{5})(3.9 \times 10^{-7})}{7.8 \times 10^{-4}}$

SOLUTION We group the numbers between 1 and 10 separately from the powers of 10:

$$\frac{(6.8 \times 10^{5})(3.9 \times 10^{-7})}{7.8 \times 10^{-4}} = \frac{(6.8)(3.9)}{7.8} \times \frac{(10^{5})(10^{-7})}{10^{-4}}$$

$$= 3.4 \times 10^{5+(-7)-(-4)}$$

$$= 3.4 \times 10^{2}$$

6. Simplify: $\dfrac{(0.000035)(45,000)}{0.000075}$

EXAMPLE 6 Simplify: $\dfrac{(35,000)(0.0045)}{7,500,000}$

SOLUTION We write each number in scientific notation, and then we proceed as we have in the examples above.

$$\frac{(35,000)(0.0045)}{7,500,000} = \frac{(3.5 \times 10^{4})(4.5 \times 10^{-3})}{7.5 \times 10^{6}}$$

$$= \frac{(3.5)(4.5)}{7.5} \times \frac{(10^{4})(10^{-3})}{10^{6}}$$

$$= 2.1 \times 10^{4+(-3)-6}$$

$$= 2.1 \times 10^{-5}$$

Getting Ready for Class

After reading through the preceding section, respond in your own words and in complete sentences.

1. How is the commutative property used when multiplying or dividing with scientific notation?

2. How is the associative property used when multiplying or dividing with scientific notation?

3. The following problem is not complete. Why not?

$$(6.0 \times 10^{3})(5.2 \times 10^{4}) = 31.2 \times 10^{7}$$

4. Explain why it is easier to multiply very large or very small numbers when they are written in scientific notation, rather than standard form.

Answers
4. 2.0×10^{-10} **5.** 3.4×10^{4}
6. 2.1×10^{4}

Problem Set F

Find each product. Write all answers in scientific notation. [Examples 1, 2]

1. $(2 \times 10^4)(3 \times 10^6)$
6×10^{10}

2. $(3 \times 10^3)(1 \times 10^5)$
3×10^8

3. $(2.5 \times 10^7)(6 \times 10^3)$
1.5×10^{11}

4. $(3.8 \times 10^6)(5 \times 10^3)$
1.9×10^{10}

5. $(7.2 \times 10^3)(9.5 \times 10^{-6})$
6.84×10^{-2}

6. $(8.5 \times 10^5)(4.2 \times 10^{-9})$
3.57×10^{-3}

7. $(36,000)(450,000)$
1.62×10^{10}

8. $(25,000)(620,000)$
1.55×10^{10}

9. $(4,200)(0.00009)$
3.78×10^{-1}

10. $(0.0000065)(86,000)$
5.59×10^{-1}

Find each quotient. Write all answers in scientific notation. [Examples 3, 4]

11. $\dfrac{3.6 \times 10^5}{1.8 \times 10^2}$
2×10^3

12. $\dfrac{9.3 \times 10^{15}}{3.0 \times 10^5}$
3.1×10^{10}

13. $\dfrac{8.4 \times 10^{-6}}{2.1 \times 10^3}$
4×10^{-9}

14. $\dfrac{6.0 \times 10^{-10}}{1.5 \times 10^3}$
4×10^{-13}

15. $\dfrac{3.5 \times 10^5}{7.0 \times 10^{-10}}$
5×10^{14}

16. $\dfrac{1.6 \times 10^7}{8.0 \times 10^{-14}}$
2×10^{20}

17. $\dfrac{540,000}{9,000}$
6×10^1

18. $\dfrac{750,000,000}{250,000}$
3×10^3

19. $\dfrac{0.00092}{46,000}$
2×10^{-8}

20. $\dfrac{0.00000047}{235,000}$
2×10^{-12}

Simplify each expression, and write all answers in scientific notation. [Examples 5, 6]

21. $\dfrac{(3 \times 10^7)(8 \times 10^4)}{6 \times 10^5}$
4×10^6

22. $\dfrac{(4 \times 10^9)(6 \times 10^5)}{8 \times 10^3}$
3×10^{11}

23. $\dfrac{(2 \times 10^{-3})(6 \times 10^{-5})}{3 \times 10^{-4}}$
4×10^{-4}

24. $\dfrac{(4 \times 10^{-5})(9 \times 10^{-10})}{6 \times 10^{-6}}$
6×10^{-9}

25. $\dfrac{(3.5 \times 10^{-4})(4.2 \times 10^5)}{7 \times 10^3}$
2.1×10^{-2}

26. $\dfrac{(2.4 \times 10^{-6})(3.6 \times 10^3)}{9 \times 10^5}$
9.6×10^{-9}

27. $\dfrac{(0.00087)(40,000)}{1,160,000}$
3×10^{-5}

28. $\dfrac{(0.0045)(24,000)}{270,000}$
4×10^{-4}

29. $\dfrac{(525)(0.0000032)}{0.0025}$
6.72×10^{-1}

30. $\dfrac{(465)(0.000004)}{0.0093}$
2×10^{-1}

■ Applying the Concepts

Super Bowl Advertising and Viewers The cost of a 30-second television ad along with the approximate number of viewers for four different Super Bowls is shown below. Complete the table by finding the cost per viewer by dividing the ad cost by the number of viewers.

	Year	Super Bowl	Ad Cost	Number of Viewers	Cost per Viewer
31.	1967	I	4.2×10^4	4.0×10^6	1.05×10^{-2}
32.	1977	XI	1.62×10^5	6.2×10^7	2.6×10^{-3}
33.	1987	XXI	5.75×10^5	8.7×10^7	6.61×10^{-3}
34.	1997	XXXI	1.2×10^6	8.8×10^7	1.36×10^{-2}

35. Pyramids and Scientific Notation The Great Pyramid at Giza is one of the largest and oldest man-made structures in the world. It weighs over 10^{10} kilograms. If each stone making up the pyramid weighs approximately 4,000 kilograms, how many stones make up the structure? Write your answer in scientific notation.

2,500,000 or 2.5×10^6 stones

36. Technology A CD-ROM holds about 700 megabytes, or 7.0×10^8 bytes, of data. A four-and-a-half minute song downloaded from the Internet uses 5 megabytes, or 5.0×10^6 bytes, of storage space. How many four-and-a-half minute songs can fit on a CD?

Music Video

140 or 1.4×10^2 songs

Solutions to Selected Practice Problems

Solutions to all practice problems that require more than one step are shown here. Before you look back here to see where you have made a mistake, you should try the problem you are working on twice. If you do not get the correct answer the second time you work the problem, then the solution here should show you where you went wrong.

Chapter 1

Section 1.2

1.
$$63$$
$$+25$$
$$\overline{88}$$

2.
$$342$$
$$+605$$
$$\overline{947}$$

3. a.
$$\overset{1}{3}75$$
$$121$$
$$+473$$
$$\overline{969}$$

b.
$$\overset{2\,2}{4}95$$
$$699$$
$$+978$$
$$\overline{2{,}172}$$

4. a.
$$\overset{11\ 11}{5}7{,}904$$
$$7{,}193$$
$$655$$
$$\overline{65{,}752}$$

b.
$$\overset{1\ 1\ 2\ 3}{6}8{,}495$$
$$7{,}236$$
$$878$$
$$29$$
$$5$$
$$\overline{76{,}643}$$

7. a. $6 + 2 + 4 + 8 + 3 = (6 + 4) + (2 + 8) + 3 = 10 + 10 + 3 = 23$
b. $24 + 17 + 36 + 13 = (24 + 36) + (17 + 13) = 60 + 30 = 90$

8. a. $n = 8$, since $8 + 9 = 17$
b. $n = 8$, since $8 + 2 = 10$
c. $n = 1$, since $8 + 1 = 9$
d. $n = 6$, since $16 = 6 + 10$

9. a. $7 + 7 + 7 + 7 = 28$ ft **b.** $88 + 88 + 33 + 33 = 242$ in. **c.** $44 + 66 + 77 = 187$ yd

Section 1.3

5. a. Food $ 5,296
Car   4,847
Total $10,143 = $10,140 to the nearest ten dollars

b. Savings $2,149
Taxes   6,137
Total $8,286 = $8,300 to the nearest hundred dollars

c. House $10,200
Taxes   6,137
Misc.   6,142
Car   4,847
Savings 2,149
Total $29,475 = $29,000 to the nearest thousand dollars

6. a. We round each of the four numbers in the sum to the nearest thousand, and then we add the rounded numbers.

5,287	rounds to	5,000
2,561	rounds to	3,000
888	rounds to	1,000
+4,898	rounds to	+ 5,000
		14,000

We estimate the answer to this problem to be approximately 14,000. The actual answer, found by adding the original, unrounded numbers, is 13,634.

b. We round each of the four numbers in the sum to the nearest thousand, and then we add the rounded numbers.

702	rounds to	1,000
3,944	rounds to	4,000
1,001	rounds to	1,000
+3,500	rounds to	+ 4,000
		10,000

We estimate the answer to this problem to be approximately 10,000. The actual answer, found by adding the original, unrounded numbers, is 9,147.

Section 1.4

1. a.
$$684$$
$$-431$$
$$\overline{253}$$

b.
$$7{,}406$$
$$-3{,}405$$
$$\overline{4{,}001}$$

2. a.
$$6{,}857$$
$$-405$$
$$\overline{6{,}452}$$

b.
$$345$$
$$-234$$
$$\overline{111}$$

3. a. $63 = 6$ tens $+ 3$ ones $= 5$ tens $+ 13$ ones
$\underline{-47} = \underline{4$ tens 7 ones $} = \underline{4$ tens 7 ones$}$
                                        1 ten $+$ 6 ones

Answer: 16

b. $532 = 5$ hundreds $+ 3$ tens $+ 2$ ones $= 5$ hundreds $+ 2$ tens $+ 12$ ones
$\underline{-403} = \underline{4$ hundreds 0 tens 3 tens$} = \underline{4$ hundreds 0 tens 3 ones$}$
                                                    1 hundred $+$ 2 tens $+$ 9 ones

Answer: 129

4. a. $\overset{5\,15}{6\,\cancel{5}6}$
$\underline{-283}$
373

b. $\overset{2\,\,16}{3{,}\cancel{7}\cancel{2}9}$
$\underline{-1{,}749}$
$1{,}980$

Section 1.5

1. a. $4 \cdot 70 = 70 + 70 + 70 + 70$
            $= 280$

b. $4 \cdot 700 = 700 + 700 + 700 + 700$
        $= 2{,}800$

c. $4 \cdot 7{,}000 = 7{,}000 + 7{,}000 + 7{,}000 + 7{,}000$
        $= 28{,}000$

4. a. $\overset{5}{5}7$
$\underline{\times\ 8}$
456

b. $\overset{5}{5}70$
$\underline{\times\ 8}$
$4{,}560$

5. a. 45
$\underline{\times 62}$
$90\ \longleftarrow 2(45) = 90$
$\underline{+2{,}700}\ \longleftarrow 60(45) = 2{,}700$
$2{,}790$

b. $\overset{1}{6}20$
$\underline{\times 45}$
$3{,}100\ \longleftarrow 5(620) = 3{,}100$
$\underline{+24{,}800}\ \longleftarrow 40(620) = 24{,}800$
$27{,}900$

6. a. 356
$\underline{\times 641}$
$356\ \longleftarrow 1(356) = 356$
$14{,}240\ \longleftarrow 40(356) = 14{,}240$
$\underline{213{,}600}\ \longleftarrow 600(356) = 213{,}600$
$228{,}196$

b. $3{,}560$
$\underline{\times 641}$
$3{,}560\ \longleftarrow 1(3{,}560) = 3{,}560$
$142{,}400\ \longleftarrow 40(3{,}560) = 142{,}400$
$\underline{2{,}136{,}000}\ \longleftarrow 600(3{,}560) = 2{,}136{,}000$
$2{,}281{,}960$

7. 365
$\underline{\times\ 550}$
$18{,}250$
$\underline{182{,}500}$
$200{,}750$ mg

8. $36(\$12) = \$432$ Total weekly earnings
$\$432 - \$109 = \$323$ Take-home pay

9. Fat: $3(10) = 30$ grams of fat; sodium: $3(160) = 480$ milligrams of sodium

10. Bowling for 3 hours burns $3(265) = 795$ calories. Eating two bags of chips means you are consuming $2(3)(160) = 960$ calories. No; bowling won't burn all the calories.

13. a. Area $= s^2 = 4^2 = 16$ feet^2
b. Area $= lw = (7)(5) = 35$ inches^2

Section 1.6

1. a. 74
$4\overline{)296}$
$\underline{28}\downarrow$
16
$\underline{16}$
0

b. 740
$4\overline{)2{,}960}$
$\underline{2\ 8}\downarrow$
16
$\underline{16}$
00

2. a. 283
$24\overline{)6{,}792}$
$\underline{4\ 8}\downarrow$
$1\ 99$
$\underline{1\ 92}\downarrow$
72
$\underline{72}$
0

b. $2{,}830$
$24\overline{)67{,}920}$
$\underline{48}\downarrow$
$19\ 9$
$\underline{19\ 2}\downarrow$
72
$\underline{72}$
00

3. 208
$9\overline{)1{,}872}$
$\underline{1\ 8}\downarrow$
07
$\underline{0}\downarrow$
72
$\underline{72}$
0

4. a. 69 R 20, or $69\frac{20}{27}$
$27\overline{)1{,}883}$
$\underline{1\ 62}\downarrow$
263
$\underline{243}$
20

b. 104 R 11, or $104\frac{11}{18}$
$18\overline{)1{,}883}$
$\underline{1\ 8}\downarrow$
08
$\underline{0}\downarrow$
83
$\underline{72}$
11

5. 156 The family spent $\$156$ per day
$12\overline{)1{,}872}$
$\underline{1\ 2}\downarrow$
67
$\underline{60}\downarrow$
72
$\underline{72}$
0

Section 1.7

1. Base 5, exponent 2; 5 to the second power, or 5 squared   **2.** Base 2, exponent 3; 2 to the third power, or 2 cubed
3. Base 1, exponent 4; 1 to the fourth power   **4.** $5^2 = 5 \cdot 5 = 25$ **5.** $9^2 = 9 \cdot 9 = 81$ **6.** $2^3 = 2 \cdot 2 \cdot 2 = 8$
7. $1^4 = 1 \cdot 1 \cdot 1 \cdot 1 = 1$ **8.** $2^5 = 2 \cdot 2 \cdot 2 \cdot 2 \cdot 2 = 32$ **9.** $7^1 = 7$ **10.** $4^1 = 4$ **11.** $9^0 = 1$ **12.** $1^0 = 1$

13. a. $5 \cdot 7 - 3 \cdot 6 = 35 - 18$
$= 17$

b. $5 \cdot 70 - 3 \cdot 60 = 350 - 180$
$= 170$

14. $7 + 3(6 + 4) = 7 + 3(10)$
$= 7 + 30$
$= 37$

15. a. $28 \div 7 - 3 = 4 - 3$
$= 1$

b. $6 \cdot 3^2 + 64 \div 2^4 - 2 = 6 \cdot 9 + 64 \div 16 - 2$
$= 54 + 4 - 2$
$= 58 - 2$
$= 56$

16. a. $5 + 3[24 - 5(6 - 2)] = 5 + 3[24 - 5(4)]$
$= 5 + 3[24 - 20]$
$= 5 + 3[4]$
$= 5 + 12$
$= 17$

b. $50 + 30[240 - 50(6 - 2)] = 50 + 30[240 - 50(4)]$
$= 50 + 30[240 - 200]$
$= 50 + 30(40)$
$= 50 + 1,200$
$= 1,250$

Chapter 2

Section 2.1

6. $\dfrac{2}{3} = \dfrac{2 \cdot 4}{3 \cdot 4} = \dfrac{8}{12}$ **7.** $\dfrac{2}{3} = \dfrac{2 \cdot 4x}{3 \cdot 4x} = \dfrac{8x}{12x}$ **8.** $\dfrac{15}{20} = \dfrac{15 \div 5}{20 \div 5} = \dfrac{3}{4}$ **10.** $\dfrac{1}{3} \cdot \dfrac{4}{4} = \dfrac{4}{12}; \dfrac{1}{6} \cdot \dfrac{2}{2} = \dfrac{2}{12}; \dfrac{1}{4} \cdot \dfrac{3}{3} = \dfrac{3}{12}$

Section 2.2

1. 37 and 59 are prime numbers; 39 is divisible by 3 and 13; 51 is divisible by 3 and 17.

2. a. $90 = 9 \cdot 10$
$= 3 \cdot 3 \cdot 2 \cdot 5$
$= 2 \cdot 3^2 \cdot 5$

b. $900 = 9 \cdot 100$
$= 3 \cdot 3 \cdot 25 \cdot 4$
$= 3 \cdot 3 \cdot 5 \cdot 5 \cdot 2 \cdot 2$
$= 2^2 \cdot 3^2 \cdot 5^2$

4. $\dfrac{12}{18} = \dfrac{12 \div 6}{18 \div 6} = \dfrac{2}{3}$

5. $\dfrac{15}{20} = \dfrac{3 \cdot 5}{2 \cdot 2 \cdot 5} = \dfrac{3}{4}$

6. a. $\dfrac{30}{35} = \dfrac{2 \cdot 3 \cdot 5}{5 \cdot 7} = \dfrac{6}{7}$ **b.** $\dfrac{300}{350} = \dfrac{2 \cdot 2 \cdot 3 \cdot 5 \cdot 5}{2 \cdot 5 \cdot 5 \cdot 7} = \dfrac{6}{7}$ **7. a.** $\dfrac{8}{72} = \dfrac{2 \cdot 2 \cdot 2 \cdot 1}{2 \cdot 2 \cdot 2 \cdot 3 \cdot 3} = \dfrac{1}{9}$ **b.** $\dfrac{16}{144} = \dfrac{2 \cdot 2 \cdot 2 \cdot 2}{2 \cdot 2 \cdot 2 \cdot 2 \cdot 3 \cdot 3} = \dfrac{1}{9}$

8. $\dfrac{5}{50} = \dfrac{5 \cdot 1}{5 \cdot 2 \cdot 5} = \dfrac{1}{10}$ **9.** $\dfrac{120}{25} = \dfrac{2 \cdot 2 \cdot 2 \cdot 3 \cdot 5}{5 \cdot 5} = \dfrac{24}{5}$

Section 2.3

1. $\dfrac{2}{3} \cdot \dfrac{5}{9} = \dfrac{10}{27}$ **2.** $\dfrac{2}{5} \cdot 7 = \dfrac{2}{5} \cdot \dfrac{7}{1}$
$= \dfrac{14}{5}$ **3.** $\dfrac{1}{3}\left(\dfrac{4}{5} \cdot \dfrac{1}{3}\right) = \dfrac{1}{3}\left(\dfrac{4}{15}\right)$
$= \dfrac{4}{45}$

4. a. $\dfrac{12}{25} \cdot \dfrac{5}{6} = \dfrac{12 \cdot 5}{25 \cdot 6}$
$= \dfrac{(2 \cdot 2 \cdot 3) \cdot 5}{(5 \cdot 5) \cdot (2 \cdot 3)}$
$= \dfrac{2}{5}$

b. $\dfrac{12}{25} \cdot \dfrac{50}{60} = \dfrac{12 \cdot 50}{25 \cdot 60}$
$= \dfrac{(2 \cdot 2 \cdot 3) \cdot (2 \cdot 5 \cdot 5)}{(5 \cdot 5) \cdot (2 \cdot 2 \cdot 3 \cdot 5)}$
$= \dfrac{2}{5}$

5. a. $\dfrac{8}{3} \cdot \dfrac{9}{24} = \dfrac{8 \cdot 9}{3 \cdot 24}$
$= \dfrac{(2 \cdot 2 \cdot 2) \cdot (3 \cdot 3)}{3 \cdot (2 \cdot 2 \cdot 2 \cdot 3)}$
$= \dfrac{1}{1}$
$= 1$

b. $\dfrac{8}{30} \cdot \dfrac{90}{24} = \dfrac{8 \cdot 90}{30 \cdot 24}$
$= \dfrac{(2 \cdot 2 \cdot 2) \cdot (2 \cdot 3 \cdot 3 \cdot 5)}{(2 \cdot 3 \cdot 5) \cdot (2 \cdot 2 \cdot 2 \cdot 3)}$
$= \dfrac{1}{1}$
$= 1$

6. $\dfrac{3}{4} \cdot \dfrac{8}{3} \cdot \dfrac{1}{6} = \dfrac{3 \cdot 8 \cdot 1}{4 \cdot 3 \cdot 6}$
$= \dfrac{(3 \cdot 2 \cdot 2 \cdot 2) \cdot 1}{(2 \cdot 2) \cdot 3 \cdot (2 \cdot 3)}$
$= \dfrac{1}{3}$

7. $\left(\dfrac{2}{3}\right)^2 = \dfrac{2}{3} \cdot \dfrac{2}{3}$
$= \dfrac{4}{9}$

8. a. $\left(\dfrac{3}{4}\right)^2 \cdot \dfrac{1}{2} = \dfrac{3}{4} \cdot \dfrac{3}{4} \cdot \dfrac{1}{2}$
$= \dfrac{9}{32}$

b. $\left(\dfrac{2}{3}\right)^3 \cdot \dfrac{9}{8} = \dfrac{2}{3} \cdot \dfrac{2}{3} \cdot \dfrac{2}{3} \cdot \dfrac{9}{8}$
$= \dfrac{2 \cdot 2 \cdot 2 \cdot 9}{3 \cdot 3 \cdot 3 \cdot 8}$
$= \dfrac{2 \cdot 2 \cdot 2 \cdot (3 \cdot 3)}{3 \cdot 3 \cdot 3 \cdot (2 \cdot 2 \cdot 2)}$
$= \dfrac{2 \cdot 2 \cdot 2 \cdot (3 \cdot 3)}{3 \cdot 3 \cdot 3 \cdot (2 \cdot 2 \cdot 2)}$
$= \dfrac{1}{3}$

9. a. $\dfrac{2}{3} \cdot \dfrac{1}{2} = \dfrac{2 \cdot 1}{3 \cdot 2}$ **b.** $\dfrac{3}{5}(15) = \dfrac{3}{5}\left(\dfrac{15}{1}\right)$ **10. a.** $\dfrac{2}{3}(12) = \dfrac{2}{3}\left(\dfrac{12}{1}\right)$ **b.** $\dfrac{2}{3}(120) = \dfrac{2}{3}\left(\dfrac{120}{1}\right)$

$\qquad\qquad = \dfrac{1}{3}$ $\qquad\qquad = \dfrac{3 \cdot 3 \cdot 5}{5}$ $\qquad\qquad\qquad = \dfrac{2 \cdot 2 \cdot 2 \cdot 3}{3 \cdot 1}$ $\qquad\qquad = \dfrac{2 \cdot 2 \cdot 2 \cdot 2 \cdot 3 \cdot 5}{3}$

$\qquad\qquad\qquad = \dfrac{9}{1}$ $\qquad\qquad\qquad = \dfrac{8}{1}$ $\qquad\qquad = \dfrac{80}{1}$

$\qquad\qquad\qquad = 9$ $\qquad\qquad\qquad = 8$ $\qquad\qquad = 80$

11. $A = \dfrac{1}{2}(7)(10)$ **12.**

$\qquad = 35 \text{ in}^2$

$A = 4 \times 4 = 16 \text{ ft}^2$

$A = \dfrac{1}{2} \times 2 \times 2$

$= 2 \text{ ft}^2$

$A = 8 \times 2 = 16 \text{ ft}^2$

Total area $= 2 + 16 + 16 = 34 \text{ ft}^2$

Section 2.4

1. a. $\dfrac{1}{3} \div \dfrac{1}{6} = \dfrac{1}{3} \cdot \dfrac{6}{1}$ **b.** $\dfrac{1}{30} \div \dfrac{1}{60} = \dfrac{1}{30} \cdot \dfrac{60}{1}$ **2.** $\dfrac{5}{9} \div \dfrac{10}{3} = \dfrac{5}{9} \cdot \dfrac{3}{10}$ **3. a.** $\dfrac{3}{4} \div 3 = \dfrac{3}{4} \cdot \dfrac{1}{3}$ **b.** $\dfrac{3}{5} \div 3 = \dfrac{3}{5} \cdot \dfrac{1}{3}$ **c.** $\dfrac{3}{7} \div 3 = \dfrac{3}{7} \cdot \dfrac{1}{3}$

$\qquad = \dfrac{6}{3}$ $\qquad\qquad = \dfrac{1 \cdot 2 \cdot 2 \cdot 3 \cdot 5}{2 \cdot 3 \cdot 5 \cdot 1}$ $\qquad = \dfrac{5 \cdot 3}{3 \cdot 3 \cdot 2 \cdot 5}$ $\qquad = \dfrac{1}{4}$ $\qquad = \dfrac{1}{5}$ $\qquad = \dfrac{1}{7}$

$\qquad = 2$ $\qquad\qquad = \dfrac{2}{1}$ $\qquad = \dfrac{1}{6}$

$\qquad\qquad = 2$

4. $4 \div \left(\dfrac{1}{5}\right) = 4(5)$ **5. a.** $\dfrac{5}{32} \div \dfrac{10}{42} = \dfrac{5}{32} \cdot \dfrac{42}{10}$ **b.** $\dfrac{15}{32} \div \dfrac{30}{42} = \dfrac{15}{32} \cdot \dfrac{42}{30}$

$\qquad = 20$ $\qquad\qquad = \dfrac{5 \cdot (2 \cdot 3 \cdot 7)}{2 \cdot 2 \cdot 2 \cdot 2 \cdot 2 \cdot 2 \cdot 5}$ $\qquad\qquad = \dfrac{(3 \cdot 5) \cdot (2 \cdot 3 \cdot 7)}{(2 \cdot 2 \cdot 2 \cdot 2 \cdot 2) \cdot (2 \cdot 3 \cdot 5)}$

$\qquad\qquad = \dfrac{21}{32}$ $\qquad\qquad = \dfrac{21}{32}$

6. $\dfrac{12}{25} \div 6 = \dfrac{12}{25} \cdot \dfrac{1}{6}$ **b.** $\dfrac{24}{25} \div 6 = \dfrac{24}{25} \cdot \dfrac{1}{6}$ **7. a.** $12 \div \left(\dfrac{4}{3}\right) = 12\left(\dfrac{3}{4}\right)$ **b.** $12 \div \dfrac{4}{5} = 12\left(\dfrac{5}{4}\right)$ **c.** $12 \div \dfrac{4}{7} = 12\left(\dfrac{7}{4}\right)$

$\qquad = \dfrac{2 \cdot 2 \cdot 3 \cdot 1}{5 \cdot 5 \cdot 2 \cdot 3}$ $\qquad = \dfrac{2 \cdot 2 \cdot 2 \cdot 3 \cdot 1}{(5 \cdot 5) \cdot (2 \cdot 3)}$ $\qquad\qquad = 9$ $\qquad\qquad = 15$ $\qquad\qquad = 21$

$\qquad = \dfrac{2}{25}$ $\qquad = \dfrac{4}{25}$

8. $\dfrac{5}{4} \div \dfrac{1}{8} + 8 = \dfrac{5}{4} \cdot \dfrac{8}{1} + 8$ **9.** $18 \div \left(\dfrac{3}{5}\right)^2 + 48 \div \left(\dfrac{2}{5}\right)^2 = 18 \div \dfrac{9}{25} + 48 \div \dfrac{4}{25}$ **10.** $12 \div \dfrac{3}{4} = 12 \cdot \dfrac{4}{3}$

$\qquad\qquad = 10 + 8$ $\qquad\qquad\qquad\qquad = 18 \cdot \dfrac{25}{9} + 48 \cdot \dfrac{25}{4}$ $\qquad\qquad = 4 \cdot 4$

$\qquad\qquad = 18$ $\qquad\qquad\qquad\qquad = 50 + 300$ $\qquad\qquad = 16 \text{ blankets}$

$\qquad\qquad\qquad\qquad = 350$

Section 2.5

1. $\dfrac{3}{10} + \dfrac{1}{10} = \dfrac{3+1}{10}$ **2.** $\dfrac{a+5}{12} + \dfrac{3}{12} = \dfrac{a+5+3}{12}$ **3.** $\dfrac{8}{7} - \dfrac{5}{7} = \dfrac{8-5}{7}$ **4.** $\dfrac{5}{9} + \dfrac{8}{9} + \dfrac{5}{9} = \dfrac{5+8+5}{9}$

$\qquad\qquad = \dfrac{4}{10}$ $\qquad\qquad = \dfrac{a+8}{12}$ $\qquad\qquad = \dfrac{3}{7}$ $\qquad\qquad = \dfrac{18}{9}$

$\qquad\qquad = \dfrac{2}{5}$ $\qquad\qquad = 2$

5. a. $\left.\begin{array}{l}18 = 2 \cdot 3 \cdot 3 \\ 14 = 2 \cdot 7\end{array}\right\}$ LCD $= 2 \cdot 3 \cdot 3 \cdot 7$
$= 126$

b. $\left.\begin{array}{l}36 = 2 \cdot 2 \cdot 3 \cdot 3 \\ 28 = 2 \cdot 2 \cdot 7\end{array}\right\}$ LCD $= 2 \cdot 2 \cdot 3 \cdot 3 \cdot 7$
$= 252$

8. a. $\dfrac{2}{9} + \dfrac{4}{15} = \dfrac{2 \cdot 5}{9 \cdot 5} + \dfrac{4 \cdot 3}{15 \cdot 3}$

$= \dfrac{10}{45} + \dfrac{12}{45}$

$= \dfrac{22}{45}$

b. $\dfrac{2}{27} + \dfrac{4}{45} = \dfrac{2 \cdot 5}{27 \cdot 5} + \dfrac{4 \cdot 3}{45 \cdot 3}$

$= \dfrac{10}{135} + \dfrac{12}{135}$

$= \dfrac{22}{135}$

9. LCD $= 100$; $\dfrac{8}{25} - \dfrac{3}{20} = \dfrac{8 \cdot 4}{25 \cdot 4} - \dfrac{3 \cdot 5}{20 \cdot 5}$

$= \dfrac{32}{100} - \dfrac{15}{100}$

$= \dfrac{17}{100}$

10. LCD $= 20$; $\dfrac{3}{4} - \dfrac{1}{5} = \dfrac{3 \cdot 5}{4 \cdot 5} - \dfrac{1 \cdot 4}{5 \cdot 4}$

$= \dfrac{15}{20} - \dfrac{4}{20}$

$= \dfrac{11}{20}$

11. a. LCD $= 36$; $\dfrac{1}{9} + \dfrac{1}{4} + \dfrac{1}{6} = \dfrac{1 \cdot 4}{9 \cdot 4} + \dfrac{1 \cdot 9}{4 \cdot 9} + \dfrac{1 \cdot 6}{6 \cdot 6}$

$= \dfrac{4}{36} + \dfrac{9}{36} + \dfrac{6}{36}$

$= \dfrac{19}{36}$

b. $\dfrac{1}{90} + \dfrac{1}{40} + \dfrac{1}{60} = \dfrac{1 \cdot 4}{90 \cdot 4} + \dfrac{1 \cdot 9}{40 \cdot 9} + \dfrac{1 \cdot 6}{60 \cdot 6}$

$= \dfrac{4}{360} + \dfrac{9}{360} + \dfrac{6}{360}$

$= \dfrac{19}{360}$

12. $2 - \dfrac{3}{4} = \dfrac{2}{1} - \dfrac{3}{4}$

$= \dfrac{2 \cdot 4}{1 \cdot 4} - \dfrac{3}{4}$

$= \dfrac{8}{4} - \dfrac{3}{4}$

$= \dfrac{5}{4}$

Section 2.6

1. $5\dfrac{2}{3} = 5 + \dfrac{2}{3}$

$= \dfrac{5}{1} + \dfrac{2}{3}$

$= \dfrac{5 \cdot 3}{1 \cdot 3} + \dfrac{2}{3}$

$= \dfrac{15}{3} + \dfrac{2}{3}$

$= \dfrac{17}{3}$

2. $3\dfrac{1}{6} = 3 + \dfrac{1}{6}$

$= \dfrac{3}{1} + \dfrac{1}{6}$

$= \dfrac{3 \cdot 6}{1 \cdot 6} + \dfrac{1}{6}$

$= \dfrac{18}{6} + \dfrac{1}{6}$

$= \dfrac{19}{6}$

3. $5\dfrac{2}{3} = \dfrac{(3 \cdot 5) + 2}{3}$

$= \dfrac{17}{3}$

4. $6\dfrac{4}{9} = \dfrac{(9 \cdot 6) + 4}{9}$

$= \dfrac{58}{9}$

5. $\begin{array}{r} 3 \\ 3\overline{)11} \\ 9 \\ \hline 2 \end{array}$ so $\dfrac{11}{3} = 3\dfrac{2}{3}$

6. $\begin{array}{r} 2 \\ 5\overline{)14} \\ 10 \\ \hline 4 \end{array}$ so $\dfrac{14}{5} = 2\dfrac{4}{5}$

7. $\begin{array}{r} 7 \\ 26\overline{)207} \\ 182 \\ \hline 25 \end{array}$ so $\dfrac{207}{26} = 7\dfrac{25}{26}$

Section 2.7

1. $2\dfrac{3}{4} \cdot 4\dfrac{1}{3} = \dfrac{11}{4} \cdot \dfrac{13}{3}$

$= \dfrac{143}{12}$

$= 11\dfrac{11}{12}$

2. $2 \cdot 3\dfrac{5}{8} = \dfrac{2}{1} \cdot \dfrac{29}{8}$

$= \dfrac{58}{8}$

$= 7\dfrac{2}{8}$

$= 7\dfrac{1}{4}$

3. $1\dfrac{3}{5} \div 3\dfrac{2}{5} = \dfrac{8}{5} \div \dfrac{17}{5}$

$= \dfrac{8}{5} \cdot \dfrac{5}{17}$

$= \dfrac{8}{17}$

4. $4\dfrac{5}{8} \div 2 = \dfrac{37}{8} \div \dfrac{2}{1}$

$= \dfrac{37}{8} \cdot \dfrac{1}{2}$

$= \dfrac{37}{16}$

$= 2\dfrac{5}{16}$

Section 2.8

1. $3\dfrac{2}{3} + 2\dfrac{1}{4} = 3 + \dfrac{2}{3} + 2 + \dfrac{1}{4}$

$= (3 + 2) + \left(\dfrac{2}{3} + \dfrac{1}{4}\right)$

$= 5 + \left(\dfrac{2 \cdot 4}{3 \cdot 4} + \dfrac{1 \cdot 3}{4 \cdot 3}\right)$

$= 5 + \left(\dfrac{8}{12} + \dfrac{3}{12}\right)$

$= 5 + \dfrac{11}{12} = 5\dfrac{11}{12}$

2. $\begin{array}{l} 5\dfrac{3}{4} = 5\dfrac{3 \cdot 5}{4 \cdot 5} = 5\dfrac{15}{20} \\ + 6\dfrac{4}{5} = 6\dfrac{4 \cdot 4}{5 \cdot 4} = 6\dfrac{16}{20} \\ \hline 11\dfrac{31}{20} = 11 + 1\dfrac{11}{20} = 12\dfrac{11}{20} \end{array}$

3. $\begin{array}{l} 6\dfrac{3}{4} = 6\dfrac{3 \cdot 2}{4 \cdot 2} = 6\dfrac{6}{8} \\ + 2\dfrac{7}{8} = 2\dfrac{7}{8} \quad = 2\dfrac{7}{8} \\ \hline 8\dfrac{13}{8} = 9\dfrac{5}{8} \end{array}$

4.
$$2\frac{1}{3} = 2\frac{1\cdot 4}{3\cdot 4} = 2\frac{4}{12}$$
$$1\frac{1}{4} = 1\frac{1\cdot 3}{4\cdot 3} = 1\frac{3}{12}$$
$$+\,3\frac{11}{12} = 3\frac{11}{12} = 3\frac{11}{12}$$
$$6\frac{18}{12} = 7\frac{6}{12} = 7\frac{1}{2}$$

5.
$$4\frac{7}{8}$$
$$-1\frac{5}{8}$$
$$3\frac{2}{8} = 3\frac{1}{4}$$

6.
$$12\frac{7}{10} = \quad 12\frac{7}{10} = \quad 12\frac{7}{10}$$
$$-\,7\frac{2}{5} = -7\frac{2\cdot 2}{5\cdot 2} = -7\frac{4}{10}$$
$$5\frac{3}{10}$$

7.
$$10 = \quad 9\frac{7}{7}$$
$$-\,5\frac{4}{7} = -5\frac{4}{7}$$
$$4\frac{3}{7}$$

8.
$$6\frac{1}{3} = \left(5 + \frac{3}{3}\right) + \frac{1}{3} = \quad 5\frac{4}{3}$$
$$-2\frac{2}{3} = \qquad\qquad -2\frac{2}{3} = -2\frac{2}{3}$$
$$3\frac{2}{3}$$

9.
$$6\frac{3}{4} = \quad 6\frac{3\cdot 3}{4\cdot 3} = \quad 6\frac{9}{12} = \quad 5\frac{21}{12}$$
$$-2\frac{5}{6} = -2\frac{5\cdot 2}{6\cdot 2} = -2\frac{10}{12} = -2\frac{10}{12}$$
$$3\frac{11}{12}$$

Section 2.9

1.
$$4 + \left(1\frac{1}{2}\right)\left(2\frac{3}{4}\right) = 4 + \left(\frac{3}{2}\right)\left(\frac{11}{4}\right)$$
$$= 4 + \frac{33}{8}$$
$$= \frac{32}{8} + \frac{33}{8}$$
$$= \frac{65}{8}$$
$$= 8\frac{1}{8}$$

2.
$$\left(\frac{2}{3} + \frac{1}{6}\right)\left(2\frac{5}{6} + 1\frac{1}{3}\right) = \left(\frac{5}{6}\right)\left(4\frac{1}{6}\right)$$
$$= \frac{5}{6}\left(\frac{25}{6}\right)$$
$$= \frac{125}{36}$$
$$= 3\frac{17}{36}$$

3.
$$\frac{3}{7} + \frac{1}{3}\left(1\frac{1}{2} + 4\frac{1}{2}\right)^2 = \frac{3}{7} + \frac{1}{3}(6)^2$$
$$= \frac{3}{7} + \frac{1}{3}(36)$$
$$= \frac{3}{7} + 12$$
$$= 12\frac{3}{7}$$

4.
$$\frac{\frac{2}{3}}{\frac{5}{9}} = \frac{2}{3} \div \frac{5}{9}$$
$$= \frac{2}{3}\cdot\frac{9}{5}$$
$$= \frac{18}{15}$$
$$= \frac{6}{5} = 1\frac{1}{5}$$

5.
$$\frac{\frac{1}{2} + \frac{3}{4}}{\frac{2}{3} - \frac{1}{4}} = \frac{12\left(\frac{1}{2} + \frac{3}{4}\right)}{12\left(\frac{2}{3} - \frac{1}{4}\right)}$$
$$= \frac{12\cdot\frac{1}{2} + 12\cdot\frac{3}{4}}{12\cdot\frac{2}{3} - 12\cdot\frac{1}{4}}$$
$$= \frac{6 + 9}{8 - 3}$$
$$= \frac{15}{5} = 3$$

6.
$$\frac{4 + \frac{2}{3}}{3 - \frac{1}{4}} = \frac{12\left(4 + \frac{2}{3}\right)}{12\left(3 - \frac{1}{4}\right)}$$
$$= \frac{12\cdot 4 + 12\cdot\frac{2}{3}}{12\cdot 3 - 12\cdot\frac{1}{4}}$$
$$= \frac{48 + 8}{36 - 3}$$
$$= \frac{56}{33} = 1\frac{23}{33}$$

7.
$$\frac{12\frac{1}{3}}{6\frac{2}{3}} = 12\frac{1}{3} \div 6\frac{2}{3}$$
$$= \frac{37}{3} \div \frac{20}{3}$$
$$= \frac{37}{3}\cdot\frac{3}{20}$$
$$= \frac{37}{20}$$
$$= 1\frac{17}{20}$$

Chapter 3

Section 3.1

1. $700 + 80 + 5 + \frac{4}{10} + \frac{6}{100} + \frac{2}{1{,}000}$ **2. a.** Six hundredths **b.** Seven tenths **c.** Eight thousandths

3. a. Five and six hundredths **b.** Four and seven tenths **c.** Three and eight thousandths
4. a. Five and ninety-eight hundredths **b.** Five and ninety-eight thousandths **5.** Three hundred five and four hundred six thousandths

Section 3.2

1. a.
$$38.45 = \quad 38\frac{45}{100} = \quad 38\frac{450}{1{,}000}$$
$$+456.073 = \quad 456\frac{73}{1{,}000} = 456\frac{73}{1{,}000}$$
$$494\frac{523}{1{,}000} = 494.523$$

b.
$$38.045 = \quad 38\frac{45}{1{,}000} = \quad 38\frac{45}{1{,}000}$$
$$+456.73 = \quad 456\frac{73}{100} = 456\frac{730}{1{,}000}$$
$$494\frac{775}{1{,}000} = 494.775$$

2. 78.674
      −23.431
      ‾‾‾‾‾‾
       55.243

3.   16.000
        0.033
        4.600
      + 0.080
      ‾‾‾‾‾‾
       20.713

4. a. 6.70   **b.** 6.7000
        −2.05   −2.0563
        ‾‾‾‾   ‾‾‾‾‾‾
         4.65   4.6437

5.   7.000   10.567
       +3.567   and   − 5.890
       ‾‾‾‾‾   ‾‾‾‾‾
       10.567   4.677

6. $10.00   1 quarter + 2 dimes + 4 pennies = 0.25 + 0.20 + 0.04 = 0.49, which is too much change.
      − 9.56   One of the dimes should be a nickel. Tell the clerk that you have been given too much change.
      ‾‾‾‾‾
      $ .44

7. a. $P = 1.38 + 1.38 + 1.38 + 1.38 = 5.52$ in.

b. $P = 6.6 + 4.7 + 4.7 = 16.0$ cm

Section 3.3

1. a. $0.4 \times 0.6 = \dfrac{4}{10} \times \dfrac{6}{10}$

$= \dfrac{24}{100}$

$= 0.24$

b. $0.04 \times 0.06 = \dfrac{4}{100} \times \dfrac{6}{100}$

$= \dfrac{24}{10,000}$

$= 0.0024$

2. a. $0.5 \times 0.007 = \dfrac{5}{10} \times \dfrac{7}{1,000}$

$= \dfrac{35}{10,000}$

$= 0.0035$

b. $0.05 \times 0.07 = \dfrac{5}{100} \times \dfrac{7}{100}$

$= \dfrac{35}{10,000}$

$= 0.0035$

3. a. $3.5 \times 0.04 = 3\dfrac{5}{10} \times \dfrac{4}{100}$

$= \dfrac{35}{10} \times \dfrac{4}{100}$

$= \dfrac{140}{1,000}$

$= \dfrac{14}{100}$

$= 0.14$

b. $0.35 \times 0.4 = \dfrac{35}{100} \times \dfrac{4}{10}$

$= \dfrac{140}{1,000}$

$= \dfrac{14}{100}$

$= 0.14$

4. a. 3 + 2 = 5 digits to the right   **b.** 2 + 4 = 6 digits to the right

5. a.   4.03
           × 5.22
           ‾‾‾‾
            806
           8060
          201500
          ‾‾‾‾‾
          21.0366

b.   40.3
        × 0.522
        ‾‾‾‾
         806
        8060
       201500
       ‾‾‾‾‾
       21.0366

6. a. $80 \times 6 = 480$

b. $40 \times 180 = 7,200$

c. $8^2 = 64$

7. a. $0.03(5.5 + 0.02) = 0.03(5.52)$

$= 0.1656$

b. $0.03(0.55 + 0.002) = 0.03(0.552)$

$= 0.01656$

8. a. $5.7 + 14(2.4)^2 = 5.7 + 14(5.76)$

$= 5.7 + 80.64$

$= 86.34$

b. $0.57 + 1.4(2.4)^2 = 0.57 + 1.4(5.76)$

$= 0.57 + 8.064$

$= 8.634$

9. a. $A = s^2 = 1.38^2 = 1.90$ in^2

b. $A = lw = (39.6)(25.1) = 993.96$ mm^2

10. $6.82(36) + 10.23(14) = 245.52 + 143.22$

$= \$388.74$

11. $C = 3.14(3)$

$= 9.42$ cm

12. a. $C = \pi d \approx (3.14)(0.92) \approx 2.89$ in.

b. $C = 2\pi r \approx 2(3.14)(13.20) \approx 82.90$ mm

13. Radius $= \dfrac{1}{2}(20) = 10$ ft

$A = \pi r^2 = (3.14)(10)^2$

$= 314$ ft^2

14. Radius $= 2(0.125) = 0.250$

$V = \pi r^2 h$

$= (3.14)(0.250)^2(6)$

$= 1.178$ in^3

Section 3.4

1.
```
        154.2
30)4,626.0
      3 0↓
      ‾‾‾
      1 62
      1 50↓
      ‾‾‾‾
       126
       120↓
       ‾‾‾
        6 0
        6 0
        ‾‾‾
          0
```

2. a.
```
       6.7
5) 33.5
   30↓
   ‾‾
    3 5
    3 5
    ‾‾
      0
```

b.
```
       6.9
5)34.5
  30↓
  ‾‾
   4 5
   4 5
   ‾‾
     0
```

c.
```
       7.1
5)35.5
  35↓
  ‾‾
   0 5
     5
   ‾‾
     0
```

3. a.
```
        2.636
18)47.448
   36↓
   ‾‾
   11 4
   10 8↓
   ‾‾‾
      64
      54↓
      ‾‾
      108
      108
      ‾‾‾
        0
```

b.
```
        26.36
18)474.48
   36↓
   ‾‾
   114
   108
   ‾‾‾
    6 4
    5 4
    ‾‾
    1 08
    1 08
    ‾‾‾
       0
```

4. a.
$$
\begin{array}{r}
45.54 \\
25\overline{)1,138.50} \\
\underline{1\ 00}\downarrow \\
138 \\
\underline{125}\downarrow \\
13\ 5 \\
\underline{12\ 5}\downarrow \\
1\ 00 \\
\underline{1\ 00} \\
0
\end{array}
$$

b.
$$
\begin{array}{r}
4.554 \\
25\overline{)113.850} \\
\underline{100}\downarrow \\
13\ 8 \\
\underline{12\ 5}\downarrow \\
1\ 35 \\
\underline{1\ 25}\downarrow \\
100 \\
\underline{100} \\
0
\end{array}
$$

5. a.
$$
\begin{array}{r}
3.15 \\
4.2.\overline{)13.2.30} \\
126\downarrow \\
6\ 3 \\
\underline{4\ 2}\downarrow \\
2\ 10 \\
\underline{2\ 10} \\
0
\end{array}
$$

b.
$$
\begin{array}{r}
31.5 \\
0.42.\overline{)13.23.0} \\
12\ 6\downarrow \\
63 \\
\underline{42} \\
21\ 0 \\
\underline{21\ 0} \\
0
\end{array}
$$

6.
$$
\begin{array}{r}
1.422 \\
0.32.\overline{)0.45.530} \\
32\downarrow \\
13\ 5 \\
\underline{12\ 8}\downarrow \\
73 \\
\underline{64}\downarrow \\
90 \\
\underline{64} \\
26
\end{array}
$$
Answer to nearest hundredth is 1.42

7. a.
$$
\begin{array}{r}
3\ 16.66 \\
0.06.\overline{)19.00.00} \\
18\downarrow \\
1\ 0 \\
\underline{6}\downarrow \\
40 \\
\underline{36}\downarrow \\
4\ 0 \\
\underline{3\ 6}\downarrow \\
40 \\
\underline{36} \\
4
\end{array}
$$
Answer to nearest tenth is 316.7

b.
$$
\begin{array}{r}
31.66 \\
0.06.\overline{)1.90.00} \\
18\downarrow \\
10 \\
\underline{6}\downarrow \\
4\ 0 \\
\underline{36}\downarrow \\
40 \\
\underline{36} \\
4
\end{array}
$$
Answer to nearest tenth is 31.7

8.
$$
\begin{array}{r}
28.5 \text{ hours} \\
6.54.\overline{)186.39.0} \\
130\ 8\downarrow \\
55\ 59 \\
\underline{52\ 32}\downarrow \\
3\ 27\ 0 \\
\underline{3\ 27\ 0} \\
0
\end{array}
$$

9. $\dfrac{4.39 - 0.43}{0.33} = \dfrac{3.96}{0.33}$

= 12 additional minutes

The call was 13 minutes long.

10. GPA $= \dfrac{48}{15} = 3.20$

Class	units	grade	value	grade points
Algebra	5	B	3	$5 \times 3 = 15$
Chemistry	4	B	3	$4 \times 3 = 12$
English	3	A	4	$3 \times 4 = 12$
History	3	B	3	$3 \times 3 = 9$
Total Units:	15			Total Grade Points: 48

Section 3.5

1. a.
$$
\begin{array}{r}
.4 \\
5\overline{)2.0} \\
\underline{2\ 0} \\
0
\end{array}
$$
so $\dfrac{2}{5} = 0.4$

b.
$$
\begin{array}{r}
0.6 \\
5\overline{)3.0} \\
\underline{3\ 0} \\
0
\end{array}
$$
so $\dfrac{3}{5} = 0.6$

c.
$$
\begin{array}{r}
.8 \\
5\overline{)4.0} \\
\underline{4\ 0} \\
0
\end{array}
$$
so $\dfrac{4}{5} = 0.8$

2. a.
$$
\begin{array}{r}
0.9166 \\
12\overline{)11.0000} \\
10\ 8\downarrow \\
20 \\
\underline{12}\downarrow \\
80 \\
\underline{72}\downarrow \\
80 \\
\underline{72} \\
8
\end{array}
$$
so $\dfrac{11}{12} = 0.917$ to the nearest thousandth

b.
$$
\begin{array}{r}
.9230 \\
13\overline{)12.0000} \\
11\ 7\downarrow \\
30 \\
\underline{26}\downarrow \\
40 \\
\underline{39}\downarrow \\
10 \\
\underline{0} \\
10
\end{array}
$$
so $\dfrac{12}{13} = 0.923$ to the nearest thousandth

3.

$$11\overline{)5.0000} = 0.4545 \quad \text{so} \quad \frac{5}{11} = 0.\overline{45}$$

$$\begin{array}{r} 4\,4\downarrow \\ \hline 60 \\ 55\downarrow \\ \hline 50 \\ 44\downarrow \\ \hline 60 \\ 55 \\ \hline 5 \end{array}$$

4. a. $0.48 = \dfrac{48}{100} = \dfrac{12}{25}$

b. $0.048 = \dfrac{48}{1{,}000} = \dfrac{6}{125}$

5. $0.025 = \dfrac{25}{1{,}000} = \dfrac{1}{40}$

6. $12.8 = 12\dfrac{8}{10} = 12\dfrac{4}{5}$

7. $\dfrac{14}{25}(2.43 + 0.27)$

$= 0.56(2.43 + 0.27)$

$= 0.56(2.70)$

$= 1.512$

8. $\dfrac{1}{4} + 0.25\left(\dfrac{3}{5}\right) = \dfrac{1}{4} + \dfrac{1}{4}\left(\dfrac{3}{5}\right)$

$= \dfrac{1}{4} + \dfrac{3}{20}$

$= \dfrac{5}{20} + \dfrac{3}{20}$

$= \dfrac{8}{20}$

$= \dfrac{2}{5} \text{ or } 0.4$

9. $\left(\dfrac{1}{3}\right)^3(5.4) + \left(\dfrac{1}{5}\right)^2(2.5) = \dfrac{1}{27}(5.4) + \dfrac{1}{25}(2.5) = 0.2 + 0.1 = 0.3$

10. $35.50 - \dfrac{1}{4}(35.50) = \dfrac{3}{4}(35.50) = 26.625 = \$26.63$ to the nearest cent

11. $A = \dfrac{1}{2}bh = \dfrac{1}{2}(6.6)(3.3) = 10.89 \text{ cm}^2$

12. $V = \pi r^2 h + \dfrac{1}{2} \cdot \dfrac{4}{3}\pi r^3 = (3.14)(10)^2(10) + \dfrac{1}{2} \cdot \dfrac{4}{3}(3.14)(10)^3$

$= 3{,}140 + \dfrac{2}{3}(3{,}140)$

$= 3{,}140 + 2{,}093.3$

$= 5{,}233.3 \text{ in}^3$

Chapter 4

Section 4.1

1. a. $\dfrac{32}{48} = \dfrac{2}{3}$ **b.** $\dfrac{3.2}{4.8} = \dfrac{2}{3}$ **c.** $\dfrac{0.32}{0.48} = \dfrac{2}{3}$

2. a. $\dfrac{\frac{3}{5}}{\frac{9}{10}} = \dfrac{3}{5} \cdot \dfrac{10}{9} = \dfrac{2}{3}$ **b.** $\dfrac{0.6}{0.9} = \dfrac{2}{3}$

3. a. $\dfrac{0.06}{0.12} = \dfrac{0.06 \times 100}{0.12 \times 100} = \dfrac{6}{12} = \dfrac{1}{2}$ **b.** $\dfrac{600}{1{,}200} = \dfrac{1}{2}$

4. $\dfrac{12}{16} = \dfrac{3}{4}$

5. Alcohol to water: $\dfrac{4}{12} = \dfrac{1}{3}$; water to alcohol: $\dfrac{12}{4} = \dfrac{3}{1}$; water to total solution: $\dfrac{12}{16} = \dfrac{3}{4}$

Section 4.2

1. $\dfrac{107 \text{ miles}}{2 \text{ hours}} = 53.5$ miles/hour

2. $\dfrac{192 \text{ miles}}{6 \text{ gallons}} = 32$ miles/gallon

3. $\dfrac{48\cent}{5.5 \text{ ounces}} = 8.7\cent$/ounce; $\dfrac{75\cent}{11.5 \text{ ounces}} = 6.5\cent$/ounce; $\dfrac{219\cent}{46 \text{ ounces}} = 4.8\cent$/ounce

(Answers are rounded to the nearest tenth.)

Section 4.3

1. $\dfrac{8 \cdot n}{8} = n$

2. $\dfrac{3 \cdot y}{3} = y$

3. $\dfrac{8 \cdot n}{8} = \dfrac{40}{8}$

$n = 5$

4. $\dfrac{35}{7} = \dfrac{7 \cdot a}{7}$

$5 = a$

Section 4.4

1. First term = 2, second term = 3, third term = 6, fourth term = 9, means: 3 and 6; extremes: 2 and 9

2. a. $5 \cdot 18 = 90$

$6 \cdot 15 = 90$

b. $13 \cdot 3 = 39$

$39 \cdot 1 = 39$

c. $\frac{2}{3} \cdot 5 = \frac{10}{3}$

$\frac{5}{3} \cdot 2 = \frac{10}{3}$

d. $0.12(3) = 0.36$

$0.18(2) = 0.36$

3. a. $3 \cdot x = 4 \cdot 9$

$3 \cdot x = 36$

$\frac{3 \cdot x}{3} = \frac{36}{3}$

$x = 12$

b. $5 \cdot x = 8 \cdot 3$

$5 \cdot x = 24$

$\frac{5 \cdot x}{5} = \frac{24}{5}$

$x = 4.8$

4. $2 \cdot 19 = 8 \cdot y$

$38 = 8 \cdot y$

$\frac{38}{8} = \frac{8 \cdot y}{8}$

$4.75 = y$

5. a. $15 \cdot n = 6(0.3)$

$15 \cdot n = 1.8$

$\frac{15 \cdot n}{15} = \frac{1.8}{15}$

$n = 0.12$

b. $0.35(100) = n \cdot 7$

$35 = n \cdot 7$

$\frac{35}{7} = \frac{n \cdot 7}{7}$

$5 = n$

6. a. $\frac{3}{4} \cdot 8 = 7 \cdot x$

$6 = 7 \cdot x$

$\frac{6}{7} = \frac{7 \cdot x}{7}$

$\frac{6}{7} = x$

b. $6 \cdot x = \frac{3}{5} \cdot 15$

$6 \cdot x = 9$

$\frac{6 \cdot x}{6} = \frac{9}{6}$

$x = \frac{3}{2}$

7. $\frac{b}{18} = \frac{0.5}{1}$

$b \cdot 1 = 18(0.5)$

$b = 9$

Section 4.5

1. a. $\frac{x}{10} = \frac{288}{6}$

$x \cdot 6 = 10 \cdot 288$

$x \cdot 6 = 2{,}880$

$\frac{x \cdot 6}{6} = \frac{2{,}880}{6}$

$x = 480$ miles

b. $\frac{x}{11} = \frac{288}{6}$

$x \cdot 6 = 11 \cdot 288$

$x \cdot 6 = 3{,}168$

$\frac{x \cdot 6}{6} = \frac{3{,}168}{6}$

$x = 528$ miles

2. a. $\frac{x}{54} = \frac{10}{18}$

$x \cdot 18 = 54 \cdot 10$

$x \cdot 18 = 540$

$\frac{x \cdot 18}{18} = \frac{540}{18}$

$x = 30$ hits

b. $\frac{x}{27} = \frac{10}{18}$

$x \cdot 18 = 27 \cdot 10$

$x \cdot 18 = 270$

$\frac{x \cdot 18}{18} = \frac{270}{18}$

$x = 15$ hits

3. $\frac{x}{35} = \frac{8}{20}$

$x \cdot 20 = 35 \cdot 8$

$x \cdot 20 = 280$

$\frac{x \cdot 20}{20} = \frac{280}{20}$

$x = 14$ milliliters of alcohol

4. $\frac{x}{4.75} = \frac{105}{1}$

$x \cdot 1 = 4.75(105)$

$x = 498.75$ miles

Section 4.6

1. $\frac{x}{14} = \frac{25}{10}$

$10x = 350$

$x = 35$

2. $\frac{h}{120} = \frac{360}{160}$

$\frac{h}{120} = \frac{9}{4}$ reduce to lowest terms

$4h = 1080$

$h = 270$ pixels

3. We see AC has a length of 3 units and BC has a length of 4 units. Since AC is proportional to GI, which has a length of 6 units, we set up a proportion to find the length of a new side, HI.

$\frac{HI}{BC} = \frac{GI}{AC}$

$\frac{HI}{4} = \frac{6}{3}$

$\frac{HI}{4} = 2$

$HI = 8$

Now we can draw HI with length 8 units, and complete the triangle by drawing line GH

4. $\frac{x}{18} = \frac{42}{12}$

$12x = 756$

$x = 63$ ft

5. $\frac{b}{15} = \frac{32}{24}$

$24b = 480$

$b = 20$ in.

Chapter 5

Section 5.1

21. $\dfrac{82}{100} = \dfrac{41}{50}$

22. $\dfrac{6.5}{100} = \dfrac{65}{1000} = \dfrac{13}{200}$

23. $\dfrac{42\frac{1}{2}}{100} = \dfrac{\frac{85}{2}}{100}$

$\quad = \dfrac{85}{2} \cdot \dfrac{1}{100}$

$\quad = \dfrac{85}{200}$

$\quad = \dfrac{17}{40}$

24. a. $\dfrac{9}{10} = 0.9 = 90\%$ **b.** $\dfrac{9}{20} = 0.45 = 45\%$

25. a. $\dfrac{5}{8} = 0.625 = 62.5\%$ **b.** $\dfrac{9}{8} = 1.125 = 112.5\%$ **26. a.** $\dfrac{7}{12} = 0.58\overline{3} = 58\frac{1}{3}\%$ or $\approx 58.3\%$ **b.** $\dfrac{13}{12} = 1.08\overline{3} = 108\frac{1}{3}\%$ or $\approx 108.3\%$

27. a. $3\dfrac{3}{4} = 3.75 = 375\%$ **b.** $3\dfrac{7}{8} = 3.875 = 387.5\%$

Section 5.2

1. a. $n = 0.25(74)$
$\quad = 18.5$

b. $n = 0.50(74)$
$\quad = 37$

2. a. $n \cdot 84 = 21$
$\dfrac{n \cdot 84}{84} = \dfrac{21}{84}$
$n = 0.25$
$n = 25\%$

b. $n \cdot 84 = 42$
$\dfrac{n \cdot 84}{84} = \dfrac{42}{84}$
$n = 0.50$
$n = 50\%$

3. a. $35 = 0.40 \cdot n$
$\dfrac{35}{0.40} = \dfrac{0.40 \cdot n}{0.40}$
$87.5 = n$

b. $70 = 0.40 \cdot n$
$\dfrac{70}{0.40} = \dfrac{0.40 \cdot n}{0.40}$
$175 = n$

4. $n = 0.635(45)$
$n \approx 28.6$

5. $n \cdot 85 = 11.9$
$\dfrac{n \cdot 85}{85} = \dfrac{11.9}{85}$
$n = 0.14$
$n = 14\%$

6. $62 = 0.39 \cdot n$
$\dfrac{62}{0.39} = \dfrac{0.39 \cdot n}{0.39}$
$159.0 \approx n$

7. 25 is what percent of 160?
$25 = n \cdot 160$
$\dfrac{25}{160} = n$
$n = 0.156 = 15.6\%$ to the nearest tenth of a percent

8. a. $\dfrac{25}{100} = \dfrac{n}{74}$
$25 \cdot 74 = 100 \cdot n$
$1850 = 100 \cdot n$
$18.5 = n$

b. $\dfrac{50}{100} = \dfrac{n}{74}$
$50 \cdot 74 = 100 \cdot n$
$3{,}700 = 100 \cdot n$
$37 = n$

9. a. $\dfrac{n}{100} = \dfrac{21}{84}$
$84 \cdot n = 21 \cdot 100$
$84 \cdot n = 2100$
$n = 25$
25%

b. $\dfrac{n}{100} = \dfrac{42}{84}$
$84 \cdot n = 42 \cdot 100$
$84 \cdot n = 4{,}200$
$n = 50$
50%

10. a. $\dfrac{40}{100} = \dfrac{35}{n}$
$40 \cdot n = 35 \cdot 100$
$40 \cdot n = 3500$
$n = 87.5$

b. $\dfrac{40}{100} = \dfrac{70}{n}$
$40 \cdot n = 70 \cdot 100$
$40 \cdot n = 7{,}000$
$n = 175$

Section 5.3

1. 114 is what percent of 150?
$114 = n \cdot 150$
$\dfrac{114}{150} = \dfrac{n \cdot 150}{150}$
$n = 0.76$
$n = 76\%$

2. What is 75% of 40?
$n = 0.75(40)$
$n = 30$ milliliters HCl

3. 3,360 is 42% of what number?
$3{,}360 = 0.42 \cdot n$
$\dfrac{3{,}360}{0.42} = \dfrac{0.42 \cdot n}{0.42}$
$n = 8{,}000$ students

4. What is 35% of 300?
$n = 0.35(300)$
$\quad = 105$ students

Section 5.4

1. What is 6% of $625?
$n = 0.06(625)$
$n = \$37.50$

2. $4.35 is 3% of what number?
$4.35 = 0.03 \cdot n$
$n = \$145$ Purchase price
Total price $= \$145 + \$4.35$
$\quad = \$149.35$

3. $11.82 is what percent of $197?
$11.82 = n \cdot 197$
$n = 0.06 = 6\%$

4. What is 3% of 115,000?
$n = 0.03(115{,}000)$
$n = \$3{,}450$

5. 10% of what number is $115?
$0.10 \cdot n = 115$
$n = \$1{,}150$

6. $105 is what percent of $750?
$105 = n \cdot 750$
$n = 0.14 = 14\%$

Section 5.5

1. $0.07(18,000) = 1,260$

$18,000	Old salary
+ 1,260	Raise
$19,260	New salary

2. $0.89(271,000) = 241,190$

271,000	Drunk drivers in 1986
+241,190	Increase
512,190	= 512,000 to the nearest thousand

3. $\$35 - \$28 = \$7$ Decrease

$7 is what percent of $35?

$7 = n \cdot 35$

$n = 0.20 = 20\%$ Decrease

4. What is 15% of $550?

$n = 0.15(550)$

$n = \$82.50$ Discount

$550.00	Original price
− 82.50	Less discount
$467.50	Sale price

5. What is 15% of $45?

$n = 0.15(45)$

$n = \$6.75$ Discount

$45.00	Original price
− 6.75	Less discount
$38.25	Sale price

What is 5% of $38.25?

$n = 0.05(38.25)$

$n = \$1.91$ to the nearest cent

$38.25	Sale price
+ 1.91	Sales tax
$40.16	Total price

Section 5.6

1. Interest $= 0.08(\$3,000)$

$= \$240$

$3,000	Principal
+ 240	Interest
$3,240	Amount after 1 year

2. Interest $= 0.12(\$7,500)$

$= \$900$

$7,500	Principal
+ 900	Interest
$8,400	Total amount to pay back

3. $I = P \cdot R \cdot T$

$I = 700 \times 0.04 \times \dfrac{90}{360}$

$I = 700 \times 0.04 \times \dfrac{1}{4}$

$I = \$7$ Interest

4. $I = P \cdot R \cdot T$

$I = 1,200 \times 0.095 \times \dfrac{120}{360}$

$I = 1,200 \times 0.095 \times \dfrac{1}{3}$

$I = \$38$ Interest

$1,200	Principal
+ 38	Interest
$1,238	Total amount withdrawn

5. Interest after 1 year is

$0.06(\$5,000) = \$300$

Total in account after 1 year is

$5,000	Principal
+ 300	Interest
$5,300	

Interest paid the second year is

$0.06\ (\$5,300) = \$318$

Total in account after 2 years is

$5,300	Principal
+ 318	Interest
$5,618	

6. Interest at the end of first quarter

$I = \$20,000 \times 0.08 \times \dfrac{1}{4} = \$400$

Total in account at end of first quarter

$\$20,000 + \$400 = \$20,400$

Interest for the second quarter

$I = \$20,400 \times 0.08 \times \dfrac{1}{4} = \$408$

Total in account at end of second quarter

$\$20,400 + \$408 = \$20,808$

Interest for the third quarter

$I = \$20,808 \times 0.08 \times \dfrac{1}{4} = \$416.16$

Total in account at the end of third quarter

$\$20,808 + \$416.16 = \$21,224.16$

Interest for the fourth quarter

$I = \$21,224.16 \times 0.08 \times \dfrac{1}{4} = \$424.48$ to the nearest cent

Total in account at end of 1 year

$21,224.16	
+ 424.48	
$21,648.64	

Chapter 6

Section 6.1

1.

187
273
150
173
227
1010

$\dfrac{1010}{5} = 202$ miles

2. First we place them in order from smallest to largest

150   173   187   227   273

Because there are 5 numbers, the one in the middle, 187, is the median.

3. We first put the numbers in order from smallest to largest. Because there is an even number of numbers, we find the mean of the middle two:

$$\frac{146{,}320 + 242{,}635}{2} = \frac{388{,}955}{2} = 194{,}477.5$$

The median is \$194,477.50.

4. The most frequently occurring score is 74. It occurs three times. The mode is 74.

5. The highest score is 97, and the lowest score is 45. The range is $97 - 45 = 52$.

Section 6.2

1. 14, 25, 7, 28, 36, 25, 17, 46, 9, 12, 16, 21, 26, 32, 38

Stem	Leaf
0	7, 9
1	4, 7, 2, 6
2	5, 8, 5, 1, 6
3	6, 2, 8
4	6

2. 11, 5, 8, 0, 12, 7, 9, 10, 22, 15, 13, 16, 5, 20, 8, 12, 16, 7, 25, 18

Interval	Tally	Frequency.	Relative Freq.
0–5	|||	3	0.15
6–11	||||| ||	7	0.35
12–17	|||||		6	0.30
18–23	|||	3	0.15
24–29			1	0.05

3. 9, 16, 3, 27, 36, 21, 11, 10, 17, 8, 29, 30, 20, 28, 12, 23

4. 3, 8, 9, 10, 11, 12, 16, 17, 20, 21, 23, 27, 28, 29, 30, 36

$$\text{Median} = \frac{17 + 20}{2} = 18.5 \qquad Q2 = 18.5$$

$$Q1 = \frac{11 + 10}{2} = 10.5$$

$$Q3 = \frac{27 + 28}{2} = 27.5$$

5. 3, 8, 9, 10, 11, 12, 16, 17, 20, 21, 23, 27, 28, 29, 30, 36

Five number summary = 3, 10.5, 18.5, 27.5, 36

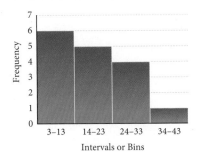

Section 6.3

1. a. $9 + 11 + 16 + 10 = 46$ **b.** $\dfrac{11}{46}$ **c.** $\dfrac{9}{16}$

2. a. $0.76(600) = 456$ people
   b. $0.24(600) = 144$ people

3.

☐ Free Space **60%**

☐ Used Space **40%**

4.

☐ Publisher **50%**

☐ Bookstore **45%**

☐ Author **5%**

Section 6.4

3. $S = \{1, 2, 3, 4, 5, 6, 7, 8, 9, 10, 11, 12\}$

   a. $>7 = \{8, 9, 10, 11, 12\}$

   $P(>7) = \dfrac{5}{12}$

   b. odd $= \{1, 3, 5, 7, 9, 11\}$

   $P(\text{odd}) = \dfrac{6}{12} = \dfrac{1}{2}$

   c. multiple of 3 $A = \{3, 6, 9, 12\}$

   $P(A) = \dfrac{4}{12} = \dfrac{1}{3}$

4. One more blue added

   blue   4

   $\dfrac{\text{red}\quad 2}{\text{total}\quad 6}$

   a. $P(\text{blue}) = \dfrac{4}{6} = \dfrac{2}{3}$

   b. $P(\text{red}) = \dfrac{2}{6} = \dfrac{1}{3}$

   b. $P(\text{blue or red}) = \dfrac{6}{6} = 1$

5. a. $P(\text{sum} \geq 7) = \dfrac{15}{36} = \dfrac{5}{12}$

   b. $P(\text{sum} = 9) = \dfrac{4}{36} = \dfrac{1}{9}$

   c. $P(\text{both even}) = \dfrac{9}{36} = \dfrac{1}{4}$

6. a. $P(\text{black}) = \dfrac{26}{52} = \dfrac{1}{2}$

   b. $P(\text{even}) = \dfrac{20}{52} = \dfrac{5}{13}$

   c. $P(\text{king or ace}) = \dfrac{8}{52} = \dfrac{2}{13}$

7. a. $P(\text{Bing}) = 0.07 = \dfrac{7}{100}$

   b. $P(\text{Bing + Yahoo}) = 0.07 + 0.28$

   $= 0.35 = \dfrac{35}{100}$

   c. $P(\text{not Bing}) = 1.00 - 0.07 = 0.93 = \dfrac{93}{100}$

8. a. $P(\text{undecided or no plans})$

   $= \dfrac{8}{300} = 0.027$

   b. $P(\text{military}) = \dfrac{13}{300} = 0.04$

   c. $P(\text{not a 2-yr college}) = \dfrac{289}{300} = 0.963$

Chapter 7

Section 7.1

1. $8 \text{ ft} = 8 \times 12 \text{ in.}$

   $= 96 \text{ in.}$

2. $26 \text{ ft} = 26 \text{ ft} \times \dfrac{1 \text{ yd}}{3 \text{ ft}}$

   $= \dfrac{26}{3} \text{ yd}$

   $= 8\dfrac{2}{3} \text{ yd, or } 8.67 \text{ yd}$

3. $220 \text{ yd} = 220 \text{ yd} \times \dfrac{3 \text{ ft}}{1 \text{ yd}} \times \dfrac{12 \text{ in.}}{1 \text{ ft}}$

   $= 220 \times 3 \times 12 \text{ in.}$

   $= 7{,}920 \text{ in.}$

4. $67 \text{ cm} = 67 \text{ cm} \times \dfrac{1 \text{ m}}{100 \text{ cm}}$

   $= \dfrac{67 \text{ m}}{100}$

   $= 0.67 \text{ m}$

5. $78.4 \text{ mm} = 78.4 \text{ mm} \times \dfrac{1 \text{ m}}{1{,}000 \text{ mm}} \times \dfrac{10 \text{ dm}}{1 \text{ m}}$

   $= \dfrac{78.4 \times 10}{1{,}000} \text{ dm}$

   $= 0.784 \text{ dm}$

6. $6 \text{ pens} = 6 \text{ pens} \times \dfrac{28 \text{ feet of fencing}}{1 \text{ pen}} \times \dfrac{1.72 \text{ dollars}}{1 \text{ foot of fencing}}$

   $= 6 \times 28 \times 1.72 \text{ dollars}$

   $= \$288.96$

7. $1{,}100 \text{ feet per minute} = \dfrac{1{,}100 \text{ feet}}{1 \text{ minute}} \cdot \dfrac{1 \text{ mile}}{5{,}280 \text{ feet}} \cdot \dfrac{60 \text{ minutes}}{1 \text{ hour}}$

   $= 1{,}100 \cdot \dfrac{60 \text{ miles}}{5{,}280 \text{ hours}}$

   $= 12.5 \text{ miles per hour, which is a reasonable speed for a chair lift.}$

Section 7.2

1. $1 \text{ yd}^2 = 1 \text{ yd} \times \text{yd} \times \dfrac{3 \text{ ft}}{1 \text{ yd}} \times \dfrac{3 \text{ ft}}{1 \text{ yd}} = 3 \text{ ft} \times 3 \text{ ft} = 9 \text{ ft}^2$

2. Length $= 36 \text{ in.} + 12 \text{ in.} = 48 \text{ in.}$; Width $= 24 \text{ in.} + 12 \text{ in.} = 36 \text{ in.}$;

   Area $= 48 \text{ in.} \times 36 \text{ in.} = 1{,}728 \text{ in}^2$

   Area in square feet $= 1{,}728 \text{ in}^2 \times \dfrac{1 \text{ ft}^2}{144 \text{ in}^2} = \dfrac{1{,}728}{144} \text{ ft}^2 = 12 \text{ ft}^2$

3. $A = 1.5 \times 45$

   $= 67.5 \text{ yd}^2$

   $67.5 \text{ yd}^2 = 67.5 \text{ yd}^2 \times \dfrac{9 \text{ ft}^2}{1 \text{ yd}^2}$

   $= 607.5 \text{ ft}^2$

4. $55 \text{ acres} = 55 \text{ acres} \times \dfrac{43{,}560 \text{ ft}^2}{1 \text{ acre}}$

   $= 55 \times 43{,}560 \text{ ft}^2$

   $= 2{,}395{,}800 \text{ ft}^2$

5. $960 \text{ acres} = 960 \text{ acres} \times \dfrac{1 \text{ mi}^2}{640 \text{ acres}}$

   $= \dfrac{960}{640} \text{ mi}^2$

   $= 1.5 \text{ mi}^2$

6. $1 \text{ m}^2 = 1 \text{ m}^2 \times \dfrac{100 \text{ dm}^2}{1 \text{ m}^2} \times \dfrac{100 \text{ cm}^2}{1 \text{ dm}^2}$

$\qquad = 10{,}000 \text{ cm}^2$

7. $5 \text{ gal} = 5 \text{ gal} \times \dfrac{4 \text{ qt}}{1 \text{ gal}} \times \dfrac{2 \text{ pt}}{1 \text{ qt}}$

$\qquad = 5 \times 4 \times 2 \text{ qt}$

$\qquad = 40 \text{ pt}$

8. $2{,}000 \text{ qt} = 2{,}000 \text{ qt} \times \dfrac{1 \text{ gal}}{4 \text{ qt}}$

$\qquad = \dfrac{2{,}000}{4} \text{ gal}$

$\qquad = 500 \text{ gal}$

The number of 10-gal containers in

500 gal is $\dfrac{500}{10} = 50$ containers.

9. $3.5 \text{ liters} = 3.5 \text{ liters} \times \dfrac{1{,}000 \text{ mL}}{1 \text{ liter}}$

$\qquad = 3.5 \times 1{,}000 \text{ mL}$

$\qquad = 3{,}500 \text{ mL}$

Section 7.3

1. $15 \text{ lb} = 15 \text{ lb} \times \dfrac{16 \text{ oz}}{1 \text{ lb}}$

$\qquad = 15 \times 16 \text{ oz}$

$\qquad = 240 \text{ oz}$

2. $5 \text{ T} = 5 \text{ T} \times \dfrac{2{,}000 \text{ lb}}{1 \text{ T}}$

$\qquad = 10{,}000 \text{ lb}$

$10{,}000 \text{ lb}$ is the equivalent of 5 tons.

3. $5 \text{ kg} = 5 \text{ kg} \times \dfrac{1{,}000 \text{ g}}{1 \text{ kg}} \times \dfrac{1{,}000 \text{ mg}}{1 \text{ g}}$

$\qquad = 5 \times 1{,}000 \times 1{,}000 \text{ mg}$

$\qquad = 5{,}000{,}000 \text{ mg}$

4. Total number of milligrams in bottle $= 75 \times 200 = 15{,}000 \text{ mg}$.

$\qquad 15{,}000 \text{ mg} = 15{,}000 \text{ mg} \times \dfrac{1 \text{ g}}{1{,}000 \text{ mg}}$

$\qquad\qquad\qquad = \dfrac{15{,}000}{1{,}000} \text{ g}$

$\qquad\qquad\qquad = 15 \text{ g}$

Section 7.4

1. $10 \text{ in.} = 10 \text{ in.} \times \dfrac{2.54 \text{ cm}}{1 \text{ in.}}$

$\qquad = 10 \times 2.54 \text{ cm}$

$\qquad = 25.4 \text{ cm}$

2. $16.4 \text{ ft} = 16.4 \text{ ft} \times \dfrac{1 \text{ m}}{3.28 \text{ ft}}$

$\qquad = \dfrac{16.4}{3.28} \text{ m}$

$\qquad = 5 \text{ m}$

3. $10 \text{ liters} = 10 \text{ liters} \times \dfrac{1 \text{ gal}}{3.79 \text{ liters}}$

$\qquad = \dfrac{10}{3.79} \text{ gal}$

$\qquad = 2.64 \text{ gal}$ (rounded to the nearest hundredth)

4. $2.2 \text{ liters} = 2.2 \text{ liters} \times \dfrac{1{,}000 \text{ mL}}{1 \text{ liter}} \times \dfrac{1 \text{ in}^3}{16.39 \text{ mL}}$

$\qquad = \dfrac{2.2 \times 1{,}000}{16.39} \text{ in}^3$

$\qquad = 134 \text{ in}^3$ (rounded to the nearest cubic inch)

5. $165 \text{ lb} = 165 \text{ lb} \times \dfrac{1 \text{ kg}}{2.20 \text{ lb}}$

$\qquad = \dfrac{165}{2.20} \text{ kg}$

$\qquad = 75 \text{ kg}$

6. $F = \dfrac{9}{5}(40) + 32$

$\qquad = 72 + 32$

$\qquad = 104°F$

7. $C = \dfrac{5(101.6 - 32)}{9}$

$\qquad = 38.7°C$ (rounded to the nearest tenth)

Section 7.5

1. a. $2 \text{ hr } 45 \text{ min} = 2 \text{ hr} \times \dfrac{60 \text{ min}}{1 \text{ hr}} + 45 \text{ min}$

$\qquad\qquad\qquad = 120 \text{ min} + 45 \text{ min}$

$\qquad\qquad\qquad = 165 \text{ min}$

b. $2 \text{ hr } 45 \text{ min} = 2 \text{ hr} + 45 \text{ min} \times \dfrac{1 \text{ hr}}{60 \text{ min}}$

$\qquad\qquad\qquad = 2 \text{ hr} + 0.75 \text{ hr}$

$\qquad\qquad\qquad = 2.75 \text{ hr}$

2. $\begin{array}{r} 4 \text{ min } \ 27 \text{ sec} \\ + 8 \text{ min } \ 46 \text{ sec} \\ \hline 12 \text{ min } \ 73 \text{ sec} \end{array}$

Since there are 60 seconds in every minute, we write 73 seconds as
1 minute 13 seconds. We have

$\qquad 12 \text{ min } 73 \text{ sec} = 12 \text{ min} + 1 \text{ min } 13 \text{ sec}$

$\qquad\qquad\qquad\qquad = 13 \text{ min } 13 \text{ sec}$

3.

6 hr	25 min		5 hr	85 min
−	42 min	=		− 42 min
			5 hr	43 min

4. First, we multiply each unit by 4:

3 lb	8 oz
×	4
12 lb	32 oz

To convert the 32 ounces to pounds, we multiply the ounces by the conversion factor

$$12 \text{ lb } 32 \text{ oz} = 12 \text{ lb} + 32 \text{ oz} \times \frac{1 \text{ lb}}{16 \text{ oz}}$$
$$= 12 \text{ lb} + 2 \text{ lbs}$$
$$= 14 \text{ lb}$$

Finally, we multiply the 14 lb and $5.00 for a total price of $70.00.

Chapter 8

Section 8.1

1. $P = 2(9) + 2(6)$
$= 18 + 12$
$= 30$ yards

2. a. $P = 4s = 4(1.38) = 5.52$ in.
b. $P = a + b + c = 6.6 + 4.7 + 4.7 = 16$ cm
c. $P = 2l + 2w = 2(39.6) + 2(25.1) = 129.4$ mm

3. a. $C = \pi d \approx (3.14)(0.92) \approx 2.89$ in.
b. $C = 2\pi r \approx 2(3.14)(13.20) \approx 82.90$ mm

4. $6{,}790 = \pi d$
$6{,}790 = 3.14d$
$d = \dfrac{6{,}790}{3.14}$
$d = 2{,}160$ miles (to the nearest ten)

Section 8.2

1. $A = bh = 3 \cdot 2 = 6$ cm²

2. $A = \dfrac{1}{2}bh = \dfrac{1}{2} \cdot 4 \cdot 2 = 4$ cm²

3. a. $A = s^2 = 1.38^2 = 1.90$ in² **b.** $A = \dfrac{1}{2}bh = \dfrac{1}{2}(6.6)(3.3) = 10.89$ cm² **c.** $A = lw = (39.6)(25.1) = 993.96$ mm²

4. $A = \pi r^2 \approx 3.14(5)^2$
$= 3.14(25) = 78.5$ ft²

5. $A = 10^2 - 5^2\pi$
$= 100 - 25\pi$
$= 21.5$ cm² (to the nearest tenth)

Section 8.3

1. a. Surface area $= 2(15 \cdot 8) + 2(8 \cdot 12) + (15 \cdot 12) = 612$ ft² **b.** 2 gallons will cover it, with some paint left over.

2. $S = 2\pi rh$
$= 2(3.14)(0.25)(6)$
$= 9.42$ in²

3. $S = 4\pi r^2$
$\approx 4(3.14)(6)^2$
$= 452.16$ in²

4. $S = \pi r^2 + 2\pi rh + \dfrac{1}{2}(4\pi r^2)$
$= (3.14)(10)^2 + 2(3.14)(10)(10) + \dfrac{1}{2}[4(3.14)(10)^2]$
$= 314 + 628 + 628$
$= 1{,}570$ in²

Section 8.4

1. $V = 15 \cdot 12 \cdot 8 = 1{,}440$ ft³

2. Radius $= 2(0.125) = 0.250$
$V = \pi r^2 h$
$= (3.14)(0.250)^2(6)$
$= 1.178$ in³

3. $V = \dfrac{1}{3}\pi r^2 h$
$= \dfrac{1}{3}(3.14)(2^2)(4)$
$= \dfrac{1}{3}(3.14)(4)(4)$
$= 16.747$ ft³

4. $V = \dfrac{4}{3}\pi r^3$
$\approx \dfrac{4}{3}(3.14)(4)^3$
$= 267.95$ cm³

5. $V = \pi r^2 h + \dfrac{1}{2} \cdot \dfrac{4}{3}\pi r^3$
$= (3.14)(10)^2(10) + \dfrac{1}{2} \cdot \dfrac{4}{3}(3.14)(10)^3$
$= 3{,}140 + \dfrac{2}{3}(3{,}140)$
$= 3{,}140 + 2{,}093.3$
$= 5{,}233.3$ in³

Section 8.5

1. $4\sqrt{25} = 4 \cdot 5$
$\quad\quad\quad = 20$

2. $\sqrt{36} + \sqrt{4} = 6 + 2$
$\quad\quad\quad\quad\quad = 8$

3. $\sqrt{\dfrac{36}{100}} = \dfrac{6}{10}$
$\quad\quad\quad\quad = \dfrac{3}{5}$

4. $14\sqrt{36} = 14 \cdot 6$
$\quad\quad\quad\quad = 84$

5. $\sqrt{81} - \sqrt{25} = 9 - 5$
$\quad\quad\quad\quad\quad\quad = 4$

6. $\sqrt{\dfrac{64}{121}} = \dfrac{8}{11}$

8. $\sqrt{405} + \sqrt{147} \approx 20.124612 + 12.124356$
$\quad\quad\quad\quad\quad\quad = 32.248968$
$\quad\quad\quad\quad\quad\quad = 32.25$ to the nearest hundredth

9. $\sqrt{\dfrac{7}{12}} \approx \sqrt{0.5833333}$
$\quad\quad\quad \approx 0.7637626$
$\quad\quad\quad = 0.764$ to the nearest thousandth

10. a. $c = \sqrt{5^2 + 5^2}$
$\quad\quad = \sqrt{25 + 25}$
$\quad\quad = \sqrt{50}$
$\quad c = 7.07$ ft (to the nearest hundredth)

b. $c = \sqrt{16^2 + 12^2}$
$\quad\quad = \sqrt{256 + 144}$
$\quad\quad = \sqrt{400}$
$\quad c = 20$ cm

11. $c = \sqrt{12^2 + 5^2} = \sqrt{144 + 25}$
$\quad\quad\quad\quad\quad\quad = \sqrt{169}$
$\quad\quad\quad\quad\quad\quad = 13$ ft

Chapter 9

Section 9.1

9.

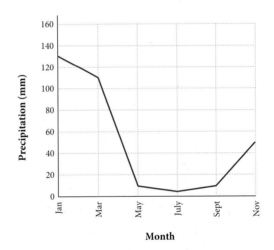

Section 9.2

1. $2 + (-5) = -3$ **2.** $-2 + 5 = 3$ **3.** $-2 + (-5) = -7$ **4.** $2 + 6 = 8$ **5.** $2 + (-6) = -4$ **6.** $-2 + 6 = 4$

7. $-2 + (-6) = -8$ **8.** $\quad 15 + \quad 12 = 27$
$\quad\quad\quad\quad\quad\quad\quad\quad\quad 15 + (-12) = 3$
$\quad\quad\quad\quad\quad\quad\quad\quad -15 + \quad 12 = -3$
$\quad\quad\quad\quad\quad\quad\quad\quad -15 + (-12) = -27$

9. $12 + (-3) + (-7) + 5 = 9 + (-7) + 5$
$\quad\quad\quad\quad\quad\quad\quad\quad\quad = 2 + 5$
$\quad\quad\quad\quad\quad\quad\quad\quad\quad = 7$

10. $[-2 + (-12)] + [7 + (-5)] = [-14] + [2]$
$\quad\quad\quad\quad\quad\quad\quad\quad\quad\quad\quad\quad\quad = -12$

11. $-5.76 + (-3.24) = -9.00$ **12.** $6.88 + (-8.55) = -1.67$ **13.** $\dfrac{5}{6} + \left(-\dfrac{2}{6}\right) = \dfrac{3}{6} = \dfrac{1}{2}$ **14.** $\dfrac{1}{2} + \left(-\dfrac{3}{4}\right) + \left(-\dfrac{5}{8}\right) = \dfrac{1 \cdot 4}{2 \cdot 4} + \left(-\dfrac{3 \cdot 2}{4 \cdot 2}\right) + \left(-\dfrac{5}{8}\right)$
$\quad\quad\quad\quad\quad\quad\quad\quad\quad\quad\quad\quad\quad\quad\quad\quad\quad\quad\quad\quad\quad\quad\quad\quad\quad = \dfrac{4}{8} + \left(-\dfrac{6}{8}\right) + \left(-\dfrac{5}{8}\right)$
$\quad\quad\quad\quad\quad\quad\quad\quad\quad\quad\quad\quad\quad\quad\quad\quad\quad\quad\quad\quad\quad\quad\quad\quad\quad = -\dfrac{2}{8} + \left(-\dfrac{5}{8}\right)$
$\quad\quad\quad\quad\quad\quad\quad\quad\quad\quad\quad\quad\quad\quad\quad\quad\quad\quad\quad\quad\quad\quad\quad\quad\quad = -\dfrac{7}{8}$

Section 9.3

1. $7 - 3 = 7 + (-3)$
$\quad\quad\quad = 4$

2. $-7 - 3 = -7 + (-3)$
$\quad\quad\quad\quad = -10$

3. $-8 - 6 = -8 + (-6)$
$\quad\quad\quad\quad = -14$

4. $10 - (-6) = 10 + 6$
$\quad\quad\quad\quad = 16$

5. $-10 - (-15) = -10 + 15$
$\quad\quad\quad\quad\quad = 5$

6. a. $8 - 5 = 8 + (-5)$ **b.** $-8 - 5 = -8 + (-5)$ **c.** $8 - (-5) = 8 + 5$ **d.** $-8 - (-5) = -8 + 5$ **e.** $12 - 10 = 12 + (-10)$
$\quad = 3$ $\quad\quad\quad = -13$ $\quad\quad\quad = 13$ $\quad\quad\quad = -3$ $\quad\quad\quad = 2$

f. $-12 - 10 = -12 + (-10)$ **g.** $12 - (-10) = 12 + 10$ **h.** $-12 - (-10) = -12 + 10$ **7.** $-4 + 6 - 7 = -4 + 6 + (-7)$
$\quad = -22$ $\quad\quad\quad\quad = 22$ $\quad\quad\quad\quad = -2$ $\quad\quad\quad\quad = 2 + (-7)$
$\quad\quad\quad\quad\quad\quad\quad\quad\quad\quad\quad\quad\quad\quad\quad\quad\quad = -5$

8. $15 - (-5) - 8 = 15 + 5 + (-8)$ **9.** $-8 - 2 = -8 + (-2)$ **10.** $7 - (-5) = 7 + 5$ **11.** $-8 - (-6) = -8 + 6$
$\quad\quad = 20 + (-8)$ $\quad\quad\quad = -10$ $\quad\quad\quad = 12$ $\quad\quad\quad = -2$
$\quad\quad = 12$

12. $-57.8 - 70.4 = -57.8 + (-70.4)$ **13.** $-\dfrac{5}{8} - \dfrac{3}{8} = -\dfrac{5}{8} + \left(-\dfrac{3}{8}\right)$ **14.** $42 - (-42) = 42 + 42 = 84°F$
$\quad\quad = -128.2$
$\quad\quad\quad\quad\quad\quad\quad\quad\quad\quad\quad = -\dfrac{8}{8}$
$\quad\quad\quad\quad\quad\quad\quad\quad\quad\quad\quad = -1$

Section 9.4

1. $2(-6) = (-6) + (-6)$ **2.** $-2(6) = 6(-2) = (-2) + (-2) + (-2) + (-2) + (-2) + (-2)$ **3.** $-2(-6) = 12$ **10.** $-5(2)(-4) = -10(-4)$
$\quad = -12$ $\quad\quad\quad\quad\quad\quad\quad\quad = -12$ $\quad\quad\quad\quad\quad\quad\quad\quad\quad\quad\quad\quad = 40$

11. a. $(-8)^2 = (-8)(-8) = 64$ **12.** $-2[5 + (-8)] = -2[-3]$ **13.** $-3 + 4(-7 + 3) = -3 + 4(-4)$ **14.** $-3(5) + 4(-4) = -15 + (-16)$
$\quad$ **b.** $-8^2 = -8 \cdot 8 = -64$ $\quad\quad\quad\quad = 6$ $\quad\quad\quad\quad\quad\quad = -3 + (-16)$ $\quad\quad\quad\quad\quad\quad = -31$
$\quad$ **c.** $(-3)^3 = (-3)(-3)(-3) = -27$ $\quad\quad\quad\quad\quad\quad\quad\quad\quad\quad\quad = -19$
$\quad$ **d.** $-3^3 = -3 \cdot 3 \cdot 3 = -27$

15. $-2(3 - 5) - 7(-2 - 4) = -2(-2) - 7(-6)$ **16.** $(-6 - 1)(4 - 9) = (-7)(-5)$ **17.** $\dfrac{3}{4}\left(-\dfrac{4}{7}\right) = -\dfrac{3 \cdot 4}{4 \cdot 7} = -\dfrac{3}{7}$
$\quad\quad\quad\quad\quad\quad\quad\quad = 4 - (-42)$ $\quad\quad\quad\quad\quad\quad = 35$
$\quad\quad\quad\quad\quad\quad\quad\quad = 4 + 42$
$\quad\quad\quad\quad\quad\quad\quad\quad = 46$

18. $\left(-\dfrac{5}{6}\right)\left(-\dfrac{9}{20}\right) = \dfrac{5 \cdot 9}{6 \cdot 20} = \dfrac{5 \cdot 3 \cdot 3}{2 \cdot 3 \cdot 4 \cdot 5} = \dfrac{3}{8}$ **19.** $(-3)(6.7) = -20.1$ **20.** $(-0.6)(-0.5) = 0.30$

Section 9.5

6. $\dfrac{8(-5)}{-4} = \dfrac{-40}{-4}$ **7.** $\dfrac{-20 + 6(-2)}{7 - 11} = \dfrac{-20 + (-12)}{-4}$ **8.** $-3(4^2) + 10 \div (-5) = -3(16) + 10 \div (-5)$ **9.** $-80 \div 2 \div 10 = -40 \div 10$
$\quad\quad = 10$ $\quad\quad\quad\quad\quad\quad = \dfrac{-32}{-4}$ $\quad\quad\quad\quad\quad\quad\quad\quad = -48 + (-2)$ $\quad\quad\quad\quad\quad\quad = -4$
$\quad\quad\quad\quad\quad\quad\quad\quad = 8$ $\quad\quad\quad\quad\quad\quad\quad\quad = -50$

Section 9.6

1. $5(7a) = (5 \cdot 7)a$ **2.** $-3(9x) = (-3 \cdot 9)x$ **3.** $5(-8y) = [5(-8)]y$ **4.** $6 + (9 + x) = (6 + 9) + x$
$\quad = 35a$ $\quad\quad\quad = -27x$ $\quad\quad\quad = -40y$ $\quad\quad\quad = 15 + x$

5. $(3x + 7) + 4 = 3x + (7 + 4)$ **6.** $6(x + 4) = 6(x) + 6(4)$ **7.** $7(a - 5) = 7(a) - 7(5)$ **8.** $6(4x + 5) = 6(4x) + 6(5)$
$\quad\quad\quad\quad = 3x + 11$ $\quad\quad\quad = 6x + 24$ $\quad\quad\quad = 7a - 35$ $\quad\quad\quad = (6 \cdot 4)x + 6(5)$
$\quad\quad\quad\quad\quad\quad\quad\quad\quad\quad\quad\quad\quad\quad\quad\quad\quad\quad\quad\quad\quad = 24x + 30$

9. $3(8a - 4) = 3(8a) - 3(4)$ **10.** $8(3x + 4y) = 8(3x) + 8(4y)$ **11.** $A = s^2 = 12^2 = 144$ ft^2
$\quad\quad\quad = 24a - 12$ $\quad\quad\quad\quad = 24x + 32y$ $\quad\quad\quad P = 4s = 4(12) = 48$ ft

12. $A = lw = 100(53) = 5{,}300$ yd^2
$\quad P = 2l + 2w = 2(100) + 2(53) = 200 + 106 = 306$ yd

Chapter 10

Section 10.1

1. $6(x + 4) = 6(x) + 6(4)$ **2.** $-3(2x + 4) = -3(2x) + (-3)(4)$ **3.** $\dfrac{1}{2}(2x - 4) = \dfrac{1}{2}(2x) - \dfrac{1}{2}(4)$ **4.** $6x - 2 + 3x + 8 = 6x + 3x + (-2) + 8$
$\quad\quad = 6x + 24$ $\quad\quad\quad = -6x + (-12)$ $\quad\quad\quad\quad = x - 2$ $\quad\quad\quad\quad\quad = 9x + 6$
$\quad\quad\quad\quad\quad\quad = -6x - 12$

5. $2(4x + 3) + 7 = 2(4x) + 2(3) + 7$
$\qquad\qquad\quad = 8x + 6 + 7$
$\qquad\qquad\quad = 8x + 13$

6. $3(2x + 1) + 5(4x - 3) = 3(2x) + 3(1) + 5(4x) - 5(3)$
$\qquad\qquad\qquad\qquad\quad = 6x + 3 + 20x - 15$
$\qquad\qquad\qquad\qquad\quad = 26x - 12$

10. $A = lw$
$\qquad = 25(8 + 2x)$
$\qquad = 25(8) + 25(2x)$
$\qquad = 200 + 50x \text{ cm}^2$

11. a. $x = 90° - 45° = 45°$
$\quad$ **b.** $x = 180° - 60° = 120°$

Section 10.2

1. When $\qquad\qquad x = 3$
$\quad$ the equation $\quad 5x - 4 = 11$
$\qquad$ becomes $\quad 5(3) - 4 = 11$
$\qquad\qquad$ or $\qquad 15 - 4 = 11$
$\qquad\qquad\qquad\qquad\quad 11 = 11$

2. When $\qquad\qquad\qquad a = -3$
$\quad$ the equation $\qquad 6a - 3 = 2a + 4$
$\quad$ becomes $\qquad 6(-3) - 3 = 2(-3) + 4$
$\qquad\qquad\qquad\quad -18 - 3 = -6 + 4$
$\qquad\qquad\qquad\qquad\quad -21 = -2$

This is a false statement, so $a = -3$ is not a solution.

3. $\qquad\qquad x + 5 = -2$
$\qquad x + 5 + (-5) = -2 + (-5)$
$\qquad\qquad\qquad x + 0 = -7$
$\qquad\qquad\qquad\qquad x = -7$

4. $\qquad a - 2 = 7$
$\quad a - 2 + 2 = 7 + 2$
$\qquad\quad a + 0 = 9$
$\qquad\qquad\quad a = 9$

5. $\qquad y + 6 - 2 = 8 - 9$
$\qquad\qquad\quad y + 4 = -1$
$\quad y + 4 + (-4) = -1 + (-4)$
$\qquad\qquad\quad y + 0 = -5$
$\qquad\qquad\qquad\quad y = -5$

6. $\quad 5x - 3 - 4x = 4 - 7$
$\qquad\qquad\quad x - 3 = -3$
$\qquad x - 3 + 3 = -3 + 3$
$\qquad\qquad\quad x + 0 = 0$
$\qquad\qquad\qquad x = 0$

7. $\qquad -5 - 7 = x + 2$
$\qquad\qquad\quad -12 = x + 2$
$\quad -12 + (-2) = x + 2 + (-2)$
$\qquad\qquad\quad -14 = x + 0$
$\qquad\qquad\quad -14 = x$

8. $\qquad a - \dfrac{2}{3} = \dfrac{5}{6}$
$\quad a - \dfrac{2}{3} + \dfrac{2}{3} = \dfrac{5}{6} + \dfrac{2}{3}$
$\qquad\qquad\quad a = \dfrac{9}{6} = \dfrac{3}{2}$

9. $5(3a - 4) - 14a = 25$
$\quad 15a - 20 - 14a = 25$
$\qquad\qquad a - 20 = 25$
$\quad a - 20 + 20 = 25 + 20$
$\qquad\qquad\quad a = 45$

Section 10.3

1. $\qquad \dfrac{1}{3}x = 5$
$\quad 3 \cdot \dfrac{1}{3}x = 3 \cdot 5$
$\qquad\qquad x = 15$

2. $\qquad \dfrac{1}{5}a + 3 = 7$
$\quad \dfrac{1}{5}a + 3 + (-3) = 7 + (-3)$
$\qquad\qquad \dfrac{1}{5}a = 4$
$\qquad 5 \cdot \dfrac{1}{5}a = 5 \cdot 4$
$\qquad\qquad a = 20$

3. $\qquad \dfrac{3}{5}y = 6$
$\quad \dfrac{5}{3} \cdot \dfrac{3}{5}y = \dfrac{5}{3} \cdot 6$
$\qquad\qquad y = 10$

4. $\qquad -\dfrac{3}{4}x = \dfrac{6}{5}$
$\quad -\dfrac{4}{3}\left(-\dfrac{3}{4}x\right) = -\dfrac{4}{3} \cdot \dfrac{6}{5}$
$\qquad\qquad x = -\dfrac{8}{5}$

5. $\qquad 6x = -42$
$\qquad \dfrac{6x}{6} = -\dfrac{42}{6}$
$\qquad\quad x = -7$

6. $\qquad -5x + 6 = -14$
$\quad -5x + 6 + (-6) = -14 + (-6)$
$\qquad\qquad -5x = -20$
$\qquad\qquad \dfrac{-5x}{-5} = \dfrac{-20}{-5}$
$\qquad\qquad\quad x = 4$

7. $\qquad 3x - 7x + 5 = 3 - 18$
$\qquad\qquad -4x + 5 = -15$
$\quad -4x + 5 + (-5) = -15 + (-5)$
$\qquad\qquad -4x = -20$
$\qquad\qquad \dfrac{-4x}{-4} = \dfrac{-20}{-4}$
$\qquad\qquad\quad x = 5$

8. $\qquad -5 + 4 = 2x - 11 + 3x$
$\qquad\qquad -1 = 5x - 11$
$\quad -1 + 11 = 5x - 11 + 11$
$\qquad\qquad 10 = 5x$
$\qquad\qquad \dfrac{10}{5} = \dfrac{5x}{5}$
$\qquad\qquad 2 = x$

Section 10.4

1. $\qquad 4(x + 3) = -8$
$\qquad\quad 4x + 12 = -8$
$\quad 4x + 12 + (-12) = -8 + (-12)$
$\qquad\qquad 4x = -20$
$\qquad\qquad \dfrac{4x}{4} = \dfrac{-20}{4}$
$\qquad\qquad\quad x = -5$

2. $\qquad 6a + 7 = 4a - 3$
$\quad 6a + (-4a) + 7 = 4a + (-4a) - 3$
$\qquad\qquad 2a + 7 = -3$
$\quad 2a + 7 + (-7) = -3 + (-7)$
$\qquad\qquad 2a = -10$
$\qquad\qquad \dfrac{2a}{2} = \dfrac{-10}{2}$
$\qquad\qquad a = -5$

3. $\qquad 5(x - 2) + 3 = -12$
$\qquad\quad 5x - 10 + 3 = -12$
$\qquad\qquad 5x - 7 = -12$
$\quad 5x - 7 + 7 = -12 + 7$
$\qquad\qquad 5x = -5$
$\qquad\qquad \dfrac{5x}{5} = \dfrac{-5}{5}$
$\qquad\qquad x = -1$

4.
$$3(4x - 5) + 6 = 3x + 9$$
$$12x - 15 + 6 = 3x + 9$$
$$12x - 9 = 3x + 9$$
$$12x + (-3x) - 9 = 3x + (-3x) + 9$$
$$9x - 9 = 9$$
$$9x - 9 + 9 = 9 + 9$$
$$9x = 18$$
$$\frac{9x}{9} = \frac{18}{9}$$
$$x = 2$$

5.
$$\frac{x}{3} + \frac{x}{6} = 9$$
$$6\left(\frac{x}{3} + \frac{x}{6}\right) = 6(9)$$
$$6\left(\frac{x}{3}\right) + 6\left(\frac{x}{6}\right) = 6(9)$$
$$2x + x = 54$$
$$3x = 54$$
$$x = 18$$

6.
$$3x + \frac{1}{4} = \frac{5}{8}$$
$$8\left(3x + \frac{1}{4}\right) = 8\left(\frac{5}{8}\right)$$
$$8(3x) + 8\left(\frac{1}{4}\right) = 8\left(\frac{5}{8}\right)$$
$$24x + 2 = 5$$
$$24x = 3$$
$$x = \frac{1}{8}$$

7.
$$\frac{4}{x} + 3 = \frac{11}{5}$$
$$5x\left(\frac{4}{x} + 3\right) = 5x\left(\frac{11}{5}\right)$$
$$5x\left(\frac{4}{x}\right) + 5x(3) = 5x\left(\frac{11}{5}\right)$$
$$20 + 15x = 11x$$
$$20 = -4x$$
$$-5 = x$$

8.
$$\frac{1}{5}x - 2.4 = 8.3$$
$$\frac{1}{5}x - 2.4 + 2.4 = 8.3 + 2.4$$
$$\frac{1}{5}x = 10.7$$
$$5\left(\frac{1}{5}x\right) = 5(10.7)$$
$$x = 53.5$$

9.
$$7a - 0.18 = 2a + 0.77$$
$$7a + (-2a) - 0.18 = 2a + (-2a) + 0.77$$
$$5a - 0.18 = 0.77$$
$$5a - 0.18 + 0.18 = 0.77 + 0.18$$
$$5a = 0.95$$
$$\frac{5a}{5} = \frac{0.95}{5}$$
$$a = 0.19$$

Section 10.5

1. STEP 1 *Read and list.*

Known items: The numbers 3 and 10

Unknown item: The number in question

STEP 2 *Assign a variable and translate the information.*

Let x = the number asked for in the problem.

Then "The sum of a number and 3" translates to $x + 3$.

STEP 3 *Reread and write an equation.*

The sum of x and 3 is 10.

$$\underbrace{x + 3} \quad \overset{\downarrow \ \downarrow}{= 10}$$

STEP 4 *Solve the equation.*

$$x + 3 = 10$$
$$x = 7$$

STEP 5 *Write your answer.*

The number is 7.

STEP 6 *Reread and check.*

The sum of **7** and 3 is 10.

2. STEP 1 *Read and list.*

Known items: The numbers 4 and 34, twice a number, and three times a number

Unknown item: The number in question

STEP 2 *Assign a variable and translate the information.*

Let x = the number asked for in the problem.

Then "The sum of twice a number and three times the number" translates to $2x + 3x$.

STEP 3 *Reread and write an equation.*

| 4 added to | the sum of twice a number and three times the number | is 34 |

$$\underset{\downarrow}{4 +} \quad \underset{\downarrow}{2x + 3x} \quad \overset{\downarrow \ \downarrow}{= \ 34}$$

STEP 4 *Solve the equation.*

$$4 + 2x + 3x = 34$$
$$5x + 4 = 34$$
$$5x = 30$$
$$x = 6$$

STEP 5 *Write your answer.*

The number is 6.

STEP 6 *Reread and check.*

Twice **6** is 12 and three times **6** is 18. Their sum is 12 + 18 = 30. Four added to this is 34. Therefore, 4 added to the sum of twice **6** and three times **6** is 34.

3. **STEP 1 *Read and list.***

Known items: Length is twice width;
                         perimeter 42 cm

Unknown items: The length and the width

STEP 2 *Assign a variable and translate the information.*

Let x = the width. Since the length is twice the width, the length must be $2x$. Here is a picture.

                                          x (width)

                    $2x$ (length)

STEP 3 *Reread and write an equation.*

The perimeter is the sum of the sides, and is given as 42; therefore,

$x + x + 2x + 2x = 42$

STEP 4 *Solve the equation.*

$$x + x + 2x + 2x = 42$$
$$6x = 42$$
$$x = 7$$

STEP 5 *Write your answer.*

The width is 7 centimeters and the length is
$2(7) = 14$ centimeters

STEP 6 *Reread and check.*

The length, 14, is twice the width, 7. The perimeter is $7 + 7 + 14 + 14 = 42$ centimeters.

4. **STEP 1 *Read and list.***

Known items: Three angles are in a triangle. One is 3 times the smallest. The largest is 5 times the smallest.

Unknown item: The three angles

STEP 2 *Assign a variable and translate the information.*

Let x = the smallest angle. The other two angles are $3x$ and $5x$.

STEP 3 *Reread and write an equation.*

The three angles must add up to 180°, so

$x + 3x + 5x = 180°$

STEP 4 *Solve the equation.*

$x + 3x + 5x = 180°$
$9x = 180°$ Add similar terms on left side
$x = 20°$ Divide each side by 9

STEP 5 *Write the answer.*

The three angles are, 20°, $3(20°) = 60°$, and
$5(20°) = 100°$.

STEP 6 *Reread and check.*

The sum of the three angles is $20° + 60° + 100° = 180°$. One angle is 3 times the smallest, while the largest is 5 times the small-est.

5. **STEP 1 *Read and list.***

Known items: Joyce is 21 years older than Travis. Six years from now their ages will add to 49.

Unknown items: Their ages now

STEP 2 *Assign a variable and translate the information.*

Let x = Travis's age now; since Joyce is 21 years older than that, she is presently $x + 21$ years old.

STEP 3 *Reread and write an equation.*

	Now	in 6 years
Joyce	$x + 21$	$x + 27$
Travis	x	$x + 6$

$x + 27 + x + 6 = 49$

STEP 4 *Solve the equation.*

$$x + 27 + x + 6 = 49$$
$$2x + 33 = 49$$
$$2x = 16$$
$$x = 8$$

STEP 5 *Write your answer.*

Travis is now 8 years old, and Joyce is
$8 + 21 = 29$ years old.

STEP 6 *Reread and check.*

Joyce is 21 years older than Travis. In six years, Joyce will be 35 years old and Travis will be 14 years old. At that time, the sum of their ages will be
$35 + 14 = 49$.

6. STEP 1 *Read and list.*

Known items:	Charges are $11 per day and 16 cents per mile. Car is rented for 2 days.
	Total charge is $41.
Unknown items:	How many miles the car was driven

STEP 2 *Assign a variable and translate the information.*

Let x = the number of miles the car was driven. Two days rental is 2(11). The cost for driving x miles is $0.16x$.

STEP 3 *Reread and write an equation.*

The total cost is the two days' rental plus the mileage cost. It must add up to 41. The equation is
$$2(11) + 0.16x = 41$$

STEP 4 *Solve the equation.*

$$2(11) + 0.16x = 41$$
$$22 + 0.16x = 41$$
$$22 + (-22) + 0.16x = 41 + (-22)$$
$$0.16x = 19$$
$$\frac{0.16x}{0.16} = \frac{19}{0.16}$$
$$x = 118.75$$

STEP 5 *Write your answer.*

The car was driven 118.75 miles.

STEP 6 *Reread and check.*

The charge for two days is $2(11) = \$22$. The 118.75 miles adds $118.75(0.16) = \$19$. The total is $\$22 + \$19 = \$41$, which checks with the total charge given in the problem.

7. STEP 1 *Read and list.*

Known items:	We have dimes and quarters. There are 7 more dimes than quarters, and the total value of the coins is $1.75.
Unknown items:	How many of each type of coin Amy has

STEP 2 *Assign a variable and translate the information.*

Let x = the number of quarters. Here is a table that summarizes the information in the problem.

	Quarters	Dimes
Number of	x	$x + 7$
Value of	$0.25x$	$0.10(x + 7)$

STEP 3 *Reread and write an equation.*

The value of the quarters plus the value of the dimes must add to 1.75. Therefore, our equation is
$$0.25x + 0.10(x + 7) = 1.75$$

STEP 4 *Solve the equation.*

$$0.25x + 0.10(x + 7) = 1.75$$
$$0.25x + 0.10x + 0.70 = 1.75$$
$$0.35x + 0.70 = 1.75$$
$$0.35x = 1.05$$
$$x = 3$$

STEP 5 *Write your answer.*

She has 3 quarters. The number of dimes is 7 more than that, which is 10.

STEP 6 *Reread and check.*

3 quarters are worth $0.75. 10 dimes are worth $1.00. The total of the two is $1.75, which checks with the information in the problem.

Section 10.6

1.   When $P = 80$ and $w = 6$
the formula $P = 2l + 2w$
becomes $80 = 2l + 2(6)$
$$80 = 2l + 12$$
$$68 = 2l$$
$$34 = l$$
The length is 34 feet.

2.   When $F = 77$
the formula $C = \dfrac{5}{9}(F - 32)$

becomes $C = \dfrac{5}{9}(77 - 32)$

$$= \dfrac{5}{9}(45)$$

$$= \dfrac{5}{9} \cdot \dfrac{45}{1}$$

$$= \dfrac{225}{9}$$

$$= 25 \text{ degrees Celsius}$$

3.   When $x = 0$
the formula $y = 2x + 6$
becomes $y = 2 \cdot 0 + 6$
$$= 0 + 6$$
$$= 6$$

4.   When $x = -3$
the formula $2x + 3y = 4$
becomes $2(-3) + 3y = 4$
$$-6 + 3y = 4$$
$$3y = 10$$
$$y = \dfrac{10}{3}$$

5. a. $11 - 9 = 2$ hr
b. $d = 60 \text{ mi/hr} \cdot 2 \text{ hr}$
$$d = 60 \cdot 2$$
$$d = 120 \text{ miles}$$

6. With $x = 35°$ we use the formulas for finding the complement and the supplement of an angle:
The complement of $35°$ is $90° - 35° = 55°$
The supplement is $35°$ is $180° - 35° = 145°$

Section 10.7

1.

2.

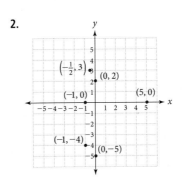

Appendices

Appendix D

1. $2^{-4} = \dfrac{1}{2^4}$

$= \dfrac{1}{16}$

2. $4^{-2} = \dfrac{1}{4^2}$

$= \dfrac{1}{16}$

3. $(-2)^{-3} = \dfrac{1}{(-2)^3}$

$= \dfrac{1}{-8}$

$= -\dfrac{1}{8}$

4. $3^4 \cdot 3^{-7} = 3^{4+(-7)}$

$= 3^{-3}$

$= \dfrac{1}{3^3}$

$= \dfrac{1}{27}$

5. $x^6 \cdot x^{-10} = x^{6+(-10)}$

$= x^{-4}$

$= \dfrac{1}{x^4}$

6. $\dfrac{2^6}{2^8} = 2^{6-8}$

$= 2^{-2}$

$= \dfrac{1}{2^2}$

$= \dfrac{1}{4}$

7. $\dfrac{10^{-5}}{10^3} = 10^{-5-3}$

$= 10^{-8}$

$\dfrac{1}{10^8} = \dfrac{1}{100,000,000}$

8. $\dfrac{10^{-6}}{10^{-8}} = 10^{-6-(-8)}$

$= 10^{-6+8}$

$= 10^2 = 100$

9. $4x^{-3} \cdot 7x = 4x^{-3} \cdot 7x^1$

$= (4 \cdot 7)(x^{-3} \cdot x^1)$

$= 28x^{-3+1}$

$= 28x^{-2} = \dfrac{28}{x^2}$

10. $\dfrac{x^{-5} \cdot x^2}{x^{-8}} = \dfrac{x^{-5+2}}{x^{-8}}$

$= \dfrac{x^{-3}}{x^{-8}}$

$= x^{-3-(-8)}$

$= x^{-3+8}$

$= x^5$

Appendix F

1. $(2.5 \times 10^6)(1.4 \times 10^2) = (2.5)(1.4) \times (10^6)(10^2)$

$= 3.5 \times 10^{6+2}$

$= 3.5 \times 10^8$

2. $(2,200,000)(0.00015) = (2.2 \times 10^6)(1.5 \times 10^{-4})$

$= (2.2)(1.5) \times (10^6)(10^{-4})$

$= 3.3 \times 10^{6+(-4)}$

$= 3.3 \times 10^2$

3. $\dfrac{6 \times 10^5}{2 \times 10^{-4}} = \dfrac{6}{2} \times \dfrac{10^5}{10^{-4}}$

$= 3.0 \times 10^{5-(-4)}$

$= 3.0 \times 10^{5+4}$

$= 3.0 \times 10^9$

4. $\dfrac{0.0038}{19,000,000} = \dfrac{3.8 \times 10^{-3}}{1.9 \times 10^7}$

$= \dfrac{3.8}{1.9} \times \dfrac{10^{-3}}{10^7}$

$= 2.0 \times 10^{-3-7}$

$= 2.0 \times 10^{-10}$

5. $\dfrac{(6.8 \times 10^{-4})(3.9 \times 10^2)}{7.8 \times 10^{-6}} = \dfrac{(6.8)(3.9)}{(7.8)} \times \dfrac{(10^{-4})(10^2)}{10^{-6}}$

$= 3.4 \times 10^{-4+2-(-6)}$

$= 3.4 \times 10^4$

6. $\dfrac{(0.000035)(45,000)}{0.000075} = \dfrac{(3.5 \times 10^{-5})(4.5 \times 10^4)}{7.5 \times 10^{-5}}$

$= \dfrac{(3.5)(4.5)}{(7.5)} \times \dfrac{(10^{-5})(10^4)}{10^{-5}}$

$= 2.1 \times 10^{-5+4-(-5)}$

$= 2.1 \times 10^4$

Answers to Odd-Numbered Problems

Chapter 1

Pretest for Chapter 1

1. $7000 + 60 + 2$ **2.** Three million, four hundred nine thousand, twenty-one **3.** 18,507 **4.** 597 **5.** 5,410 **6.** 211
7. 264 **8.** 216 **9.** 21,440 **10.** 32 **11.** 174 R 16 **12.** 510 **13.** 6,800 **14.** 31 **15.** 74 **16.** $6(12 - 8) = 24$

Getting Ready for Chapter 1

TABLE 1 Addition Facts										
+	0	1	2	3	4	5	6	7	8	9
0	0	1	2	3	4	5	6	7	8	9
1	1	2	3	4	5	6	7	8	9	10
2	2	3	4	5	6	7	8	9	10	11
3	3	4	5	6	7	8	9	10	11	12
4	4	5	6	7	8	9	10	11	12	13
5	5	6	7	8	9	10	11	12	13	14
6	6	7	8	9	10	11	12	13	14	15
7	7	8	9	10	11	12	13	14	15	16
8	8	9	10	11	12	13	14	15	16	17
9	9	10	11	12	13	14	15	16	17	18

TABLE 2 Multiplication Facts										
×	0	1	2	3	4	5	6	7	8	9
0	0	0	0	0	0	0	0	0	0	0
1	0	1	2	3	4	5	6	7	8	9
2	0	2	4	6	8	10	12	14	16	18
3	0	3	6	9	12	15	18	21	24	27
4	0	4	8	12	16	20	24	28	32	36
5	0	5	10	15	20	25	30	35	40	45
6	0	6	12	18	24	30	36	42	48	54
7	0	7	14	21	28	35	42	49	56	63
8	0	8	16	24	32	40	48	56	64	72
9	0	9	18	27	36	45	54	63	72	81

Problem Set 1.1

1. 8 ones, 7 tens **3.** 5 ones, 4 tens **5.** 8 ones, 4 tens, 3 hundreds **7.** 8 ones, 0 tens, 6 hundreds
9. 8 ones, 7 tens, 3 hundreds, 2 thousands **11.** 9 ones, 6 tens, 5 hundreds, 3 thousands, 7 ten thousands, 2 hundred thousands
13. Ten thousands **15.** Hundred millions **17.** Ones **19.** Hundred thousands **21.** $600 + 50 + 8$ **23.** $60 + 8$
25. $4,000 + 500 + 80 + 7$ **27.** $30,000 + 2,000 + 600 + 70 + 4$ **29.** $3,000,000 + 400,000 + 60,000 + 2,000 + 500 + 70 + 7$
31. $400 + 7$ **33.** $30,000 + 60 + 8$ **35.** $3,000,000 + 4,000 + 8$ **37.** Twenty-nine **39.** Forty **41.** Five hundred seventy-three
43. Seven hundred seven **45.** Seven hundred seventy **47.** Twenty-three thousand, five hundred forty
49. Three thousand, four **51.** Three thousand, forty **53.** One hundred four million, sixty-five thousand, seven hundred eighty
55. Five billion, three million, forty thousand, eight **57.** Two million, five hundred forty-six thousand, seven hundred thirty-one
59. 325 **61.** 5,432 **63.** 86,762 **65.** 2,000,200 **67.** 2,002,200
69. a. Twenty-eight thousand, six hundred thirty-one **b.** Ninety-three thousand, three hundred thirty-three
71. Hundred thousands **73.** Three million, one hundred seventy-three thousand, four hundred three
75. Twenty-one thousand, four hundred eighty **77.** Seven hundred fifty dollars and no cents **79.** 304,000,000
81. One hundred twenty-seven million **83.** 36,000,000 **85.** Ten million, nine hundred thousand

Problem Set 1.2

1. 15 **3.** 14 **5.** 24 **7.** 15 **9.** 20 **11.** 68 **13.** 98 **15.** 7,297 **17.** 6,487 **19.** 96 **21.** 7,449 **23.** 65
25. 102 **27.** 875 **29.** 829 **31.** 10,391 **33.** 16,204 **35.** 155,554 **37.** 111,110 **39.** 17,391 **41.** 14,892 **43.** 180
45. 2,220 **47.** 18,285 **49.**

First Number a	Second Number b	Their Sum $a + b$
61	38	99
63	36	99
65	34	99
67	32	99

51.

First Number a	Second Number b	Their Sum $a + b$
9	16	25
36	64	100
81	144	225
144	256	400

53. $9 + 5$ **55.** $8 + 3$ **57.** $4 + 6$ **59.** $1 + (2 + 3)$ **61.** $2 + (1 + 6)$ **63.** $(1 + 9) + 1$ **65.** $4 + (n + 1)$ **67.** $n = 4$
69. $n = 5$ **71.** $n = 8$ **73.** $n = 8$ **75.** The sum of 4 and 9 **77.** The sum of 8 and 1 **79.** The sum of 2 and 3 is 5.
81. a. $5 + 2$ **b.** $8 + 3$ **83. a.** $m + 1$ **b.** $m + n$ **85.** 12 in. **87.** 16 ft **89.** 26 yd **91.** 18 in. **93. a.** 150 **b.** 1,125
95. $349 **97. a.** $62,377.00 **b.** $55,177.00 **c.** $7,200.00

Problem Set 1.3

1. 40   **3.** 50   **5.** 50   **7.** 80   **9.** 460   **11.** 470   **13.** 56,780   **15.** 4,500   **17.** 500   **19.** 800   **21.** 900   **23.** 1,100
25. 5,000   **27.** 39,600   **29.** 5,000   **31.** 10,000   **33.** 1,000   **35.** 658,000   **37.** 510,000   **39.** 3,789,000

Original Number	Rounded to the Nearest		
	Ten	Hundred	Thousand
41. 7,821	7,820	7,800	8,000
43. 5,999	6,000	6,000	6,000
45. 10,985	10,990	11,000	11,000
47. 99,999	100,000	100,000	100,000

49. 1,200   **51.** 1,900   **53.** 58,000   **55.** 33,400   **57.** 190,000   **59.** 81,400
61. a. 4,265,997 babies   **b.** Yes   **c.** 2,300,000 babies   **d.** 112,000 babies
63. 160 miles per hour   **65.** Answers will vary, but 70 miles per hour is a good estimate.
67.

Problem Set 1.4

1. 32   **3.** 22   **5.** 10   **7.** 111   **9.** 312   **11.** 403   **13.** 1,111   **15.** 4,544   **17.** 15   **19.** 33   **21.** 5   **23.** 33   **25.** 95
27. 152   **29.** 274   **31.** 488   **33.** 538   **35.** 163   **37.** 1,610   **39.** 46,083
41.

First Number a	Second Number b	The Difference of a and b $a - b$
25	15	10
24	16	8
23	17	6
22	18	4

43.

First Number a	Second Number b	The Difference of a and b $a - b$
400	256	144
400	144	256
225	144	81
225	81	144

45. The difference of 10 and 2   **47.** The difference of a and 6   **49.** The difference of 8 and 2 is 6.   **51.** 3   **53.** 8   **55.** 23
57. $8 - 3$ **59.** $y - 9$ **61.** $3 - 2 = 1$ **63.** $37 - 9x = 10$ **65.** $2y - 15x = 24$ **67.** $(x + 2) - (x + 1) = 1$ **69.** $255
71. $172,500   **73.** 91 mph   **75.** 173 GB
77. a.

State	Energy (MegaWatts)
Texas	2,768
California	2,361
Iowa	936
Washington	818

b. 407 MW

Problem Set 1.5

1. 300   **3.** 600   **5.** 3,000   **7.** 5,000   **9.** 21,000   **11.** 81,000   **13.** 100   **15.** 228   **17.** 36   **19.** 1,440   **21.** 950
23. 1,725   **25.** 121   **27.** 1,552   **29.** 4,200   **31.** 66,248   **33.** 279,200   **35.** 12,321   **37.** 106,400   **39.** 198,592
41. 612,928   **43.** 333,180   **45.** 18,053,805   **47.** 263,646,976
49.

First Number a	Second Number b	Their Product ab
11	11	121
11	22	242
22	22	484
22	44	968

51.

First Number a	Second Number b	Their Product ab
25	10	250
25	100	2,500
25	1,000	25,000
25	10,000	250,000

53.

First Number a	Second Number b	Their Product ab
12	20	240
36	20	720
12	40	480
36	40	1,440

55. The product of 6 and 7   **57.** The product of 2 and n

59. The product of 9 and 7 is 63.   **61.** $7 \cdot n$ **63.** $6 \cdot 7 = 42$ **65.** $0 \cdot 6 = 0$ **67.** Products: $9 \cdot 7$ and 63
69. Products: $4(4)$ and 16   **71.** Factors: 2, 3, and 4   **73.** Factors: 2, 2, and 3   **75.** $9(5)$ **77.** $7 \cdot 6$ **79.** $(2 \cdot 7) \cdot 6$
81. $(3 \times 9) \times 1$ **83.** $7(2) + 7(3) = 35$ **85.** $9(4) + 9(7) = 99$ **87.** $3x + 3$ **89.** $2x + 10$ **91.** $n = 3$ **93.** $n = 9$ **95.** $n = 0$
97. 2,860 mi   **99.** $7.18   **101.** 148,800 jets   **103.** 2,081 calories   **105.** 280 calories   **107.** Yes   **109.** 1 in^2 **111.** 1.125 in^2
113. 8,000   **115.** 1,500,000   **117.** 1,400,000   **119.** 40   **121.** 54

Problem Set 1.6
1. $6 \div 3$ **3.** $45 \div 9$ **5.** $r \div s$ **7.** $20 \div 4 = 5$ **9.** $2 \cdot 3 = 6$ **11.** $9 \cdot 4 = 36$ **13.** $6 \cdot 8 = 48$ **15.** $7 \cdot 4 = 28$ **17.** 5   **19.** 8
21. Undefined   **23.** 45   **25.** 23   **27.** 1,530   **29.** 1,350   **31.** 18,000   **33.** 16,680   **35.** a   **37.** b   **39.** 1   **41.** 2
43. 4   **45.** 6   **47.** 45   **49.** 49   **51.** 432   **53.** 1,438   **55.** 705   **57.** 3,020
59.

First Number a	Second Number b	The Quotient of a and b $\frac{a}{b}$
100	25	4
100	26	3 R 22
100	27	3 R 19
100	28	3 R 16

61. 61 R 4   **63.** 90 R 1   **65.** 13 R 7   **67.** 234 R 6

69. 402 R 4   **71.** 35 R 35   **73.** $3,525   **75.** 79¢   **77.** 3 bottles   **79.** 6 glasses, with 2 ounces left over   **81.** $3,900,000
83. 665 mg   **85.** 5 mi

Problem Set 1.7
1. Base 4; exponent 5   **3.** Base 3; exponent 6   **5.** Base 8; exponent 2   **7.** Base 9; exponent 1   **9.** Base 4; exponent 0   **11.** 36
13. 8   **15.** 1   **17.** 1   **19.** 81   **21.** 10   **23.** 12   **25.** 1   **27.** 12   **29.** 100   **31.** 4   **33.** 43   **35.** 16   **37.** 84
39. 14   **41.** 74   **43.** 12,768   **45.** 104   **47.** 416   **49.** 66   **51.** 21   **53.** 7   **55.** 16   **57.** 84   **59.** 40   **61.** 41
63. 18   **65.** 405   **67.** 124   **69.** 11   **71.** 91   **73.** 7   **75.** $8(4 + 2) = 48$ **77.** $2(10 + 3) = 26$ **79.** $3(3 + 4) + 4 = 25$
81. $(20 \div 2) - 9 = 1$ **83.** $(8 \cdot 5) + (5 \cdot 4) = 60$ **85.** 255 calories   **87.** 465 calories   **89.** Big Mac has twice the calories.
91. 4   **93.** 16

Chapter 1 Review
1. One thousand, three hundred seventy-six   **3.** 5,245,652   **5.** $1,000,000 + 20,000 + 5,000 + 600 + 30 + 9$ **7.** d   **9.** c   **11.** b
13. g   **15.** 749   **17.** 8,272   **19.** 314   **21.** 3,149   **23.** 584   **25.** 3,717   **27.** 173   **29.** 428   **31.** 3,781,090   **33.** 3,800,000
35. 79   **37.** 222   **39.** 8   **41.** 32   **43.** $3(4 + 6) = 30$ **45.** $2(17 - 5) = 24$ **47.** $P = 22$ m

Chapter 1 Test
1. Twenty thousand, three hundred forty-seven   **2.** 2,045,006   **3.** $100,000 + 20,000 + 3,000 + 400 + 7$ **4.** f   **5.** c   **6.** a   **7.** e
8. 876   **9.** 16,383   **10.** 524   **11.** 3,085   **12.** 1,674   **13.** 22,258   **14.** 85   **15.** 21   **16.** 520,000   **17.** 11   **18.** 4
19. 107   **20.** $3x - 6$ **21.** $2(11 + 7) = 36$ **22.** $(20 \div 5) + 9 = 13$ **23.** $P = 46$ m   **24.** $131,363,606   **25.** $912,251,368

A Glimpse of Algebra
1. $36x^2$ **3.** $16x^2$ **5.** $27a^3$ **7.** $8a^3b^3$ **9.** $81x^2y^2$ **11.** $25x^2y^2z^2$ **13.** $1,296x^4y^2$ **15.** $576x^6$ **17.** $200x^5$ **19.** $7,200a^7$
21. $432x^5y^5$ **23.** $400x^6y^6z^6$ **25.** $x^5y^7z^6$ **27.** $324a^{14}b^{16}$ **29.** $40x^{11}y^{12}$

Chapter 2

Pretest for Chapter 2

1. $\frac{4}{5}$ **2.** $2^4 \cdot 7$ **3.** 6   **4.** 12   **5.** $\frac{28}{25}$ **6.** $\frac{1}{12}$ **7.** $\frac{53}{80}$ **8.** $\frac{19}{24}$ **9.** $\frac{23}{5}$ **10.** $2\frac{5}{8}$ **11.** $3\frac{17}{20}$ **12.** $3\frac{15}{19}$

13. $5\frac{3}{10}$ **14.** $2\frac{5}{6}$ **15.** $\frac{1}{16}$ **16.** 12   **17.** $12\frac{81}{100}$ **18.** 1   **19.** $\frac{2}{3}$ **20.** $1\frac{2}{7}$

Getting Ready for Chapter 2

1. a. > **b.** > **c.** < **d.** >   **2.** 10   **3.** 2   **4.** 16   **5.** 23   **6.** 16   **7.** 0   **8.** 24   **9.** 101   **10.** 5   **11.** 2 R 3   **12.** 8 R 16
13. 201 R 5   **14.** 507 R 10   **15.** $(2 + 3) \cdot 7$ **16.** $2^2 \cdot 3^3$

Problem Set 2.1

1. 1   **3.** 2   **5.** x **7.** a **9.** 5   **11.** 1   **13.** 12   **15.**

Numerator a	Denominator b	Fraction $\frac{a}{b}$
3	5	$\frac{3}{5}$
1	7	$\frac{1}{7}$
x	y	$\frac{x}{y}$
$x + 1$	x	$\frac{x + 1}{x}$

17. $\frac{3}{4}, \frac{1}{2}, \frac{9}{10}$

19. True   **21.** False   **23.** $\frac{3}{4}$ **25.** $\frac{43}{47}$ **27.** $\frac{4}{3}$ **29.** $\frac{13}{17}$ **31.** $\frac{4}{6}$ **33.** $\frac{5}{6}$ **35.** $\frac{8}{12}$ **37.** $\frac{8}{12}$ **39.** $\frac{2x}{12x}$ **41.** $\frac{48a}{24a}$

43. $\frac{120a}{24a}$ **45.** Answers will vary   **47.** 3   **49.** 2   **51.** 37   **53. a.** $\frac{1}{2}$ **b.** $\frac{1}{2}$ **c.** $\frac{1}{4}$ **d.** $\frac{1}{4}$

55.–63.   **65.** $\frac{1}{20} < \frac{4}{25} < \frac{3}{10} < \frac{2}{5}$ **67.** $\frac{3}{12}$ inch

69.

How Often Workers Send Non-Work-Related E-Mail From the Office	Fraction of Respondents Saying Yes
never	$\frac{4}{25}$
1 to 5 times a day	$\frac{47}{100}$
5 to 10 times a day	$\frac{8}{25}$
more than 10 times a day	$\frac{1}{20}$

71. $\frac{4}{5}$ **73.** $\frac{311}{500}$ **75.** $\frac{19}{33}$ **77. a.** $\frac{90}{360}$ **b.** $\frac{45}{360}$ **c.** $\frac{180}{360}$ **d.** $\frac{270}{360}$

79. d   **81.** a   **83.** 108   **85.** 60   **87.** 4   **89.** 5   **91.** 7   **93.** 51   **95.** 23   **97.** 32   **99.** 16   **101.** 18

Problem Set 2.2

1. Prime   **3.** Composite; 3, 5, and 7 are factors   **5.** Composite; 3 is a factor   **7.** Prime   **9.** $2^2 \cdot 3$ **11.** 3^4 **13.** $5 \cdot 43$ **15.** $3 \cdot 5$

17. $\frac{1}{2}$ **19.** $\frac{2}{3}$ **21.** $\frac{4}{5}$ **23.** $\frac{9}{5}$ **25.** $\frac{7}{11}$ **27.** $\frac{3}{5}$ **29.** $\frac{1}{7}$ **31.** $\frac{7}{9}$ **33.** $\frac{7}{5}$ **35.** $\frac{1}{5}$ **37.** $\frac{11}{7}$ **39.** $\frac{5}{3}$ **41.** $\frac{8}{9}$ **43.** $\frac{42}{55}$

45. $\frac{17}{19}$ **47.** $\frac{14}{33}$ **49. a.** $\frac{2}{17}$ **b.** $\frac{3}{26}$ **c.** $\frac{1}{9}$ **d.** $\frac{3}{28}$ **e.** $\frac{2}{19}$ **51. a.** $\frac{1}{45}$ **b.** $\frac{1}{30}$ **c.** $\frac{1}{18}$ **d.** $\frac{1}{15}$ **e.** $\frac{1}{10}$ **53. a.** $\frac{1}{3}$ **b.** $\frac{5}{6}$ **c.** $\frac{1}{5}$

55. $\frac{9}{16}$ **57.–59.** $\frac{1}{2} = \frac{2}{4} = \frac{4}{8} = \frac{8}{16}$ $\frac{3}{2} = \frac{6}{4} = \frac{12}{8} = \frac{24}{16}$ **61.** $\frac{106}{115}$ **63.** $\frac{1}{3}$ **65.** $\frac{8}{25}$ **67.** $\frac{1}{3}$ **69.** $\frac{37}{70}$

$\frac{1}{4} = \frac{2}{8} = \frac{4}{16}$ $\frac{5}{4} = \frac{10}{8} = \frac{20}{16}$

71. $\frac{1}{3}$ **73.** $\frac{1}{8}$ **75.** 3 **77.** 45 **79.** 25 **81.** $2^2 \cdot 5 \cdot 3$ **83.** $2^2 \cdot 5 \cdot 3$ **85.** 9 **87.** 25 **89.** 12 **91.** 18 **93.** 42 **95.** 53

Problem Set 2.3

1. $\frac{8}{15}$ **3.** $\frac{7}{8}$ **5.** 1 **7.** $\frac{27}{4}$ **9.** 1 **11.** $\frac{1}{24}$ **13.** $\frac{24}{125}$ **15.** $\frac{105}{8}$

17.

First Number x	Second Number y	Their Product xy
$\frac{1}{2}$	$\frac{2}{3}$	$\frac{1}{3}$
$\frac{2}{3}$	$\frac{3}{4}$	$\frac{1}{2}$
$\frac{3}{4}$	$\frac{4}{5}$	$\frac{3}{5}$
$\frac{5}{a}$	$\frac{a}{6}$	$\frac{5}{6}$

19.

First Number x	Second Number y	Their Product xy
$\frac{1}{2}$	30	15
$\frac{1}{5}$	30	6
$\frac{1}{6}$	30	5
$\frac{1}{15}$	30	2

21. $\frac{3}{5}$ **23.** 9 **25.** 1 **27.** 8 **29.** $\frac{1}{15}$ **31.** $\frac{4}{9}$ **33.** $\frac{9}{16}$ **35.** $\frac{1}{4}$ **37.** $\frac{8}{27}$ **39.** $\frac{1}{2}$ **41.** $\frac{9}{100}$ **43.** 3 **45.** 24

47. 4 **49.** 9 **51.** $\frac{3}{10}$; numerator should be 3, not 4.

53. a.

Number x	Square x^2
1	1
2	4
3	9
4	16
5	25
6	36
7	49
8	64

b. Either *larger* or *greater* will work.   **55.** 133 in²

57. $\frac{4}{9}$ ft² **59.** 3 yd² **61.** 138 in² **63. a.** $\frac{5}{4}$ in. **b.** $\frac{7}{10}$ in. **c.** 3 in. **65.** 126,500 ft³ **67.** About 8 million **69.** 846

71. Canada: > 1,668,000 Venezuela: 1,251,000 Iraq: < 834,000 **73.** $\frac{1}{27}$ **75.** $\frac{8}{27}$ **77.** 2 **79.** 3 **81.** 2 **83.** 5 **85.** 3

87. $\frac{4}{3}$ **89.** 3 **91.** $\frac{1}{7}$ **93.** 100 **95.** 9 **97.** 18 **99.** 8

Problem Set 2.4

1. $\frac{15}{4}$ **3.** $\frac{4}{3}$ **5.** 9 **7.** 200 **9.** $\frac{3}{8}$ **11.** 1 **13.** $\frac{49}{64}$ **15.** $\frac{3}{4}$ **17.** $\frac{15}{16}$ **19.** $\frac{1}{6}$ **21.** 6 **23.** $\frac{5}{18}$ **25.** $\frac{9}{2}$

27. $\frac{2}{9}$ **29.** 9 **31.** $\frac{4}{5}$ **33.** $\frac{15}{22}$ **35.** 40 **37.** $\frac{7}{10}$ **39.** 13 **41.** 12 **43.** 186 **45.** 646 **47.** $\frac{3}{5}$ **49.** 40

51. $3 \cdot 5 = 15$; $3 \div \frac{1}{5} = 3 \cdot \frac{5}{1} = 15$ **53.** 490 feet **55.** 14 blankets **57.** 6 **59.** 28 cartons **61.** 20 lots

63. $\frac{3}{6}$ **65.** $\frac{9}{6}$ **67.** $\frac{4}{12}$ **69.** $\frac{8}{12}$ **71.** $\frac{14}{30}$ **73.** $\frac{18}{30}$ **75.** $\frac{12}{24}$ **77.** $\frac{4}{24}$ **79.** $\frac{15}{36}$ **81.** $\frac{9}{36}$

83.

Number	Rounded to the Nearest		
	Ten	Hundred	Thousand
74	70	100	0
747	750	700	1,000
474	470	500	0

85. b

Problem Set 2.5

1. $\frac{2}{3}$ **3.** $\frac{1}{4}$ **5.** $\frac{1}{2}$ **7.** $\frac{1}{3}$ **9.** $\frac{3}{2}$ **11.** $\frac{x+6}{2}$ **13.** $\frac{4}{5}$ **15.** $\frac{10}{3}$

17.

First Number a	Second Number b	The Sum of a and b $a + b$
$\frac{1}{2}$	$\frac{1}{3}$	$\frac{5}{6}$
$\frac{1}{3}$	$\frac{1}{4}$	$\frac{7}{12}$
$\frac{1}{4}$	$\frac{1}{5}$	$\frac{9}{20}$
$\frac{1}{5}$	$\frac{1}{6}$	$\frac{11}{30}$

19.

First Number a	Second Number b	The Sum of a and b $a + b$
$\frac{1}{12}$	$\frac{1}{2}$	$\frac{7}{12}$
$\frac{1}{12}$	$\frac{1}{3}$	$\frac{5}{12}$
$\frac{1}{12}$	$\frac{1}{4}$	$\frac{4}{12} = \frac{1}{3}$
$\frac{1}{12}$	$\frac{1}{6}$	$\frac{3}{12} = \frac{1}{4}$

21. $\frac{7}{9}$ **23.** $\frac{7}{3}$ **25.** $\frac{7}{4}$ **27.** $\frac{7}{6}$ **29.** $\frac{9}{20}$ **31.** $\frac{7}{10}$ **33.** $\frac{19}{24}$ **35.** $\frac{13}{60}$ **37.** $\frac{31}{100}$ **39.** $\frac{67}{144}$ **41.** $\frac{29}{35}$ **43.** $\frac{949}{1,260}$

45. $\frac{13}{420}$ **47.** $\frac{41}{24}$ **49.** $\frac{53}{60}$ **51.** $\frac{5}{4}$ **53.** $\frac{88}{9}$ **55.** $\frac{3}{4}$ **57.** $\frac{1}{4}$ **59.** 19   **61.** 3   **63.** $\frac{160}{63}$ **65.** $\frac{5}{8}$ **67.** $\frac{7}{20}$ inch

69. $\frac{9}{2}$ pints   **71.** $\frac{61}{400}$ **73.** $\frac{5}{3}$ hours   **75.** $\frac{1}{3}$ **77.** 10 lots   **79.** $\frac{3}{2}$ in.   **81.** $\frac{9}{5}$ ft   **83.** $\frac{7}{3}$ **85.** 3   **87.** 59   **89.** $\frac{16}{8}$

91. $\frac{8}{8}$ **93.** $\frac{11}{4}$ **95.** $\frac{17}{8}$ **97.** $\frac{9}{8}$ **99.** 2 R 3   **101.** 8 R 16   **103.** $\frac{9}{10}$ **105.** 8   **107.** 3   **109.** 2   **111.** $\frac{2}{7}$ **113.** $\frac{15}{22}$

Problem Set 2.6

1. $\frac{14}{3}$ **3.** $\frac{21}{4}$ **5.** $\frac{13}{8}$ **7.** $\frac{47}{3}$ **9.** $\frac{104}{21}$ **11.** $\frac{427}{33}$ **13.** $1\frac{1}{8}$ **15.** $4\frac{3}{4}$ **17.** $4\frac{5}{6}$ **19.** $3\frac{1}{4}$ **21.** $4\frac{1}{27}$ **23.** $28\frac{8}{15}$

25. $\frac{11}{4}$ **27.** $\frac{37}{8}$ **29.** $\frac{14}{5}$ **31.** $\frac{9}{40}$ **33.** $\frac{3}{8}$ **35.** $\frac{32}{35}$ **37.** $\frac{4}{7}$ **39.** $\frac{4}{5}$ **41.** 9   **43.** 98

Problem Set 2.7

1. $5\frac{1}{10}$ **3.** $13\frac{2}{3}$ **5.** $6\frac{93}{100}$ **7.** $5\frac{5}{6}$ **9.** $9\frac{3}{4}$ **11.** $3\frac{1}{5}$ **13.** $12\frac{1}{2}$ **15.** $9\frac{9}{20}$ **17.** $\frac{32}{45}$ **19.** $1\frac{2}{3}$ **21.** 4   **23.** $4\frac{3}{10}$ **25.** $\frac{1}{10}$

27. $3\frac{1}{5}$ **29.** $2\frac{1}{8}$ **31.** $7\frac{1}{2}$ **33.** $\frac{11}{13}$ **35.** $5\frac{1}{2}$ cups   **37.** $1\frac{1}{3}$ **39.** $2,687\frac{1}{5}$ cents   **41.** $163\frac{3}{4}$ mi   **43.** $6\frac{758}{1,207}$ shares

45. $\$2,516\frac{2}{3}$ **47.** $182\frac{9}{16}$ ft²   **49.** $3\frac{7}{16}$ mi²

51. Can 1 contains $157\frac{1}{2}$ calories, whereas Can 2 contains $87\frac{1}{2}$ calories. Can 1 contains 70 more calories than Can 2.

53. Can 1 contains 1,960 milligrams of sodium, whereas Can 2 contains 1,050 milligrams of sodium. Can 1 contains 910 more milligrams of sodium than Can 2.

55. a. $\frac{10}{15}$ **b.** $\frac{3}{15}$ **c.** $\frac{9}{15}$ **d.** $\frac{5}{15}$ **57. a.** $\frac{5}{20}$ **b.** $\frac{12}{20}$ **c.** $\frac{18}{20}$ **d.** $\frac{2}{20}$ **59.** $\frac{13}{15}$ **61.** $\frac{14}{9} = 1\frac{5}{9}$ **63.** $\frac{3}{5}$ **65.** $\frac{3}{14}$ **67.** $2\frac{1}{4}$

69. $3\frac{1}{16}$

Problem Set 2.8

1. $5\frac{4}{5}$ **3.** $12\frac{2}{5}$ **5.** $3\frac{4}{9}$ **7.** 12   **9.** $1\frac{3}{8}$ **11.** $14\frac{1}{6}$ **13.** $4\frac{1}{12}$ **15.** $2\frac{1}{12}$ **17.** $26\frac{7}{12}$ **19.** 12   **21.** $2\frac{1}{2}$ **23.** $8\frac{6}{7}$ **25.** $3\frac{3}{8}$

27. $10\frac{4}{15}$ **29.** $2\frac{1}{15}$ **31.** $21\frac{17}{20}$ **33.** 9   **35.** $18\frac{1}{10}$ **37.** 14   **39.** 17   **41.** $24\frac{1}{24}$ **43.** $27\frac{6}{7}$ **45.** $6\frac{1}{4}$ **47.** $9\frac{7}{10}$ **49.** $5\frac{1}{2}$

51. $\frac{2}{3}$ **53.** $1\frac{11}{12}$ **55.** $3\frac{11}{12}$ **57.** $5\frac{19}{20}$ **59.** $5\frac{1}{2}$ **61.** $\frac{13}{24}$ **63.** $3\frac{1}{2}$ **65.** $\$2\frac{1}{2}$ **67.** \$250   **69.** \$300

71. a. NFL: $P = 306\frac{2}{3}$ yd; Canadian: $P = 350$ yd; Arena: $P = 156\frac{2}{3}$ yd

b. NFL: $A = 5,333\frac{1}{3}$ sq yd; Canadian: $A = 7,150$ sq yd; Arena: $A = 1,416\frac{2}{3}$ sq yd

73. $31\frac{1}{6}$ in.   **75.** $4\frac{63}{64}$ **77.** 2   **79.** $\frac{11}{8} = 1\frac{3}{8}$ **81.** $3\frac{5}{8}$ **83.** 17   **85.** 14   **87.** 104   **89.** 96   **91.** 40   **93.** $3\frac{1}{2}$

95. $5\frac{29}{40}$ **97.** $34\frac{4}{5}$

Problem Set 2.9

1. 7   **3.** 7   **5.** 2   **7.** 35   **9.** $\frac{7}{8}$ **11.** $8\frac{1}{3}$ **13.** $\frac{11}{36}$ **15.** $3\frac{2}{3}$ **17.** $6\frac{3}{8}$ **19.** $4\frac{5}{12}$ **21.** $\frac{8}{9}$ **23.** $\frac{1}{2}$ **25.** $1\frac{1}{10}$ **27.** 5

29. $\frac{3}{5}$ **31.** $\frac{7}{11}$ **33.** 5   **35.** $\frac{17}{28}$ **37.** $1\frac{7}{16}$ **39.** $\frac{13}{22}$ **41.** $\frac{5}{22}$ **43.** $\frac{15}{16}$ **45.** $1\frac{5}{17}$ **47.** $\frac{3}{29}$ **49.** $1\frac{34}{67}$ **51.** $\frac{346}{441}$

53. $5\frac{2}{5}$ **55.** 8   **57.** 5 miles²   **59.** $115\frac{2}{3}$ yd   **61.** $\frac{2}{3}$ **63.** $\frac{1}{6}$ **65.** $\frac{1}{7}$ **67.** $9\frac{7}{9}$

Chapter 2 Review

1. $\frac{3}{4}$ **3.** $\frac{11}{7}$ **5.** 1   **7.** $\frac{8}{21}$ **9.** $\frac{2}{3}$ **11.** $\frac{3}{8}$ **13.** $\frac{1}{2}$ **15.** $\frac{7}{2}$ **17.** $\frac{1}{36}$ **19.** $\frac{29}{8}$ **21.** $3\frac{3}{4}$ **23.** $\frac{8}{13}$ **25.** 12

27. $17\frac{11}{12}$ **29.** $11\frac{2}{3}$ **31.** 5   **33.** $\frac{1}{2}$ **35.** 20 items   **37.** 9   **39.** $1\frac{7}{8}$ cups   **41.** $10\frac{1}{2}$ tablespoons

43. Area = $25\frac{1}{5}$ ft²; perimeter = 28 ft

Chapter 2 Cumulative Review

1. 6,317   **3.** $\frac{81}{169}$ **5.** $\frac{1}{4}$ **7.** $\frac{4}{11}$ **9.** 24   **11.** $4\frac{8}{21}$ **13.** 625   **15.** $\frac{11}{12}$ **17.** $\frac{4}{9}$ **19.** 9   **21.** 2,274   **23.** $\frac{81}{125}$

25. 1090   **27.** $\frac{9x}{39x}$ **29.** $\frac{46}{45} = 1\frac{1}{45}$ **31.** 1,561,471 babies

Chapter 2 Test

1. $\frac{2}{5}$ **2.** $\frac{3}{8}$ **3.** $\frac{23}{5}$ **4.** $\frac{7}{10}$ **5.** $\frac{47}{36}$ **6.** $9\frac{17}{24}$ **7.** $3\frac{2}{3}$ **8.** $5\frac{2}{5}$ **9.** $\frac{1}{3}$ **10.** $\frac{1}{9}$ **11.** $\frac{5}{16}$ **12.** $\frac{5}{6}$ **13.** $2\frac{1}{2}$

14. $\frac{1}{4}$ **15.** $\frac{3}{8}$ **16.** $4\frac{1}{2}$ **17.** $6\frac{2}{3}$ **18.** $2\frac{13}{18}$ **19.** $16\frac{3}{4}$ **20.** $9\frac{11}{12}$ **21.** $\frac{1}{2}$ **22.** $1\frac{2}{3}$ **23.** $12\frac{3}{8}$ **24.** $16\frac{3}{4}$ **25.** $\frac{1}{6}$

26. $3\frac{3}{4}$ **27.** $\frac{1}{10}$ **28.** $\frac{7}{10}$ **29.** $27\frac{1}{2}$ in.   **30.** Perimeter = $23\frac{1}{3}$ ft   **31.** $8\frac{1}{5}$ in

Chapter 2 Glimpse of Algebra

1. $\frac{x+3}{4}$ **3.** $\frac{x+2}{5}$ **5.** $\frac{7x}{8}$ **7.** $\frac{2}{x}$ **9.** $\frac{3x+2}{6}$ **11.** $\frac{2x-1}{4}$ **13.** $\frac{12+3x}{4x}$ **15.** $\frac{4x-5}{5x}$ **17.** $\frac{7x+24}{12x}$ **19.** $\frac{3x+4}{4x}$

21. $\frac{12+x}{4}$ **23.** $\frac{10-x}{2}$ **25.** $\frac{28-a}{7}$ **27.** $\frac{5+2a}{5}$ **29.** $\frac{8x+3}{x}$ **31.** $\frac{2x-5}{x}$ **33.** $\frac{4x+3}{4}$ **35.** $\frac{11x}{9}$ **37.** $\frac{3a}{7}$ **39.** $\frac{5x}{4}$

Chapter 3

Pretest for Chapter 3

1. Four and thirteen thousandths   **2.** $12\frac{9}{100}$ **3.** 0.34   **4.** 0.42   **5.** 0.04, 0.4, 0.41, 0.45, 0.5, 0.51   **6.** $\frac{17}{20}$ **7.** 15.41

8. 5.21   **9.** 9.72   **10.** 567.8   **11.** 4.12   **12.** 8.7

Getting Ready for Chapter 3

1. 407,927   **2.** 25,576   **3.** 436   **4.** 663   **5.** 132,980   **6.** 728   **7.** 12,768   **8.** 96   **9.** 1,848   **10.** 298 R 14   **11.** 74

12. $\frac{1}{16}$ **13.** $\frac{3}{10}$ **14.** $1\frac{41}{64}$ **15.** 9,200   **16.** $\frac{19}{50}$ **17.** $2^4 \cdot 3$ **18.** $2^2 \cdot 3^2 \cdot 5$

Problem Set 3.1

1. Three tenths   **3.** Fifteen thousandths   **5.** Three and four tenths   **7.** Fifty-two and seven tenths   **9.** $405\frac{36}{100}$ **11.** $9\frac{9}{1,000}$

13. $1\frac{234}{1,000}$ **15.** $\frac{305}{100,000}$ **17.** Tens   **19.** Tenths   **21.** Hundred thousandths   **23.** Ones   **25.** Hundreds   **27.** 0.55   **29.** 6.9

31. 11.11   **33.** 100.02   **35.** 3,000.003   **37. a.** <   **b.** >   **39.** 0.002   0.005   0.02   0.025   0.05   0.052   **41.** 7.451,   7.54

43. $\frac{1}{4}$ **45.** $\frac{1}{8}$ **47.** $\frac{5}{8}$ **49.** $\frac{7}{8}$ **51.** 9.99   **53.** 10.05   **55.** 0.05   **57.** 0.01

	Number	Whole Number	Rounded to the Nearest Tenth	Hundredth	Thousandth
59.	47.5479	48	47.5	47.55	47.548
61.	0.8175	1	0.8	0.82	0.818
63.	0.1562	0	0.2	0.16	0.156
65.	2,789.3241	2,789	2,789.3	2,789.32	2,789.324
67.	99.9999	100	100.0	100.00	100.000

69. Hundredths   **71.**

PRICE OF 1 GALLON OF REGULAR GASOLINE	
Date	Price (Dollars)
5/5/08	3.903
5/12/08	3.919
5/19/08	3.952
5/26/08	4.099

73. Three and eleven hundredths; two and five tenths

75. Fifteen hundredths   **77.** $6\frac{31}{100}$ **79.** $6\frac{23}{50}$

81. $18\frac{123}{1000}$ **83.** $\frac{3}{16} < \frac{3}{10} < \frac{3}{8} < \frac{3}{4}$ **85.** <   **87.** >

Problem Set 3.2

1. 6.19 **3.** 1.13 **5.** 6.29 **7.** 9.042 **9.** 8.021 **11.** 11.7843 **13.** 24.343 **15.** 24.111 **17.** 258.5414 **19.** 666.66
21. 11.11 **23.** 3.57 **25.** 4.22 **27.** 120.41 **29.** 44.933 **31.** 7.673 **33.** 530.865 **35.** 27.89 **37.** 35.64
39. 411.438 **41.** 6 **43.** 1 **45.** 3.1 **47.** 5.9 **49.** 3.272 **51.** 4.001 **53.** 1.47 seconds **55.** $1,571.10 **57.** 4.5 in.
59. $5.43 **61.** 6.42 sec **63.** 2 in. **65.** $3.25; three $1 bills and a quarter **67.** 3.25 **69.** $\frac{3}{100}$ **71.** $\frac{51}{10,000}$ **73.** $1\frac{1}{2}$
75. 1,400 **77.** $\frac{3}{20}$ **79.** $\frac{147}{1,000}$ **81.** 132,980 **83.** 2,115 **85.** 12 **87.** 16 **89.** 20 **91.** 68

Problem Set 3.3

1. 0.28 **3.** 0.028 **5.** 0.0027 **7.** 0.78 **9.** 0.792 **11.** 0.0156 **13.** 24.29821 **15.** 0.03 **17.** 187.85 **19.** 0.002
21. 27.96 **23.** 0.43 **25.** 49,940 **27.** 9,876,540 **29.** 1.89 **31.** 0.0025 **33.** 5.1106 **35.** 7.3485 **37.** 4.4
39. 2.074 **41.** 3.58 **43.** 187.4 **45.** 116.64 **47.** 20.75 **49.** 371.34 meters **51.** 0.126
53. Moves it two places to the right **55.** $1,381.38 **57. a.** 83.21 mm **b.** 551.27 mm² **c.** 1,102.53 mm³ **59.** 1.18 in²
61. $C = 25.12$ in.; $A = 50.24$ in² **63.** $C = 24,492$ mi **65.** 168 in. **67.** 100.48 ft³ **69.** 50.24 ft³ **71.** 1,879 **73.** 1,516 R 4
75. 298 **77.** 34.8 **79.** 49.896
81. 825 **83.** $\frac{3}{10} < \frac{2}{5} < \frac{1}{2} < \frac{4}{5}$ **85.** $\frac{3}{2} < 1\frac{2}{3} < 1\frac{5}{6} < \frac{25}{12}$ **87.** No

Problem Set 3.4

1. 19.7 **3.** 6.2 **5.** 5.2 **7.** 11.04 **9.** 4.8 **11.** 9.7 **13.** 2.63 **15.** 4.24 **17.** 2.55 **19.** 1.35 **21.** 6.5 **23.** 9.9
25. 0.05 **27.** 89 **29.** 2.2 **31.** 1.35 **33.** 16.97 **35.** 0.25 **37.** 2.71 **39.** 11.69 **41.** 3.98 **43.** 5.98 **45.** 0.77778
47. 307.20607 **49.** 0.70945 **51.** 3,472 square miles **53.** 7.5 mi **55.** $6.65/hr **57.** 22.4 mi **59.** 5 hr **61.** 7 min
63.

Rank	Name	Number of Events	Total Earnings	Average per Event
1.	Lorena Ochoa	25	$1,838,616	$73,545
2.	Annika Sorenstam	13	$1,295,585	$99,660
3.	Paula Creamer	24	$891,804	$37,159
4.	Seon Hwa Lee	28	$656,313	$23,440
5.	Jeong Jang	27	$642,320	$23,790

65. 2.73 **67.** 0.13 **69.** $\frac{3}{4}$ **71.** $\frac{2}{3}$ **73.** $\frac{3}{8}$ **75.** $\frac{19}{50}$ **77.** $\frac{6}{10}$ **79.** $\frac{60}{100}$ **81.** $\frac{12}{15}$ **83.** $\frac{60}{15}$ **85.** $\frac{18}{15}$ **87.** 0.75
89. 0.875 **91.** 19 **93.** 3

Problem Set 3.5

1. 0.125 **3.** 0.625

5.

Fraction	$\frac{1}{4}$	$\frac{2}{4}$	$\frac{3}{4}$	$\frac{4}{4}$
Decimal	0.25	0.5	0.75	1

7.

Fraction	$\frac{1}{6}$	$\frac{2}{6}$	$\frac{3}{6}$	$\frac{4}{6}$	$\frac{5}{6}$	$\frac{6}{6}$
Decimal	$0.1\overline{6}$	$0.\overline{3}$	0.5	$0.\overline{6}$	$0.8\overline{3}$	1

9. 0.48 **11.** 0.4375 **13.** 0.92

15. 0.27 **17.** 0.09 **19.** 0.28

21.

Decimal	0.125	0.250	0.375	0.500	0.625	0.750	0.875
Fraction	$\frac{1}{8}$	$\frac{1}{4}$	$\frac{3}{8}$	$\frac{1}{2}$	$\frac{5}{8}$	$\frac{3}{4}$	$\frac{7}{8}$

23. $\frac{3}{20}$ **25.** $\frac{2}{25}$ **27.** $\frac{3}{8}$ **29.** $5\frac{3}{5}$ **31.** $5\frac{3}{50}$ **33.** $1\frac{11}{50}$

35. 2.4 **37.** 3.98 **39.** 3.02 **41.** 0.3 **43.** 0.072 **45.** 0.8 **47.** 1 **49.** 0.25 **51.** $4\frac{4}{10} = 4\frac{2}{5}$ **53.** $16.22
55. $52.66 **57.** 9 in.
59.

CHANGE IN STOCK PRICE		
Date	Gain ($)	As a Decimal ($) (To the Nearest hundredth)
Monday, March 6, 2000	$\frac{3}{4}$	0.75
Tuesday, March 7, 2000	$\frac{9}{16}$	0.56
Wednesday, March 8, 2000	$\frac{3}{32}$	0.09
Thursday, March 9, 2000	$\frac{7}{32}$	0.22
Friday, March 10, 2000	$\frac{1}{16}$	0.06

61. 104.625 calories **63.** $10.38

65. Yes **67.** 33.49 m³ **69.** 226.1 ft³ **71.** 22.28 in² **73.** 852 **75.** 20,675

Chapter 3 Review

1. Thousandths **3.** 37.0042 **5.** 98.77 **7.** 5.816 **9.** 36.381 **11.** 7.65 **13.** 7.09 **15.** 5.729 **17.** 1.008 **19.** 34.1
21. 4.16 **23.** 0.875 **25.** $\frac{141}{200}$ **27.** $14\frac{1}{8}$ **29.** 2.42 **31.** 79 **33.** 1.224 **35.** 0.4

Chapter 3 Cumulative Review

1. 4,079 **3.** 16,072 **5.** 6.22 **7.** 55.728 **9.** $\frac{1}{2}$ **11.** $15\frac{3}{4}$ **13.** 20 **15.** 9 **17.** $3(13 + 4) = 51$ **19.** False **21.** $\frac{7}{9}$
23. 0.94 **25.** $14\frac{7}{8}$ **27.** $8\frac{1}{4}$ cups **29.** 399.5 yds

Chapter 3 Test

1. Five and fifty-three thousandths **2.** Thousandths **3.** 17.0406 **4.** 46.75 **5.** 8.18 **6.** 6.056 **7.** 35.568 **8.** 8.72 **9.** 11.36
10. 8.907 **11.** 1.568 **12.** 0.24 **13.** 0.92 **14.** $\frac{14}{25}$ **15.** 14.664 **16.** 4.69 **17.** 17.129 **18.** 0.26 **19.** 6.48 **20.** 10.784
21. $11.53 **22.** $24.47 **23.** $6.55 **24.** $285.83

A Glimpse of Algebra

1. $6x^2 + 9x + 8$ **3.** $5a + 8$ **5.** $9x + 6$ **7.** $5y^3 + 5y^2 + 9y + 7$ **9.** $6x^2 + 4x + 5$ **11.** $3a^2 + 7a + 6$ **13.** $5x^3 + 7x^2 + 16x + 13$

Chapter 4

Pretest for Chapter 4

1. $\frac{3}{5}$ **2.** $\frac{8}{3}$ **3.** $\frac{5}{7}$ **4.** $\frac{16}{23}$ **5.** 62 mi/hr **6.** 15¢ **7.** 10 **8.** 5 **9.** $\frac{14}{3}$ **10.** 12 **11.** 720 mi **12.** $54.75 **13.** 8
14. 50

Getting Ready for Chapter 4

1. $\frac{1}{3}$ **2.** 2 **3.** 0.25 **4.** 0.125 **5.** 65 **6.** 1.2 **7.** 297.5 **8.** 4 **9.** 8 **10.** 12 **11.** 62.5 **12.** 0.695 **13.** 3.98
14. $\frac{3}{2}$ **15.** 8.7 **16.** 6.5

Problem Set 4.1

1. $\frac{4}{3}$ **3.** $\frac{16}{3}$ **5.** $\frac{2}{5}$ **7.** $\frac{1}{2}$ **9.** $\frac{3}{1}$ **11.** $\frac{7}{6}$ **13.** $\frac{7}{5}$ **15.** $\frac{5}{7}$ **17.** $\frac{8}{5}$ **19.** $\frac{1}{3}$ **21.** $\frac{1}{10}$ **23.** $\frac{3}{25}$ **25.** a. $\frac{1}{2}$ b. $\frac{1}{3}$ c. $\frac{2}{3}$
27. $\frac{11}{14}$ **29.** $\frac{20 \text{ mg}}{1 \text{ mL}}$ **31.** $\frac{75 \text{ mg}}{2 \text{ mL}}$ **33.** a. $\frac{13}{8}$ b. $\frac{1}{4}$ c. $\frac{3}{8}$ d. $\frac{13}{3}$ **35.** a. $\frac{6}{1}$ b. $\frac{5}{1}$ c. $\frac{4}{1}$ d. $\frac{3}{1}$ e. $\frac{4}{1}$ **37.** a. $\frac{44}{39}$ b. $\frac{1}{1}$ c. $\frac{6}{7}$
39. 18 **41.** 62.5 **43.** 0.615 **45.** 176 **47.** 184 **49.** 0.087 **51.** 0.048 **53.** $\frac{5}{8}$ **55.** $\frac{11}{2} = 5\frac{1}{2}$ **57.** $\frac{5}{14}$ **59.** 96

Problem Set 4.2

1. 55 mi/hr **3.** 84 km/hr **5.** 0.2 gal/sec **7.** 14 L/min **9.** 19 mi/gal **11.** $4.\overline{3}$ mi/L **13.** The Midwest **15.** 480 mL/hr
17. 4.95¢ per oz **19.** 34.7¢ per diaper, 31.6¢ per diaper; Happy Baby **21.** $1.00 = 0.646 Euros **23.** $1.00 = 0.509 pounds
25. The 18 oz box is the best buy at $0.277 per ounce. **27.** 54.03 mi/hr **29.** 9.3 mi/gal **31.** $64 **33.** $16,000 **35.** $n = 6$
37. $n = 4$ **39.** $n = 4$ **41.** $n = 65$ **43.** $\frac{7}{8}$ **45.** $\frac{1}{40}$ **47.** $\frac{1}{60}$ **49.** $\frac{11}{6} = 1\frac{5}{6}$ **51.** The 100 ounce size is the better value.

Problem Set 4.3

1. 35 **3.** 18 **5.** 14 **7.** n **9.** y **11.** $n = 2$ **13.** $x = 7$ **15.** $y = 7$ **17.** $n = 8$ **19.** $a = 8$ **21.** $x = 2$ **23.** $y = 1$
25. $a = 6$ **27.** $n = 5$ **29.** $x = 3$ **31.** $n = 7$ **33.** $y = 1$ **35.** $y = 9$ **37.** $n = 3\frac{1}{2}$ **39.** $x = 3\frac{1}{2}$ **41.** $a = 2\frac{2}{5}$ **43.** $y = \frac{4}{7}$
45. $y = \frac{10}{13}$ **47.** $x = 2\frac{1}{2}$ **49.** $n = 1\frac{1}{2}$ **51.** $\frac{3}{4}$ **53.** 1.2 **55.** 6.5 **57.** 0.75 **59.** 5.5 **61.** 0.03 **63.** 0.375 **65.** $\frac{17}{50}$
67. $2\frac{2}{5}$ **69.** $1\frac{3}{4}$ **71.** $\frac{7}{8}$

Problem Set 4.4

1. Means: 3, 5; extremes: 1, 15; products: 15 **3.** Means: 25, 2; extremes: 10, 5; products: 50 **5.** Means: $\frac{1}{2}$, 4; extremes: $\frac{1}{3}$, 6; products: 2
7. Means: 5, 1; extremes: 0.5, 10; products: 5 **9.** 10 **11.** $\frac{12}{5}$ **13.** $\frac{3}{2}$ **15.** $\frac{10}{9}$ **17.** 7 **19.** 14 **21.** 18 **23.** 6 **25.** 40
27. 50 **29.** 108 **31.** 3 **33.** $\frac{2}{5}$ **35.** $\frac{1}{4}$ **37.** 108 **39.** 65 **41.** 41 **43.** 108 **45.** 20 **47.** 297.5 **49.** 450
51. 5 **53.** Tens **55.** 26.516 **57.** 0.39

Section 4.5

1. 329 mi **3.** 360 points **5.** 15 pt **7.** 427.5 mi **9.** 900 eggs **11.** 35.5 mg/pill **13.** 5.5 mL **15.** 2.5 tablets **17.** 435 in. = 36.25 ft **19.** $313.50 **21.** 265 g **23.** 91.3 L **25.** 60,113 people **27.** 78 teachers **29.** 850 meters **31.** 15 mL **33.** 900 mg/day **35.** 2 **37.** 147 **39.** 20 **41.** 147 **43.** 1.35 **45.** 3.816 **47.** 4 **49.** 160 **51.** 183.79

Section 4.6

1. 9 **3.** 14 **5.** 12 **7.** 25 **9.** 32

11.   **13.**   **15.** **17.**

19. 45 in. **21.** 960 pixels **23.** 1,440 pixels **25.** 57 ft **27.** 177 ft **29.** 13.99 **31.** 40.999 **33.** 0.10545 **35.** 18

37. $4\frac{1}{6}$ **39.** 4 **41. a.** $\frac{1}{2}$ **b.** 18 rectangles should be shaded. **c.** $\frac{1}{3}$

Chapter 4 Review

1. $\frac{3}{10}$ **3.** $\frac{3}{4}$ **5.** $\frac{7}{5}$ **7.** $\frac{1}{2}$ **9.** $\frac{1}{3}$ **11.** $\frac{9}{2}$ **13.** $\frac{1}{4}$ **15.** 19 mi/gal

17. 9.05¢/ounce; 8.41¢/ounce; 32-ounce carton is the better buy. **19.** 49 **21.** $\frac{1}{10}$ **23.** 1,500 mL **25.** 5 weeks **27.** 3 tablets

29. 9 **31.** 160

Chapter 4 Cumulative Review

1. 10,522 **3.** 18 **5.** $506\frac{3}{31}$ **7.** 47 **9.** 74 **11.** 310 **13.** 71.48 **15.** 4.5 **17.** 80 **19.** $\frac{25}{42}$ **21.** 25

23. $P = 42$ in.; $A = 72$ in^2 **25.** $x = 16$ cm **27.** $80\frac{9}{16}$ in. **29.** 150 sections **31.** $\frac{1}{3}$

Chapter 4 Test

1. $\frac{4}{3}$ **2.** $\frac{9}{10}$ **3.** $\frac{3}{2}$ **4.** $\frac{3}{10}$ **5.** $\frac{3}{5}$ **6.** $\frac{24}{5}$ **7.** $\frac{6}{25}$ **8.** 23 mi/gal

9. 16-ounce can: 16.2¢/ounce; 12-ounce can: 15.8¢/ounce; 12-ounce can is the better buy **10.** 36 **11.** 8 **12.** 24 hits

13. 135 mi **14.** $h = 16$ **15.** 27 mg **16.** 33.15 mg **17.** 1,053 students

A Glimpse of Algebra

1. $x^2 + 6x + 8$ **3.** $6x^2 + 13x + 6$ **5.** $21x^2 + 34x + 8$ **7.** $x^2 + 7x + 10$ **9.** $2x^2 + 11x + 12$ **11.** $14x^2 + 41x + 15$

13. $9x^2 + 12x + 4$ **15.** $4a^2 + 9a + 5$ **17.** $42y^2 + 111y + 72$ **19.** $8 + 24x + 18x^2$

Chapter 5

Pretest for Chapter 5

1. 0.68 **2.** 0.02 **3.** 0.215 **4.** 39% **5.** 38.6% **6.** 398% **7.** $\frac{33}{100}$ **8.** $\frac{9}{20}$ **9.** $\frac{17}{200}$ **10.** 67% **11.** 80% **12.** 225%

13. 1.2 **14.** 15% **15.** 50

Getting Ready for Chapter 5

1. 141.44 **2.** 225 **3.** 1,477,432 **4.** $\frac{13}{40}$ **5.** 20 **6.** 489 **7.** 9.45 **8.** 0.352 **9.** 0.0362 **10.** 117.2 **11.** 4

12. $\frac{9}{25}$ **13.** $\frac{9}{200}$ **14.** $\frac{65}{2}$ **15.** 0.375 **16.** $0.41\overline{6}$ **17.** 2.5 **18.** 62.5 **19.** 15,300 **20.** 2,976.74

Section 5.1

1. $\frac{20}{100}$ **3.** $\frac{60}{100}$ **5.** $\frac{24}{100}$ **7.** $\frac{65}{100}$ **9.** 0.23 **11.** 0.92 **13.** 0.09 **15.** 0.034 **17.** 0.0634 **19.** 0.009 **21.** 23% **23.** 92%

25. 45% **27.** 3% **29.** 60% **31.** 80% **33.** 27% **35.** 123% **37.** $\frac{3}{5}$ **39.** $\frac{3}{4}$ **41.** $\frac{1}{25}$ **43.** $\frac{53}{200}$ **45.** $\frac{7,187}{10,000}$

47. $\frac{3}{400}$ **49.** $\frac{1}{16}$ **51.** $\frac{1}{3}$ **53.** 50% **55.** 75% **57.** $33\frac{1}{3}$% **59.** 80% **61.** 87.5% **63.** 14% **65.** 325% **67.** 150%

69. 48.8% **71. a.** 0.506 **b.** 0.527 **c.** 0.537 **73. a.** $\frac{27}{50}, \frac{7}{25}, \frac{3}{20}, \frac{3}{100}$ **b.** 0.54, 0.28, 0.15, 0.03 **c.** About two times as likely

75. 78.4% **77.** 11.8% **79.** 72.2% **81.** 18.5 **83.** 10.875 **85.** 0.5 **87.** 62.5 **89.** 0.5 **91.** 0.125 **93.** 0.625

95. 0.0625 **97.** 0.3125 **99.** 2 **101.** 2 **103.** 2 **105.** 2

Section 5.2
1. 8 **3.** 24 **5.** 20.52 **7.** 7.37 **9.** 50% **11.** 10% **13.** 25% **15.** 75% **17.** 64 **19.** 50 **21.** 925 **23.** 400 **25.** 5.568
27. 120 **29.** 13.72 **31.** 22.5 **33.** 50% **35.** 942.684 **37.** 97.8 **39.** What number is 25% of 350?
41. What percent of 24 is 16? **43.** 46 is 75% of what number? **45.** 4.8% calories from fat; healthy
47. 50% calories from fat; not healthy **49.** 0.80 **51.** 0.76 **53.** 48 **55.** 0.25 **57.** 0.5 **59.** $\frac{5}{8}, \frac{3}{4}, \frac{7}{8}$ **61.** $\frac{1}{4}$ **63.** 0.25
65. 0.75 **67.** 0.125 **69.** 0.375 **71.** $\frac{1}{8}, \frac{1}{4}, \frac{3}{8}, \frac{1}{2}, \frac{5}{8}, \frac{3}{4}, \frac{7}{8}$

Section 5.3
1. 70% **3.** 84% **5.** 45 mL **7.** 18.2 acres for farming; 9.8 acres are not available for farming **9.** $11.20
11. Bush 286; Kerry 251 **13.** 34,266,960 **15.** 3,000 students **17.** 400 students **19.** 1,664 female students **21.** 31.25%
23. 50% **25.** About 19.2 million **27.** 33 **29.** 8,685 **31.** 136 **33.** 0.05 **35.** 15,300 **37.** 0.15 **39.** $\frac{1}{5}$ **41.** $\frac{5}{12}$
43. $\frac{3}{4}$ **45.** $\frac{2}{3}$ **47.** 39.4% **49.** 94 hits **51.** At least 16 hits

Section 5.4
1. $52.50 **3.** $2.70; $47.70 **5.** $150; $156 **7.** 5% **9.** $420.90 **11.** $2,820 **13.** $200 **15.** 14% **17.** 26.9%
19. 62.8 cents or $0.628% **21.** $560 **23.** $11.93 **25.** 4.5% **27.** $3,995 **29.** 1,100 **31.** 75 **33.** 0.16 **35.** 4
37. 396 **39.** 415.8 **41.** $\frac{1}{2}$ **43.** $2\frac{2}{3}$ **45.** $1\frac{1}{2}$ **47.** $4\frac{1}{2}$

Section 5.5
1. $24,610 **3.** $7,020 **5.** $13,200 **7.** 10% **9.** 20% **11.** 21% **13.** $45; $255 **15.** $381.60 **17.** 13.9% **19.** 16%
21. 21.8 in. to 23.2 in. **23.** $46,595.88 **25. a.** 51.9% **b.** 7.8% **27.** 140 **29.** 4 **31.** 152.25 **33.** 3,434.7 **35.** 10,150
37. 10,456.78 **39.** 2,140 **41.** 3,210 **43.** 1 **45.** $\frac{3}{4}$ **47.** $1\frac{5}{12}$ **49.** 6

Section 5.6
1. $2,160 **3.** $665 **5.** $8,560 **7.** $2,160 **9.** $5 **11.** $813.33 **13.** $406.34 **15.** $5,618 **17.** $8,407.56
19. $974.59 **21. a.** $13,468.55 **b.** $13,488.50 **c.** $12,820.37 **d.** $12,833.59 **23.** 30% **25.** $16\frac{2}{3}$% **27.** 108 **29.** 162
31. 8 **33.** 3 **35.** $\frac{1}{2}$ **37.** $\frac{3}{8}$ **39.** $\frac{2}{3}$ **41.** $\frac{3}{2} = 1\frac{1}{2}$ **43.** $\frac{1}{12}$ **45.** $1\frac{1}{4}$ **47.** $\frac{16}{21}$ **49.** $\frac{64}{525}$ **51.** $30.78
53. Percent increase in production cost: *Star Wars* 1 to 2 = 63.6%; *Star Wars* 2 to 3 = 80.6%; *Star Wars* 3 to 4 = 253.8%

Chapter 5 Review
1. 0.35 **3.** 0.05 **5.** 95% **7.** 49.5% **9.** $\frac{3}{4}$ **11.** $1\frac{9}{20}$ **13.** 30% **15.** $66\frac{2}{3}$% **17.** 16.8 **19.** 50% **21.** 80 **23.** 75%
25. $477 **27.** $4.93 **29.** 55.4% increase **31.** $60; 20% off

Chapter 5 Cumulative Review
1. 7,714 **3.** 45,084 **5.** 33 **7.** $\frac{125}{216}$ **9.** 1.322 **11.** $\frac{1}{6}$ **13.** $\frac{23}{24}$ **15.** 42 **17.** 6 **19.** $\frac{1}{4}$ **21.** 648 in² **23.** $\frac{23}{50}$
25. 67 **27.** 20% **29.** 47¢ **31.** 100°C **33.** 345 miles **35.** P = 34 in., A = 72.25 in² **37.** $7 per hour

Chapter 5 Test
1. 0.18 **2.** 0.04 **3.** 0.005 **4.** 45% **5.** 70% **6.** 135% **7.** $\frac{13}{20}$ **8.** $1\frac{23}{50}$ **9.** $\frac{7}{200}$ **10.** 35% **11.** 37.5% **12.** 175%
13. 45 **14.** 45% **15.** 80 **16.** 92% **17.** $960 **18.** $40; 16% off **19.** $220.50 **20.** $100 **21.** $2,520 **22.** $1,064
23. 2,940 people

A Glimpse of Algebra
1. 9 **3.** 180 **5.** 8 **7.** $\frac{8}{15}$ **9.** 20 **11.** 36 **13.** $\frac{17}{13} = 1\frac{4}{13}$ **15.** $\frac{22}{23}$ **17.** 140 **19.** 25 **21.** 3 **23.** 1 **25.** 21

Chapter 6

Pretest for Chapter 6
1. mean: 7, median: 6 **2.** mean: 33, median: 33 **3.** mean: 17.5, median: 15.5 **4.** mode: 6, range: 9 **5.** mode: 1, range: 12
6. mode: none, range: 19 **7.**

Stem	Leaf
0	4
1	7, 6, 9
2	8, 7, 3
3	1

8.

Getting Ready for Chapter 6

1. 2.1   **2.** 4.9   **3.** 7.9   **4.** 14.2   **5.** 5,169   **6.** 7,335   **7.** 347.2   **8.** 182.2   **9.** 23,126   **10.** 17,943   **11.** 216   **12.** 90
13. 86.8   **14.** 36.44   **15.** 2,890.75   **16.** 3,588.6   **17.** 60%   **18.** 25%   **19.** 1.25%   **20.** 1.5%

Problem Set 6.1

1. 3   **3.** 6   **5.** 16,194   **7.** 7.5   **9.** 11   **11.** 50   **13.** 900   **15.** 3.2   **17.** 18   **19.** 87   **21.** 1   **23.** 22   **25.** 2.9
27. 38   **29.** mean = 79.5, median = 83   **31.** Both are $31,000   **33. a.** 78.5   **b.** 76   **c.** 76   **35.** $6,868.83, $6,993
37. $19,985, $19,788   **39.** 62   **41.** $3,190   **43.** $1,530   **45. a.** 3,055   **b.** mean   **47.** 7

Problem Set 6.2

1.

Stem	Leaf
1	9, 8
2	4, 7, 2, 9, 0, 6
3	2, 0, 0, 1, 4

3.

Stem	Leaf
1	6
2	7, 9
3	4, 5, 5
4	6, 8
5	2, 8, 1, 1
6	7
7	2, 6, 3
8	5, 4, 3, 6
9	4, 8

5.

Stem	Leaf
3	9, 5, 4, 6
4	7, 7, 1, 0, 3, 8, 5, 6, 0, 2, 3
5	8, 4, 2, 3, 4, 3, 9, 8, 6, 2, 0
6	0, 1, 3, 0, 4

7.

Interval	Tally	Frequency	Relative Freq.
47–56	I	1	$\frac{1}{20}$ = 0.05
57–66	III	3	$\frac{3}{20}$ = 0.15
67–76	IIII IIII	10	$\frac{10}{20}$ = 0.5
77–86	IIII	5	$\frac{5}{20}$ = 0.25
87–96	I	1	$\frac{1}{20}$ = 0.05

9.

11. a. *(below)*   **b.** $\frac{6}{22}$ = 0.27   **c.** $\frac{12}{22}$ = 0.55   **13. a.** *(below)*   **b.** 21   **c.** $\frac{10}{21}$ = 0.48   **d.** $\frac{9}{21}$ = 0.43   **15. a.** 29   **b.** 36

17. Q1: 18.5   Q2: 23   Q3: 29   **19.** Q1: 1.3   Q2: 2.35   Q3: 3.6   **21.** Q1: 64   Q2: 80.5   Q3: 85   Min: 64   Max: 91
23. $x > 75$ or $x < 75$ or $70 < x < 85$ **25.** 70   **27.** 75   **29.** $x > 85$ or $x < 85$ or $75 < x < 90$ **31.** 75   **33.** 85
35. Q1: 2   Q2: 3.5   Q3: 4.5   Min: 1   Max: 5

Problem Set 6.3

1. a. $\frac{41}{100}$ **b.** $\frac{38}{41}$ **c.** $\frac{31}{50}$ **d.** $\frac{31}{19}$ **3. a.** 78%   **b.** 10%   **c.** 18%   **d.** 22%

5. a. 240 people   **b.** 960 people   **c.** 750 people   **d.** 1,800 people

7.

A 25%
B 40%
C 35%

9.

Bedrooms 37%
Living Room 25%
Bathrooms 8%
Kitchen 17%
Dining Room 13%

11. $\frac{8}{3}$ or $2\frac{2}{3}$ **13.** $\frac{1}{40}$ **15.** $\frac{73}{20}$ or $3\frac{13}{20}$ **17.** $\frac{62}{25}$ or $2\frac{12}{25}$ **19.** $\frac{4}{3}$ or $1\frac{1}{3}$

Problem Set 6.4

1. a. $\frac{1}{2}$ **b.** 0   **c.** 1   **d.** $\frac{1}{2}$ **3. a.** $\frac{1}{36}$ **b.** $\frac{1}{18}$ **c.** $\frac{1}{2}$ **d.** $\frac{5}{6}$ **5. a.** $\frac{1}{13}$ **b.** $\frac{1}{4}$ **c.** $\frac{12}{13}$ **d.** $\frac{10}{13}$ **7. a.** $\frac{1}{8}$ **b.** $\frac{1}{4}$ **c.** $\frac{1}{2}$ **d.** $\frac{1}{8}$
9. a. $\frac{1}{3}$ **b.** $\frac{1}{2}$ **c.** $\frac{1}{2}$ **d.** $\frac{5}{6}$ **11. a.** $\frac{4}{7}$ **b.** $\frac{3}{7}$ **c.** 1   **d.** 0   **13.** 0.8 = $\frac{4}{5}$ **15. a.** $\frac{1}{2}$ **b.** $\frac{5}{36}$ **c.** $\frac{23}{36}$ **d.** $\frac{13}{36}$

Chapter 6 Review

1. a. 12.6 cents/cup **b.** 10 cents/cup **c.** 27 cents/cup   **3.** 2

5.

Stem	Leaf
1	6, 9
2	8, 1, 0
3	2

7.

9.

Interval	Tally	Frequency	Relative Freq.
17–25	ⵌⵑ	6	$\frac{6}{15} = 0.4$
26–34	ⵑⵑ	4	$\frac{4}{15} = 0.267$
35–43	ⵑ	3	$\frac{3}{15} = 0.2$
44–52	ⵑ	1	$\frac{1}{15} = 0.067$
53–61	ⵑ	1	$\frac{1}{15} = 0.067$

11. a. 72% **b.** 54 **c.** 28%   **13.** $\frac{3}{13}$ **15.** $\frac{5}{6}$

17. a. $\frac{33}{95}$ **b.** $\frac{2}{95}$ **c.** $\frac{64}{95}$

Chapter 6 Cumulative Review

1. 42   **3.** $\frac{3}{28}$ **5.** $17\frac{1}{2}$ **7.** 9.648   **9.** $1\frac{5}{7}$ **11.** 7.617   **13.** 4.65   **15.** $\frac{5}{4}$ **17.** 16   **19.** $17   **21.** $24   **23.** 3

25. 7.5 tablespoons   **27.** 204 in. = 17 ft   **29.** $\frac{1}{13}$

Chapter 6 Test

1. a. 6.6 seconds **b.** 11.4 seconds **c.** 10.8 sec   **2. a.** $2,036 **b.** $2,443 **c.** $2,443 **d.** $3,564

3.

Stem	Leaf
0	9, 4, 3, 6
1	9, 6, 2
2	0, 4
3	0

4.

5.

6. What People Like to Barbecue

- Beef **38%**
- Seafood **19%**
- Chicken **23%**
- Vegetables **5%**
- Hot Dogs **6%**
- Pork **8%**
- Fruit **1%**

7. $\frac{1}{4}$ **8.** $\frac{5}{13}$ **9.** $\frac{5}{8}$ **10.** $\frac{3}{8}$ **11.** $\frac{1}{2}$ **12.** $\frac{7}{80}$

Chapter 7

Pretest for Chapter 7

1. 96 in.   **2.** $2\frac{1}{2}$ yd   **3.** 3,200 cm   **4.** 6.1 cm   **5.** 270 ft²   **6.** 3 ft²   **7.** 6 mi²   **8.** 14,000 cm²   **9.** 12 qt   **10.** 9 gal

11. 0.251 L   **12.** 64 oz   **13.** 2.142 g   **14.** 9.84 yd   **15.** 11.37 L   **16.** 40°C   **17.** 66 ft/sec   **18.** $6.86

Getting Ready for Chapter 7

1. $\frac{2}{5}$ **2.** $\frac{4}{1}$ **3.** 192   **4.** 12,500   **5.** 3,267,000   **6.** 3,600   **7.** 9.3375   **8.** 190.4   **9.** $2\frac{2}{3}$ **10.** 0.025   **11.** 450

12. 0.4   **13.** 50   **14.** 3.65   **15.** 750   **16.** 24   **17.** 122   **18.** 38.9   **19.** 0.75   **20.** Perimeter = 120 in., Area = 864 in²

Section 7.1

1. 60 in.   **3.** 120 in.   **5.** 6 ft   **7.** 162 in.   **9.** $2\frac{1}{4}$ ft   **11.** 13,200 ft   **13.** $1\frac{1}{3}$ yd   **15.** 1,800 cm   **17.** 4,800 m   **19.** 50 cm

21. 0.248 km   **23.** 670 mm   **25.** 34.98 m   **27.** 6.34 dm   **29.** 5.3 miles   **31.** 20 yd   **33.** 80 in.   **35.** 244 cm

37. 2,960 chains   **39.** 120,000 μm   **41.** 7,920 ft   **43.** 80.7 ft/sec   **45.** 19.5 mi/hr   **47.** 1,023 mi/hr   **49.** 3,965,280 ft

51. 179,352 in.   **53.** 2.7 mi   **55.** 18,094,560 ft   **57.** 144   **59.** 8   **61.** 1,000   **63.** 3,267,000   **65.** 6   **67.** 0.4   **69.** 405

71. 450   **73.** 45   **75.** 2,200   **77.** 607.5   **79.** $\frac{1}{3}$ **81.** 6   **83.** $3\frac{1}{2}$ **85.** 6   **87.** 6   **89.** $\frac{7}{10}$

91. 10,000 steps $\cdot \dfrac{2.5 \text{ ft}}{1 \text{ step}} \cdot \dfrac{1 \text{ mi}}{5,280 \text{ ft}} = 4.7$ mi

Section 7.2

1. 432 in²   **3.** 2 ft²   **5.** 1,306,800 ft²   **7.** 1,280 acres   **9.** 3 mi²   **11.** 108 ft²   **13.** 1,700 mm²   **15.** 28,000 cm²

17. 0.0012 m²   **19.** 500 m²   **21.** 700 a   **23.** 3.42 ha   **25.** 135 ft³   **27.** 48 fl oz   **29.** 8 qt   **31.** 20 pt   **33.** 480 fl oz

35. 8 gal   **37.** 6 qt   **39.** 9 yd³   **41.** 5,000 mL   **43.** 0.127 L   **45.** 4,000,000 mL   **47.** 14,920 L   **49.** 2,177,280 acres

51. 30 a   **53.** 5,500 bricks   **55.** 16 cups   **57.** 34,560 in³   **59.** 48 glasses   **61.** 20,288,000 acres   **63.** 3,230.93 mi²

65. 23.35 gal   **67.** 21,492 ft³   **69.** 192   **71.** 6,000   **73.** 300,000   **75.** 12.5   **77.** $\frac{5}{8}$ **79.** 9   **81.** $\frac{1}{3}$ **83.** $\frac{17}{144}$

Section 7.3

1. 128 oz   **3.** 4,000 lb   **5.** 12 lb   **7.** 0.9 T   **9.** 32,000 oz   **11.** 56 oz   **13.** 13,000 lb   **15.** 2,000 g   **17.** 40 mg

19. 200,000 cg   **21.** 508 cg   **23.** 4.5 g   **25.** 47.895 cg   **27.** 1.578 g   **29.** 0.42 kg   **31.** 48 g   **33.** 4 g   **35.** 9.72 g

37. 120 g   **39.** 3 L   **41.** 1.5 L   **43.** 0.561 grams   **45. a.** 3 capsules   **b.** 1 capsule   **c.** 2 capsules   **47.** 20.32   **49.** 6.36

51. 50   **53.** 50   **55.** 122   **57.** 248   **59.** 40   **61.** $\frac{9}{50}$ **63.** $\frac{9}{100}$ **65.** $\frac{4}{5}$ **67.** $1\frac{3}{4}$ **69.** 0.75   **71.** 0.85   **73.** 0.6

75. 3.625   **77.** $\frac{1}{8}$ **79.** $6\frac{1}{4}$ **81.** 0.125   **83.** 6.25

Section 7.4

1. 15.24 cm   **3.** 13.12 ft   **5.** 6.56 yd   **7.** 32,200 m   **9.** 5.98 yd²   **11.** 24.7 acres   **13.** 8,195 mL   **15.** 2.12 qt   **17.** 75.8 L

19. 339.6 g   **21.** 33 lb   **23.** 365°F   **25.** 30°C   **27.** 58°C   **29.** 7.5 mL   **31.** 3.94 in.   **33.** 7.62 m   **35.** 46.23 L

37. 17.67 oz   **39.** Answers will vary.   **41.** 91.46 m   **43.** 20.90 m²   **45.** 88.55 km/hr   **47.** 2.03 m   **49.** 38.3°C   **51.** 75

53. 82   **55.** 3.25   **57.** 22   **59.** 41   **61.** 48   **63.** 195   **65.** 3.26   **67.** $90   **69.** mean = 8, range = 6

71. mean = 6, range = 9   **73.** median = 21, range = 14   **75.** median = 40, range = 16   **77.** mode = 14, range = 7

79. a. 73   **b.** 71   **c.** 70   **d.** 23   **81.** 381.8 mg/day; 1.53 mL/day

Section 7.5

1. a. 270 min   **b.** 4.5 hr   **3. a.** 320 min   **b.** 5.33 hr   **5. a.** 390 sec   **b.** 6.5 min   **7. a.** 320 sec   **b.** 5.33 min

9. a. 40 oz   **b.** 2.5 lb   **11. a.** 76 oz   **b.** 4.75 lb   **13. a.** 54 in.   **b.** 4.5 ft   **15. a.** 69 in.   **b.** 5.75 ft   **17. a.** 9 qt   **b.** 2.25 gal

19. 11 hr   **21.** 22 ft 4 in.   **23.** 11 lb   **25.** 5 hr 40 min   **27.** 3 hr 47 min   **29.** 52 min   **31.** 7.5 seconds   **33.** 8:18:18; 9:08:01

35. 00:06:15   **37.** $104   **39.** 10 hr   **41.** $150   **43.** $6   **45.**   **47.** 1.79 sec

CAFFEINE CONTENT IN SOFT DRINKS	
Drink	Caffeine (In Milligrams)
Jolt	100
Mountain Dew	55
Coca-Cola	45
Diet Pepsi	36
7 up	0

Chapter 7 Review

1. 144 in.   **3.** 0.49 m   **5.** 435,600 ft²   **7.** 576 in²   **9.** 6 gal   **11.** 128 oz   **13.** 5,000 g   **15.** 10.16 cm   **17.** 7.42 qt

19. 141.5 g   **21.** 248°F   **23.** 8.52 liters   **25.** 4,383.23 mi²   **27.** 402.5 km   **29.** 600 bricks   **31.** 80 glasses   **33.** 117 mi/hr

35. 322 km/hr   **37.** 13 lb

Chapter 7 Cumulative Review

1. 16,759   **3.** 12   **5.** $490\frac{1}{32}$ **7.** 21   **9.** 38   **11.** 13   **13.** 11.07   **15.** 16.2   **17.** 153   **19.** $6\frac{2}{5}$ **21.** 0.75   **23.** $14\frac{4}{5}$

25. 11.5   **27.** 72 in., 207 in²   **29.** 47   **31.** 1,788   **33.** 42   **35.** 87%

Chapter 7 Test

1. 21 ft   **2.** 0.75 km   **3.** 130,680 ft²   **4.** 3 ft²   **5.** 10,000 mL   **6.** 8.05 km   **7.** 10.6 qt   **8.** 26.7° C   **9.** 2,400 lb   **10.** 9 lb

11. 3.5 ft²   **12.** 450 m²   **13.** 6.5 yd³   **14.** 104°F   **15.** 0.26 gal   **16.** 20,844 in.   **17.** 0.24 ft³   **18.** 70.75 liters   **19.** 74.70 m

20. 7.55 liters   **21.** 6.30 in.   **22.** 8.05 km   **23.** 109.65 cm²   **24.** 17.29 acres   **25.** 4.72 L   **26.** 7.73 kg   **27.** 90 tiles

28. 64 glasses   **29. a.** 330 min   **b.** 5.5 hr   **30.** 11 lb   **31.** 0.51 km

Chapter 8

Pretest for Chapter 8
1. $P = 16$ in., $A = 16$ in^2 **2.** $P = 18$ cm, $A = 18$ cm^2 **3.** $C = 31.4$ in., $A = 78.5$ in^2 **4.** 54 in^2 **5.** 212.5 m^2 **6.** 180 ft^2
7. 258 m^2 **8.** 527.52 ft^2 **9.** 113.04 mm^2 **10.** 9   **11.** $\frac{4}{7}$ **12.** -6 **13.** $h = 13$ m

Getting Ready for Chapter 8
1. 140   **2.** 12.56   **3.** 73.005   **4.** 3.2656   **5.** 26   **6.** 54   **7.** 9   **8.** $1\frac{41}{64} \approx 1.64$ **9.** 8   **10.** $6\frac{3}{8} = 6.375$
11. $\frac{88}{7} \approx 12.57$ **12.** 154   **13.** $\frac{729}{4} = 182.25$ **14.** 30.96   **15.** 5.1   **16.** 114.4   **17.** 452.16   **18.** ≈ 33.49 **19.** $\frac{3,168}{7} \approx 452.57$
20. $\frac{704}{21} \approx 33.52$ **21.** 7,930   **22.** 2,162

Problem Set 8.1
1. 16 yds   **3.** 12.8 ft   **5.** 22 ft   **7.** 10 yds   **9.** 40.4 ft   **11.** 41 in.   **13.** 50 in.   **15.** 40 yds   **17.** 56 in.   **19.** 37.68 yds
21. 69.08 ft   **23.** 18.84 ft   **25. a.** 10.2 in. **b.** 7.68 in.   **27.** 38.94 mm   **29.** 98 in.   **31.** 1040 ft   **33.** Yes, when $w = l = 5$ ft
35. 2 in.   **37.** 9   **39.** 1.64   **41.** 660.19   **43.** 30.96   **45.** 91.5 m   **47. a.** 6.30 in. **b.** 5.09 in.   **49.** 18.28 in.

Problem Set 8.2
1. 9 in^2 **3.** 4.84 yd^2 **5.** 135 yd^2 **7.** 18 yd^2 **9.** 1.73 ft^2 **11.** 18 mi^2 **13.** 24 ft^2 **15.** 58.3 cm^2 **17.** 113.04 in^2
19. 156 cm^2 **21.** 59.13 ft^2 **23.** 37.74 ft^2 **25. a.** 5.4 in^2 **b.** .864 in^2 **27.** 120.70 mm^2 **29.** 588 in^2
31. a. 24 **b.** 40 **c.** 48 **d.** 49 **e.** 62.42 **f.** Circle   **33.** 16 cm   **35.** 24   **37.** 72   **39.** 4.71   **41.** 547   **43.** 200 yd^2
45. 5 mi^2 **47.** 22.28 in^2

Problem Set 8.3
1. 54 m^2 **3.** 88 in^2 **5.** 108 yd^2 **7.** 31.4 in^2 **9.** 149.15 cm^2 **11.** 2,198 ft^2 **13.** 78.5 m^2 **15.** 153.86 ft^2 **17.** 162.78 in^2
19. 87.92 in^2 **21.** 901.18 cm^2 **23.** 100 m^2 **25.** 439.6 in^2 **27. a.** 1.354 in **b.** 93.5 in^2 **c.** yes   **29.** 288 ft^2
31. 60,288,000 mi^2 **33.** 282.6 cm^2 **35.** 27   **37.** $\frac{2}{3}$ **39.** 0.294   **41.** 785   **43.** 1,728 in^3 **45.** 1.5 gal

Problem Set 8.4
1. 27 m^3 **3.** 20.4 in^3 **5.** 20.48 m^3 **7.** 70.65 yd^3 **9.** 14.47 in^3 **11.** 121.52 m^3 **13.** 7.07 m^3 **15.** 66.99 cm^3
17. 10.60 cm^3 **19.** 267.95 ft^3 **21.** 4,186.67 cm^3 **23.** 1,837.85 m^3 **25.** 169.56 in^3 **27.** 0.21 ft^3 **29.** 80 ft^3 **31.** 49.63 cm^3
33. 22.5 m^3 **35.** $\frac{1}{81}$ **37.** $\frac{25}{36}$ **39.** 0.25   **41.** 1.44   **43.** 25   **45.** 100   **47.** $\frac{3}{2}$ **49.** $\frac{8}{3}$ **51.** $\frac{2}{3}$ **53.** $\frac{6}{7}$ **55.** 1
57. $\frac{8}{5}$ **59.** $\frac{1}{5}$ **61.** $\frac{1}{16}$ **63.** No

Problem Set 8.5
1. 8   **3.** 9   **5.** 6   **7.** 5   **9.** 15   **11.** 48   **13.** 45   **15.** 48   **17.** 15   **19.** 1   **21.** 78   **23.** 9   **25.** $\frac{4}{7}$ **27.** $\frac{3}{4}$ **29.** False
31. True   **33.** 10 in.   **35.** 13 ft   **37.** 6.40 in.   **39.** 17.49 m   **41.** 1.1180   **43.** 11.1803   **45.** 3.46   **47.** 11.18   **49.** 0.58
51. 0.58   **53.** 12.124   **55.** 9.327   **57.** 12.124   **59.** 12.124   **61.** 6.7 miles   **63.** 30 ft   **65.** 25 ft   **67.** 5 miles
69. $16 \cdot 2$ **71.** $25 \cdot 3$ **73.** $25 \cdot 2$ **75.** $4 \cdot 10$ **77.** $16 \cdot 2$ **79.** $49 \cdot 2$ **81.** $16 \cdot 3$ **83.** $\frac{2}{5}$ **85.** $9\frac{8}{25}$ **87.** 8   **89.** $2\frac{4}{5}$
91. $\frac{7}{16}$ **93.** 19

Chapter 8 Review
1. $\frac{1}{2}$ mm   **3.** 14.7 in.   **5.** $24\frac{9}{16}$ cm   **7.** 27 in^2 **9.** $\frac{1}{7}$ m^2 **11.** 19.625 in^2 **13.** 32 cm^2 **15.** Perimeter = 40 ft; area = 84 ft^2
17. $V = 997.80$ km^3; $S = 482.81$ km^2 **19.** 628 in^3 **21.** 183.17 ft^3 **23.** 701,201.25 ft^3

Chapter 8 Cumulative Review
1. 5,555   **3.** 73.8   **5.** $\frac{1}{2}$ **7.** 8.936   **9.** 1.156   **11.** $\frac{1}{9}$ **13.** $2\frac{1}{10}$ **15.** $1\frac{1}{8}$ **17.** $\frac{2}{3}$ **19.** 1,600 acres   **21.** $\frac{11}{20}$
23. $3 \cdot 10^4 + 4 \cdot 10^2 + 5$ **25.** $66\frac{2}{3}\%$ **27.** 80.5 km/hr   **29.** 0.54   **31.** $41.07

Chapter 8 Test
1. 34 ft   **2.** 14.4 cm   **3.** 38 in.   **4.** 62.8 yd   **5.** 24 m   **6.** 49 cm^2 **7.** 52 in^2 **8.** $\frac{5}{3}$ ft^2 **9.** 77.13 mm^2 **10.** 28 in^2
11. 84 ft^3 **12.** 68.39 m^3 **13.** 113.04 cm^3 **14.** 284.69 in^3 **15.** Volume = 96 in^3; surface area = 136 in^2 **16.** 61 ft
17. 989 mm^2 **18.** 3.75 cm   **19.** 1 ft   **20.** 1.88 meters

Chapter 9

Pretest for Chapter 9

1. -10 **2.** 3   **3.** $\frac{6}{5} > -\frac{5}{6}$ **4.** $2 < |-4|$ **5.** -8 **6.** 1   **7.** -10 **8.** -3.47 **9.** -1 **10.** $-\frac{17}{20}$ **11.** -33 **12.** -20
13. $\frac{2}{5}$ **14.** -3 **15.** 8   **16.** 0   **17.** -8 **18.** -14 **19.** -3 **20.** $3x + 13$ **21.** $15y - 10$ **22.** $-b$ **23.** $35°$

Getting Ready for Chapter 9

1. $(5 \cdot 3)2$ **2.** $4(7 - 2)$ **3.** 110.1   **4.** 9   **5.** 0.32   **6.** 0   **7.** 125   **8.** $\frac{9}{10}$ **9.** 6   **10.** 2   **11.** 3   **12.** 1   **13.** $\frac{5}{16}$
14. 8   **15.** 3   **16.** 4   **17.** 24 in.   **18.** 7,500 ft²

Problem Set 9.1

1. 4 is less than 7.   **3.** 5 is greater than -2.   **5.** -10 is less than -3.   **7.** 0 is greater than -4.   **9.** $30 > -30$ **11.** $-10 < 0$
13. $-3 > -15$ **15.** $3 < 7$ **17.** $7 > -5$ **19.** $-6 < 0$ **21.** $-12 < -2$ **23.** $-\frac{1}{2} > -\frac{3}{4}$ **25.** $-0.75 < 0.25$ **27.** $-0.1 < -0.01$
29. $-3 < |6|$ **31.** $15 > |-4|$ **33.** $|-2| < |-7|$ **35.** 2   **37.** 100   **39.** 8   **41.** 231   **43.** $\frac{3}{4}$ **45.** 200   **47.** 8   **49.** 231
51. -3 **53.** 2   **55.** -75 **57.** 0   **59.** 0.123   **61.** $-\frac{7}{8}$ **63.** 2   **65.** 8   **67.** -2 **69.** -8 **71.** 0   **73.** Positive
75. -100 **77.** -20 **79.** -360 **81.** -450 feet   **83.** $-3,060$ feet   **85.** $-\$5,000; -\$2,750$ **87.** $-61°F, -51°F$
89. $-5°F, -15°F$ **91.** New Orleans $-6{:}00$ GMT   **93.** $-7°F$ **95.** $10°F$ and 25-mph wind
97.

99. 25   **101.** 5   **103.** 6   **105.** 19   **107.** 4,313   **109.** 56   **111.** $5 + 3$

113. $(7 + 2) + 6$ **115.** $x + 4$ **117.** $y + 5$ **119.** -3
121. The opposite of a number is the number that is the same distance from 0, but on the opposite side of 0.
123. The opposite of the absolute value of -3. It simplifies to -3.

Problem Set 9.2

1. 5   **3.** 1   **5.** -2 **7.** -6 **9.** 4   **11.** 4   **13.** -9 **15.** 15   **17.** -3 **19.** -11 **21.** -7 **23.** -3 **25.** -16 **27.** -8
29. -127 **31.** 49   **33.** 34   **35.**

First Number a	Second Number b	Their Sum $a + b$
5	-3	2
5	-4	1
5	-5	0
5	-6	-1
5	-7	-2

37.

First Number x	Second Number y	Their Sum $x + y$
-5	-3	-8
-5	-4	-9
-5	-5	-10
-5	-6	-11
-5	-7	-12

39. 10   **41.** 445   **43.** 107   **45.** -20 **47.** -17 **49.** -50 **51.** -7 **53.** 3   **55.** 50   **57.** -73 **59.** -11 **61.** 17
63. -3.8 **65.** 14.4   **67.** -9.89 **69.** -1 **71.** $-\frac{2}{7}$ **73.** $-\frac{3}{5}$ **75.** -0.86 **77.** -4.2 **79.** $-\frac{1}{4}$ **81.** -21 **83.** -5
85. -4 **87.** 7   **89.** 10   **91.** 380 feet above the trailhead   **93.** $\$10$ **95.** -2 **97.** 4   **99.** $-\frac{2}{5}$ **101.** 30   **103.** -60.3
105. 2   **107.** 3   **109.** 604   **111.** 0   **113.** $10 - x$ **115.** $y - 17$

Problem Set 9.3

1. 2   **3.** 2   **5.** -8 **7.** -5 **9.** 7   **11.** 12   **13.** 3   **15.** -7 **17.** -3 **19.** -13 **21.** -50 **23.** -100 **25.** 399
27. -21 **29.** -11.41 **31.** -1.9 **33.** -1 **35.** $-\frac{5}{12}$ **37.** $-\frac{11}{15}$ **39.** -7 **41.** -9 **43.** -14 **45.** -65 **47.** -11
49. 202   **51.** -400 **53.** -17.5 **55.** $-\frac{1}{12}$ **57.** 11   **59.** -4 **61.** 8   **63.** 6   **65.** b   **67.** a   **69.** -100
71. -16 degrees   **73.** 7,603 feet   **75.** -100 items   **77.** $\$1,760$ **79.** $\$3,009$ **81.** $-11 - (-22) = 11°$ F   **83.** $3 - (-24) = 27°$ F
85. $60 - (-26) = 86°$ F   **87.** $-14 - (-26) = 12°$ F   **89.** 30   **91.** 36   **93.** 64   **95.** 48   **97.** 41   **99.** 40   **101.** 17   **103.** 32
105. 25   **107.** 72   **109.** $3 \cdot 5$ **111.** $7x$ **113.** $5(3)$ **115.** $(5 \cdot 7) \cdot 8$ **117.** $2(3) + 2(4) = 6 + 8 = 14$ **119.** $3 - 5 \neq 5 - 3$
121. You have a balance of $\$10$ in your checkbook, and you write a check for $\$12$. Your new balance is $-\$2$.   **123.** $-5, -10$ **125.** 2, 6

Problem Set 9.4

1. -56 **3.** -60 **5.** 56 **7.** 81 **9.** -9.03 **11.** $\frac{3}{7}$ **13.** -8 **15.** -24 **17.** 24 **19.** -6 **21. a.** 16 **b.** -16
23. a. -125 **b.** -125 **25. a.** 16 **b.** -16
27.

Number x	Square x^2
-3	9
-2	4
-1	1
0	0
1	1
2	4
3	9

29.

First Number x	Second Number y	Their Product xy
6	2	12
6	1	6
6	0	0
6	-1	-6
6	-2	-12

31. -4 **33.** 50 **35.** 1 **37.** -35 **39.** -22 **41.** -30 **43.** -25 **45.** 9 **47.** -13 **49.** -11 **51.** 19 **53.** 6
55. -6 **57.** -4 **59.** -17 **61.** a **63.** d **65.** a **67.** b **69.** $-6°C$ **71.** -16 degrees **73.** $400 remains **75.** 7
77. 5 **79.** -5 **81.** 9 **83.** 4 **85.** 17 **87.** 405 **89.** $12 \div 6$ or $\frac{12}{6}$ **91.** $6 \div 3 = 2$ **93.** $5 \cdot 2 = 10$ **95.** 89
97. $-54, 162$ **99.** $54, -162$ **101.** 44 **103.** 19 **105.** -17

Problem Set 9.5

1. -3 **3.** -5 **5.** 3 **7.** 2 **9.** -4 **11.** -2 **13.** 0 **15.** -5
17.

First Number a	Second Number b	The Quotient of a and b $\frac{a}{b}$
100	-5	-20
100	-10	-10
100	-25	-4
100	-50	-2

19.

First Number a	Second Number b	The Quotient of a and b $\frac{a}{b}$
-100	-5	20
-100	5	-20
100	-5	-20
100	5	20

21. -5 **23.** 35 **25.** 6 **27.** 1 **29.** -6 **31.** -2 **33.** -1 **35.** -1 **37.** 2 **39.** -3 **41.** -7 **43.** 30 **45.** 4
47. -5 **49.** -20 **51.** -5 **53.** -1 **55.** c **57.** a **59.** d **61.** $-$9,810.50
63.

65. $x + 3$ **67.** $(5 + 7) + a$ **69.** $(3 \cdot 4)y$ **71.** $5(3) + 5(7)$ **73.** 36 **75.** 64 **77.** 350
79. 7,500 **81.** 4 **83.** -12 **85.** 12 **87.** -32 **89.** 32 **91.** -2 **93.** -4 **95.** 4 **97.** -1 **99.** -1

Problem Set 9.6

1. $20a$ **3.** $48a$ **5.** $-18x$ **7.** $-27x$ **9.** $-10y$ **11.** $-60y$ **13.** $5 + x$ **15.** $13 + x$ **17.** $10 + y$ **19.** $8 + y$ **21.** $5x + 6$
23. $6y + 7$ **25.** $12a + 21$ **27.** $7x + 28$ **29.** $7x + 35$ **31.** $6a - 42$ **33.** $2x - 2y$ **35.** $20 + 4x$ **37.** $6x + 15$ **39.** $18a + 6$
41. $12x - 6y$ **43.** $35 - 20y$ **45.** $8x$ **47.** $4a$ **49.** $4x$ **51.** $5y$ **53.** $-10a$ **55.** $-5x$
57. $x($3,300 - $300) - $250 = $3,000x - 250 **59.** $A = 36$ ft^2; $P = 24$ ft **61.** $A = 81$ in^2; $P = 36$ in. **63.** $A = 200$ in^2; $P = 60$ in.
65. $A = 300$ ft^2; $P = 74$ ft **67.** $20°$ C **69.** $5°$ C **71.** $-10°$ C

Chapter 9 Review

1. -17 **3.** 4.6 **5.** -6 **7.** 2 **9.** 4 **11.** 6 **13.** -2 **15.** -971 **17.** -12 **19.** 7 **21.** -20 **23.** $-1,736$
25. -3 **27.** 2 **29.** 36 **31.** -8 **33.** -5 **35.** -8 **37.** -1 **39.** -4 **41.** -42 **43.** -11 **45.** -27 **47.** 2 **49.** False
51. True **53.** False **55.** $58 + (-$86) = -28 **57.** $24°$ **59.** $3x + 12$ **61.** $-21a$ **63.** $4x + 12$ **65.** $21y - 56$ **67.** $3x$
69. $4y$

Chapter 9 Cumulative Review

1. $\frac{31}{35}$ **3.** 316 **5.** $\frac{16}{81}$ **7.** $-\frac{1}{16}$ **9.** 37.65 **11.** Thirty-eight thousand six hundred nine **13.** 126 **15.** $\frac{23}{24}$ **17.** -1
19. $\frac{2}{5}$ **21.** $8\frac{1}{6}$ **23.** 37.5% **25.** 1 **27.** 0.35 km **29.** 0.56 **31.** $\frac{11}{4}$ **33.** 20 women **35.** 97 mi. **37.** $10.80
39. 65 more

Chapter 9 Test

1. -14 **2.** $\frac{2}{3}$ **3.** $-1 > -4$ **4.** $|-4| > |2|$ **5.** 7 **6.** -2 **7.** -9 **8.** -5.9 **9.** $-\frac{22}{15}$ **10.** -36 **11.** 42 **12.** 6
13. -5 **14.** 5 **15.** -3.6 **16.** $-\frac{7}{12}$ **17.** -14 **18.** -7 **19.** $-\frac{3}{10}$ **20.** $\frac{7}{6}$ **21.** 9 **22.** -8 **23.** -11 **24.** -15
25. 7 **26.** -4 **27.** -74 **28.** -45 **29.** 11 **30.** 4 **31.** $\frac{1}{2}$ **32.** 4 **33.** 19 **34.** $-\frac{5}{2}$ **35.** -61 **36.** -7
37. 24 **38.** -5 **39.** -14 **40.** -5 **41.** $-\$35$ **42.** $25°$ **43.** -21 million visitors

Chapter 10

Pretest for Chapter 10

1. $-a + 7$ **2.** $14y - 12$ **3.** -6 **4.** -5 **5.** 15 **6.** -1 **7.** 4 **8.** 60 **9.** -10 **10.** No   **11.** -23 **12.** 8

Getting Ready for Chapter 10

1. 5 **2.** 135 **3.** -6 **4.** $\frac{11}{8}$ **5.** -20 **6.** -2 **7.** 18 **8.** 1 **9.** $-\frac{2}{3}$ **10.** 13 **11.** 7 **12.** 35 **13.** $10x$
14. $-12x$ **15.** $4x - 20$ **16.** x **17.** $x + 2$ **18.** $P = 8x$

Problem Set 10.1

1. $10x$ **3.** y **5.** $3a$ **7.** $8x + 16$ **9.** $6a + 14$ **11.** $x + 2$ **13.** $6x + 11$ **15.** $2x + 2$ **17.** $-a + 12$ **19.** $4y - 4$
21. $-2x + 4$ **23.** $8x - 6$ **25.** $5a + 9$ **27.** $-x + 3$ **29.** $17y + 3$ **31.** $a - 3$ **33.** $6x + 16$ **35.** $10x - 11$ **37.** $19y + 32$
39. $30y - 18$ **41.** $6x + 14$ **43.** $27a + 5$ **45.** 14 **47.** 27 **49.** -19 **51.** 7 **53.** 1 **55.** 18 **57.** 12 **59.** -10
61. 28 **63.** 40 **65.** 26 **67.** 4 **69.** 3 **71.** 0 **73.** 15 **75.** 6 **77.** $6(x + 4) = 6x + 24$ **79.** $4x + 4$ **81.** $10x - 4$
83. $5°$ **85.** $55°$; complementary angles   **87.** $20°$; complementary angles
89. a. Yes **b.** No, he should earn $108 for working 9 hours **c.** No, he should earn $84 for working 7 hours **d.** Yes
91. a. $32°F$ **b.** $22°F$ **c.** $-18°F$ **93. a.** 27 **b.** 47 **95.** 0 **97.** -6 **99.** -3 **101.** $\frac{11}{8}$ **103.** 0 **105.** x **107.** $y - 2$
109. -9 **111.** 6 **113.** a **115.** c   **117.** c   **119.** $-\frac{2}{3}$ **121.** 18 **123.** $-\frac{1}{12}$

Problem Set 10.2

1. Yes   **3.** Yes   **5.** No   **7.** Yes   **9.** No   **11.** 6 **13.** 11 **15.** -15 **17.** 1 **19.** -3 **21.** -1 **23.** $\frac{7}{5}$ **25.** -10
27. -4 **29.** -3 **31.** 2 **33.** -6 **35.** -6 **37.** -1 **39.** -2 **41.** -16 **43.** -3 **45.** 10 **47.** $x = 4$ **49.** $x = 12$
51. $58°$ celsius   **53.** $67°$ **55. a.** 225 **b.** $\$11,125$ **57.** $\frac{1}{4}$ **59.** 2 **61.** $\frac{3}{2}$ **63.** 1 **65.** 1 **67.** 1 **69.** 1 **71.** x
73. $7x - 11$ **75.** 2 **77.** $\frac{5}{14}$ **79.** $-\frac{1}{15}$ **81.** $-\frac{7}{6}$ **83.** Equation: $x + 12 = 30; x = 18$ **85.** Equation: $8 - 5 = x + 7; x = -4$

Problem Set 10.3

1. 8 **3.** -6 **5.** -6 **7.** 6 **9.** 16 **11.** 16 **13.** $-\frac{3}{2}$ **15.** -7 **17.** -8 **19.** 6 **21.** 2 **23.** 3 **25.** 4 **27.** -24
29. 12 **31.** -8 **33.** 15 **35.** 3 **37.** -1 **39.** 1 **41.** 3 **43.** 1 **45.** -1 **47.** $-\frac{1}{3}$ **49.** -14 **51.** 9 **53.** 8
55. 300.7 ft/sec   **57.** $\$35.00$ **59.** $97,500,000$ or 97.5 million viewers   **61.** $2x + 5 = 19; x = 7$ **63.** $5x - 6 = -9; x = -\frac{3}{5}$
65. $6a - 16$ **67.** $-15x + 3$ **69.** $3y - 9$ **71.** $16x - 6$

Problem Set 10.4

1. 3 **3.** 2 **5.** -3 **7.** -4 **9.** 1 **11.** 0 **13.** 2 **15.** -2 **17.** 3 **19.** -1 **21.** 7 **23.** -3 **25.** 1 **27.** -2 **29.** 4
31. 10 **33.** -5 **35.** $-\frac{1}{12}$ **37.** -3 **39.** 20 **41.** -1 **43.** 5 **45.** 4 **47.** 2.05 **49.** -0.064 **51.** 12.03 **53.** 0.44
55. -0.175 **57.** 2 **59.** 10 **61.** 5 **63.** $1,250$ feet   **65.** 13 **67.** 30 hours   **69.** $x + 2$ **71.** $2x$ **73.** $2(x + 6)$ **75.** $x - 4$
77. $2x + 5$ **79.** $<$ **81.** $>$ **83.** $0.001, 0.003, 0.01, 0.013, 0.03, 0.031$ **85. a.** $4x + 6(x - 100) = 2,400$ **b.** $x = 300$ **c.** 500 people

Problem Set 10.5

1. $x + 3$ **3.** $2x + 1$ **5.** $5x - 6$ **7.** $3(x + 1)$ **9.** $5(3x + 4)$ **11.** The number is 2.   **13.** The number is -2.
15. The number is 3.   **17.** The number is 5.   **19.** The number is -2.   **21.** The length is 10 m and the width is 5 m.
23. The length of one side is 8 cm.   **25.** The measures of the angles are $45°, 45°,$ and $90°$.   **27.** The angles are $30°, 60°,$ and $90°$.
29. Patrick is 33 years old, and Pat is 53 years old.   **31.** Sue is 35 years old, and Dale is 39 years old.   **33.** 87 mi   **35.** 147 mi
37. 8 nickels, 18 dimes   **39.** 16 dimes, 32 quarters   **41.** $x = 8, y = 6, z = 9$ **43.** 39 hours   **45.** 60 miles per hour   **47.** 35
49. 65 **51.** 2 **53.** 14 **55.** $-\frac{2}{3}$ **57.** $0.75, 75\%$ **59.** $1.2, 120\%$ **61.** $\frac{37}{100}, 0.37$ **63.** $\frac{17}{500}, 0.034$ **65.** 20.25 **67.** 75

Problem Set 10.6

1. 704 ft^2 **3.** $\frac{9}{8}$ in^2 **5.** $\$240$ **7.** $\$285$ **9.** 12 ft   **11.** 8 ft   **13.** $\$140$ **15.** 58 in.   **17.** $3\frac{1}{4} = \frac{13}{4}$ ft   **19.** $C = 100°C$; yes
21. $C = 20°C$; yes   **23.** $0°C$ **25.** $5°F$

27.

AGE (YEARS)	MAXIMUM HEART RATE (BEATS PER MINUTE)
18	202
19	201
20	200
21	199
22	198
23	197

29.

RESTING HEART RATE	TRAINING HEART RATE
60	144
65	146
70	148
75	150
80	152
85	154

31. a. 4 hrs **b.** 220 miles

33. a. 4 hours **b.** 65 mph   **35.** 360 in³   **37.** 1 yd³   **39.** $y = 7$ **41.** $y = -3$ **43.** $y = -2$ **45.** $x = 3$ **47.** $x = 5$

49. $x = 8$ **51.** $y = 1$ **53.** $y = 3$ **55.** $y = \dfrac{5}{2}$ **57.** $y = 0$ **59.** $y = \dfrac{13}{3}$ **61.** $y = 4$ **63.** $x = 0$ **65.** $x = \dfrac{13}{4}$ **67.** $x = 3$

69. Complement: 45°; supplement: 135°   **71.** Complement: 59°; supplement: 149°   **73. a.** 13,330 kilobytes **b.** 2,962 kilobytes

75. a. About 58° Celcius **b.** 328 K   **77.** $\dfrac{3}{4}$ **79.** 3   **81.** 2   **83.** 6

Problem Set 10.7

1.–17.

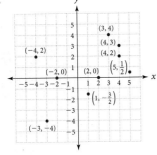

19. $(2, 2)$ **21.** $(-3, 2)$ **23.** $(3, -3)$ **25.** $(-4, 0)$ **27.** yes   **29.** No   **31.** Yes

33. No   **35.** (1985, 20), (1990, 34), (1995, 45)

37. a. (5, 40), (10, 80), (20, 160) **b.** $320 **c.** 30 hours **d.** No, if she works 35 hours, she should be paid $280.   **39.** xy^2 **41.** $\dfrac{1}{xy}$

43. $\dfrac{4x + 15}{20}$ **45.** $\dfrac{3x - 1}{x}$ **47.** $A = (1, 2), B = (6, 7)$ **49.** $A = (2, 2), B = (2, 5), C = (7, 5)$

Chapter 10 Review

1. $17x$ **3.** $11a - 3$ **5.** $5x + 4$ **7.** $10a - 4$ **9.** 42   **11.** 1   **13.** -9 **15.** 7   **17.** Yes   **19.** 9   **21.** 3   **23.** 9

25. 5   **27.** -1 **29.** $-\dfrac{1}{8}$ **31.** 9   **33.** 7   **35.** -16 **37.** 2   **39.** -2 **41.** -4 **43.** The length is 14 m, and the width is 7 m.

45. 15° and 75°   **47.** 18°, 54°, 108°   **49.** $y = 6$ **51.** $y = 3$ **53.** $x = 0$ **55.** $x = 2$ **57.** $x = -3$ **59.** $x = -9$

61–67.

Chapter 10 Cumulative Review

1. 5,996   **3.** 4.559   **5.** 938,135   **7.** 42   **9.** 440,000   **11.** $6\dfrac{1}{3}$ **13.** 80%   **15.** $1\dfrac{6}{25}$ **17.** $\dfrac{4}{81}$ **19.** -7 **21.** 4

23. 56   **25.** 5   **27.** 8   **29.** Ben is 17, Ryan is 9   **31.** $80, 20%   **33.** $14.40   **35.** 64   **37.** 240   **39.** $\dfrac{4}{1}$

Chapter 10 Test

1. $6x - 5$ **2.** $3b - 4$ **3.** $2x - 18$ **4.** $14x - 12$ **5.** -3 **6.** 9   **7.** Yes   **8.** No   **9.** 8   **10.** -6 **11.** 4   **12.** -4.9

13. 27   **14.** 6   **15.** -4 **16.** 1   **17.** $\dfrac{2}{3}$ **18.** 1   **19.** all real numbers   **20.** 5   **21.** -8 **22.** 22 mi/hr

23. Length = 9 cm; width = 5 cm   **24.** Susan is 11, Karen is 6.   **25.** 20°, 40°, 120°   **26.** 4 quarters, 11 dimes   **27.** 22.5°, and 67.5°

28. 4.5 m   **29.** 20 ft, 240 ft   **30.**

Appendices

Problem Set D

1. $\dfrac{1}{32}$ **3.** $\dfrac{1}{100}$ **5.** $\dfrac{1}{x^3}$ **7.** $\dfrac{1}{16}$ **9.** $-\dfrac{1}{125}$ **11.** $\dfrac{1}{4}$ **13.** 1,000   **15.** $\dfrac{1}{x^7}$ **17.** 9   **19.** $\dfrac{1}{8}$ **21.** 1,000   **23.** $\dfrac{1}{x^{12}}$ **25.** 2

27. 4   **29.** $\dfrac{1}{4}$ **31.** x **33.** $\dfrac{1}{x}$ **35.** $\dfrac{1}{10^7}$ **37.** $\dfrac{1}{10^7}$ **39.** 1,000   **41.** x^{24} **43.** 4   **45.** 10,000   **47.** $15x^5$ **49.** $\dfrac{6}{x^5}$

51. $-\dfrac{12}{x^7}$ **53.** $42x^2$ **55.** x^5 **57.** x^2

Problem Set E

1. 4.25×10^5 **3.** 6.78×10^6 **5.** 1.1×10^4 **7.** 8.9×10^7 **9.** 38,400   **11.** 57,100,000   **13.** 3,300   **15.** 89,130,000

17. 3.5×10^{-4} **19.** 7×10^{-4} **21.** 6.035×10^{-2} **23.** 1.276×10^{-1} **25.** 0.00083   **27.** 0.0625   **29.** 0.3125   **31.** 0.005

33. $\$4.2 \times 10^4$; 4,000,000   **35.** $\$5.75 \times 10^5$; 87,000,000   **37.**   **39.** 1.024×10^3

41. 1.074×10^9

Jupiter's Moon	Period (Seconds)	
Io	153,000	1.53×10^5
Europa	307,000	3.07×10^5
Ganymede	618,000	6.18×10^5
Callisto	1,440,000	1.44×10^6

Problem Set F

1. 6×10^{10} **3.** 1.5×10^{11} **5.** 6.84×10^{-2} **7.** 1.62×10^{10} **9.** 3.78×10^{-1} **11.** 2×10^3 **13.** 4×10^{-9} **15.** 5×10^{14}

17. 6×10^1 **19.** 2×10^{-8} **21.** 4×10^6 **23.** 4×10^{-4} **25.** 2.1×10^{-2} **27.** 3×10^{-5} **29.** 6.72×10^{-1} **31.** $\$1.05 \times 10^{-2}$

33. $\$6.61 \times 10^{-3}$ **35.** 2,500,000 stones or 2.5×10^6

Index